Introduction to the

Theory of Integration

This is Volume 13 in
PURE AND APPLIED MATHEMATICS
A Series of Monographs and Textbooks
Editors: Paul A. Smith and Samuel Eilenberg
A complete list of titles in this series appears at the end of this volume

Introduction to the Theory of Integration

T. H. HILDEBRANDT
Department of Mathematics
University of Michigan
Ann Arbor, Michigan

1963

ACADEMIC PRESS New York and London

ACADEMIC PRESS, INC.
111 Fifth Avenue, New York, New York 10003

United Kingdom Edition published by
ACADEMIC PRESS, INC. (LONDON) LTD.
Berkeley Square House, London W1X 6BA

Library of Congress Catalog Card Number: 62-13099

Second Printing, 1971

PRINTED IN THE UNITED STATES OF AMERICA

Preface

This book is an outgrowth of lectures given at the University of Michigan by the author on the subject of integration during a period of more than a quarter of a century. The assumption at the beginning of the course was that the student was familiar with the salient facts of functions of a real variable, that is had a basic knowledge of the topological properties of the real line, continuous functions, functions of bounded variation, derivatives, and Riemann integrals. This same background is assumed here. At no time was it possible to include in the course of lectures all the material included in the book. It represents what we would have liked to discuss if there had been time.

The subject matter presented is essentially the classical theory of Stieltjes and Lebesgue integration. In that way it is reactionary relative to the present style of graduate mathematical instruction, which veers strongly toward the abstract and sometimes overlooks the concrete basic ideas. We have tried to include as far as possible the ideas which form the basis of abstract procedures in the theory of integration, and hope that we have thereby made the latter a little more understandable.

Since the book is essentially of a textbook character, we have been rather sparing with references and giving credit for various ideas. The difficulty is that so often one overlooks an important work and disappoints the originators of ideas by neglecting to mention them. Then, too, most of the ideas presented are by this time in the public domain.

By way of acknowledgment, we are grateful to Professor R. E. Langer of the United States Army Mathematical Research Center at the University of Wisconsin for the opportunity of spending several fruitful months at the Center. Also, we appreciate having the chance to discuss certain problems with Professor P. Porcelli of Louisiana State University. We cannot overlook the patience of the graduate students who have formed captive audiences while some of the material here presented was under development. We have not burdened anyone with a critical reading of the manuscript. As a consequence all awkwardness of presentation and errors in reasoning are the sole responsibility of the author.

T. H. Hildebrandt

Ann Arbor, Michigan
January 1963

CONTENTS

Chapter VIII

Classes of Measurable and Integrable Functions

Chapter IX

Other Methods of Defining the Class of Lebesgue Integrable Functions. Abstract Integrals

Chapter X

Product Measures. Iterated Integrals. Fubini Theorem

Chapter XI

Derivatives and Integrals

CHAPTER I

A GENERAL THEORY OF LIMITS

The theory of integration depends on limits of a variety of types. To avoid deriving properties of each of these limits separately, we present a general theory of limits as developed by E. H. Moore and H. L. Smith which includes as special cases the limits used in this book.

1. Directed Sets. The Moore-Smith General Limit

To set up a general theory of limits, we examine some of the limits which occur in analysis and note their common features.

The simplest limit is that of a sequence $\{a_n\}$ of real numbers and is defined as follows: the sequence $\{a_n\}$ has a as a limit written $\lim_n a_n = a$, if for every positive e, there exists an integer n_e depending on e, such that if $n > n_e$, then $| a_n - a | < e$, or $a - e < a_n < a + e$. If we introduce the Peano symbolism where $\supset$ = implies, $\exists$ = there exists, $\ni$ = such that, then this limit definition can be written

$$e > 0 \supset \exists\, n_e \ni n > n_e \supset | a_n - a | < e.$$

Next we have the limit of a function $f(x)$ defined on an interval $a \leqq x \leqq b$, at a point x_0 of $[a, b]$, viz., $\lim_{x \to x_0} f(x) = c$ if and only if for every $e > 0$, there exists a d_e such that if $0 < | x - x_0 | < d_e$, then $| f(x) - c | < e$, or

$$e > 0 \supset \exists\, d_e \ni 0 < | x - x_0 | < d_e \supset | f(x) - c | < e.$$

A slightly different type of limit occurs in connection with the Riemann integral. If $f(x)$ is defined on the interval $a \leqq x \leqq b$, σ stands for the subdivision of $[a, b]$ by the points $a = x_0 < x_1 < x_2 < \dots < x_n = b$ and $x_{i-1} \leqq x_i' \leqq x_i$, then $\int_a^b f(x)dx$ is defined as the limit of the approximating sums $\Sigma_{i=1}^n f(x_i') (x_i - x_{i-1})$ as the maximum of the lengths of the subintervals $[x_i, x_{i-1}]$ or $| x_i - x_{i-1} |$ approaches zero. If we denote the maximum of $| x_i - x_{i-1} |$ for $i = 1, \ldots n$ by $| \sigma |$, the *norm* of σ, then

$$\int_a^b f(x)dx = \lim_{|\sigma| \to 0} \sum_{i=1}^n f(x_i') (x_i - x_{i-1})$$

or

$$e > 0 \supset \exists\, d_e \ni | \sigma | < d_e \supset | \sum_{i=1}^n f(x_i') (x_i - x_{i-1}) - \int_a^b f(x)dx | < e.$$

This differs from the preceding cases in that $\Sigma_{i=1}^n f(x_i') (x_i - x_{i-1})$ considered as a function of σ is a many-valued function.

A fourth type of limit occurs in the definition of total variation of a function of bounded variation on an interval $[a, b]$. If $f(x)$ is of bounded variation on $[a, b]$, then the total variation $V_a^b f$ is defined as the least upper bound (l.u.b.) of $\Sigma_{i=1}^n | f(x_i) - f(x_{i-1}) |$ for all subdivisions σ of $[a, b]$. However, the function of σ: $g(\sigma) = \Sigma_{i=1}^n | f(x_i) - f(x_{i-1}) |$ has a monotonic character relative to σ, in the sense that if we add additional points to σ, then $g(\sigma)$ does not diminish. Consequently, if we mean by $\sigma_1 \geq \sigma_2$ that the subsdivision σ_1 contains all of the points of σ_2, then we have

$$e > 0 \supset \exists\, \sigma_e \ni \sigma \geq \sigma_e \supset V_a^b f - \sum_{i=1}^n | f(x_i) - f(x_{i-1}) | < e.$$

A similar situation occurs in connection with the upper and lower Darboux integrals $\overline{\int_a^b} f(x)dx$ and $\underline{\int_a^b} f(x)dx$ of a bounded function on $[a, b]$.

Let us now examine these instances of definition of limits in order to deduce their common characteristics. We note in the first place that the notion of *limit applies only to functions*. A sequence is a function of the integers, the approximating sums in integration and variation are functions of the subdivision of the fundamental interval. Secondly, some sort of order is involved in each of these definitions, for sequences, the order of the integers, for functions of x, the order established by the distance $| x - x_0 |$, for Riemann integration the order defined by the norm $| \sigma |$, and in total variation the order $\sigma_1 \geq \sigma_2$ defined by inclusion.

In order to bring the second and third cases in line with the other two, we rephrase them as follows:

$$\lim_{x \to x_0} f(x) = c$$
$$\equiv e > 0 \supset \exists\, x_e \ni 0 < |x - x_0| < |x_e - x_0| \supset |f(x) - c| < e$$

and

$$\lim_{|\sigma| \to 0} \sum_{\sigma} f(x_i') (x_i - x_{i-1}) = \int_a^b f(x)dx$$

$$\equiv e > 0 \supset \exists\, \sigma_e \ni |\sigma| < |\sigma_e| \supset \left| \sum_{\sigma} f(x_i') (x_i - x_{i-1}) - \int_a^b f(x)dx \right| < e.$$

These considerations suggest the following generalization: Let Q be a general class of elements q and $f(q)$ a real valued function on Q. In Q assume a relation R holding between some pairs of elements q_1 and q_2 of Q, i.e., for some q_1 and q_2, we have q_1Rq_2. For R we postulate the minimum condition associated with order, viz., R has the *transitive* property: *if* q_1Rq_2 *and* q_2Rq_3, *then* q_1Rq_3.

We then define *the general limit*: $\lim_q f(q) = a$, if and only if *for every* $e > 0$ *there exists a* q_e *such that if* qRq_e, *then* $|f(q) - a| < e$, or

$$\lim_q f(q) = a \equiv e > 0 \supset \exists\, q_e \ni qRq_e \supset |f(q) - a| < e.$$

It is fairly obvious how each of the instances of limits we have considered follows this pattern. Also we note that the same set of elements may be ordered in different ways, giving rise to different definitions of limit.

Since in the sequel we shall have frequent occasion to use the statement involved in the definition of limit, we shall abbreviate it: $(e, q_e, qRq_e) : |f(q) - a| < e$.

In any general theory of limits it is desirable to preserve as far as possible the basic properties valid in the simpler instances. Among these one of the most important facts is that if $\lim_q f(q)$ exists, then this limit is unique. This means that if $\lim_q f(q) = a$ and $\lim_q f(q) = b$, then $a = b$. Now if $\lim_q f(q) = a$, then $(e, q_e', qRq_e') : |f(q) - a| < e$, and if $\lim_q f(q) = b$, then $(e, q_e'', qRq_e'') : |f(q) - b| < e$. In order to draw any conclusions from these two statements, we need to know that for every $e > 0$ there exists at least one q_{0e} such that $q_{0e}Rq_e'$ and $q_{0e}Rq_e''$ simultaneously. Then it follows that for every $e > 0$, $|a - b| < 2e$, i.e., $a = b$. This suggests the following additional postulate on R, which we call the *compositive* property: *for any two* q_1 *and* q_2 *there exists a* q_3 *such that* q_3Rq_1 *and* q_3Rq_2, which might be stated, any two elements of Q have a successor.

We have then proved that: *if R has the transitive and compositive property and if* $\lim_q f(q)$ *exists, then this limit is unique.*

It turns out that the transitive and compositive properties of the relation R are sufficient for setting up a theory of limits which contains the elementary cases as special instances. As a consequence we apply a special label to general classes Q with such an R and define:

1.1. Definition. A general set Q with a binary relation R holding between some pairs of elements of Q is called a *directed set* if the relation R is transitive and compositive.

As additional instances of directed sets we note the following:

(1) Let P be any set of elements and let Q consist of all finite subsets of P, and let the elements of Q be directed by inclusion, i.e., if q_1 and q_2 are any two sets in Q, then $q_1 R q_2$ if and only if q_1 contains all of the elements of q_2.

(2) Let P be any set of elements and let Q consist of all finite or denumerable subsets of P, directed by inclusion.

(3) Let P be any set of elements and Q be a collection of subsets of P which with any two sets q_1 and q_2 contains also the union or sum of the two sets, direction being by inclusion.

Other instances will occur later in the book.

It is possible to add $+\infty$ and $-\infty$ as possible limits in the usual way, i.e., $\lim_q f(q) = +\infty$ is equivalent to the statement, for every $e > 0$ there exists a q_e such that if qRq_e, then $f(q) > e$; and $\lim_q f(q) = -\infty$ if for every $e > 0$ there exists a q_e such that if qRq_e, then $f(q) < -e$.

In case we allow $+\infty$ and $-\infty$ as values for the set of real numbers $\mathfrak{R}$, we shall call the result the *extended line* denoted $\mathfrak{R}^*$.

It is apparent that in the definition of limit we can replace e by ke where k is fixed relative to e and positive, since ke covers the same ground as e. As a consequence the definition for finite limit could also read $(ke, q_e, qRq_e) : |f(q) - a| < ke$.

If Q is a directed set, if $f(q)$ is on Q to the reals, and if the general limit $\lim_q f(q)$ exists, finite or infinite, this limit is called a *Moore-Smith* or *directed limit.*

2. Properties of Limits

We proceed to show that the properties of limits of sequences are essentially preserved in the more general setting. For the sake of convenience, we shall assume that the limits involved in this section are finite.

2.1. If $\lim_q f(q) = a$, and b is any constant, then $\lim_q bf(q) = ba$.

For $(e, q_e, qRq_e) : |f(q) - a| < e$ implies $|bf(q) - ba| < |b|e$.

2.2. If $\lim_q f(q) = a$, then $\lim_q |f(q)| = |a|$.

For $||f(q)| - |a|| \leqq |f(q) - a|$.

2.3. If $\lim_q f(q) = a$, and $\lim_q g(q) = b$, then $\lim_q (f(q) + g(q)) = a + b = \lim_q f(q) + \lim_q g(q)$.

For $(e, q_e', qRq_e') : |f(q) - a| < e$ and $(e, q_e'', qRq_e'') : |g(q) - b| < e$ imply $(e, q_e''', qRq_e''') : |f(q) + g(q) - (a + b)| \leqq |f(q) - a| + |g(q) - b| < 2e$, where q_e''' is determined by the compositive property of R so that $q_e''' R q_e'$ and $q_e''' R q_e''$.

2.4. If $\lim_q f(q) = a$, then the set of values of $f(q)$ is ultimately bounded, i.e., there exists a q_0 and a $b > 0$ such that for qRq_0 we have $|f(q)| < b$.

This is obvious from the definition of limit.

2.5. If $\lim_q f(q) = a$, and $\lim_q g(q) = b$, then $\lim_q f(q)g(q) = ab = \lim_q f(q) \cdot \lim_q g(q)$.

This follows from the inequality

$$|f(q) \cdot g(q) - ab| \leqq |f(q)||g(q) - b| + |b||f(q) - a|$$

and the ultimate boundedness of $f(q)$.

2.6. If $\lim_q f(q) = a$ and $a \neq 0$, then $\lim_q (1/f(q)) = 1/a = 1/\lim_q f(q)$.

For if $a \neq 0$ and if $e < |a|/2$, then $|f(q)| > |a|/2$ for qRq_e, so that $|1/f(q) - 1/a| = |f(q) - a|/|a||f(q)| < 2|f(q) - a|/|a|^2$.

A combination of I.2.5 and I.2.6 yields the usual theorem on the limit of a quotient of two functions. All of these theorems are special cases of the general theorem:

2.7. If $F(x_1, x_2, ..., x_n)$ is defined on the value space of $f_1(q), f_2(q), ..., f_n(q)$ and continuous at $(a_1, ..., a_n)$ where $\lim_q f_1(q) = a_1$, $\lim_q f_2(q) = a_2, ..., \lim_q f_n(q) = a_n$, then

$$\lim_q F(f_1(q), f_2(q), ..., f_n(q)) = F(a_1, a_2, ..., a_n)$$
$$= F(\lim_q f_1(q), \lim_q f_2(q), ..., \lim_q f_n(q)).$$

For a directed set the notion of subsequence is replaced by that of *cofinality* with Q. We define:

2.8. Definition. A subset Q' of Q is *cofinal* with Q if for every q of Q, there exists a q' in Q' such that $q'Rq$.

A set Q' cofinal with Q is also a directed set with the same R, as can easily be verified.

2.9. If $\lim_q f(q) = a$ and Q' is cofinal with Q, then $\lim_{q'} f(q') = a$.

This is a generalization of the statement that if a sequence a_n converges, then every subsequence converges to the same limit. The proof is obvious. There is a converse:

2.10. If $f(q)$ and a are such that for every Q' cofinal with Q, there exists a subset Q'' cofinal with Q' and therefore with Q, such that $\lim_{q''} f(q'') = a$, then $\lim f(q) = a$.

For suppose that $f(q)$ does not have a as a limit. Then there exists an $e > 0$ such that for every q there exists a q_q with $q_q Rq$ such that $|f(q_q) - a| > e$. Now the set Q' consisting of q_q is cofinal with Q, and so there exists a subset Q'' cofinal with Q' and so with Q such that $\lim_{q''} f(q'') = a$, which obviously contradicts the inequality $|f(q'') - a| > e$ for every q''.

2.11. A necessary and sufficient condition that $f(q)$ have a finite limit is that the *Cauchy condition of convergence* hold, viz., for $e > 0$ there exists q_e such that $q_1 Rq_e$, $q_2 Rq_e$ implies $|f(q_1) - f(q_2)| < e$.

The necessity follows in the usual way. For the sufficiency take $e = 1/n$ (or any monotonic sequence $e_n \to 0$). Select q_n so that $q_n R q_{n-1}$ and so that $q'Rq_n$ and $q''Rq_n$ implies $|f(q') - f(q'')| < 1/n$. Then from the transitive property of R it follows that $|f(q_{n+1}) - f(q_{n+m})| < 1/n$ for all n and m, so that $f(q_n)$ is a Cauchy sequence of real numbers and consequently $\lim_n f(q_n)$ exists. If this limit is a, then $(e, n_e, n > n_e): |f(q_n) - a| < e$. Further, $|f(q_n) - f(q)| < e$ if $n - 1 > 1/e$ and qRq_{n-1}. If we set $q_e = q_{n-1}$ for n greater than n_e and $1 + 1/e$, then $(e, q_e, qRq_e): |f(q) - a| < 2e$, i.e., $\lim_q f(q) = a$.

In these properties of limits, no mention has been made of the possible multiple valuedness of the functions involved. An examination of the proofs will show that the properties hold even if the functions are multiple valued, provided it is understood that if $f(q)$ belongs to the class C and $g(q)$ belongs to the class D, then $f(q)+g(q)$ belongs to a subset of the sum of any element in C with any in D. Similarly for $f(q)\cdot g(q)$.

2.12. Definition. We define a function $f(q)$ on a directed set Q *monotone nondecreasing* (nonincreasing) if $f(q)$ is single valued and q_1Rq_2 implies $f(q_1)\geqq f(q_2)$ $(f(q_1)\leqq f(q_2))$.

As in the case of monotonic sequences we have:

2.13. THEOREM. If $f(q)$ is monotonic nondecreasing and bounded above, then $\lim_q f(q)$ exists as the least upper bound (l.u.b.) of $f(q)$ in q. Otherwise, $\lim_q f(q)=+\infty$. A similar statement holds for non-increasing functions.

For if $a=$ l.u.b.$_q f(q)$, then for $e>0$ there exists q_e such that $a-e<f(q)\leqq a$. In view of the monotoneity of $f(q)$, it then follows that $(e,\ q_e,\ qRq_e):|f(q)-a|<e$.

3. Values Approached

Obviously $\lim_q f(q)$ for a function on a directed set Q need not exist. However, as we shall see, for any function on a directed set there exists at least one number a on the extended real axis $-\infty\leqq a\leqq\infty$, which is a *value approached* (or quasi-limit), which notion we define as follows:

3.1. Definition. a is a value approached of $f(q)$ on the directed set Q if for every $e>0$ and q, there exists a q_{eq} such that $q_{eq}Rq$ and $|f(q_{eq})-a|<e$, if a is finite, $f(q_{eq})>e$ if $a=+\infty$, and $f(q_{eq})<-e$ if $a=-\infty$. Or $(e,\ q;\ q_{eq}):\ q_{eq}Rq,\ |f(q_{eq})-a|<e$ for a finite, $f(q_{eq})>e$ for $a=+\infty$ and $f(q_{eq})<-e$ for $a=-\infty$.

The notion of value approached is a close relative of the inaccurate definition of limit of a sequence a_n which states that a is a limit of a_n if a_n can be made to differ from a by as little as one pleases by making n large enough.

The set of values approached (abbreviated v.ap.) of a function $f(q)$ on a directed set Q can be obtained as follows: Let E_q be the set of values $f(q')$ for $q'Rq$, and F_q the closure of E_q obtained by adding to E_q all of its limiting points. Obviously the sets F_q are monotonic nonincreasing in q in the sense that q_1Rq_2 implies F_{q_1} is contained in F_{q_2}. Then:

3.2. THEOREM. The set $F_0 = \Pi_q F_q$, the set of numbers contained in all of the F_q, is the set of values approached of $f(q)$ and is not vacuous.

For suppose a is a v.ap. and suppose, if possible, that a is not in F_0. Then there exists a q_0 such that F_{q_0} does not contain a. Since F_{q_0} is closed there exists a vicinity $V(a)$ containing no point of F_{q_0}. Since the sets F_q are monotone nonincreasing in q, $V(a)$ will have no point in common with F_q for qRq_0. This contradicts the definition of v.ap.

On the other hand, suppose that a is in F_0. Then for every q there exists a $q_q = q'$ with $q'Rq$ such that either a belongs to $E_{q'}$ or is a limiting point of $E_{q'}$. In either case, $(e, q, q_{eq}): q_{eq}Rq, |f(q_{eq}) - a| < e$, for a finite and similarly for $a = \pm\infty$, i.e., a is a v.ap. of $f(q)$.

To show that F_0 is not vacuous, we proceed contrapositively, or suppose that F_0 is empty. If a is any value $-\infty \leqq a \leqq +\infty$, then as above there exists a vicinity $V(a)$ and a q_a such that qRq_a implies that F_q and $V(a)$ have no points in common. The Borel theorem holds on $-\infty \leqq a \leqq +\infty$ and consequently there exist a finite number of points $a_1,\ldots,a_n$ and corresponding $q_1,\ldots,q_n$ such that $\Sigma_{i=1}^n V(a_i)$ covers $-\infty \leqq a \leqq +\infty$. Consequently, if $q_0Rq_1,\ldots q_0Rq_n$, which q_0 exists by the compositive property of R, then for qRq_0 the sets F_q are vacuous, which is contrary to their definition. Hence F_0 is not vacuous. F_0 being the product or common part of closed sets is closed.

As an alternative way of obtaining v.ap. by $f(q)$ we have:

3.3. THEOREM. a is a v.ap. of $f(q)$ on the directed set Q if and only if for every q there exists a monotone increasing sequence of q_n such that q_nRq and $\lim_n f(q_n) = a$.

For the necessity we need only apply the definition of v.ap. with $e = 1/n$, $n = 1, 2, \ldots$, q_1Rq, and q_nRq_{n-1}. For the sufficiency we note that under the conditions of the theorem a belongs to all F_q and so is a v.ap.

In the case of sequences of real numbers a_n, any v.ap. is also the limit of a subsequence a_{n_m} of a_n. If we define a as a sublimit of $f(q)$ if there exists a subset Q' cofinal with Q such that $\lim_{q'} f(q') = a$, then we see at once that any sublimit is also a v.ap. But we do not know whether conversely every v.ap. is also a sublimit.

4. Extreme Limits

Since the class F_0 of v.ap. for a function $f(q)$ is closed, it has both a maximum and a minimum on $-\infty \leqq a \leqq +\infty$. These two special v.ap. are designated *the greatest of the limits of* $f(q)$ $(\overline{\lim}_q f(q))$ or limit superior (lim sup) and *least of the limits* $(\underline{\lim}_q f(q))$ or limit inferior (lim inf), respectively. Since the second designations are frequently referred to as lim sups and lim infs, which have a rather non-mathematical suggestion, we shall usually speak of the greatest and least of the limits. From the extremal characterization of these notions we find at once:

4.1. THEOREM. If $f(q)$ is defined on the directed set Q, then

$$\overline{\lim}_q f(q) = \text{g.l.b.}[\text{l.u.b.}(f(q') \text{ for } q'Rq) \mid \text{for } q \text{ in } Q]$$

and

$$\underline{\lim}_q f(q) = \text{l.u.b.}[\text{g.l.b.}(f(q') \text{ for } q'Rq) \mid \text{for } q \text{ in } Q].$$

Here g.l.b. is the abbreviation for greatest lower bound and l.u.b. for least upper bound.

If we set $g(q) = \text{l.u.b.}[f(q') \text{ for } q'Rq]$, then $g(q)$ is the maximum of the set F_q and is monotone nonincreasing in q, so that $\overline{\lim}_q f(q) = \lim_q g(q)$. From this we obtain the following alternative definition of $\overline{\lim}_q f(q)$, if it is finite:

4.2. $\overline{\lim}_q f(q) = a$ if for every $e > 0$ there exists a q_e such that for qRq_e we have $f(q) < a + e$, and for every e and q there exists a q_{eq} such that $q_{eq}Rq$ and $f(q_{eq}) > a - e$. Or $(e, q_e, qRq_e): f(q) < a + e$ and $(e, q, q_{eq}): q_{eq}Rq,\ f(q_{eq}) > a - e$.

This definition combines one inequality from the definition of limit with the reverse inequality from the statement for v. ap. For if $\overline{\lim}_q f(q) = a$, then $\lim_q g(q) = a$, so that $(e, q_e, qRq_e) : f(q) \leqq g(q) < a + e$. On the other hand, since $g(q) \geqq \overline{\lim}_q f(q) = a$, for all q, and $g(q)$ is the maximum of the set F_q, then for any e and q there exists $q_{eq}Rq$ such that $f(q_{eq}) \geqq g(q) - e > a - e$. Conversely, if $(e, q_e, qRq_e): f(q) < a + e$, then for qRq_e we have $g(q) \leqq a + e$; and if $(e, q, q_{eq}) : q_{eq}Rq,\ f(q) > a - e$, then for all q we have $g(q) \geqq a - e$. Hence $\overline{\lim}_q f(q) = \lim_q g(q) = a$.

Similar considerations show that if $\overline{\lim}_q f(q) = +\infty$, only the second statement is needed, i.e., $\overline{\lim}_q f(q) = +\infty$ if and only if for every $e > 0$ and q there exists a q_{eq} such that $q_{eq}Rq$ and $f(q_{eq}) > e$.

The other condition is automatically fulfilled. For $\overline{\lim}_q f(q) = -\infty$, only the first type of condition is needed, i.e., (e, q_e, qRq_e), $f(q) < -e$. It follows that if $\overline{\lim}_q f(q) = -\infty$, then $\lim_q f(q) = -\infty$.

The modifications in the above considerations needed for $\underline{\lim}_q f(q)$ are obvious, or can be deduced from the observation that:

4.3. $\underline{\lim}_q f(q) = -\overline{\lim}_q (-f(q))$.

From the various definitions of $\overline{\lim}_q f(q)$ and $\underline{\lim}_q f(q)$, when compared with those for $\lim_q f(q)$, it follows at once:

4.4. A necessary and sufficient condition that $\lim_q f(q)$ exist is that $\overline{\lim}_q f(q) = \underline{\lim}_q f(q)$.

We note the following properties of the extreme limits:

4.5. The statement $\overline{\lim}_q f(q) \leqq a$, for a finite is equivalent to (e, q_e, qRq_e): $f(q) < a + e$.

For if $\overline{\lim}_q f(q) = b$ and $b \leqq a$, then $(e, q_e, qRq_e) : f(q) < b + e \leqq a + e$. On the other hand, if $\overline{\lim}_q f(q) = b$, then (e, q, q_{eq}): $q_{eq}Rq$, $f(q) > b - e$. This combined with $(e, q_e, q'Rq_e)$: $f(q) < a + e$ for $q' = q_{eq} = q_{eq_e}$ gives $b - e < a + e$ for all $e > 0$, so that $b \leqq a$.

4.6. If $f(q)$ and $g(q)$ are any two functions on the directed set Q, then

$$\underline{\lim}_q f(q) + \underline{\lim}_q g(q) \leqq \underline{\lim}_q (f(q) + g(q)) \leqq \overline{\lim}_q f(q) + \underline{\lim}_q g(q)$$
$$\leqq \overline{\lim}_q (f(q) + g(q)) \leqq \overline{\lim}_q f(q) + \overline{\lim}_q g(q).$$

We demonstrate this set of inequalities for the case when all of the limits are finite. If $\overline{\lim}_q f(q) = a$ and $\overline{\lim}_q g(q) = b$, then (e, q_e, qRq_e): $f(q) < a + e$ and (e, q_e', qRq_e'): $g(q) < b + e$. It follows that $(e, q_e'', qRq_e'') : f(q) + g(q) < a + b + 2e$, where $q_e''Rq_e$ and $q_e''Rq_e'$. Consequently, by 4.5 $\overline{\lim}_q (f(q) + g(q)) \leqq a + b = \overline{\lim}_q f(q) + \overline{\lim}_q g(q)$. From this inequality, we obtain $\overline{\lim}_q (f(q) + g(q)) - \overline{\lim}_q f(q) \leqq \overline{\lim}_q g(q)$. On setting $f(q) + g(q) = h(q)$ and $k(q) = -f(q)$, so that $g(q) = h(q) + k(q)$, and using the relation between $\overline{\lim}$ and $\underline{\lim}$, we get $\overline{\lim}_q h(q) + \underline{\lim}_q k(q) \leqq \overline{\lim}_q (h(q) + k(q))$. The other two inequalities in the series follow from those already derived by using the relation $\overline{\lim}_q f(q) = -\underline{\lim}_q (-f(q))$.

The verification that these inequalities still hold if $+\infty$ and $-\infty$ are permitted as values for the limits, provided the ambiguous expression $+\infty - \infty$ does not occur is left as an exercise.

4.7. We note that if $\lim_q f(q)$ exists, i.e., $\overline{\lim}_q f(q) = \underline{\lim}_q f(q)$, then as a result of these inequalities $\overline{\lim}$ and $\underline{\lim}$ are distributive relative to addition, for example, $\overline{\lim}_q (f(q)+g(q)) = \lim_q f(q) + \overline{\lim}_q g(q)$.

5. Directed Sets of Sequential Character

A directed set Q is said to be of *sequential character* if there exists a sequence $\{q_n\}$ of elements of Q cofinal with Q.

The directed sets of sequential character are important because limit of a function on such sets is essentially a sequential limit. Of the instances of directed sets considered, those based on a metric or norm, i.e., where there exists a positive valued $|q|$ such that q_1Rq_2 is equivalent to $|q_1| \leqq |q_2|$, are of sequential character, any sequence $\{q_n\}$ such that $|q_n| \to 0$ monotonically will serve as the sequence of the definition. Special instances are $\lim_{x \to x_0} f(x)$ and the definition of Riemann integrals. However, if Q consists of all finite subsets of a general set P directed by inclusion, then usually Q will not be of sequential character.

The important property of limits on directed sets Q of sequential character is contained in the following theorem:

5.1. THEOREM. If Q is a directed set of sequential character, and $f(q)$ is on Q to real numbers, then $\lim_q f(q) = a$ if and only if for every monotone sequence $\{q_n\}$ cofinal with Q we have $\lim_n f(q_n) = a$.

The sequence q_n is monotone if for every n: q_nRq_{n-1}. If $\{q_n\}$ is any sequence cofinal with Q, then there exist monotone sequences cofinal with Q, the sequence $\{q_n'\}$, which is determined serially by the conditions $q_n'Rq_n$ and $q_n'Rq_{n-1}'$, being such a sequence.

That the condition stated is necessary follows from the definition of $\lim_q f(q) = a$. Observe, however, that the condition that the sequence $\{q_n\}$ be monotone is essential here.

For the sufficiency, suppose if possible that for every monotone sequence $\{q_n\}$ cofinal with Q we have $\lim_n f(q_n) = a$, but that $\lim_q f(q) \neq a$. Then there exists $e > 0$, such that for every q, there is a q_q with q_qRq and $|f(q_q) - a| > e$. Let $\{q_n\}$ be a sequence cofinal with Q. We can then determine for each n: q_n' such that $q_n'Rq_n$ and $q_n'Rq_{n-1}'$, such that $|f(q_n') - a| > e$, since there exists a q for which qRq_n and qRq_{n-1}' and a q_q with q_qRq such that $|f(q_q) - a| > e$. Then q_n' is monotone and cofinal with Q, but $\lim_n f(q_n') \neq a$, leading to a contradiction.

We have assumed that a is finite. The case when $a = \pm\infty$ follows similarly.

6. General Sums

As a very useful application of the theory of limits on directed sets, we define the notion of $\Sigma_p f(p)$, for a function f on a general set P to real numbers. We note that the sum of an infinite series $\Sigma_n a_n$ is defined as the limit of $s_n = \Sigma_{m=1}^n a_n$, a finite number of terms, when this limit exists. Similarly for $\Sigma_p f(p)$, we denote by q any finite number of elements: $p_1, \dots p_n$ of P and consider $g(q) = \Sigma_{p \text{ on } q} f(p) = \Sigma_{i=1}^n f(p_i)$. Now the class of finite subsets of P is a directed set ordered by inclusion. Hence we define:

6.1. Definition. The sum $\Sigma_p f(p) = \lim_q \Sigma_q f(p) = \lim_q \Sigma_{i=1}^n f(p_i)$, when this limit exists as a finite number.

We then have the following theorem:

6.2. If $f(p)$ is a real valued function on P, then $\Sigma_p f(p)$ exists if and only if $f(p)$ vanishes except for a denumerable set of elements: $p_1, \dots, p_n, \dots$ of P and $\Sigma_n | f(p_n) |$ is convergent. Then $\Sigma_n f(p_n)$ is absolutely convergent and is the value of $\Sigma_p f(p)$.

If $\lim_q \Sigma_q f(p)$ exists as a finite number, then the Cauchy condition of convergence applies and we have $(e, q_e, q_1 \supseteq q_e, q_2 \supseteq q_e)$: $| \Sigma_{q_1} f(p) - \Sigma_{q_2} f(p) | < e$. If we take $e = 1/n$, $q_2 = q_e$ and $q_1 = (q_e, p)$, where p is any element of P not in q_e, then $| f(p) | < 1/n$. Then the set of points of P for which $| f(p) | \geqq 1/n$ belong to q_e with $e = 1/n$ and is finite. Hence the set of points for which $f(p) \neq 0$ is denumerable. If we use the same inequality, set $q_1 = (q_2, p_1', \dots p_k')$ where $p_1', \dots p_k'$ are any points not in q_1 for which $f(p) > 0$, then $\Sigma_i f(p_i') < e$. It follows that $\Sigma_{p'} f(p')$ for p' ranging over the points for which $f(p') > 0$ is convergent. Similarly one shows that $\Sigma_{p''} f(p'')$ for p'' the points for which $f(p'') < 0$ is also convergent. Then if $p_1, \dots, p_n, \dots$ are the elements of P for which $f(p_n) \neq 0$, we have $\Sigma_n | f(p_n) |$ convergent, so that $\Sigma_n f(p_n)$ is absolutely convergent. Because of the convergence of $\Sigma_n | f(p_n) |$, we have $(e, n_e, m > n_e)$: $\Sigma_m^\infty | f(p_n) | < e$. If we take $q_e = (p_1, \dots, p_{n_e})$ and $q \supseteq q_e$, then

$$| \textstyle\sum_q f(p) - \sum_n f(p_n) | \leq \displaystyle\sum_{n_e+1}^{\infty} | f(p_n) | < e.$$

This says that $\lim_q \Sigma_q f(p) = \Sigma_n f(p_n)$.

We note that we have here a means of defining absolute convergence of an infinite series Σa_n without recourse to absolute values, via the property that $\lim_q \Sigma_q a_n$ with $q = (n_1, \ldots, n_m)$ exists.

The theorem is immediately extensible to the case when $f(p)$ is complex valued. In the case where $f(p)$ has values in a more general space with linear properties, the existence of $\lim_q \Sigma_q f(p)$ defines unconditional convergence rather than absolute convergence.

7. Double and Iterated Limits

If we have two directed sets Q_1 with relation R_1 and Q_2 with relation R_2 (Q_1 and Q_2 may be the same sets with the same or different relations), we can make the product set $Q_1 \times Q_2$ into a directed set by assuming that $q_1'q_2'Rq_1''q_2''$ is equivalent to $q_1'R_1q_1''$ and $q_2'R_2q_2''$, as a check on the postulates for directed sets shows at once. [If Q_α are any collection of directed sets with relations R_α, then the product set $Q = \Pi_\alpha Q_\alpha$ is a directed set if $q'Rq''$ is equivalent to $q_\alpha'R_\alpha q_\alpha''$ for all α.] We shall limit ourselves to two directed sets P and Q each with an order relation R of its own. For a function $f(p, q)$ defined on the product set $P \times Q$, we can then define the double limit:

7.1. Definition.

$$\lim_{pq} f(p, q) = a \equiv (e, p_e, q_e, pRp_e, qRq_e) : |f(p, q) - a| < e,$$

and similarly if $a = \pm\infty$.

In addition there are also the iterated limits: $\lim_p \lim_q f(p, q)$ and $\lim_q \lim_p f(p, q)$, where we assume that all the limits indicated exist. Of constant occurrence in analysis is the relationship between the double limit and the iterated limits, and the interchange of order of of limits in the iterated limits. We have the following:

7.2. THEOREM. If $\lim_{pq} f(p, q)$ exists as a finite number and $\lim_q f(p, q)$ exists for pRp_0, then $\lim_p \lim_q f(p, q)$ exists and is equal to $\lim_{pq} f(p, q)$.

For suppose $\lim_q f(p, q) = g(p)$ for pRp_0. Then

$$(e, pRp_0, q_{ep}, qRq_{ep}) : |f(p, q) - g(p)| < e.$$

If $\lim_{pq} f(p, q) = a$, then

$$(e, p_e, q_e, pRp_e, qRq_e) : |f(p, q) - a| < e.$$

Consequently, $(e, p_e', pRp_e') : |g(p) - a| < 2e$, where $p_e'Rp_0$ and $p_e'Rp_e$. For, for any pRp_e', we can select a q such that qRq_{ep} and qRq_e.

As an immediate consequence we have:

7.3. Corollary. If $\lim_{pq} f(p, q)$ exists as a finite number, $\lim_q f(p, q)$ exists for pRp_0 and $\lim_p f(p, q)$ exists for qRq_0, then $\lim_p \lim_q f(p, q)$ and $\lim_q \lim_p f(p, q)$ both exist and are equal to each other and to $\lim_{pq} f(p, q)$.

An easily remembered and useful condition for the interchange of order of limits in iterated limits is embodied in what we call:

7.4. The Iterated Limits Theorem. *If* $\lim_p f(p, q)$ *exists finitely for all* q, *and* $\lim_q f(p, q)$ *exists finitely for all* p *and uniformly on* P, *then* $\lim_p \lim_q f(p, q)$, $\lim_q \lim_p f(p, q)$, *and* $\lim_{pq} f(p, q)$ *all exist and are equal.*

Let $\lim_p f(p, q) = g(q)$ and $\lim_q f(p, q) = h(p)$. Then since $\lim_q f(p, q)$ exists uniformly on P, the corresponding Cauchy condition of convergence also holds uniformly on P, i.e.,

$$(e, q_e, q'Rq_e, q''Rq_e, p): |f(p, q') - f(p, q'')| < e.$$

On taking limits as to p, we have

$$(e, q_e, q'Rq_e, q''Rq_e) : | g(q') - g(q'') | < e,$$

so that $\lim_q g(q)$ or $\lim_q \lim_q f(p, q)$ exists. Call this limit a. By combining

$$(e, q_e', qRq_e', p) : | f(p, q) - h(p) | < e \tag{1}$$

$$(e, q, p_{eq}, pRp_{eq}) : | f(p, q) - g(p) | < e \tag{2}$$

$$(e, q_e'', qRq_e'') : | g(q) - a | \qquad < e \tag{3}$$

we get

$$(e, p_e, pRp_e) : | h(p) - a | < 3\,e \tag{4}$$

provided we take $p_e = p_{eq}$, with q any such that qRq_e' and qRq_e''. Then $\lim_p h(p) = a$, or $\lim_p \lim_q f(p, q) = \lim_q \lim_p f(p, q)$, so that both iterated limits exist and are equal. By combining statements (1) and (4), we get

$$(e, p_e, q_e', pRp_e, qRq_e') : | f(p, q) - a | < 4\,e \tag{5}$$

so that the double limit $\lim_{pq} f(p, q)$ also exists and is equal to the iterated limits. This completes the proof of the theorem.

We might note that by combining statements (3) and (5), we get

$$(e, p_e, q_e, pRp_e, qRq_e) : | f(p, q) - g(q) | < 5\,e \tag{6}$$

where q_eRq_e' and q_eRq_e''. This statement is a kind of ultimate uniformity as to q and is equivalent to $\lim_{pq}(f(p, q) - g(q)) = 0$. In the case where Q is the set of positive integers N in their natural order, we can deduce actual uniformity as to $N = Q$, i.e., we have:

7.5. Corollary. If $f(p, n) = f_n(p)$ is on $P \times N$, where P is a directed set, $\lim_p f_n(p)$ exists for each n, $\lim_n f_n(p)$ exists uniformly in p, then $\lim_n \lim_p f_n(p)$, $\lim_p \lim_n f_n(p)$ and $\lim_{np} f_n(p)$ all exist and are equal. Moreover, $\lim_p f_n(p)$ is uniform as to n.

For statement (6) in this setting reads $(e, n_e, p_e, n > n_e, pRp_e)$: $| f_n(p) - g_n | < 5\,e$. Now there are only a finite number of n's less than or equal to n_e for any given e and for each of these n's there exists a p_{en}, such that pRp_{en} implies $| f_n(p) - g_n | < 5\,e$. If we take p_e' so that $p_e'Rp_e$, $p_e'Rp_{en}$, $n = 1, \ldots, n_e$, then we have (e, p_e', pRp_e', n) : $| f_n(p) - g_n) | < 5\,e$, which means that $f_n(p)$ converges uniformly to g_n in n.

A careful examination of the proof of the iterated limits theorem shows that the uniformity of one of the inner limits is stronger than necessary and that a condition of the form of statement (6) will carry the argument. As a matter of fact, we have:

7.6 THEOREM. If $\lim_p f(p, q) = g(q)$ for each q, $\lim_q f(p, q) = h(p)$ for each p and if $\lim_{pq}(f(p, q) - h(p)) = 0$, then $\lim_p \lim_q f(p, q)$, $\lim_q \lim_p f(p, q)$, and $\lim_{pq} f(p, q)$ all exist and are equal.

For from $\lim_{pq}(f(p, q) - h(p)) = 0$ it follows that $(e, p_e, q_e, pRp_e, q'Rq_e, q''Rq_e)$: $| f(p, q') - h(p) | < e$, and $| f(p, q'') - h(p) | < e$. Then $| f(p, q') - f(p, q'') | < 2\,e$. If we take limits as to p, we deduce that $| g(q') - g(q'') | < 2\,e$ for $q'Rq_e$, $q''Rq_e$. Then $\lim_q g(q)$ exists. The remainder of the proof requires only slight alterations in statements (1) and (4) in the proof of the iterated limits theorem.

Many theorems of analysis are consequences of the iterated limits theorem. For instance: "if $f_n(x)$ on $[a, b]$ are continuous at $x = x_0$ and converge to $f(x)$ uniformly in some vicinity of x_0, then $f(x)$ is continuous at x_0" is such a theorem. We order the integers n in their natural order, and the x by the condition $x'Rx'' \equiv | x' - x_0 | < | x'' - x_0 |$. By Corollary I.7.5 we can conclude, moreover, that the measure of continuity d_{en} such that $| f_n(x) - f_n(x_0) | < e$ for $e > 0$, $| x - x_0 | < d_{en}$, is independent of n, i.e., the functions $f_n(x)$ are equally continuous at x_0. This suggests also the conjugate theorem: "if the functions $f_n(x)$ converge to $f(x)$ for $0 < | x - x_0 | < d$, and $f_n(x)$ are equally continuous at x_0, then $\lim_{x \to x_0} f(x) = \lim_n f_n(x_0)$." If we further assume convergence and equal continuity at all points of the closed interval $[a, b]$ and then apply statement (6) above with $P = N$, $Q = 0 < | x - x_0 | < d$ for each x_0, we obtain $(e, n_{ex_0}, d_{ex_0}, n > n_{ex_0}, \ 0 \leq | x - x_0 | < d_{ex_0}) : | f_n(x) - f(x) | < e$, x being permitted to be equal to x_0 because of the convergence at x_0. Applying the Borel theorem to the intervals $0 \leqq | x - x_0 | < d_{ex_0}$ yields a finite number of points $x_1,\ldots,x_m$, a finite number of intervals $0 \leqq | x - x_i | < d_{ex_i}$ covering $[a, b]$, a finite number of n's: $n_{ex_1}, \ldots, n_{ex_m}$, of which we can chose the largest n_e. As a consequence for $n > n_e$ and $a \leq x \leq b$, we have $| f_n(x) - f(x) | < e$, giving us the well known:

7.7 THEOREM. If $f_n(x)$ is a set of equally continuous functions on $[a, b]$ converging to $f(x)$ at all points of $[a, b]$, then the convergence of f_n to f is uniform on $[a, b]$ and $f(x)$ is continuous.

The conditions of uniformity in the hypothesis of the iterated limits theorem, while sufficient are not necessary for the existence of the iterated limits and the double limit and their equality. A situation which under certain conditions makes the uniformity condition necessary is covered by the following:

7.8. THEOREM. If P and Q are directed sets, if $f(p, q)$ on $P \times Q$ is monotonic nondecreasing in q for each p, and if $\lim_p \lim_q f(p, q) = \lim_q \lim_p f(p, q)$ where the limits exist as finite numbers, then $\lim_{pq} f(p, q)$ exists and is equal to the iterated limits. In particular, if either P or Q, Q say, is the set of positive integers N in their natural order, then $\lim_p f(p, q)$ is uniform as to $Q = N$.

Obviously, "nondecreasing" can be replaced by "nonincreasing."

Suppose $\lim_p f(p, q) = g(q)$ and $\lim_q f(p, q) = h(p)$ with $\lim_q g(q) = \lim_p h(p) = a$. Then obviously $g(q)$ is also nondecreasing in q and $\lim_q g(q) = \text{l.u.b. } g(q)$. Because of the monotoneity of $f(p, q)$ in q, we have $f(p, q) \leqq h(p)$ for all p and q. If we adjoin the fact that $\lim_p h(p) = a$, then $(e, p_e, pRp_e, q) : f(p, q) \leqq h(p) < a + 2e$. On the other hand, since $\lim_q g(q) = a$, we have $(e, q_e, qRq_e) : g(q) > a - e$. Fix q' so that $q'Rq_e$. Then $(e, q', p_e' = p_{eq'}, pRp_e') : f(p, q') > g(q') - e$. Consequently, for qRq' and pRp_e' we have: $f(p, q) \geqq f(p, q') \geqq g(q') - e > a - 2e$. If now we assume that $p_e''Rp_e$ and $p_e''Rp_e'$, then a combination of these statements yields: $(e, p_e'', q_e', pRp_e'', qRq_e') : a - 2e < f(p, q) < a + 2e$, which is the definition of $\lim_{pq} f(p, q) = a$.

The uniformity in case either P or Q is the set of positive integers in their natural order then follows from Corollary I.7.5 of the iterated limits theorem.

As a special case we have: if a_{mn} is a double sequence which is monotone nondecreasing in n for each m, and if $\lim_m \lim_n a_{mn} = \lim_n \lim_m a_{mn}$, then both the inner limits are uniform.

If we examine the proof of Theorem I.7.8, we note that we use only the fact that $\lim_q f(p, q) \leqq h(p)$ for all p.

This gives the following:

7.9. Corollary. If $f(p, q)$ is monotonic nondecreasing in q for each p, and if $\lim_q f(p, q) \leqq h(p)$ for each p, and $\lim_p h(p) = \lim_q \lim_p f(p, q)$ then $\lim_{pq} f(p, q)$ exists and is equal to $\lim_q \lim_p f(p, q)$.

8. Filters

The notion of filters was introduced into mathematical thinking by the Bourbaki group and has gained widespread recognition as a tool in analysis, even to the extent of displacing the more easily understood concept of directed set. We consequently devote this section to the relation between directed sets and filters.

8.1. Definition. If P is a fundamental class of elements, then a filter $\mathfrak{F}$ is a class of subsets of P which satisfies the following conditions:

(1) if F belongs to $\mathfrak{F}$, and the set E contains F then E belongs to $\mathfrak{F}$;

(2) if F_1 and F_2 belong to $\mathfrak{F}$, then F_3, their intersection or the set of all elements in both F_1 and F_2, belongs to $\mathfrak{F}$;

(3) the null set does not belong to $\mathfrak{F}$.

The conditions on a filter are strongly reminiscent of the conditions on a set of vicinities of a point in topological space. In particular, if no vicinity of p consists of p only, then the vicinities of a point p with p omitted form a filter, provided condition (1) is satisfied.

If $f(p)$ is a function on P, then limit of $f(p)$ relative to the filter $\mathfrak{F}$ is defined:

8.2. Definition. $\lim_{\mathfrak{F}} f(p) = a$ if and only if for every $e > 0$,there exists a set F_e in the filter $\mathfrak{F}$ such that $|f(p) - a| < e$ for all p in F_e, or $(e, F_e, p \text{ in } F_e) : |f(p) - a| < e$.

A class $\mathfrak{B}$ of subsets B of P is called a *base* for $\mathfrak{F}$ if $\mathfrak{B}$ is a subclass of $\mathfrak{F}$, and if for every F of $\mathfrak{F}$, there exists a B of $\mathfrak{B}$ contained in F.

Then:

8.3. THEOREM. If $\mathfrak{B}$ is a base for the filter $\mathfrak{F}$, then $\lim_{\mathfrak{F}} f(p) = a$ if and only if $\lim_{\mathfrak{B}} f(p) = a$.

For suppose $\lim_{\mathfrak{F}} f(p) = a$, i.e., $(e, F_e, p \text{ in } F_e): |f(p) - a| < e$. If B_e is contained in F_e, then obviously $(e, B_e, p \text{ in } B_e): |f(p) - a| < e$, i.e., $\lim_{\mathfrak{B}} f(p) = a$. Since $\mathfrak{B}$ is contained $\mathfrak{F}$, the converse is obvious.

If we desire that $\mathfrak{B}$ generate $\mathfrak{F}$ by adding to $\mathfrak{B}$ all the subsets of P which contain a set B of $\mathfrak{B}$, then $\mathfrak{F}$ will be a filter if we assume that $\mathfrak{B}$ has the properties: (2′) if B_1 and B_2 belong to $\mathfrak{B}$, then there exists in $\mathfrak{B}$ a set B_3 contained in the intersection of B_1 and B_2; and (3) $\mathfrak{B}$ is not vacuous and does not contain the null set.

For if F_1 contains B_1 and F_2 contains B_2, then the intersection of F_1 and F_2 will contain any B_3 contained in both B_1 and B_2.

In order to apply the notion of filters to the convergence of a sequence of real numbers a_n, we let P be the set N of positive integers. The filter $\mathfrak{F}$ consists of all subsets of N obtained by omitting a finite number of elements from N. A base $\mathfrak{B}$ of $\mathfrak{F}$ consists of all sets N_k defined by the integers $n > k$.

8.4. THEOREM. Any directed set Q with relation R gives rise to a filter $\mathfrak{F}$ on Q.

We define the sets B_q = [the set of all q' such that $q'Rq$]. Then the class $\mathfrak{B}$ of B_q satisfies the conditions (2′) and (3). For B_{q_1} and B_{q_2} will contain the set B_{q_3} where the q_3 such that q_3Rq_1 and q_3Rq_2 exists by the compositive property. Moreover, B_q is not vacuous since the compositive property applied to q and q assures the existence of an element q_1 such that q_1Rq. As a consequence, if we add to $\mathfrak{B}$ all subsets of Q containing a set B, then the resulting class of sets is a filter. Moreover, $\lim_q f(q) = a$ is by definition equivalent to $\lim_{\mathfrak{B}} f(q) = a$ and so to $\lim_{\mathfrak{F}} f(q) = a$.

8.5. Conversely, a filter is a directed set.

For suppose $\mathfrak{F}$ is a filter on P. If we call $\mathfrak{F}$ the set Q and define q_1Rq_2 by inclusion, i.e., $F_1 \subset F_2$, then Q is a directed set. The function $f(p)$ on P to reals gives rise to the many-valued function $f(F)$ on Q or the filter $\mathfrak{F}$, where $f(F)$ includes all $f(p)$ for p in F. Then $\lim_{\mathfrak{F}} f(p) = a$ is obviously equivalent to $\lim_{\mathfrak{F}} f(F) = \lim_q f(q) = a$.

We see then that limits via filters or directed sets are in a sense equivalent. We shall restrict ourselves to directed sets, since we consider them a simpler concept than filters.

The contrast between directed sets and filters is illustrated by considering the definition of unconditional convergence of an infinite series $\Sigma_n a_n$ as being equivalent to the existence of the $\lim_q \Sigma_q a_n$, where

$q = (n_1, \ldots, n_m)$, finite subsets of the integers N. One might perhaps expect that the filter connected with this limit would be determined by the complements of finite subsets of the integers N. This is not the case. Our basic Q is the set of all finite subsets q of N. Consequently, the equivalent filter has as its base $\mathfrak{B}$, the sets B_q, where B_q is the class of all finite subsets of N containing the set q. To characterize the sets F of the filter $\mathfrak{F}$ adds additional complications.

EXERCISES

1. Show that if $\pm\infty$ are allowed as values of $\lim_q f(q)$ and $\lim_q g(q)$, where f and g are defined on the directed set Q, then $\lim_q (f(q) + g(q)) = \lim_q f(q) + \lim_q g(q)$, excepting for the ambiguous case $+\infty - \infty$.

2. Show that if $\pm\infty$ are allowed as values of $\overline{\lim}_q$ and $\underline{\lim}_q$, then for two functions $f(q)$ and $g(q)$ on the directed set Q we have:

$$\underline{\lim}_q f(q) + \underline{\lim}_q g(q) \leqq \underline{\lim}_q (f(q) + g(q)) \leqq \overline{\lim}_q f(q) + \underline{\lim}_q g(q)$$
$$\leqq \overline{\lim}_q (f(q) + g(q)) \leqq \overline{\lim}_q f(q) + \overline{\lim}_q g(q),$$

provided $+\infty - \infty$ is not involved.

3. Under what conditions would relations similar to those of Exs. 1 and 2 hold for limits of products and products of limits of two functions?

4. Given $f(p, q)$ on the product $P \times Q$ of the directed sets P and Q. Let $g(q)$ be the many-valued function v.ap.$_p f(p, q)$. Show that if $\lim_{pq} f(p, q)$ exists as a finite number, then $\lim_q g(q) = \lim_{pq} f(p, q)$.

5. Deduce properties of a generalized iterated limit of a function $f(p, q)$ on the product $P \times Q$ of the directed sets P and Q, defined: for every $e > 0$, there exists p_e such that if pRp_e, then there exists q_{ep} such that if qRq_{ep}, then $|f(p, q) - a| < e$.

6. If $f_n(x)$ is a sequence of continuous functions on the closed interval $[a, b]$ such that $f_{n+1}(x) \geqq f_n(x)$ for every n and x, and if $\lim_n f_n(x) = f(x)$ is continuous, then the convergence of $f_n(x)$ to $f(x)$ is uniform on $[a, b]$.

7. If $f_n(x)$ is a sequence of monotonic nondecreasing functions on the closed interval $[a, b]$, and if $\lim_n f_n(x) = f(x)$ and $f(x)$ is continuous, show that the convergence of $f_n(x)$ to $f(x)$ is uniform on $[a, b]$.

8. Suppose the double sequence a_{mn} is such that (a) $\Sigma_n |a_{mn}|$ converges for each m, (b) $\lim_m a_{mn} = a_n$ for each n, and (c) $\lim_m \Sigma_n |a_{mn}| = \Sigma_n |a_n|$. Show that $\lim_m \Sigma_n |a_{mn} - a_n| = 0$.

REFERENCES

On Moore-Smith general limit:

E. H. MOORE: Definition of limit in general analysis, *Proc. Natl. Acad. Sci.* **1** (1915) 628.

E. H. MOORE and H. L. SMITH: A general theory of limits, *Am. J. Math.* **44** (1922) 102-121.

H. L. SMITH: A general theory of limits, *Natl. Math. Mag.* **12** (1938) 371-379.

G. BIRKHOFF: Moore-Smith convergence in general topology. *Ann. Math.* (2) **38** (1937) 39-56.

E. J. MCSHANE: Partial orderings and Moore-Smith limits, *Am. Math. Mon.* **59** (1952) 1-10.

On Filters:

N. BOURBAKI: Elements de Mathematiques XVI. Pt. I, livre III: Topologie Generale, Actualités sci. et ind. No. 1196. (1953) p. 8 ff.

9. Linear Spaces

Although not immediately connected with the notion of general limits, the idea of linear spaces has so many of its roots in the theory of integration that it seems desirable to devote a paragraph of this introductory chapter to a summary of some of the important basic concepts connected with such spaces.

9.1. Definition. A *space* is any collection of elements usually subjected to certain conditions or having certain properties.

9.2. Definition. A *linear or vector space* X of elements $x, y, z, \ldots$ is a set of elements subjected to the following conditions:

(a) There is an operation $+$ between any two elements of X to an element of X, under which X forms an Abelian group, that is:

(1) for every x, y of X there exists a z of X such that $z = x + y$,

(2) for every x, y of X: $x + y = y + x$,

(3) for every x, y, z of X: $x + (y + z) = (x + y) + z$,

(4) for every x, y of X there exists a z in X such that $x + z = y$.

As a consequence there exists a unique element of X its zero denoted 0 such that for all x: $x + 0 = 0 + x = x$.

(b) To every number a and element x of X there corresponds an element ax such that

(5) $1 \cdot x = x$ for all x,

(6) for all numbers a and b, and x of X: $(ab)x = a(bx)$,

(7) for all numbers a and x, y of X: $a(x + y) = ax + ay$,

(8) for all numbers a and b and x of X: $(a + b)\, x = ax + bx$.

It follows that $0 \cdot x = \mathit{0}$ for all x. Here numbers may be limited to the field of real numbers or may be the field of complex numbers. We shall limit ourselves to the real numbers, i.e., to *real linear spaces*.

Most simple instances of linear spaces are classes of functions on some range P. If $f(p)$ and $g(p)$ are two such functions, then usually $(f + g)(p) = f(p) + g(p)$, and $(af)(p) = a \cdot f(p)$ for all p of P. Instances of linear spaces are: (1) the set of all functions on a range P; (2) the set of all bounded functions on a range P; (3) if Q is a directed set, then the set of all functions $f(q)$ for which $\lim_q f(q)$ exists forms a linear space (this is another way of stating the first part of Theorems I.2.1 and I.2.3); (3′) the set of all functions $f(q)$ on the directed set Q such that $\lim_q f(q) = 0$ is a linear space; (4) the set of all functions on a range P for which $\Sigma_p f(p)$ as defined in I.6 exists. This set is identical with the set of all functions for which $\Sigma_p | f(p) | < \infty$; (5) the set of all sequences a_n such that $\Sigma_n a_n$ exists; (6) the set of all continuous functions on an interval $[a, b]$.

The linear spaces which parallel the class of real numbers in their properties are the normed linear spaces. We define:

9.3. Definition. X is a *normed linear space* if there exists on X a norm: $\| x \|$ satisfying the conditions:

(1) for every x of X: $\| x \| \geqq 0$;

(2) for every x and y of X: $\| x + y \| \leq \| x \| + \| y \|$, or equivalently:

(2′) for every x, y, z of X: $\| x - z \| \leqq \| x - y \| + \| y - z \|$, which is usually called the triangle property;

(3) for every number a and x of X: $\| ax \| = | a | \cdot \| x \|$;

(4) $\| x \| = 0$ if and only if $x = \mathit{0}$.

If X is the set of all bounded functions $f(p)$ on P, then $\| f \|$ can defined as the l.u.b. $| f(p) |$ for p on P. If X is the set of all functions $f(p)$ on P such that $\Sigma_p | f(p) | < \infty$, then $\| f \|$ can be defined as $\Sigma_p | f(p) |$.

In terms of the norm, it is customary to define the notion of limit:

$$\lim_n x_n = x \text{ is equivalent to } \lim_n \| x_n - x \| = 0,$$

or if Q is a directed set

$$\lim_q x_q = x \text{ is equivalent to } \lim_q \| x_q - x \| = 0.$$

However, limits in linear spaces need not be limited to such norm limits. For instance, if X is a space of functions on P, we can define "lim"$_n f_n$ by pointwise convergence: $\lim_n f_n(p) = f(p)$ for all p of P. Or we can define "lim"$_n f_n = f$ as $\lim_n f_n(p) = f(p)$ uniformly on P. Or we may define "lim"$_n f_n = f$ provided there exists a set of subsets of P: P_a such that $P = \Sigma_a P_a$ and $\lim_n f_n(p) = f(p)$ uniformly on each P_a. Similar statements hold for directed limits.

Of particular importance among linear spaces are the linear normed complete spaces. We define:

9.4. Definition. X is a *linear normed complete space* if it satisfies the Cauchy conditon of convergence relative to the norm, i.e., if for every sequence of elements x_n such that $\lim_{m,n} \| x_m - x_n \| = 0$ there exists an element x in X such that $\lim_n \| x_n - x \| = 0$.

Such spaces are frequently called Banach spaces. We prefer the terminology "linear normed complete" because these spaces were considered by many mathematicians before Banach, and also because the terminology adequately describes the character of these spaces in contrast to other linear spaces.

In addition to completeness relative to sequences one might also have completeness relative to any or some directed sets Q, in the sense that if $x(q)$ is on the directed set Q to X and such that $\lim_{q_1 q_2} \| x(q_1) - x(q_2) \| = 0$, then there exists an element x of X such that $\lim_q \| x(q) - x \| = 0$. Following the proof as given for the special case when $x(q)$ are real numbers in I.2.11, it is easy to show that:

9.5. THEOREM. If X is a linear normed complete space, then it has the completeness property also relative to any function $x(q)$ on any directed set Q to X.

For limits in a linear space, it is not always true that a sequential type of completeness when it exists and holds carries with it completeness relative to all directed sets.

A *functional* on a linear space is in fact a function; f on the space X assigns to elements x real numbers.

Of particular interest are the linear functionals, defined:

9.6. Definition. $f(x)$ is a linear functional or form on the linear space X if it assigns a real number to each x of X and if for a and b real numbers and x and y elements of X we have $f(ax + by) = af(x) + bf(y)$.

9.7. Definition. In a linear normed space, a linear functional is *continuous* if $\lim_n \| x_n - x \| = 0$ implies $\lim_n f(x_n) = f(x)$ or $\lim_n f(x_n - x) = 0$. It is an easy matter to prove:

9.8 THEOREM. A necessary and sufficient condition that a linear functional on a linear space X be continuous is that there exists a constant M such that $| f(x) | \leqq M \| x \|$ for all x of X, or that $f(x)$ be bounded (or limited) on X.

As an example of a linear functional, we might note that if X is the class of real valued functions f on the directed set Q, such that $\lim_q f(q)$ exists, then $\lim_q f(q)$ is a linear functional on this linear class, which is another way of stating Theorems I.2.1 and I.2.3.

CHAPTER II

RIEMANNIAN TYPE OF INTEGRATION

In this chapter, we take up some types of integrals suggested by the Riemann definition of integral. We consider first functions defined on a subinterval of the real line, and consider later the extension to two or higher dimensions. As a basis we develop first the properties of integrals of functions of intervals, using the theory of the Riemann integral as a guide. Properties of functions of bounded variation are summarized as an instance of integrals of functions of intervals. Then Riemann-Stieltjes integrals are developed first for the case of any two functions, and then particularly for the case where the function with respect to which the integral is taken is of bounded variation. Finally the integration theory for one-dimensional space is in part extended to two or more dimensions in the next chapter.

1. Functions of Intervals

We assume a basic finite interval $[a, b] \equiv a \leqq x \leqq b$, denoted by X. Subintervals $[c, d]$ with $a \leqq c \leqq x \leqq d \leqq b$ will be denoted by I. Although we have indicated that $I = [c, d]$ means the closed interval $c \leqq x \leqq d$, for most of the considerations of this chapter, it is immaterial whether I be closed, open, or half-open.

1.1. Definition. An *interval function*, or *function of intervals* $f(I)$ is assumed to be defined for all subintervals of $[a, b]$ and may be many valued.

We mention some examples of functions of intervals. Suppose $g(x)$ is a bounded point function on $[a, b]$. Then $g(x)$ gives rise to the following interval functions:

(1) $f(I) = g(x)$ for $c \leqq x \leqq d$;

(2a) $f(I) =$ l.u.b. $g(x)$ for x on $[c, d]$;

(2b) $f(I) =$ g.l.b. $g(x)$ for x on $[c, d]$;

(3) $f(I) = g(d) - g(c)$;

(4) $f(I) = | g(d) - g(c) |$;

(5) $f(I) =$ *oscillation* of $g(x)$ on $[c, d] =$ l.u.b. $[|g(x_1) - g(x_2)|$ for x_1, and x_2 on $[c, d]] = \omega(g; I) =$ l.u.b. of interval function (4) for all I' contained in I;

(6) $f(I) = g(x)\,(d - c) = g(x) l(I)$ for all x of $[c, d]$;

(6a) $f(I) =$ (l.u.b. $f(x)$ on $[c, d]$) $(d - c) = M(d - c)$;

(6b) $f(I) =$ (g.l.b. $f(x)$ on $[c, d]$) $(d - c) = m(d - c)$;

(6c) $f(I) = g(c)\,(d - c)$ or $f(I) = g(d)\,(d - c)$;

(7) $f(I) = (g(d) - g(c))/(d - c)$ of interest in connection with derivatives;

(8) $f(I) = (g(d) - g(c))^2/(d - c)$.

If we have two point functions $g(x)$ and $h(x)$ we get:

(9) $f(I) = g(x')\,(h(d) - h(c))$ with $c \leqq x \leqq d$, which leads to Riemann-Stieltjes integrals. Some modifications of this are:

(9a) $f(I) = g(c)\,(h(d) - h(c))$ or $f(I) = g(d)\,(h(d) - h(c))$;

(9b) $f(I) = (g(c) + g(d))\,(h(d) - h(c))/2$;

(9c) $f(I) = (g(x_1) + \ldots g(x_k))\,(h(d) - h(c))/k$, where $x_1, \ldots, x_k$ are points, possibly restricted, of $[c, d]$;

(10) $f(I) = (g(d) - g(c))/(h(d) - h(c))$ where $h(c) \neq h(d)$ for all c, d of $[a, b]$;

(11) $f(I) = (g(d) - g(c))^2/(h(d) - h(c))$, which occurs in the theory of Hellinger integrals.

A function of intervals in turn can give rise to other functions of intervals, e.g., if $f(I)$ is a function of intervals then $| f(I) |$; l.u.b. $f(I)$; g.l.b. $f(I)$; l.u.b. $[f(I')$ for I' contained in $I]$; g.l.b. $[f(I')$ for I' contained in $I]$ are functions of intervals.

1.2. Definition. A single-valued function of intervals is said to be *additive* if for every division of any I into a finite number of adjacent intervals $I_1, \ldots, I_k$, so that $I = I_1 + I_2 + \ldots + I_k$, we have $f(I) = \Sigma_{i=1}^k f(I_i)$. A single-valued function $f(I)$ is said to be *upper semiadditive* if under the same conditions $f(I) \leqq \Sigma_{i=1}^k f(I_i)$, *lower semiadditive* if $f(I) \geqq \Sigma_{i=1}^k f(I_i)$.

If $f(I)$ is additive, then obviously $| f(I) |$ is upper semiadditive. The indefinite Riemann integral is an additive function of intervals.

Example (6 a) above is lower semiadditive, and (6 b) is upper semiadditive.

If $f(I)$ is an additive function of intervals of $[a, b]$, then $f(I)$ is completely determined by the point function $g(x) = f[a, x]$, since $f[c, d] = f[a, d] - f[a, c] = g(d) - g(c)$.

2. Integrals of Functions of Intervals

We call a *subdivision* (or partition) of $[a, b]$ a division of $[a, b]$ into a finite number of adjacent intervals by the points $a = x_0 < x_1 < \ldots < x_n = b$ or by the intervals I_i: $[x_{i-1} \leqq x \leqq x_i]$, $i = 1 \ldots n$. We shall denote such a subdivision by σ, where σ can mean either $(x_0, x_1, \ldots, x_n)$ or $(I_1, \ldots, I_n)$. We shall say that σ_1 is *finer* than or a *refinement* of σ_2, denoted by $\sigma_1 \geq \sigma_2$, if every x_i of σ_2 is contained in σ_1 or every interval of σ_1 is a subinterval of some interval in σ_2. For one-dimensional space, it is usually more convenient to assume σ given by the points of subdivision. We shall denote by $\sigma_1 + \sigma_2$, the totality of dividing points in both σ_1 and σ_2 arranged in linear order.

As indicated in I.1, it is possible to make a directed set out of the subdivisions of $[a, b]$ in two distinct ways: (a) by introducing a metric or *norm* and defining $|\sigma| =$ maximum of lengths of I_i or of $x_i - x_{i-1}$, the norm order relation $\sigma_1 R \sigma_2$ being equivalent to $|\sigma_1| \leqq |\sigma_2|$; (b) by defining $\sigma_1 R \sigma_2$ by set inclusion, i.e., $\sigma_1 \geq \sigma_2$ if σ_1 contains all of the points of σ_2, or σ_1 is finer than σ_2.

Any interval function $f(I)$ and a subdivision σ of $[a, b]$ give rise to a function of $g(\sigma) = \Sigma_{i=1}^{n} f(I_i)$, where $\sigma = (I_1, \ldots, I_n)$. The two methods of ordering subdivisions then give rise to two types of integrals for interval functions.

2.1. Definition. We shall say that: *the interval function $f(I)$ on* $[a, b]$ *has a norm integral on* $[a, b]$ (denoted $N \int_a^b f(dI)$), *if* $\lim_{|\sigma| \to 0} g(\sigma) = \lim_{|\sigma| \to 0} \Sigma_{i=1}^{n} f(I_i)$ *exists.*

2.2. Definition. *The function $f(I)$ on* $[a, b]$ *has a σ-integral* (denoted $\sigma \int_a^b f(dI)$), *if* $\lim_\sigma g(\sigma) = \lim_\sigma \Sigma_i f(I_i)$ *exists in the sense of successive subdivisions or refinements.*

The Riemann integral $\int_a^b g(x)dx$ is a norm integral based on the interval function (6): $f(I) = g(x)\,(d - c)$, $c \leqq x \leqq d$, the Darboux upper and lower integrals $\overline{\int}_a^b g(x)dx$ and $\underline{\int}_a^b g(x)dx$ are σ-integrals based on the interval functions (6 a) and (6 b), viz., $f(I) =$ (g.l.b. $g(x)$ on

$[c, d])$ $(d-c)$ and $f(I) = $ (l.u.b. $g(x)$ on $[c, d])$ $(d-c)$, respectively. Obviously, if $f(I)$ is additive, then for all σ, $\Sigma_\sigma f(I) = f(X)$, so that $\int_a^b f(dI)$ exists in either sense and has the value $f(X)$.

If $\Sigma_\sigma f(I)$ does not have a limit, we have values approached and greatest and least of the limits. As a consequence we define $N \overline{\int_a^b} f(dI) = \overline{\lim}_{|\sigma| \to 0} \Sigma_\sigma f(I)$ and $\sigma \overline{\int_a^b} f(dI) = \overline{\lim}_\sigma \Sigma_\sigma f(I)$ and similarly for the lower integrals $N \underline{\int_a^b} f(dI)$ and $\sigma \underline{\int_a^b} f(dI)$. The Darboux upper and lower intergrals for a point function $g(x)$ are the upper and lower σ-integrals for $f(I) = g(x)\,(d-c)$ with $c \leqq x \leqq d$.

3. Existence Theorems

Since the two types of integrals we are considering are special cases of limits of real valued functions on directed sets, we are able to apply the general theory. We therefore have:

3.1. THEOREM (Cauchy condition of convergence). A necessary and sufficient condition that $N \int_a^b f(dI)$ or $\sigma \int_a^b f(dI)$ exist is that the corresponding Cauchy condition of convergence holds, i.e.,

for the norm integral:

$$(e, d_e, |\sigma_1| < d_e, |\sigma_2| < d_e) : |\sum_{\sigma_1} f(I) - \sum_{\sigma_2} f(I)| < e$$

for the σ-integral:

$$(e, \sigma_e, \sigma_1 \geq \sigma_e, \sigma_2 \geq \sigma_e) : |\sum_{\sigma_1} f(I) - \sum_{\sigma_2} f(I)| < e.$$

These statements can be replaced by

$$\lim_{(|\sigma_1|, |\sigma_2|) \to (0,0)} (\sum_{\sigma_1} f(I) - \sum_{\sigma_2} f(I)) = 0$$

and

$$\lim_{\sigma_1 \sigma_2} (\sum_{\sigma_1} f(I) - \sum_{\sigma_2} f(I)) = 0,$$

respectively. Also since from $|\Sigma_{\sigma_3} f(I) - \Sigma_{\sigma_1} f(I)| < e$ and $|\Sigma_{\sigma_3} f(I) - \Sigma_{\sigma_2} f(I)| < e$, it follows that $|\Sigma_{\sigma_1} f(I) - \Sigma_{\sigma_2} f(I)| < 2e$, an equivalent statement can be obtained by replacing the condition on σ_2 in each case by $\sigma_2 \geq \sigma_1$, so that for instance for the norm integral, the Cauchy condition of convergence might read: $(e, d_e, |\sigma_1| < d_e, \sigma_2 \geq \sigma_1) : |\Sigma_{\sigma_2} f(I) - \Sigma_{\sigma_1} f(I)| < e$. For we can compare $\Sigma_{\sigma_1} f(I)$

and $\Sigma_{\sigma_2} f(I)$ with $\Sigma_{\sigma_1+\sigma_2} f(I)$ since $|\sigma_1| < d_e$ and $|\sigma_2| < d_e$ implies $|\sigma_1 + \sigma_2| < d_e$.

A second existence theorem is the following:

3.2. THEOREM. A necessary and sufficient condition that $\int_a^b f(dI)$ exist is that the corresponding upper and lower integrals: $\overline{\int}_a^b f(dI)$ and $\underline{\int}_a^b f(dI)$ be finite and equal.

Note that these upper and lower integrals are defined in terms of extreme limits, not as in the case of Riemann integrals as least upper and greatest lower bounds.

For the norm integral there exists a reduction of the norm limit to sequential limits, so that we have:

3.3. THEOREM. A necessary and sufficient condition that $N \int_a^b f(dI)$ exist is that for every sequence of subdivisions σ_n of $[a, b]$ such that $\lim_n |\sigma_n| = 0$ the approximating sums $\Sigma_{\sigma_n} f(I)$ shall converge to a finite limit.

The necessity is obvious since any sequence σ_n such that $\lim_n |\sigma_n| = 0$, is cofinal with $|\sigma| \to 0$. On the other hand, if $\lim_n \Sigma_{\sigma_n} f(I)$ exists for every σ_n such that $|\sigma_n| \to 0$, then this limit is the same for all sequences, since any two sequences σ_n and σ_n' could be combined into a single sequence σ_n'' having the same property, for which $\lim_n \Sigma_{\sigma_n''} f(I)$ exists uniquely. Suppose then $\lim_{|\sigma| \to 0} \Sigma_\sigma f(I)$ does not exist or is not equal to this common limit a. Then there exists $e > 0$, such that for every n there exists σ_n with $|\sigma_n| < 1/n$ and $|\Sigma_{\sigma_n} f(I) - a| > e$. Consequently, $\lim_n \Sigma_{\sigma_n} f(I) \neq a$, which leads to a contradiction.

We observe that we have demonstrated essentially that if a directed set Q is directed via a norm: $|q|$ so that $\lim_q f(q)$ is equivalent to $\lim_{|q| \to 0} f(q)$, then a necessary and sufficient condition that $\lim_q f(q)$ exist is that $\lim_n f(q_n)$ exist for every sequence $\{q_n\}$ such that $|q_n| \to 0$ (compare I.5.1.).

For the case when $f(I)$ is single valued and upper semiadditive (lower semiadditive) the sums $\Sigma_\sigma f(I)$ are monotonic nondecreasing (nonincreasing) as functions of σ. Consequently:

3.4. THEOREM. If $f(I)$ is single-valued and upper (lower) semiadditive and $\Sigma_\sigma f(I)$ is bounded above (below) as to σ, then $\sigma \int_a^b f(dI)$ exists and is equal to $\text{l.u.b.}_\sigma \Sigma_\sigma f(I)$ $(\text{g.l.b.}_\sigma \Sigma_\sigma f(I))$.

As an instance, we note that if $g(x)$ is a point function on $[a, b]$ and $f(I) = |g(d) - g(c)|$ then $f(I)$ is upper semiadditive, so that if $g(x)$ is of bounded variation, the total variation of g is the $\sigma \int_a^b f(dI)$. We shall consequently write $V_a^b g(x) = \int_a^b |dg|$. Further, the Darboux integrals of a bounded point function $g(x)$ are σ-integrals of the interval functions (6a) and (6b) listed in Section 1 above.

For a slightly more sophisticated existence theorem, we define the oscillation function: $\omega(Sf; I)$, which is an interval function, as follows:

3.5. Definition. $\omega(Sf; I) =$ l.u.b. $[| \Sigma_{\sigma_1} f - \Sigma_{\sigma_2} f |$, for all σ_1 and σ_2 of $I]$.
Here $\Sigma_\sigma f$ stands for the sum of $f(I')$ over all the intervals I' belonging to σ.

This oscillation functions $\omega(Sf; I)$ is positive and lower semiadditive. For if $I = I_1 + I_2$, with I_1 and I_2 adjacent, then for $e > 0$, there exist subdivisions σ_1' and σ_1'' of I_1 and σ_2' and σ_2'' of I_2 such that

$$0 \leqq \omega(Sf; I_1) - (\textstyle\sum_{\sigma_1'} f - \sum_{\sigma_1''} f) < e$$

and

$$0 \leqq \omega(Sf; I_2) - (\textstyle\sum_{\sigma_2'} f - \sum_{\sigma_2''} f) < e.$$

Then

$$\omega(Sf; I_1) + \omega(Sf; I_2) < 2e + (\textstyle\sum_{\sigma'} f - \sum_{\sigma''} f) \leqq 2e + \omega(Sf; I),$$

where $\sigma' = \sigma_1' + \sigma_2'$ and $\sigma'' = \sigma_1'' + \sigma_2''$. Since the inequality holds for all e, we get $\omega(Sf; I_1) + \omega(Sf; I_2) \leqq \omega(Sf; I)$, the lower semi-additivity of $\omega(Sf; I)$.

With the aid of this oscillation function, we obtain a third existence theorem for integrals of interval functions.

3.6. THEOREM. A necessary and sufficient condition that $N \int_a^b f(dI)$ exist is that $N \int_a^b \omega(Sf; dI) = 0$; that $\sigma \int_a^b f(dI)$ exist is that

$$\sigma \int_a^b \omega(Sf; dI) = 0, \quad \text{or} \quad \text{g.l.b.}_\sigma \textstyle\sum_\sigma \omega(Sf; I) = 0.$$

We shall prove only the first half of this theorem, i.e., for the norm integral, the case for the σ-integral follows the same line of argument. We show that the conditions of the theorem are equivalent to the Cauchy condition of convergence.

Suppose $N \int_a^b \omega(Sf; dI) = 0$. Then

$$(e, d_e, |\sigma| < d_e) : \textstyle\sum_\sigma \omega(Sf; I) < e.$$

Suppose $|\sigma_1| < d_e$ and $\sigma_2 \geq \sigma_1$. Then by rearrangement of terms, so as to bring together the terms in each subinterval of σ_1, we find that

$$|\sum_{\sigma_1} f(I) - \sum_{\sigma_2} f(I)| \leq \sum_{\sigma_1} \omega(Sf; I) < e,$$

so that the Cauchy condition of convergence holds in its second form. On the other hand suppose for $e > 0$, d_e is determined by the Cauchy condition of convergence, and select σ so that $|\sigma| < d_e$. Let σ consist of the n points $a = x_0 < x_1 < \ldots < x_n = b$. Then on $[x_{i-1}, x_i]$, we can find σ_i' and σ_i'' so that

$$\sum_{\sigma_i'} f - \sum_{\sigma_i''} f \geqq 0,$$

and

$$\omega(Sf; [x_{i-1}, x_i]) \leqq \sum_{\sigma_i'} f - \sum_{\sigma_i''} f + e/n.$$

If we set $\sigma' = \Sigma_i \sigma_i'$ and $\sigma'' = \Sigma_i \sigma_i''$ then $|\sigma'| < d_e$ and $|\sigma''| < d_e$ and

$$0 \leqq \sum_{\sigma} \omega(Sf; [x_{i-1}, x_i]) \leqq \sum_i (\sum_{\sigma_i'} f - \sum_{\sigma_i''} f) + e$$

$$\leqq \sum_{\sigma'} f - \sum_{\sigma''} f + e < 2e.$$

Then $N \int_a^b \omega(Sf; dI) = 0$.

3.7. Definition. We shall call an interval function *pseudoadditive at a point x if*

$$\lim_{d', d'' \to (0,0)} (f[x - d', x + d''] - f[x - d', x] - f[x, x + d'']) = 0,$$

with $d' > 0$ and $d'' > 0$.

Then the Cauchy condition of convergence gives rise to the following necessary condition for the existence of the norm integral of an interval function $f(I)$:

3.8. THEOREM. A necessary condition that $N \int_a^b f(dI)$ exist is that $f(I)$ be pseudoadditive at every interior point of $[a, b]$.

This results from a comparison of $\Sigma_{\sigma_1} f$ and $\Sigma_{\sigma_2} f$, where σ_1 and σ_2 agree excepting that in σ_2, the interval $[x - d', x + d'']$ of σ_1 is replaced by the two intervals $[x - d', x]$ and $[x, x + d'']$.

For the σ-integral, since we can always include any given point x in a subdivision, the corresponding necessary condition is one sided, i.e., we have:

3.9. THEOREM. A necessary condition for the existence of $\sigma\int_a^b f(dI)$ is that for every x: $\lim_{x''\to x}(f[x, x'') - f[x, x'] - f[x', x'']) = 0$, $x < x' < x''$ and $\lim_{x''\to x}(f[x'', x] - f[x'', x'] - f[x', x]) = 0$, $x'' < x' < x$.

We could call these two properties pseudoadditivity on the right and left, respectively. It is to be noted that $f(I)$ can be pseudoadditive both on the left and right without being pseudoadditive.

The importance of the pseudoadditive condition is that it is the connecting link between the norm and σ-integrals. We have:

3.10. THEOREM. A necessary and sufficient condition that the norm integral of an interval function $f(I)$ exists is that the σ-integral exist and that $f(I)$ be pseudoadditive at every interior point of $[a, b]$.

Since $\sigma_1 \geq \sigma_2$ implies that $|\sigma_1| \leqq |\sigma_2|$, it follows that if the norm integral exists, the σ-integral exists and the values agree. Conversely, suppose $\sigma\int_a^b f(dI)$ exists. Then $(e, \sigma_e, \sigma \geq \sigma_e) : |\Sigma_\sigma f(I) - \sigma\int_a^b f(dI)| < e$. Let σ_e consist of the $n+2$ points: $a = x_0, x_1, \ldots, x_n, x_{n+1} = b$. Since $f(I)$ is pseudoadditive at $x_1, \ldots, x_n$, there exists a d_e such that if $0 < d_i', d_i'' < d_e$, then $|f[x_i - d_i', x_i + d_i''] - f[x_i - d_i', x_i] - f[x_i, x_i + d_i'']| < e/n$. For the d_e so determined consider any subdivision σ with $|\sigma| < d_e$. Let $\sigma_0 = \sigma + \sigma_e$ and compare $\Sigma_\sigma f$ and $\Sigma_{\sigma_0} f$, using the same value of f for any interval of σ which contains no point of σ_e as an interior point. If $x_i' - d_i', x_i + d_i''$ are the end points of intervals of σ containing a point of σ_e, then

$$|\textstyle\sum_\sigma f(I) - \sum_{\sigma_0} f(I)| \leqq \sum_i |f[x_i - d_i', x_i + d_i''] \\ - f[x_i - d_i', x_i] - f[x_i, x_i + d_i'']| < e.$$

But since $\sigma_0 \geq \sigma_e$, it follows that

$$(e, d_e, |\sigma| < d_e) : |\textstyle\sum_\sigma f(I) - \sigma\displaystyle\int_a^b f(dI)| \leqq |\textstyle\sum_\sigma f(I) - \sum_{\sigma_0} f(I)| \\ + |\textstyle\sum_{\sigma_0} f(I) - \sigma\displaystyle\int_a^b f(dI)| < 2e.$$

This means that $N\int_a^b f(dI)$ exists and is equal to $\sigma\int_a^b f(dI)$.

The interval function $f(I) = g(x)(d-c)$, $c \leqq x \leqq d$, with $g(x)$ bounded is pseudoadditive since $f(I) \leqq (\text{l.u.b. } g(x)) \cdot (d-c)$. It follows that in the definition of the Riemann integral, limits of the approximating sums can be taken either as $|\sigma| \to 0$ or as σ becomes finer. This is the import of the Darboux theorem on the existence of a Riemann integral.

4. The Integral of an Interval Function as a Function of Intervals

4.1. THEOREM. If $f(I)$ is an interval function on $[a, b]$ and $\int_a^b f(dI)$ exists, and if $a \leqq c < d \leqq b$, then $\int_c^d f(dI)$ exists.

We apply II.3.6. Suppose σ is a subdivision of $[a, b]$ containing the points c and d such that $\Sigma_\sigma \omega(Sf; I) \leqq e$. Then obviously $\Sigma_{\sigma'} \omega(Sf; I) < e$, if σ' is a subdivision of $[c, d]$ agreeing with σ on this interval.

If follows that $\int_c^d f(dI)$ defines a single-valued interval function on $[a, b]$ which we denote: $\int_I f(dI)$.

4.2. THEOREM. If $\int_a^b f(dI)$ exists and $a < c < b$, then $\int_a^c f(dI) + \int_c^b f(dI) = \int_a^b f(dI)$.

Since all of the integrals in the formula exist, for $e > 0$ and for the same d_e, we determine $\sigma' = \sigma(a, c)$, $\sigma'' = \sigma(c, b)$, and $\sigma = \sigma(a, b)$ such that $|\sigma'|$, $|\sigma''|$, $|\sigma| < d_e$, and $|\int_a^c f(dI) - \Sigma_{\sigma'} f(I)| < e$, $|\int_c^b f(dI) - \Sigma_{\sigma''} f(I)| < e$, and $|\int_a^b f(dI) - \Sigma_\sigma f(I)| < e$. If $\sigma = \sigma' + \sigma''$, then $|\int_a^c f(dI) + \int_c^b f(dI) - \int_a^b f(dI)| < 3\,e$, from which we deduce the equality in the theorem. Since the interval $[a, b]$ can be replaced by any subinterval $I = [c, d]$, we conclude that:

4.3. Corollary. If $\int_a^b f(dI)$ exists and if $I = I_1 + I_2$, where I is any subinterval of $[a, b]$ and I_1 and I_2 are adjacent, then $\int_I f(dI) = \int_{I_1} f(dI) + \int_{I_2} f(dI)$, or $\int_I f(dI)$ is an additive function of intervals on $[a, b]$. In particular there exists then a point function $g(x)$ so that $g(x) = \int_a^x f(dI)$, which defines the interval function $\int_I f(dI)$.

The reasoning for the case where we deal with a σ-integral instead of a norm integral, is similar.

For the converse, we have separate results for the norm and the σ-integrals.

4.4σ. THEOREM. If $\sigma \int_a^c f(dI)$ and $\sigma \int_c^b f(dI)$ exist, then $\sigma \int_a^b f(dI)$ exists and is equal to the sum of these two integrals.

For

$$(e, \sigma_e(a, c), \sigma' \geq \sigma_e(a, c)) : \sum_{\sigma'} \omega(Sf; I) < e$$

and

$$(e, \sigma_e(c, b), \sigma'' \geq \sigma_e(c, b)) : \sum_{\sigma''} \omega(Sf; I) < e$$

imply

$$(e, \sigma = \sigma' + \sigma'') : \sum_\sigma \omega(Sf; I) = \sum_{\sigma'} \omega(Sf; I) + \sum_{\sigma''} \omega(Sf; I) < 2\,e.$$

Then $\sigma \int_a^b f(dI)$ exists.

The additional condition needed for the corresponding result in the case of norm integrals is suggested by the fact that if the norm integral of $f(I)$ exists, then $f(I)$ is pseudoadditive at every interior point of $[a, b]$. We have:

4.4N. THEOREM. If $N \int_a^c f(dI)$ and $N \int_c^b f(dI)$ both exist and $f(I)$ is pseudoadditive at the point c, then $N \int_a^b f(dI)$ exists and is equal to the sum of these two integrals.

For under the hypothesis of the theorem, $f(I)$ will be pseudoadditive at every interior point of $[a, b]$. Moreover, the $\sigma \int_a^c f(dI)$ and $\sigma \int_c^b f(dI)$ will exist, so that $\sigma \int_a^b f(dI)$ exists also. Hence by Theorem II.3.10, $N \int_a^b f(dI)$ exists.

In view of the additive properties of the integral we have:

4.5. Approximation Theorem. If σ is any subdivision of $[a, b]$ and if $\int_a^b f(dI)$ exists, then $| \int_a^b f(dI) - \Sigma_\sigma f(I) | \leqq \Sigma_\sigma \omega(Sf, I)$.

For if $\sigma = (I_1, \ldots, I_i, \ldots, I_n)$, then $\int_a^b f(dI) = \Sigma_i \int_{I_i} f(dI)$ and obviously $| \int_{I_i} f(dI) - f(I_i) | \leqq \omega(Sf; I_i)$.

For the case of Riemann integrals, the indefinite integral $\int_a^x g(x)dx$ is a continuous function of x. For integrals of interval functions, this property becomes:

4.6. THEOREM. If $N \int_a^b f(dI)$ exists, then $(e, d_e, l(I) < d_e)$: $| N \int_I f(dI) - f(I) | < e$, or $\lim_{l(I)\to 0} | N \int_I f(dI) - f(I) | = 0$, and uniformly on $[a, b]$.

Here $l(I)$ is the length of the interval I. This theorem is an immediate consequence of the existence theorem II.3.6 and the approximation theorem II.4.5.

The corresponding theorem for σ-integrals reads:

4.7. THEOREM. If $\sigma \int_a^b f(dI)$ exists, then for every point x of $[a, b]$ and $d > 0$:

$$\lim_{d\to 0}(f[x-d, x] - \sigma \int_{x-d}^{x} f(dI)]$$

$$= \lim_{d\to 0}(f[x, x+d] - \sigma \int_{x}^{x+d} f(dI)) = 0.$$

For the interval $[a, x]$ we have

$$(e, \sigma_e(a, x), \sigma \geq \sigma_e(a, x)) : \textstyle\sum_\sigma \omega(Sf; I) < e.$$

Let $x - d_0$ be the point of σ preceding x. Then obviously $\omega(Sf; [x - d, x]) < e$ for $0 < d < d_0$. Consequently, for $d < d_0$

$$\left| \int_{x-d}^{x} f(dI) - f[x - d, x] \right| \leqq \omega(Sf, [x - d, x]) < e.$$

Similarly for the right of the point x.

These two theorems can be interpreted as saying that in a certain sense, the single-valued additive interval function $\int_I f(dI)$ is *differentially equivalent* to $f(I)$. If we base the continuity of the interval function on its behavior as $l(I) \to 0$, then these theorems assert that the continuity properties of the point function determined by $\int_a^x f(dI)$ are governed by those of $f(I)$.

The differential equivalence also shows up in a substitution theorem. If $f(I)$ is an interval function on $[a, b]$ and $h(x)$ is a bounded point function, then in an obvious way $h(x') \cdot f(I)$ for x' on I defines an interval function and may have an integral. We have:

4.8. Substitution Theorem. If $f(I)$ is an interval function on $[a, b]$ such that $\int_a^b f(dI)$ exists and $g(I) = \int_I f(dI)$; if further $h(x)$ is a bounded function on $[a, b]$, then $\int_a^b h(x)f(dI)$ exists if and only if $\int_a^b h(x)g(dI)$ exists, and the two integrals are then equal.

The same type of integral (norm or σ) is assumed throughout. For if σ is any subdivision of $[a, b]$ and $|h(x)| < M$ on $[a, b]$, then by the approximation theorem II.4.5, and the existence of $\int_a^b f(dI)$ we have

$$\begin{aligned} &\left| \sum_\sigma h(x) f(I) - \sum_\sigma h(x) g(I) \right| \\ &\quad \leq \sum_\sigma |h(x)| \left| f(I) - \int_I f(dI) \right| < M \sum_\sigma \left| f(I) - \int_I f(dI) \right| \\ &\quad \leq M \sum_\sigma \omega(Sf; I) < Me \end{aligned}$$

for suitably chosen σ.

5. Integral as a Function of the Interval Function

The following two theorems are immediate consequences of corresponding theorems on limits:

5.1. THEOREM. If $\int_a^b f_1(dI)$ and $\int_a^b f_2(dI)$ exist and the values of $f_3(I)$ are contained in the class of values $f_1(I) + f_2(I)$, then $\int_a^b f_3(dI)$ exists and $\int_a^b f_3(dI) = \int_a^b (f_1 + f_2)(dI) = \int_a^b f_1(dI) + \int_a^b f_2(dI)$.

5.2. THEOREM. If $\int_a^b f(dI)$ exists, then $\int_a^b cf(dI)$ exists and is equal to $c \int_a^b f(dI)$.

The following theorem on the convergence of integrals of a sequence of interval functions is an immediate consequence of the iterated limits theorem I. 7.4.

5.3. THEOREM. If $f_n(I)$ and $f(I)$ are interval functions on $[a, b]$ such that for every value $f(I)$ there exists a sequence of values $f_n(I)$ converging to $f(I)$, and if the sequence $\int_a^b f_n(dI)$ exists uniformly in the sense that $\lim \Sigma_\sigma \omega(Sf_n; I)$ converges uniformly to zero in n, then $\int_a^b f(dI)$ exists and is equal to $\lim_n \int_a^b f_n(dI)$.

It is assumed that the integrals (norm or σ) are the same throughout this theorem.

A special convergence theorem holds for σ-integrals, for the case when the functions $f_n(I)$ are upper semiadditive:

5.4. THEOREM. If the interval functions $f_n(I)$ are single-valued and upper semiadditive on $[a, b]$, and have a finite integral, and if $\lim_n f_n(I) = f(I)$ for each I, then $f(I)$ is also upper semiadditive and $\sigma \int_a^b f(dI) \leqq \underline{\lim}_n \sigma \int_a^b f_n(dI)$.

The inequality still holds if $f(I)$ does not have a finite integral. If $\underline{\lim}_n \int_a^b f_n(dI) = +\infty$, there is nothing to prove. Let then $\underline{\lim}_n \int_a^b f_n(dI) = c < \infty$. There exists then a subsequence of $f_n(I)$ such that $\lim_m \int_a^b f_{n_m}(dI) = c$, and consequently $(e, m_e, m > m_e)$: $\int_a^b f_{n_m}(dI) < c + e$. From this it follows that for $m > m_e$ and all σ, we have $\Sigma_\sigma f_{n_m}(I) < c + e$. By taking limits as to m, we get: $\Sigma_\sigma f(I) \leqq c + e$ for all $e > 0$ and all σ. This implies that $\int_a^b f(dI) \leqq c = \underline{\lim}_n \int_a^b f_n(dI)$.

We observe that we have proved incidentally:

5.5 Corollary I. If $f_n(I)$ are upper semiadditive and converge to $f(I)$ for all I and $\sigma \int_a^b f_n(dI) \leqq M$ for all n, then $\sigma \int_a^b f(dI)$ exists $\leqq M$.

Another consequence of the theorem is:

5.6. Corollary II. If $f_n(I)$ are upper semiadditive interval functions with finite integrals on $[a, b]$, if $f_n(I)$ converges to $f(I)$ for all I, and if $\lim_n \sigma \int_a^b f_n(dI) = \sigma \int_a^b f(I)$, then $\lim_n \sigma \int_a^x f_n(dI) = \sigma \int_a^x f(dI)$ for all x of $[a, b]$.

For by the additive property of integrals, and the properties of greatest and least of limits (see I.4.6) we have:

$$\begin{aligned}\int_a^b f(dI) &= \int_a^x f(dI) + \int_x^b f(dI) \leqq \underline{\lim}_n \int_a^x f_n(dI) + \underline{\lim}_n \int_x^b f_n(dI)\\ &\leqq \underline{\lim}_n \left(\int_a^x f_n(dI) + \int_x^b f_n(dI)\right) = \lim_n \int_a^b f_n(dI)\\ &\leqq \overline{\lim}_n \int_a^x f_n(dI) + \underline{\lim}_n \int_x^b f_n(dI) \leqq \overline{\lim} \int_a^b f_n(dI)\\ &= \lim_n \int_a^b f_n(dI).\end{aligned}$$

Hence all of these inequalities become equalities. Then $\underline{\lim}_n \int_a^x f_n(dI) = \overline{\lim}_n \int_a^x f_n(dI) = \lim_n \int_a^x f_n(dI)$. Further, $\int_a^x f(dI) + \int_x^b f(dI) = \lim_n \int_a^x f_n(dI) + \underline{\lim}_n \int_x^b f_n(dI)$. Since $\int_a^x f(dI) \leqq \lim_n \int_a^x f_n(dI)$ and $\int_x^b f(dI) \leqq \underline{\lim}_n \int_x^b f_n(dI)$, it follows that $\int_a^x f(dI) = \lim_n \int_a^x f_n(dI)$ and consequently also $\lim_n \int_x^b f_n(dI) = \int_x^b f(dI)$.

Note that this second corollary is limited to σ-integrals.

EXERCISES

1. If the interval function $f(I)$ has an integral on $[a, b]$, does the integral function $|f(I)|$ also have an integral?

2. If a sequence of interval functions $f_n(I)$ converges uniformly on the set of subintervals of $[a, b]$ to $f(I)$ and if $\int_a^b f_n(dI)$ exist, does $\int_a^b f(dI)$ exist and is it equal to the possibly existing $\lim_n \int_a^b f_n(dI)$?

3. Let Q be a directed set and $f_q(I)$ a set of upper semiadditive interval functions on $[a, b]$. If $\sigma \int_a^b f_q(dI)$ exist as finite numbers and $\lim_q f_q(I) = f(I)$ for all I of $[a, b]$, show that $\sigma \int_a^b f(dI) \leqq \underline{\lim}_q \sigma \int_a^b f_q(dI)$. If in addition $\lim_q \sigma \int_a^b f_q(dI) = \sigma \int_a^b f(dI)$ is $\lim_q \sigma \int_a^x f_q(dI) = \sigma \int_a^x f(dI)$ for all x of $[a, b]$?

6. Functions of Bounded Variation

The class of functions of bounded variation on a linear interval $[a, b]$ plays an important role in real analysis. Since the total variation is an instance of an integral of an interval function, it seems justifiable to devote space to the consideration of these functions and a collection of their properties.

6.1. Definition. A function $f(x)$ on $[a, b]$ is of bounded variation on $[a, b]$ if the function of subdivisions $g(\sigma) = \Sigma_\sigma |f(x_i) - f(x_{i-1})|$ is bounded as to σ. The least upper bound of $g(\sigma)$ as to σ is called the total variation of f on $[a, b]$.

Since the interval function $F(I) = |f(d) - f(c)| = |\Delta_c^d f|$ is upper semiadditive, it follows that the total variation when it exists is the σ-limit of $g(\sigma)$, i.e., the total variation is the σ-integral of the interval function $|\Delta_c^d f|$, so that the properties of the σ-integral apply. We shall consequently represent the total variation of f on $[a, b]$ by $\int_a^b |df|$. It follows that if f is of bounded variation on $[a, b]$ it is of bounded variation on every subinterval of $[a, b]$, and that the point function $v(x) = \int_a^x |df|$ is monotonic nondecreasing. It also follows immediately from the definition that if $f(x)$ is of bounded variation so is $cf(x)$ for all constants c and $\int_a^b |dcf| = |c| \int_a^b |df|$. Further, if f and g are of bounded variation, so is $f + g$ and $\int_a^b |d(f + g)| \leqq \int_a^b |df| + \int_a^b |dg|$. These statements include the fact that the space of functions of bounded variation is linear.

Any function of bounded variation on $[a, b]$ is also bounded since $|f(x) - f(a)| \leqq v(x) \leqq \int_a^b |df|$.

A monotonic nondecreasing (nonincreasing) function is obviously of bounded variation with $\int_a^b |df| = |f(b) - f(a)|$.

As a consequence any linear combination of monotonic nondecreasing functions $\Sigma_i a_i f_i(x)$ is also of bounded variation. This statement is in a sense reversible, in that we have:

6.2. THEOREM. Every function of bounded variation on a linear interval $[a, b]$ can be expressed as the difference of two monotonic nondecreasing functions.

For if $v(x) = \int_a^x |df|$, then $v(x) + (f(x) - f(a))$ and $v(x) - (f(x) - f(a))$ are both monotone nondecreasing. For $\Delta_c^d (v(x) \pm (f(x) - f(a))) = \int_c^d |df| \pm (f(d) - f(c)) \geqq 0$ for all $c > d$. If we set $p(x) = \frac{1}{2} (v(x) + f(x) - f(a))$ and $n(x) = \frac{1}{2} (v(x) - f(x) + f(a))$ then $f(x) - f(a) = p(x) - n(x)$ and $\int_a^b |df| = p(x) + n(x)$.

The functions $p(x)$ and $n(x)$ can be obtained in another way. Suppose that for any σ of $[a, x]$ we set $P(\sigma; a, x) = \Sigma_i (f(x_i') - f(x'_{i-1}))$ where the (x'_{i-1}, x_i') are the intervals of σ for which $\Delta f \geqq 0$, and let $N(\sigma; a, x) = - \Sigma_i (f(x_i'') - f(x''_{i-1}))$, where the (x''_{i-1}, x_i'') are the intervals of σ for which $\Delta f \leqq 0$. Then $P(\sigma; a, x)$ and $N(\sigma; a, x)$ are both monotone nondecreasing in σ and if f is of bounded variation on $[a, b]$ the least upper bounds as to σ of $P(\sigma; a, x)$ and $N(\sigma; a, x)$ both exist as σ-limits converging say to $P(a, x)$ and $N(a, x)$. Now for each σ, we have $P(\sigma; a, x) - N(\sigma; a, x) = f(x) - f(a)$ and $P(\sigma, a, x) + N(\sigma; a, x) = \Sigma_\sigma |\Delta f|$. Taking limits as to σ we find $P(a; x) - N(a, x) = f(x) - f(a)$ and $P(a, x) + N(a, x) =$

$\int_a^x |df|$. From this it follows that $P(a, x) = p(x)$ and $N(a, x) = n(x)$.

This approach to functions of bounded variation is due to Jordan, who first called attention to these functions. Consequently, the formulas $f(x) - f(a) = p(x) - n(x)$ with $\int_a^x |df| = p(x) + n(x)$ give what is usually called the *Jordan decomposition* of a function of bounded variation. The functions $p(x)$ and $n(x)$ are called the *positive* and *negative variations* of $f(x)$.

The above approach suggests still another method of defining the functions $p(x)$ and $n(x)$, as well as the bounded variation of a function. Let π stand for a finite number of disjoint subintervals: $I_i = [x_i', x_i'']$, $i = 1 \ldots m$ of $[a, x]$. Then $p(x) = \text{l.u.b. } \Sigma_i(f(x_i') - f(x_i''))$ and $n(x) = - \text{g.l.b. } \Sigma_i(f(x_i') - f(x_i''))$ for all possible sets π of disjoint subintervals of $[a, x]$. This leads to the following definition of a function of bounded variation:

6.3. THEOREM. $f(x)$ on $[a, b]$ is of bounded variation if and only if $G(\pi) = \Sigma_i(f(x_i') - f(x_i''))$ is bounded as a function of $\pi = (I_1, \ldots, I_m)$, finite sets of nonoverlapping intervals of $[a, b]$. The total variation of f on $[a, b]$ is equal to $\text{l.u.b.}_\pi G(\pi) - \text{g.l.b.}_\pi G(\pi)$, $\text{l.u.b.}_\pi G(\pi)$ being the positive variation on $[a, b]$ and $\text{g.l.b.}_\pi G(\pi)$ the negative variation.

The function $p(x)$ and $n(x)$ of the Jordan decomposition enjoy the following minimal property:

6.4. THEOREM. If $f(x)$ is of bounded variation on $[a, b]$ and if $f(x) = p_1(x) - n_1(x)$, $p_1(a) = n_1(a) = 0$, and $p_1(x)$ and $n_1(x)$ monotonic nondecreasing, then $p_1(x) - p(x)$ and $n_1(x) - n(x)$ are both positive or zero monotonic nondecreasing functions on $[a, b]$.

This is equivalent to proving that $\Delta p_1 \geqq \Delta p$ and $\Delta n_1 \geqq \Delta n$ for every subinterval of $[a, b]$. By the preceding result, for every interval $[c, d]$ of $[a, b]$ and every $e > 0$, there exists a set π of disjoint intervals of $[c, d]$ such that $p(d) - p(c) - e \leqq \Sigma_\pi \Delta f \leqq p(d) - p(c)$. Since $f(x) - f(a) = p_1(x) - n_1(x)$ we have

$$\sum_\pi \Delta f = \sum_\pi \Delta p_1 - \sum_\pi \Delta n_1 \leqq \sum_\pi \Delta p_1 \leqq p_1(d) - p_1(c).$$

Consequently, $p_1(d) - p_1(c) \geqq p(d) - p(c) - e$ for all $e > 0$, or $\Delta p_1 \geqq \Delta p$ for all intervals $[c, d]$. Similarly $\Delta n_1 \geqq \Delta n$.

It follows that:

6.5. THEOREM. If $f(x)$ is of bounded variation on $[a, b]$, then $p(x)$ is the minimal monotonic nondecreasing function such that

$p(a) = 0$ and $\Delta p \geqq \Delta f$ for all intervals $[c, d]$, and $n(x)$ has the same property relative to $-f(x)$.

For if $\Delta p_1 \geqq \Delta f$ for all intervals $[c, d]$, then $\Delta n_1 = \Delta(p_1 - f) \geqq 0$ for all intervals, so that $n_1(x)$ is monotone nondecreasing and $f(x) - f(a) = p_1(x) - n_1(x)$. Consequently $\Delta p_1 \geqq \Delta p$.

7. Continuity Properties of Functions of Bounded Variation

Since the discontinuities of a monotonic function are all of the first kind, i.e., $f(x+0)$ and $f(x-0)$ exist for each x, and are at most denumerable in number, it follows that any function of bounded variation is continuous excepting at a denumerable number of points at each of which $f(x+0)$ and $f(x-0)$ exist. Moreover, since the total variation function $v(x) = \int_a^x |df|$ is an integral of an interval function, it reflects the discontinuities of $|\Delta f|$, i.e., by II.4.7 we have $v(x+0) - v(x) = |f(x+0) - f(x)|$ and $v(x) - v(x-0) = |f(x) - f(x-0)|$. It follows that if $f(x)$ is a continuous function of bounded variation, then $v(x)$, $p(x)$, and $n(x)$ are also continuous.

We define a *simple break* (or step) *function* $B(x, x_0; c, d)$ as follows: $B(x, x_0; c, d) = 0$ for $a \leqq x < x_0$; $B(x, x_0; c, d) = c$ for $x = x_0$ and $B(x, x_0; c, d) = d$ for $x_0 < x \leqq b$.

If $f(x)$ has a discontinuity of the first kind at x_0, then $f(x) - B(x, x_0; f(x_0) - f(x_0 - 0), f(x_0 + 0) - f(x_0 - 0))$ will be continuous at x_0 with value $f(x_0 - 0)$. Now if $\{x_n\}$ are the points of discontinuity of a function of bounded variation $f(x)$, then it follows that $\Sigma_n (|f(x_n) - f(x_n - 0)| + |f(x_n + 0) - f(x_n)|) \leqq \int_a^b |df|$. Consequently, the series $\Sigma_n B(x, x_n; f(x_n) - f(x_n - 0), f(x_n + 0) - f(x_n - 0))$ is absolutely and uniformly convergent on $[a, b]$, since the total variation of $B(x, x_0; c, d)$ is at most $|c| + |d - c|$. The series will consequently converge to a function whose only discontinuities are at $x = x_n$, the discontinuities matching those of $f(x)$. It follows that the function $f_c(x) = f(x) - \Sigma_n B(x, x_n; f(x_n) - f(x_n - 0), f(x_n + 0) - f(x_n - 0))$ is continuous on $[a, b]$. This gives rise to another decomposition of a function of bounded variation and we have:

7.1. THEOREM. If $f(x)$ is of bounded variation it can be written in the form $f(x) = f_c(x) + f_b(x)$, where $f_c(x)$ is continuous on $[a, b]$ and $f_b(x)$ is a pure break function, a uniformly convergent sum of simple break functions.

It is possible to define $f_b(x)$ directly in the form:

$$f_b(x) = \sum_{a \leq y < x} (f(y+0) - f(y-0)) + f(x) - f(x-0)$$

where $f(a-0) = f(a)$.

8. The Space of Functions of Bounded Variation

We have already seen that the space of functions of bounded variation on $[a, b]$ is linear. In addition it has the *multiplicative property*, viz.:

8.1. THEOREM. If $f_1(x)$ and $f_2(x)$ are of bounded variation on $[a, b]$, then $f_1(x)f_2(x)$ has the same property and $\int_a^b |d(f_1 \cdot f_2)| \leq M_1 \int_a^b |df_2| + M_2 \int_a^b |df_1|$, where $M_i = \text{l.u.b.} [|f_i(x)|, x \text{ on } [a, b]]$, $i = 1,2$.

For $|f_1(d)f_2(d) - f_1(c)f_2(c)| \leq |f_1(d)| \cdot |f_2(d) - f_2(c)| + |f_2(c)| \cdot |f_1(d) - f_1(c)|$.

Further, the space of functions of bounded variation has the *absolute property*, viz.:

8.2. THEOREM. If $f(x)$ is of bounded variation on $[a, b]$, then $|f(x)|$ is also of bounded variation on $[a, b]$ and $\int_a^b |df| \leq \int_a^b |d(|f|)|$.

For $||f(d)| - |f(c)|| \leq |f(d) - f(c)|$.

This absolute property together with linearity assures us that with any two functions $f_1(x)$ and $f_2(x)$ the space of functions of bounded variation contains also the greater $f_1 \vee f_2(x)$ and the lesser $f_1 \wedge f_2(x)$ of these functions. Here $f_1 \vee f_2(x) = f_1(x)$ if $f_1(x) \geq f_2(x)$ and $= f_2(x)$ if $f_2(x) \geq f_1(x)$, while for $f_1 \wedge f_2(x)$ the inequalities are reversed. For, as can easily be verified $f_1 \vee f_2(x) = \frac{1}{2}(f_1(x) + f_2(x) + |f_1(x) - f_2(x)|)$ and $f_1 \wedge f_2(x) = \frac{1}{2}(f_1(x) + f_2(x) - |f_1(x) - f_2(x)|)$.

These statements can be reformulated:

8.3. THEOREM. The space of functions of bounded variation on $[a, b]$ form a lattice if the order relation $f_1 \geq f_2$ means $f_1(x) \geq f_2(x)$ for all x.

8.4. Definition. A *lattice* is defined as a set of elements having an order relation ($\geq$) defined between some of its pairs of elements, and with any two elements x, y contains also the least upper bound $x \vee y$ and the greatest lower bound $x \wedge y$. Here $x \vee y$ is an element z such that (a) $z \geqq x$ and $z \geqq y$, and (b) if $u \geqq x$ and $u \geqq y$, then $u \geqq z$, the inequalities being reversed for $x \wedge y$.

It happens that the space of functions of bounded variation is also a lattice if order is defined in a different way, viz., $f_1 (\geqq) f_2$ if $f_1 - f_2$ is a monotone nondecreasing function. If we define the interval function $F(I) = f(d) - f(c)$ for $I = [c, d]$, then $f_1 (\geqq) f_2$ if and only if $F_1(I) \geqq F_2(I)$ for all I of $[a, b]$. Since the addition of a constant to the function f does not affect the value of the corresponding interval function, it follows that in this ordering two functions are equivalent, if they differ by a constant. We might therefore limit ourselves to functions f for which $f(a) = 0$.

The function f is monotonic nondecreasing if $f(\geqq)0$. Consequently, in this ordering $f \vee 0$, if it exists, is the least monotonic nondecreasing function f_1 such that $\Delta f_1 \geqq \Delta f$, for all intervals. As we have seen in II.6.5, when f is of bounded variation then this function f_1 is the positive variation p of f. Similarly, $-n = f \wedge 0$, so that the total variation $\int_a^b | df | = f \vee 0 - f \wedge 0$. For any two functions f_1 and f_2 we can show that $f_1 \vee f_2 = f_2 + (f_1 - f_2) \vee 0$, and $f_1 \wedge f_2 = f_2 + (f_1 - f_2) \wedge 0$, from which we conclude that the space of functions of bounded variation under this second type of ordering is also a lattice.

8.5. The space of functions of bounded variation becomes a *normed* space if we define $\|f\| = |f(a)| + \int_a^b |df|$, so that the distance between two functions f_1 and f_2 can be defined $\delta(f_1, f_2) = |f_1(a) - f_2(a)| + \int_a^b |d(f_1 - f_2)|$. It can easily be verified that the norm and metric properties are satisfied under these definitions.

The norm gives rise to a topology in the space of functions of bounded variation via the condition "lim"$_n f_n = f$ is equivalent to

$$\lim_n \|f_n - f\| = \lim_n(|f_n(a) - f(a)| + \int_a^b |d(f_n - f)|) = 0.$$

This norm convergence is a rather strong type of convergence. In the first place it is obvious that $\lim_n \|f_n - f\| = 0$ implies $\lim_n f_n(a) = f(a)$. Then from

$$\begin{aligned} &|f_n(x) - f(x) - (f_n(a) - f(a)| \\ &\leqq |f_n(a) - f(a)| + \int_a^x |d(f_n - f)| \leqq \|f_n - f\|, \end{aligned}$$

it follows that $\lim_n f_n(x) = f(x)$ uniformly on $[a,b]$. Also from

$$\left| \int_a^x |df_n| - \int_a^x |df| \right| \leqq \int_a^x |d(f_n - f)| \leqq \int_a^b |d(f_n - f)|,$$

it follows that $\lim_n \int_a^x |df_n| = \int_a^x |df|$ uniformly on $[a, b]$. However, it is possible to have $\lim_n f_n(x) = f(x)$ and $\lim_n \int_a^x |df_n| = \int_a^x |df|$ uniformly on $[a, b]$ without having $\lim_n \int_a^b |d(f_n - f)| = 0$. For if on $[0,1]$ we take $f_n(x) = m/n$ for $(m-1)/n < x \leqq m/n$, $m = 1,\ldots,n$, and $f_n(0) = 0$, then the $f_n(x)$ are monotone nondecreasing, $\int_a^x |df_n| = f_n(x)$, and $\lim_n f_n(x) = x$ uniformly on $[0, 1]$ but $\int_0^1 |d(f_n - f)| = 1$ for all n.

Under the norm as defined, the space of functions of bounded variation is complete, i.e., we have:

8.6. THEOREM. If for the sequence of functions $f_n(x)$ of bounded variation on $[a, b]$ we have $\lim \| f_m - f_n \| = 0$, then there exists a function $f(x)$ of bounded variation such that $\lim_n \| f - f_n \| = 0$.

Reasoning as above, we find that $\lim_n f_n(x)$ exists uniformly on $[a, b]$ and is equal to $f(x)$ say. Also, $\lim_n \int_a^b | df_n |$ exists. Now by II.5.4 we have $\int_a^b | df | \leqq \underline{\lim}_n \int_a^b | df_n | = \lim_n \int_a^b | df_n |$, since we are dealing with integrals of upper semiadditive interval functions. Then f is also of bounded variation. By the same theorem we have $\int_a^b | d(f - f_n) | \leqq \underline{\lim}_m \int_a^b | d(f_m - f_n) |$. Now by the hypothesis of our theorem we have $(e, n_e, m \geqq m_e, n \geqq n_e) : \int_a^b | d(f_m - f_n) | \leqq e$, so that for $n \geqq n_e$: $\int_a^b | d(f_n - f) | \leqq e$. As a result of these considerations we have

$$\lim_n \| f_n - f \| = \lim_n (| f_n(a) - f(a) | + \int_a^b | d(f_n - f) |) = 0.$$

8.7. From the above considerations, it is apparent that in the space of functions of bounded variation, there is a variety of modes of convergence. We list the following:

(1) Norm convergence: $\lim_n \| f_n - f \| = \lim_n (| f_n(a) - f(a) | + \int_a^b | d(f_n - f) |) = 0$.

(2) Double uniform convergence: $\lim_n f_n(x) = f(x)$ uniformly on $[a, b]$ and $\lim_n \int_a^x | df_n | = \int_a^x | df |$ uniformly on $[a, b]$. It should be noted that uniform convergence of a sequence of functions of bounded variation $f_n(x)$ to $f(x)$ does not necessarily imply that $f(x)$ is of bounded variation. For instance, the functions $f_n(x) = 0$ for $0 \leqq x \leqq 1/n$; $= x \sin(\pi/x)$ for $1/n \leqq x \leqq 1$ are each of bounded variation on $[0, 1]$, converge uniformly to $f(x) = x \sin(\pi/x)$ which is not of bounded variation on $[0, 1]$.

(3) $\lim_n f_n(x) = f(x)$ for all x of $[a, b]$ and $\lim_n \int_a^b | df_n | = \int_a^b | df |$ and so $\lim_n \int_a^x | df_n | = \int_a^x | df |$ for all x of $[a, b]$. The last remark is

a special instance of II.5.6, since the interval function $F(I) = | f(d) - f(c) |$ is upper semiadditive on $[a,b]$.

(4) $\lim_n f_n(x) = f(x)$ for all x of $[a, b]$; $\int_a^b | df_n |$ bounded in n. The second half of this condition is usually stated: the sequence f_n is uniformly of bounded variation, where:

8.8. Definition. A set of functions $\mathfrak{F}$ is *uniformly of bounded variation* if there exists a constant M such that $\int_a^b | df | \leqq M$ for all f of $\mathfrak{F}$. Since by theorem $\int_a^b | df | \leqq \underline{\lim}_n \int_a^b df_n$, it follows that in this type of limit, the limit function $f(x)$ is necessarily also of bounded variation, i.e., this type of convergence operates within the space of functions of bounded variation. It is sometimes referred to as weak convergence.

(5) $\lim_n f_n(x) = f(x)$ except at a denumerable set of points of $[a, b]$; $\int_a^b | df_n |$ is bounded in n and $\int_a^b | df | < \infty$.

In connection with the limit (4) we have an important theorem due to E. Helly which is in a sense an extension of the Weierstrass-Bolzano theorem on the space of real numbers, to functions of bounded variation.

8.9. Helly's Theorem. If $f_n(x)$ is a sequence of functions, uniformly of bounded variation on $[a, b]$ such that $f_n(a)$ is bounded in n, then there exists a subsequence $f_{n_m}(x)$ and a function $f(x)$ of bounded variation such that $\lim_m f_{n_m}(x) = f(x)$ for all x of $[a, b]$.

The proof of this theorem depends on the following lemma, which is basic in theorems of the Weierstrass-Bolzano type:

Let $\mathfrak{S}$ be the space of infinite sequences of real numbers: $S = (a_1, \ldots, a_p, \ldots) = \{a_p\}$. Then if $S_n = (a_{n1}, \ldots, a_{np}, \ldots)$ is any sequence of such sequences such that for every p the a_{np} are bounded in n, then there exists a subsequence S_{n_m} and an S such that $\lim_m S_{n_m} = S$ in the sense that for every p: $\lim_m a_{n_m p} = a_p$.

The proof of this lemma is based upon the use of the Weirstrass-Bolzano theorem in the form: if a_n is any bounded sequence of real numbers then there exists a subsequence a_{n_m} and a number a, such that $\lim_m a_{n_m} = a$. This form is equivalent to the topological statement: any bounded set of real numbers has at least one limiting point.

Since the sequence a_{n1} is bounded, there exists a subsequence $a_{n_m^{(1)}1}$ such that $\lim_m a_{n_m^{(1)}1} = a_1$. For the sequence $a_{n_m^{(1)}2}$, there exists a subsequence $n_m^{(2)}$ of $n_m^{(1)}$ such that $\lim_m a_{n_m^{(2)}2} = a_2$. Continuing in this way we get a succession of subsequences of the integers:

$$\begin{array}{c} n_1^{(1)}, n_2^{(1)}, \ldots, n_m^{(1)}, \ldots \\ n_1^{(2)}, n_2^{(2)}, \ldots, n_m^{(2)}, \ldots \\ \ldots \\ n_1^{(r)}, n_2^{(r)}, \ldots, n_m^{(r)}, \ldots \\ \ldots \end{array}$$

each row a subsequence of the preceeding row and such that $\lim_m a_{n_m^{(r)} p} = a_p$ for all $r \leqq p$. If we let r increase indefinitely, this set of sequences might have no sequence of the integers in common. In order to get a sequence effective for our purpose, we use the *diagonal procedure*, i.e., we consider the sequence of integers $n_r^{(r)}$, $r = 1, 2, \ldots$ Then for $r \geqq m$, $n_r^{(r)}$ will be a subsequence of $n_m^{(r)}$. Consequently, $\lim_r a_{n_r^{(r)} p} = a_p$, since the convergence will depend only on the terms for which $r > p$. This statement is equivalent to $\lim_r S_{n_r^{(r)}} = S$ in terms of coordinate-wise convergence.

Returning to Helly's theorem, we consider first the special case when the functions are monotonic nondecreasing, i.e., assume that $f_n(x)$ is a uniformly bounded sequence of monotonic nondecreasing functions on $[a, b]$. Let $\{x_p\}$ be a denumerable dense set of points of $[a, b]$ including a and b. Then $\{f_n(x_p)\} = S_n$ is a sequence of sequences, satisfying the conditions of our lemma so that there exists a subsequence n_m of the integers n such that $\lim_m f_{n_m}(x_p)$ exists for all p. Denote these limits by $f(x_p)$. Now $f(x)$ is monotonic nondecreasing on the x_p, i.e., $x_p \leqq x_p'$ implies $f(x_p) \leqq f(x_p')$. Consequently, we know that the function f can be extended to a monotonic nondecreasing function defined for all points x for which $f(x - 0) = f(x + 0) = f(x)$ as determined by the x_p. It now develops that if $f(x_0 + 0) = f(x_0 - 0) = f(x_0)$, then $f_{n_m}(x_0)$ converges to $f(x_0)$. For we have $(e > 0,\ d_e,\ 0 < x_p - x_0 < d_e) : f(x_0) \geqq f(x_p) - e$. For a particular such p, we take $m \geqq m_{ep}$ so that $f(x_p) > f_{n_m}(x_p) - e$. Then for the same m's:

$$f(x_0) \geqq f(x_p) - e \geqq f_{n_m}(x_p) - 2\,e \geqq f_{n_m}(x_0) - 2\,e.$$

In a similar way we may consider the approach from the left and find that for $m \geqq m_{ep'} : f(x_0) \leqq f_{n_m}(x_0) + 2\,e$, so that for $m \geqq m_{ep}$ and $m_{ep'} : f_{n_m}(x_0) - 2\,e \leqq f(x_0) \leqq f_{n_m}(x_0) + 2\,e$, and so $\lim_m f_{n_m}(x_0)$

$= f(x_0)$. This observation assures us that $\lim_m f_{n_m}(x) = f(x)$ except possibly at the points of discontinuity of $f(x)$.

Let us denote by x_p' this at most denumerable number of discontinuities of $f(x)$. Then by applying the lemma to $f_{n_m}(x_p')$ we get a subsequence $f_{n'_k}$ of functions such that $\lim_k f_{n'_k}(x_p')$ exists for all p. Consequently $\lim_k f_{n'_k}(x)$ exists for all x of $[a, b]$.

The final step is almost self-evident. We write $f_n(x) = f_n(a) + P_n(x) - N_n(x)$, where $P_n(x)$ and $N_n(x)$ are the positive and negative variations of the functions $f_n(x)$, respectively. If $f_n(x)$ is a sequence of functions uniformly of bounded variation, $P_n(x)$ and $N_n(x)$ will be uniformly bounded sequences of monotonic nondecreasing functions. We can then pick a subsequence n_m of the integers so that $f_{n_m}(a)$, $P_{n_m}(x)$, and $N_{n_m}(x)$ converge for all x and consequently $f_{n_m}(x) = f_{n_m}(a) + P_{n_m}(x) - N_{n_m}(x)$ will converge for all x.

In some of the appliations of this theorem it is sufficient to know that the subsequence $f_{n_m}(x)$ converges to a function of bounded variation $f(x)$ excepting at a denumerable set of points.

As a corollary we have an alternate form of this theorem:

8.10. THEOREM. If $\mathfrak{F} = [f(x)]$ is an infinite set of functions of bounded variation on $[a, b]$, which are uniformly of bounded variation, then there exists a sequence of distinct elements $\{f_n\}$ of $\mathfrak{F}$ and a function g of bounded variation such that $\lim_n f_n(x) = g(x)$ for all x of $[a, b]$.

8.11. Remarks on Compactness. The word "compact" as applied to a set of elements in an abstract topological space was introduced by Fréchet in his thesis [Sur quelques points du Calcul Fonctionnel, *Rend. Circ. Palermo* 22 (1906) 1-74] in connection with spaces in which the notion of a limit of a sequence is defined. According to Fréchet limits of sequences of elements have three properties: (1) $\lim_n x_n$, if it exists, is unique; (2) if $x_n = x$ for all n then $\lim_n x_n = x$; and (3) if $\lim_n x_n = x$ and n_m is a subsequence of the integers n then $\lim_m x_{n_m} = x$. In such a sequential-limit space, a limiting element of a set E has a sequence of distinct elements of E converging to it. A set E is compact if every infinite subset has at least one limiting element. As a consequence a set E of elements is compact if and only if from every sequence $\{x_n\}$ of elements of E we can extract a subsequence $\{x_{n_m}\}$ having a limit.

If we define convergence of a sequence of functions of bounded variation by means of pointwise convergence, then the Helly theorem asserts that a subset of the set of functions of bounded variation is compact if it is uniformly of bounded variation. The lemma used in the proof is equivalent to the statement that in the space of all sequences of real numbers, where limit is defined by coordinatewise convergence, a set of such sequences is compact if each coordinate value is bounded (or compact).

Recently the word "compact" has been applied to sets in a topological space, provided a form of the Borel theorem applies, i.e., any covering of the set by open sets can be reduced to a finite subset of the covering sets. To distinguish between these two types of compactness, one might label the one tied to the existence of limiting elements W-B (Weierstrass-Bolzano) compactness and the covering type B (Borel) compactness.

We state without proof the theorem:

In a metric space, in which convergence is related to a metric $\delta(x, y)$ in the sense that $\lim_n x_n = x$ is equivalent to $\lim_n \delta(x_n, x) = 0$, a set is B-compact if and only if it is W-B-compact and closed.

EXERCISES

1. Show directly from the definition, that if $f(x)$ is of bounded variation on $[a, b]$, then $f(x+0)$ and $f(x-0)$ exist for all $a < x < b$, $f(a+0)$ exists at a and $f(b-0)$ at b.

2. Show that if $f(x)$ has only discontinuities of the first kind on $[a, b]$, i.e., $f(x+0)$ and $f(x-0)$ exist for all x of $[a, b]$ as finite numbers, then $f(x)$ is bounded on $[a, b]$ and has at most a denumerable number of discontinuities.

3. Show that the indefinite integral of a Riemann integrable function $f(x) : g(x) = \int_a^x f(x)dx$ is of bounded variation and that $\int_a^b | dg(x) | = \int_a^b | f(x) | dx$.

4. If $f_q(x)$ is a directed set of functions of bounded variation such that $\lim_q f_q(x) = f(x)$ for x on $[a, b]$, is it true that $\int_a^b | df | \leq \underline{\lim}_q \int_a^b | df_q |$?

9. Riemann-Stieltjes Integrals

The Riemann-Stieltjes (R-S) integral is an integral of functions of intervals depending on two point functions: $f(x)$ and $g(x)$ with $F(I) = F[c, d] = f(x)(g(d) - g(c))$, $c \leq x \leq d$. Stieltjes, following

Cauchy, considered the case where $f(x)$ is continuous and $g(x)$ of bounded variation on $[a, b]$ and was content to note that for this combination of functions the function of subdivisions

$$G(\sigma) = \sum_i f(x_i')(g(x_i) - g(x_{i-1})) = \sum_\sigma f\Delta g, \text{ with } x_{i-1} \leqq x_i' \leqq x_i$$

converges as $|\sigma| \to 0$. Since Riemann, the emphasis has been more in the direction of determining for what combinations of functions $f(x)$ and $g(x)$ a given mode of convergence leads to an integral.

As in the case of functions of intervals, we have for $\Sigma_i f(x_i')(g(x_i) - g(x_{i-1}))$, the two modes of convergence, viz., as $|\sigma| \to 0$, leading to the norm integral: $N \int fdg$, and by successive subdivisions or refinements, leading to the σ-integral: $\sigma \int fdg$. Both integrals will be called Riemann-Stieltjes (R-S) integrals. In the early part of this section, no restrictions beyond the existence of the integrals will be placed on the functions f and g. Later we shall consider the special case when $g(x)$ is limited to being a function of bounded variation on $[a, b]$.

We note a few examples of Stieltjes integrals. If $f(x) = c$ on $[a, b]$, then for all functions $g(x)$, $\int_a^b cdg = c(g(b) - g(a))$. If $g(x) = c$ on $[a, b]$, then $\int_a^b fdg = 0$ for all $f(x)$. If $g(x) = x$, then the Riemann-Stieltjes integral becomes a Riemann integral.

If $g(x) = B(x, x_0; c, d)$ the simple break function with value c at $x = x_0$ and break d at $x = x_0$, then the only contributions to $\Sigma_\sigma f\Delta g$ are the terms which come from points in the vicinity of x_0. If σ does not include x_0, then $G(\sigma) = f(x')d$, where $x_1 \leqq x' \leqq x_2$, x_1 and x_2 being the points of σ immediately adjacent to x_0 on either side. If σ includes x_0, then $G(\sigma) = f(x'')c + f(x''')(d - c)$, where $x_1 \leqq x'' \leqq x_0$ and $x_0 \leqq x''' \leqq x_2$. If the norm integral exists these two expressions must have the same finite limit: $f(x_0)d$ as x', x'', and x''' approach x_0. If $f(x)$ is discontinuous at x_0 i.e., $\lim_{x \to x_0} f(x) \neq f(x_0)$, then $d = 0$, and so also $c = 0$, since x'' and x''' are independent of each other. Then $g(x)$ is continuous at $x = x_0$. Consequently, if $g(x)$ is discontinuous, then $f(x)$ must be continuous at x_0 and $N \int_a^b fdg = f(x_0)d = f(x_0)(g(x_0 + 0) - g(x_0 - 0))$. If the σ-integral exists, then x_0 can eventually be included in σ, so that

$$\lim_{\substack{x'' \to x_0+0 \\ x''' \to x_0-0}} (f(x'')c + f(x''')(d - c))$$

must exist and be equal to $f(x_0)c + f(x_0)(d - c) = f(x_0)d$. If $f(x)$ is discontinuous on the left, then since x'' and x''' are independent, it follows that $c = 0$, i.e., $g(x)$ is continuous on the left. If $f(x)$ is discontinuous on the right, it follows that $c - d = 0$, i.e., $g(x)$ is continuous on the right. Consequently, if $\sigma \int_a^b fdg$ exists, then $f(x)$ and $g(x) = B(x, x_0; c, d)$ do not have discontinuities on the same side of x_0 and $\int_a^b fdg = f(x_0)d = f(x_0)\ (g(x_0 + 0) - g(x_0 - 0))$.

A kind of geometrical interpretation of the Stieltjes integral is as follows: In three dimensions, $y = f(x)$ is a cylinder on the xy-plane with elements parallel to the z-axis, and $z = g(x)$ is a cylinder on the xz-plane with elements parallel to the y-axis. Consequently, $\int ydz$ is the (signed) projection onto the yz-plane of the area on the cylinder $y = f(x)$ cut off by the cylinder $z = g(x)$.

9.1. We note the following variants of the basic interval function for R-S integrals, which in some cases lead to effective integrals of Stieltjes type:

(1) $F(I) = f(c)\ (g(d) - g(c))$; left Cauchy integral;

(2) $F(I) = f(d)\ (g(d) - g(c))$; right Cauchy integral;

(3) $F(I) = \frac{1}{2}\ (f(c) + f(d))\ (g(d) - g(c))$; mean integral;

(4) $F(I) = f(x)\ (g(d) - g(c)), c < x < d$; modified integral;

(5) if $g(x)$ has only discontinuities of the first kind (or breaks): $F(I) = f(c)\ (g(c + 0) - g(c)) + f(x)\ (g(d - 0) - g(c + 0)) + f(d)\ (g(d) - g(d - 0))$, with $c < x < d$.

Both modes of convergence can be considered in each of these cases.

10. Existence Theorems for Riemann-Stieltjes Integrals

The theorems of II.3 for integrals of interval functions yield the following:

10.1. If for two functions $f(x)$ and $g(x)$ on $[a, b]$, $N \int_a^b fdg$ exists, then $\sigma \int_a^b fdg$ exists.

10.2. A necessary and sufficient condition that $N \int_a^b fdg$ $(\sigma \int_a^b fdg)$ exist is that the corresponding Cauchy condition of convergence hold for the approximating sums $\Sigma_\sigma f\Delta g$.

10.3. A necessary and sufficient condition that $N \int_a^b fdg$ $(\sigma \int_a^b fdg)$ exist is that the corresponding upper and lower integrals $\overline{\int_a^b} fdg$ and $\underline{\int_a^b} fdg$ be finite and equal.

Note that these upper and lower integrals are defined as greatest and least of limits, and not in terms of upper and lower bounds of the function f on intervals of subdivision.

10.4. A necessary and sufficient condition that $N\int_a^b fdg\ (\sigma\int_a^b fdg)$ exist is that $N\int_a^b \omega(Sf\Delta g;\ I) = 0\ (\sigma\int_a^b \omega(Sf\Delta g; I) = 0)$.

Since $\omega(Sf\Delta g;\ I) \geqq \omega(f, I)\ |\ g(I)\ |$, where $\omega(f;\ I)$ is the oscillation of f on $I = [c, d]$ and $g(I) = g(d) - g(c)$, we have:

10.5. Corollary I. If $N\int_a^b fdg$ exists, then $N\int_a^b \omega(f; I)\ |g(I)\ | = 0$; if $\sigma\int_a^b fdg$ exists, then $\sigma\int_a^b \omega(f;\ I)\ |g(I)| = 0$ or equivalently g.l.b.$_\sigma \Sigma_\sigma\ \omega(f;\ I)\ |g(I)\ | = 0$.

This leads to:

10.6. Corollary II. If $N\int_a^b fdg$ exists, then f and g have no common discontinuities on $[a, b]$. If $\sigma\int_a^b fdg$ exists, then f and g have no common discontinuities on the same side of any point of $[a, b]$.

We prove the second part of this corollary first. Suppose $\sigma\int_a^b fdg$ exists. Then by Corollary I $(e,\ \sigma_e,\ \sigma \geqq \sigma_e) : \Sigma_\sigma\ \omega(f; I)\ |\ g(I)\ | < e$. If x_0 is a point of discontinuity of $f(x)$ on the left, then by including x_0 in σ it follows that $\omega(f;\ [x', x_0])\ |\ g(x') - g(x_0)\ | < e$ where x' is the point of σ immediately to the left of x_0. Since we can add to σ any point between x' and x_0, it follows that $\omega(f; [x_0 - d, x_0])\ |\ g(x_0) - g(x_0 - d)\ | < e$ for $0 < d < x_0 - x'$. Since x_0 is a point of discontinuity of f on the left, there exists $e' > 0$ such that $0 < d < x_0 - x'$ implies $\omega(f;\ [x_0 - d,\ x_0'']) > e'$, so that $|\ g(x_0) - g(x_0 - d)\ | < e/e'$. Consequently, $\lim_{x\to x_0 - 0} g(x) = g(x_0)$, or $g(x)$ is continuous on the left at x_0. If then g is discontinuous on the left, $f(x)$ must be continuous on the left at x_0. The reasoning for the right hand is similar.

If $N\int_a^b fdg$ exists, then $(e,\ d_e,\ |\sigma\ | < d_e) : \Sigma_\sigma \omega(f,\ I)\ |g(I)\ | < e$. Let x_0 be a point of discontinuity of $f(x)$. Since $\sigma\int_a^b fdg$ exists if $N\int_a^b fdg$ exists, it follows that $g(x)$ is continuous either on the left or the right of x_0. Further, $\omega(f;\ [x_0 - d,\ x_0 + d'])\ |g(x_0 + d') - g(x_0 - d)\ | < e$ if $0 < d,\ d' < d_e$. Since $f(x)$ is discontinuous at x_0, there exists $e' > 0$ such that $\omega(f;\ [x_0 - d,\ x_0 + d']) > e'$ for $0 < d$, $d' < d_e$, and so also $|g(x_0 + d') - g(x_0 - d)\ | < e/e'$. Consequently,

$$\lim_{(d, d')\to(+0,\,+0)} (g(x_0 + d') - g(x_0 - d)) = 0.$$

Since $g(x)$ is continuous on either the left or the right, it follows that $\lim_{x\to x_0} g(x) = g(x_0)$. Then if $g(x)$ is discontinuous at x_0, $f(x)$ must be continuous.

We note that:

10.7. If either $f(x)$ or $g(x)$ is continuous at x_0, then the interval function $F(I) = F[c, d] = f(x)\,(g(d) - g(c))$ is pseudoadditive at x_0 provided f and g are bounded in the neighborhood of x_0.

This follows at once from the identity:

$F[c, d] - (F[c, x_0] + F[x_0, d]) =$
$(f(x') - f(x'''))\,(g(d) - g(x_0)) + (f(x') - f(x''))\,(g(x_0) - g(c))$
with $c \leqq x' \leqq d$, $c \leqq x'' \leqq x_0$, $c_0 \leqq x''' \leqq d$.

10.8. Conversely, if $F(I) = f(x)\,(g(d) - g(c))$ is pseudoadditive at x_0, then either $f(x)$ or $g(x)$ is continuous at this point.

For if $g(x)$ is discontinuous on the right, then there exists a sequence $x_n \to x_0 + 0$ such that $|\,g(x_0) - g(x_n)\,| > e$, for some fixed $e > 0$. If in the expression for $F[c, x_n] - (F[c, x_0] + F[x_0, x_n])$ we take $x'' = x' = x_0$, and then let $c \to x_0 - 0$ and $x_n \to x_0 + 0$, we conclude that $\lim_{x''' \to x_0 + 0} f(x''') = f(x_0)$. If we take $x''' = x_0$, and $x'' = x'$, then we conclude that $\lim_{x' \to x_0 - 0} f(x') = f(x)$. Then $f(x)$ is continuous at x_0. The same reasoning, by parity, applies if $g(x)$ is discontinuous on the left.

If we take into account II.3.10, we obtain:

10.9. THEOREM. If $f(x)$ and $g(x)$ are bounded on $[a, b]$, then a necessary and sufficient condition that $N \int_a^b fdg$ exist is that $\sigma \int_a^b fdg$ exist and f and g have no common discontinuities on $[a, b]$.

If either $f(x)$ or $g(x)$ is a continuous function on $[a, b]$, then $N \int_a^b fdg$ exists if and only if $\sigma \int_a^b fdg$ exists, and they are equal. In particular it is immaterial whether the Riemann integral $\int_a^b f(x)dx$ is defined as a norm or a σ-integral. This is essentially the burden of the Darboux theorem.

As an additional necessary condition for the existence of $\int_a^b fdg$ we have:

10.10. THEOREM. If $f(x)$ and $g(x)$ are such that $\int_a^b fdg$ exists (in either sense), then there exists a finite number of closed intervals of $[a, b]$: $[I_1, \ldots, I_n]$ such that $f(x)$ is bounded on each I_k, and $g(x)$ is constant on the closed complementary intervals: $I_1', \ldots, I'_{n+1}$. Consequently, $\int_a^b fdg$ is zero on the intervals I_k', and the value of $\int_a^b fdg$ is independent of the values assumed by $f(x)$ on these intervals.

Suppose $\sigma \int_a^b fdg$ exists. Then by II.10.5: $(e, \sigma_e, \sigma \geqq \sigma_e) : \Sigma_\sigma \omega(f; I)\,|\,g(I)\,| < e$, so that $\omega(f;\, I)\,|\,g(I)\,| < e$ for each I of σ. Let σ_e

consist of the points $a = x_0 < x_1 < \dots < x_n = b$, and suppose that f is unbounded on $[x_k, x_{k+1}]$. Then $\omega(f; I)$ is $+\infty$ on this interval so that $g(I) = g(x_{k+1}) - g(x_k) = 0$. Let x' be any interior point of $[x_k, x_{k+1}]$. Then either $\omega(f; [x_k, x'])$ or $\omega(f; [x', x_{k+1}])$ is infinite. Consequently, $g(x') = g(x_k)$ or $g(x_{k+1})$, so that $g(x)$ is constant on $[x_k, x_{k+1}]$. Since there are only a finite number of intervals in σ_e, this proves the theorem for $\sigma \int_a^b fdg$ and consequently also for $N \int_a^b fdg$. The difference between the σ and norm integral is that for the latter any point of unboundedness of $f(x)$ [i.e., in every neighborhood of which $f(x)$ is unbounded] must be interior to one of the intervals of constancy of $g(x)$, while for the σ-integral it may be an end point.

Since the value of the integral $\int_a^b fdg$ is unchanged if $f(x)$ is altered on an interval of constancy of $g(x)$, we might assume that $f(x)$ is linear on such intervals, and restrict ourselves to the case where $f(x)$ is bounded on $[a, b]$.

The function $g(x)$ is subject to the same boundedness conditions as $f(x)$. This can be shown easily by using the integration by parts theorem below.

11. Properties of Riemann-Stieltjes Integrals

11.1. The integral $\int_a^b fdg$ is a bilinear function in f and g, in the sense that if for $f_1(x),\dots f_n(x)$ and $g_1(x),\dots g_n(x)$ the integrals $\int_a^b f_i(x)dg_j(x)$ exist, and $c_1,\dots,c_n$; $d_1,\dots, d_n$ are constants, then for $f(x) = \Sigma_{i=1}^n c_i f_i(x)$ and $g(x) = \Sigma_{i=1}^n d_i g_i(x)$ the integral $\int_a^b fdg$ exists and is equal to $\Sigma_{ij}\, c_i d_j \int_a^b f_i dg_j$.

This follows from II.5.1 and II.5.2.

11.2. If $\int_a^b fdg$ exists, then for $a \leqq c \leqq d \leqq b$: $\int_c^d fdg$ exists and $\int_I fdg = \int_c^d fdg$ is an additive function of intervals.

This follows from II.4.1.

11.3. The continuity properties of the function $h(x) = \int_a^x fdg$ are determined largely by those of $g(x)$. In particular, if $g(x)$ is continuous at x_0, then $h(x)$ is continuous at x_0. If $g(x_0 - 0)$ exists, then $h(x_0 - 0)$ exists and $h(x_0) - h(x_0 - 0) = f(x_0)\,(g(x_0) - g(x_0 - 0))$. Similar statements hold for $g(x_0 + 0)$ and $h(x_0 + 0)$.

For if $x_1 < x_0$, then

$$\left| \int_{x_1}^{x_0} fdg - f(x')\,(g(x_0) - g(x_1)) \right| \leqq \omega(Sf\Delta g;\ [x_1, x_0]),$$

and the left-hand side approaches zero as $x_1 \to x_0 - 0$. If $g(x_0 - 0)$

exists and is not equal to $g(x_0)$, then $g(x)$ is discontinuous on the left and $f(x)$ is continuous on the left at x_0. Then

$$\lim_{x_1 \to x_0 - 0} \int_{x_1}^{x_0} fdg = \lim_{x_1 < x' \to x_0 - 0} f(x')\,(g(x_0) - g(x_1))$$
$$= f(x_0)\,(g(x_0) - g(x_0 - 0)).$$

11.4. Approximation Theorem. If σ is any subdivision of $[a, b]$, then $| \int_a^b fdg - \Sigma_\sigma f\Delta g | \leqq \Sigma_\sigma \omega(Sf\Delta g;\ I)$.

This is a special case of the corresponding theorem for integrals of interval functions II.4.5.

11.5. Convergence Theorem. If $\lim_n f_n(x) = f(x)$ for all x of $[a, b]$, and $\int_a^b f_n dg$ exists uniformly in the sense that $\lim_\sigma \Sigma_\sigma \omega(Sf_n\Delta g;\ I) = 0$ uniformly in n, then $\lim_n \int_a^b f_n dg$ and $\int_a^b fdg$ both exist and are equal. The integrals and corresponding limit are assumed to be the same throughout.

This is an immediate consequence of the iterated limits theorem I.7.4.

11.6. Substitution Theorem. If $f(x)$ is bounded on $[a, b]$ and $k(x) = \int_a^x g(x)dh(x)$, then $\int_a^b f(x)dk(x)$ exists if and only if $\int_a^b f(x)g(x)\,dh(x)$ exists and the two integrals are equal.

This is a special case of the substitution theorem for integrals of interval functions II.4.8 and can also be proved directly. The integrals are assumed to be of the same type throughout.

11.7. Integration by Parts Theorem. If $\int_a^b fdg$ exists, then $\int_a^b gdf$ exists and $\int_a^b fdg = f(b)\,g(b) - f(a)\,g(a) - \int_a^b gdf$.

The proof of this theorem depends on the following identity:

$$\sum_{i=1}^{n} g(x_i')\,(f(x_i) - f(x_{i-1})) = f(x_n)\,g(x_n) - f(x_0)\,g(x_0)$$
$$- \sum_{i=0}^{n} f(x_i)\,(g(x'_{i+1}) - g(x_i'))$$

where $x_0' = x_0$ and $x'_{n+1} = x_n$.

Suppose $N \int_a^b fdg$ exists. Then

$$(e, d_e, |\sigma| < d_e) : | \int_a^b fdg - \Sigma_\sigma f\Delta g | < e.$$

Then

$$| \sum_{i=1}^{n} g(x_i')\,(f(x_i) - f(x_{i-1})) - f(b)g(b) + f(a)g(a) + \int_a^b fdg |$$
$$= | \int_a^b fdg - \sum_{i=0}^{n} f(x_i)\,(g(x'_{i+1}) - g(x_i')) | \leqq e$$

provided $|\sigma| = \max(x_i - x_{i-1}) < d_e/2$, since then $\max(x_i' - x'_{i-1}) \leqq 2\max(x_i - x_{i-1}) < d_e$. Then $N\int_a^b fdg = f(b)g(b) - f(a)g(a) - N\int_a^b gdf$.

If $\sigma\int fdg$ exists, then $(e, \sigma_e, \sigma \geq \sigma_e) : |\int_a^b fdg - \Sigma_\sigma f\Delta g| < e$. Select a $\sigma \geqq \sigma_e$. Then

$$|\sum_{i=1}^{n} g(x_i')(f(x_i) - f(x_{i-1})) - f(b)g(b) + f(a)g(a) + \int_a^b fdg|$$
$$= |\sum_{i=0}^{n} f(x_i)(g(x'_{i+1}) - g(x_i')) - \int_a^b fdg|$$
$$= |\sum_{i=0}^{n}(f(x_i)(g(x'_{i+1}) - g(x_i)) + f(x_i)(g(x_i) - g(x_i')) - \int_a^b fdg| < e$$

since $\sigma' = (a = x_0 \leqq x_1' \leqq x_1 \leqq x_2' \leqq \ldots \leqq x'_{n+1} = x_n = b)$ includes σ and so $\sigma' \geqq \sigma_e$. Consequently, $\sigma\int_a^b gdf$ exists and is equal to $f(b)g(b) - f(a)g(a) - \int_a^b fdg$.

There is a slightly more complicated proof for the case of the σ-integral. From $\Sigma_\sigma f\Delta g = f(d)g(d) - f(c)g(c) - \Sigma_{\sigma'} g\Delta f$, with $\sigma = (c = x_0, x_1, \ldots, x_n = d)$ and $\sigma' = (c = x_0', x_i', \ldots, x'_{n+1} = d)$, it follows that $\Sigma_{\sigma_1} f\Delta g - \Sigma_{\sigma_2} f\Delta g = \Sigma_{\sigma'_2} g\Delta f - \Sigma_{\sigma'_1} g\Delta f$, where σ_1 and σ_1' and σ_2 and σ_2' are related subdivisions of the interval $I = [c, d]$. Then $\omega(Sf\Delta g; I) \leqq \omega(Sg\Delta f; I) \leqq \omega(Sf\Delta g; I)$ for every I, and equality holds. If then $\sigma\int_a^b \omega(Sf\Delta g; I) = 0$, then $\sigma\int_a^b \omega(Sg\Delta f; I) = 0$ and the existence of $\sigma\int_a^b fdg$ carries with it the existence of $\sigma\int_a^b gdf$. Let $\sigma = \sigma_e + \sigma_e'$, where $(e, \sigma_e, \sigma \geqq \sigma_e) : |\int_a^b fdg - \Sigma_\sigma f\Delta g| < e$, and $(e, \sigma_e', \sigma \geqq \sigma_e') : |\int_a^b gdf - \Sigma_\sigma g\Delta f| < e$. If in $\Sigma_\sigma f\Delta g$, we take $x_i' = x_{i-1}$, then

$$\sum_{i=1}^{n} f(x_{i-1})(g(x_i) - g(x_{i-1})) = f(b)g(b) - f(a)g(a) - \sum_{i=1}^{n} g(x_i)(f(x_i) - f(x_{i-1})).$$

Then for every $e > 0$:

$$|\int_a^b fdg + \int_a^b gdf - (f(b)g(b) - f(a)g(a))| < 2e.$$

The integration by parts formula follows.

Since for any function $f(x)$ and any x of $[a, b]$ we have $f(x) - f(a) = \int_a^x df$, we have

$$f(b)g(b) - f(a)g(a) = f(b)(g(b) - g(a)) + g(a)(f(b) - f(a)) = \int_a^b f(b)dg(x) + \int_a^b g(a)df(x).$$

Then the integration by parts formula can be written

$$\int_a^b (f(x) - f(b))dg(x) = \int_a^b (g(a) - g(x))df(x)$$

or:

11.8. $$\int_a^b df(x) \int_a^x dg(y) = \int_a^b dg(y) \int_y^b df(x).$$

If we assume that $\int_a^b f_1(x)df(x)$ and $\int_a^b g_1(y)dg(y)$ each exist, then the substitution theorem gives us

$$\int_a^b \int_a^x f_1(x)df(x)g_1(y)dg(y) = \int_a^b \int_y^b g_1(y)dg(y)f_1(x)df(x).$$

Because of the linearity properties of the Stieltjes integral, we can extend this linearly in the sense:

11.9. THEOREM. If $\int_a^b f_i(x)df(x)$ and $\int_a^b g_i(y)dg(y)$ exist for $i = 1, \ldots, n$ and if $h(x, y) = \Sigma_{i=1}^n f_i(x)g_i(y)$, then

$$\int_a^b df(x) \int_a^x h(x, y)dg(y) = \int_a^b dg(y) \int_y^b h(x, y)df(x).$$

This is a special case of the so called Dirichlet formula.

EXERCISES

1. Which of the theorems or properties holding for Riemann-Stieltjes integrals are also valid for variants of the interval functions for Stieltjes integrals mentioned in II.9.1?

2. Show that if $\int_a^b fdg$ exists, then $g(x)$ is bounded on a set E of a finite number of nonoverlapping subintervals of $[a, b]$, $f(x)$ being constant on the complement of E relative to $[a, b]$.

3. Is the substitution theorem still valid if the boundedness condition on $f(x)$ is dropped?

4. Show that if $f(x)$ is bounded and $\int_a^b g(x)dh(x)$, $\int_a^b f(x)g(x)dh(x)$ and $\int_a^b f(x)h(x)dg(x)$ exist, then $\int_a^b g(x)h(x)df(x)$ exists and

$$\int_a^b f(x)g(x)dh(x) + \int_a^b f(x)h(x)dg(x) + \int_a^b g(x)h(x)df(x)$$
$$= f(b)g(b)h(b) - f(a)g(a)h(a).$$

5. Show that if for a function $f(x)$ on $[a, b]$, $\int_a^b fdf$ exists, then $\int_a^b fdf = \frac{1}{2}((f(b))^2 - (f(a))^2)$. If $n > 2$, and an integer, is it true that if $\int_a^b f^n df$ exists then $\int_a^b f^n df = ((f(b))^{n+1} - (f(a))^{n+1})/(n+1)$?

12. Classes of Functions Determined by Stieltjes Integrals

Any given function $g(x)$ on $[a, b]$ determines a class $\mathfrak{F}$ of functions $f(x)$ such that $\int_a^b fdg$ exists for all f of $\mathfrak{F}$. For instance, the function $g(x) = x$ determines the class of Riemann integrable functions, the break function $\beta(x, x_0; d_1, d_2)$ with $d_1 \neq 0$ and $d_1 \neq d_2$ determines the class of functions $f(x)$ continuous at $x = x_0$. Any such class of functions is linear. In the same way, a fixed function $f(x)$ determines a linear class $\mathfrak{G}$ of functions $g(x)$ such that $\int_a^b fdg$ exists for all g of $\mathfrak{G}$.

A class $\mathfrak{G}$ of functions $g(x)$ determines a class $\mathfrak{F}$ of functions $f(x)$ such that $\int_a^b fdg$ exists for every g of $\mathfrak{G}$ and every f of $\mathfrak{F}$. The class of functions $\mathfrak{F}$ is linear and $\int_a^b fdg$ is bilinear on the product of the two classes $\mathfrak{F} \times \mathfrak{G}_1$, where $\mathfrak{G}_1$ is the linear extension of $\mathfrak{G}$, or the smallest linear class containing $\mathfrak{G}$. A similar statement is possible if $\mathfrak{F}$ and $\mathfrak{G}$ are interchanged.

In the history of the theory of integration, the class of continuous functions has had an honored role. As a matter of fact, it is often taken for granted that any integration process on a linear interval should make every continuous function $f(x)$ integrable. This raises the question of characterizing the class $\mathfrak{G}$ of functions $g(x)$ such that $\int_a^b fdg$ exists for every function $f(x)$ continuous on $[a, b]$ and every g of $\mathfrak{G}$. Since $f(x)$ is continuous, it is immaterial whether the norm or the σ-integral is involved. The following theorem is an answer to the question:

12.1. THEOREM. A necessary and sufficient condition that $\int_a^b fdg$ exist for every function $f(x)$ continuous on $[a, b]$ is that $g(x)$ be of bounded variation on $[a, b]$.

The sufficiency part of the theorem goes back to Stieltjes. We apply Theorem II.10.4. If g is of bounded variation, then a brief calculation shows that $\omega(Sf\Delta g; I) \leqq \omega(f, I) \cdot v(I)$, where $v(I) = \int_I |dg|$. The continuity and consequent uniform continuity of $f(x)$ gives $(e, d_e, l(I) \leqq d_e) : \omega(f, I) \leqq e$. Then if $|\sigma| \leqq d_e$, $\Sigma_\sigma \omega(Sf\Delta g; I) \leqq e\, \Sigma_\sigma v(I) = e \cdot v[a, b]$, and $\int_a^b fdg$ exists.

The necessity part of this theorem is a little more complicated. We have the important lemma:

12.2. Lemma. If $a_n \geqq 0$, and $\Sigma_n a_n$ is divergent, then there exist constants $c_n > 0$ such that $\lim_n c_n = 0$, and $\Sigma_n c_n a_n$ is still divergent.

Crudely expressed, this lemma states that there is no last divergent series of positive terms.

If $s_n = \Sigma_{m=1}^{n} a_m$, then $c_n = 1/s_n$ is a sequence satisfying the conditions of the lemma. For

$$\sum_{p=0}^{m} a_{n+p}/s_{n+p} \geqq \sum_{p=0}^{m} a_{n+p}/s_{n+m} = (s_{n+m} - s_{n-1})/s_{n+m} = 1 - s_{n-1}/s_{n+m}.$$

Since $s_n \to \infty$, for any n we can select m so large that $s_{n-1}/s_{n+m} < \frac{1}{2}$. It follows that $\Sigma_n a_n/s_n$ violates the Cauchy condition of convergence and is divergent.

Our lemma is a special case of the Abel-Dini theorem, which states that if $a_n \geqq 0$, and $\Sigma_n a_n$ is divergent, then $\Sigma_n a_n/s_n^k$ is divergent if $k \leqq 1$ (which follows at once from the above lemma), and convergent if $k > 1$. The harmonic series with $a_n = 1$ for all n, is a special case. A similar theorem is true if $a_n \geqq 0$ and $\Sigma_n a_n$ is convergent; if $r_n = \Sigma_{m=n}^{\infty} a_m$, then $\Sigma_n a_n/r_n^k$ is convergent if $k < 1$ and divergent if $k \geqq 1$. So there is no last convergent series of positive terms. For details the reader is referred to K. Knopp: "Infinite Series," 1928, § 39.

We also need the following local property of functions of bounded variation:

12.3. THEOREM. A function $g(x)$ is of bounded variation on $[a, b]$ if and only if for every x of $[a, b]$, there exists a vicinity $[x - d_1, x + d_2]$ such that $f(x)$ is of bounded variation on $[x - d_1, x + d_2]$, ($d_1 = 0$ if $x = a$, and $d_2 = 0$ if $x = b$).

The "only if" is obvious. The "if" follows from the Borel theorem.

Returning to our theorem, we proceed contrapositively and assume that $\int_a^b f dg$ exists for all continuous functions $f(x)$ but $g(x)$ is not of bounded variation on $[a, b]$. Then there exists a point x_0 of $[a, b]$ such that $g(x)$ is of infinite variation on every interval $[x_0 - d_1, x_0 + d_2]$, and consequently of infinite variation either on $[x_0 - d_1, x_0]$ for all d_1 or on $[x_0, x_0 + d_2]$ for all d_2. Assume that the former case holds. We can then find a monotone nondecreasing sequence of points x_n approaching x_0 on the left, such that $\Sigma_n |g(x_{n+1}) - g(x_n)| = \infty$. Consequently, by the lemma above, there exist c_n such that $\lim_n c_n = 0$ and $\Sigma_n c_n \,|\, g(x_{n+1}) - g(x_n) \,| = \infty$. Construct $f(x)$ as follows: (a) $f(x) = 0$ for $a \leqq x \leqq x_1$, and for $x \geqq x_0$; (b) $f(x_n) = 0$ for all n; (c) $f(\frac{1}{2}(x_n + x_{n+1})) = c_n \operatorname{sgn}(g(x_{n+1}) - g(x_n))$; and (d) $f(x)$ is linear between x_n and $\frac{1}{2}(x_n + x_{n+1})$ and between $\frac{1}{2}(x_n + x_{n+1})$ and x_{n+1}. Then $f(x)$ is continuous on $[a, b]$. If σ is any subdivision of $[a, b]$ with $x_k' < x_0 \leqq x'_{k+1}$, we can add x_0 and points of x_n between

x_k' and x_0 to σ so that

$$\sum_{n=m}^{p} f(\tfrac{1}{2}(x_n + x_{n+1}))\,(g(x_{n+1}) - g(x_n)) > M$$

for any given M. Consequently, $\lim_\sigma \Sigma_\sigma f\Delta g$ does not exist, contradicting the assumption that $\int_a^b fdg$ exists.

There is also a theorem if the role of f and g is interchanged, i.e., we have:

12.4. THEOREM. If $\int_a^b fdg$ exists for all functions $g(x)$ of bounded variation on $[a, b]$, then $f(x)$ is continuous on $[a, b]$.

For if we set $g(x) = \beta(x, x_0; d_1, d_2)$, the break function with discontinuity at $x = x_0$ and $d_1 \neq 0$, $d_1 \neq d_2$, then $\int_a^b fdg$ exists if and only $f(x)$ is continuous at $x = x_0$.

From these two theorems we conclude that the classes of continuous functions and functions of bounded variation are complementary or adjoint with respect to the Stieltjes integral $\int_a^b fdg$.

13. Riemann-Stieltjes Integrals with Respect to Functions of Bounded Variation. Existence Theorems

In view of the above considerations, Stieltjes integrals with respect to functions of bounded variation play a prominent role, and this is frequently the only case considered. In the following sections we derive additional properties of these integrals when $g(x)$ is of bounded variation.

13.1. THEOREM. If $g(x)$ is of bounded variation on $[a, b]$, for $I = [c, d]$, $g(I) = g(d) - g(c)$ and $v(I) = \int_I |dg|$, then

$$\omega(f, I)\,|g(I)| \leqq \omega(Sf\Delta g; I) \leqq \omega(f, I) \cdot v(I).$$

Here $\omega(f; I)\,|g(I)| = \omega(f, I) \cdot v(I) = 0$ if $v(I) = 0$.

The left-hand inequality is obvious and holds whether $g(x)$ is of bounded variation or not. For the right-hand inequality take any two subdivisions σ_1 and σ_2 of I and set $\sigma_3 = \sigma_1 + \sigma_2$. Then

$$\begin{aligned} &\Big|\sum_{\sigma_1} f(x_i')g(I_i') - \sum_{\sigma_2} f(x_j'')g(I_j'')\Big| \\ &= \Big|\sum_{\sigma_3} f(x_i')g(I_{ij}) - \sum_{\sigma_3} f(x_j'')g(I_{ij})\Big| \\ &\leqq \omega(f, I) \sum_{ij} |g(I_{ij})| \leqq \omega(f, I) \int_I |dg| \\ &= \omega(f, I) \cdot v(I). \end{aligned}$$

From these inequalities and II.10.4, we conclude at once:

13.2. THEOREM. A necessary condition that $\int_a^b fdg$ exists is that $\int_a^b \omega(f, I) \mid g(I) \mid = 0$ and a sufficient condition is that $\int_a^b \omega(f, I) \cdot v(I) = 0$.

A stronger result holds:

13.3. THEOREM. A necessary and sufficient condition that $\int_a^b fdg$ exist is that $\int_a^b \omega(f, I) \cdot v(I) = 0$.

To prove the necessity, we consider first the case of the σ-integral, and show that if $\sigma \int_a^b \omega(f, I) \mid g(I) \mid = 0$, then $\sigma \int_a^b \omega(f, I)v(I) = 0$. We can assume that $f(x)$ is bounded on $[a, b]$. Then $(e, \sigma_e, \sigma \geqq \sigma_e)$: $\Sigma_\sigma \omega(f, I) \mid g(I) \mid \leqq e$. Now by definition $(e, \sigma_e', \sigma \geqq \sigma_e') : \int_a^b \mid dg \mid \leqq \Sigma_\sigma \mid g(I) \mid + e$. As a consequence for $\sigma \geqq \sigma_e + \sigma_e'$:

$$\begin{aligned} 0 &\leqq \sum_\sigma \omega(f, I)v(I) = \sum_\sigma \omega(f, I)\left(\mid g(I) \mid + (v(I) - \mid g(I) \mid)\right) \\ &\leqq \sum_\sigma \omega(f, I) \mid g(I) \mid + \omega(f, [a, b]) \sum_\sigma (v(I) - \mid g(I) \mid) \\ &\leqq e + \omega(f, [a, b]) \left(\int_a^b \mid dg \mid - \sum_\sigma g(I)\right) \leqq e(1 + \omega(f, [a, b])). \end{aligned}$$

This proves that $\sigma \int_a^b \omega(f, I) \cdot v(I) = 0$. For the norm integral, we note that if $N \int_a^b fdg$ exists, then $\sigma \int_a^b fdg$ exists and f and g have no common discontinuities. As a consequence $\sigma \int_a^b \omega(f, I) \cdot v(I) = 0$ and f and v have no common discontinuities. But then the interval function $\omega(f, I) \cdot v(I)$ is pseudoadditive at every point, so that $N \int_a^b \omega(f, I) \cdot v(I) = \sigma \int_a^b \omega(f, I) \cdot v(I) = 0$.

Since for $g(x)$ monotonic nondecreasing $\omega(Sf\Delta g; I) = \omega(f, I) \cdot g(I)$, and $v(x)$ is monotone, the import of this theorem is:

13.4. Corollary I. A necessary and sufficient condition that $\int_a^b fdg$ exist for g of bounded variation is that $\int_a^b fdv$ exist.

Since, moreover, $P(x) = \frac{1}{2}(v(x) + g(x) - g(a))$ and $N(x) = \frac{1}{2}(v(x) - (g(x) - g(a)))$, we have:

13.5. Corollary II. If g is of bounded variation, then $\int_a^b fdg$ exists if and only if $\int_a^b fdP$ and $\int_a^b fdN$ exist and then $\int_a^b fdg = \int_a^b fdP - \int_a^b fdN$.

It follows that the definition of Stieltjes integrals with respect to functions of bounded variation could be based on that of integrals with respect to monotonic nondecreasing functions.

For the case where $g(x)$ is a monotonic nondecreasing function, and $f(x)$ is bounded, we have for any fixed subdivision σ:

$$\text{l.u.b.} \sum_\sigma f(x_i') (g(x_i) - g(x_{i-1})) = \sum_\sigma M_i(g(x_i) - g(x_{i-1}))$$

and

$$\text{g.l.b.} \sum_\sigma f(x_i') (g(x_i) - g(x_{i-1})) = \sum_\sigma m_i(g(x_i) - g(x_{i-1}))$$

where $M_i = \text{l.u.b.}[f(x) : x \text{ on } [x_{i-1}, x_i]]$, and $m_i = \text{g.l.b.} [f(x) : x$ on $[x_{i-1}, x_i]]$. As a consequence

$$\sigma \overline{\int_a^b} fdg = \underset{\sigma}{\text{g.l.b.}} \sum_\sigma M_i(g(x_i) - g(x_{i-1})) = \sigma \int_a^b M(I)g(I)$$

and

$$\sigma \underline{\int_a^b} fdg = \underset{\sigma}{\text{l.u.b.}}\, m_i(g(x_i) - g(x_{i-1})) = \sigma \int_\sigma m(I)g(I).$$

This means that if $g(x)$ is monotone then the upper and lower σ-integrals of f with respect to g, are definable in terms of upper and lower sums and their respective greatest lower and least upper bounds, that is, are of the nature of Darboux integrals.

An additional corollary of our existence theorem is:

13.6. Corollary III. If g_1 and g_2 are of bounded variation on $[a, b]$ and if for every subinterval $[c, d]$, we have $\int_c^d | dg_2 | \leqq \int_c^d | dg_1 |$, and if $\int_a^b fdg_1$ exists, then $\int_a^b fdg_2$ exists also.

For functions of bounded variation, the approximation theorem takes the form:

13.7. Approximation Theorem. If f is of bounded variation and σ is any subdivision of $[a, b]$ and if $\int_a^b fdg$ exists, then

$$\left| \int_a^b fdg - \sum_\sigma f(x_i') (g(x_i) - g(x_{i-1})) \right| \leqq \sum_\sigma \omega(f, I)\, v(I).$$

Obvious is:

If g is of bounded variation on $[a, b]$ and if $\int_a^b fdg$ exists, then $\left| \int_a^b fdg \right| \leqq M \int_a^b | dg |$, where M is the l.u.b. of f on the totality of intervals complementary to those for which $g(x)$ is constant.

The decomposition of a function of bounded variation in the form $g(x) = g_c(x) + g_b(x)$, where $g_c(x)$ is the continuous part of $g(x)$ and $g_b(x)$ is the break or saltus function of g leads to:

13.8. THEOREM. If $g(x)$ is of bounded variation on $[a, b]$ and $\int_a^b fdg$ exists, then $\int_a^b fdg_c$ and $\int_a^b fdg_b$ both exist and

$$\int_a^b fdg = \int_a^b fdg_c + \int_a^b fdg_b = \int_a^b fdg_c + \sum_x f(x) (g(x+0) - g(x-0)),$$

where $g(a-0) = g(a)$ and $g(b+0) = g(b)$.

As a consequence of II.10.10 we can assume that $f(x)$ is bounded on $[a, b]$. Since $\int_I |dg_c| \leqq \int_I |dg|$, for every interval I, it follows by II.13.6 that the existence of $\int_a^b fdg$ carries that of $\int_a^b fdg_c$ with it. Consequently, by the linear properties of the integral, $\int_a^b fdg_b$ exists also. Set $\beta(x, x_0) = \beta(x, x_0; g(x_0) - g(x_0 - 0), g(x_0 + 0) - g(x_0 - 0))$, where $\beta(x, x_0; d_1, d_2)$ is the simple break function for x_0, d_1, d_2. Then for each point of discontinuity x_0 of $g(x)$, $\int_a^b f(x)d\beta(x, x_0)$ exists also and is equal to $f(x_0)\ (g(x_0 + 0) - g(x_0 - 0))$. If $g_b(x) = \Sigma_n \beta(x, x_n)$, where x_n ranges over the discontinuities of $g(x)$, then

$$\int_a^b \left| d(g_b(x) - \sum_{m=1}^{n} \beta(x, x_m)) \right|$$

$$\leqq \sum_{m=n+1}^{\infty} (|g(x_m) - g(x_m - 0)| + |g(x_m + 0) - g(x_m)|),$$

and the right-hand side of the inequality approaches zero with n. Since

$$\left| \int_a^b f(x)d(g_b(x) - \sum_{m=1}^{n} \beta(x, x_m)) \right| \leqq M \int_a^b \left| d(g_b(x) - \sum_{m=1}^{n} \beta(x, x_m)) \right|,$$

it follows further that

$$\lim_n \int_a^b f(x)d(\sum_{m=1}^{n} \beta(x, x_m)) = \int_a^b f(x)dg_b(x),$$

so that

$$\int_a^b fdg_b = \sum_n f(x_n)(g(x_n + 0) - g(x_n - 0))$$
$$= \sum_x f(x)\ (g(x + 0) - g(x - 0)).$$

This result is not entirely reversible, since for the norm integral $f(x)$ must be continuous where $g(x)$ is discontinuous, and for the σ-integral f and g cannot have discontinuities on the same side of any point. It does suggest that if $g(x)$ is of bounded variation and $f(x)$ is bounded and if $\int_a^b fdg_c$ exists, then we might define

$$\int_a^b fdg = \int_a^b fdg_c + f(a)\ (g(a + 0) - g(a))$$
$$+ \sum_{a<x<b} f(x)\ (g(x + 0) - g(x - 0)) + f(b)\ (g(b) - g(b - 0)),$$

and similarly for any closed interval in $[a, b]$.

When $g(x)$ is of bounded variation, it is possible to obtain the σ-integral by a type of convergence which involves the norm of σ.

In σ-convergence it turns out that the points of discontinuity of $g(x)$ play an important role. Arranging these points in any convenient order as a single sequence (for instance, in decreasing order of the magnitude of the breaks $| g(x_n) - g(x_n - 0) | + | g(x_n + 0) - g(x_n) |$, we introduce an order in the subdivisions by the condition that $\sigma_1 R \sigma_2$ if $| \sigma_1 | < | \sigma_2 |$ and σ_1 contains more points of the sequence $x_1, ..., x_n ...$ of points of discontinuity of g than σ_2 does. Then it is easy to see that the order R makes a directed set of the subdivisions σ.

We then have:

13.9. THEOREM. If $g(x)$ is of bounded variation on $[a, b]$, a necessary and sufficient condition that $\sigma \int_a^b fdg$ exists is that $\Sigma_\sigma f(x_i') (g(x_i) - g(x_{i-1}))$ converge in the R sense just defined.

The sufficiency is immediate. For the necessity suppose that $\sigma \int_a^b fdg$ exists. We can then assume that f is bounded on $[a, b]$. Let $g_n(x) = g_c(x) + \Sigma_{m=1}^n \beta(x, \bar{x}_m)$, where $\beta(x, \bar{x}_m)$ is the simple break function determined by g at the point of discontinuity $\bar{x}_m$. Then $\sigma \int_a^b fdg_n$ exists both as a σ-limit and as an R-limit, and converges to $\sigma \int_a^b fdg$. Select n_0 so that simultaneously

$$\text{(a)} \qquad | \sigma \int_a^b fdg - \sigma \int_a^b fdg_{n_0} | < e,$$

and

$$\text{(b)} \qquad \textstyle\sum_\sigma | (g_{n_0}(x_i) - g_{n_0}(x_{i-1})) - (g(x_i) - g(x_{i-1})) | < e,$$

for all subdivisions σ of $[a, b]$. The latter is possible since for all σ:

$$\sum_\sigma | \Delta g_n - \Delta g | = \sum_\sigma | \Delta(g_n - g) | \leqq \int_a^b | d(g_n - g) |$$
$$\leqq \sum_{n+1}^\infty (| g(\bar{x}_m - 0) - g(\bar{x}_m) | + | g(\bar{x}_m + 0) - g(\bar{x}_m) |),$$

and the right hand side approaches zero with n. Further select d_e so that if $| \sigma | < d_e$ and σ contains $\bar{x}_1, ..., \bar{x}_{n_0}$; then:

$$\text{(c)} \qquad | \textstyle\sum_\sigma f(x_i') (g_{n_0}(x_i) - g_{n_0}(x_{i-1})) - \int_a^b fdg_{n_0} | < e.$$

Then from inequality (b) we obtain:

$$\text{(d)} \qquad | \textstyle\sum_\sigma f(x_i') (g_{n_0}(x_i) - g_{n_0}(x_{i-1}))$$
$$- \textstyle\sum_\sigma f(x_i') (g(x_i) - g(x_{i-1})) | < Me$$

where M is the l.u.b. of $|f(x)|$ on $[a, b]$. By combining inequalities (a), (c) and (d), we have:

$$\left| \int_a^b fdg - \sum_\sigma f(x_i')\,(g(x_i) - g(x_{i-1})) \right| < (2 + M)\,e,$$

provided $|\sigma| < d_e$ and σ contains $\bar{x}_1, \ldots, \bar{x}_{n_0}$.

It is obvious that the R-ordering of subdivisions σ makes of them a directed set of sequential character, the required cofinal sequence σ_n being for instance such that $|\sigma_n| < 1/n$ and σ_n contains the points $x_1, \ldots, x_n$ of points of discontinuity of $g(x)$. As a consequence of the theorem on limits of functions on a directed set of sequential character (I.5.1) we have:

13.10. THEOREM. If $g(x)$ is of bounded variation on $[a, b]$, then a necessary and sufficient condition that $\sigma \int_a^b fdg$ exist is that $\lim_n \Sigma_{\sigma_n} f(x_i')\,(g(x_i) - g(x_{i-1}))$ exist for every sequence of subdivisions σ_n such that $|\sigma_n| \to 0$, and the σ_n ultimately contain all of the points of discontinuity of $g(x)$.

Note that $\lim_{\sigma_n}$, if it exists for all $\{\sigma_n\}$ described in the theorem, will be independent of $\{\sigma_n\}$, since two such sequences $\{\sigma_n\}$ and $\{\sigma_n'\}$ can be combined into a single sequence $\{\sigma_n''\}$ of the same character by alternating σ_n and σ_n'.

For the norm integral it is possible to replace in the condition $N \int_a^b \omega(f;\ I) \cdot v(I) = 0$, the integral of an interval function by an integral of a point function. We have:

13.11. THEOREM. A necessary and sufficient condition that $N \int_a^b fdg$ exist is that $N \int_a^b \omega(f,\ x)\,dv(x) = 0$.

Here $\omega(f; x) =$ g.l.b. $[\omega(f; I)$ for all I containing $x]$, the *point oscillation function* of f.

We prove equivalence of the condition of the theorem with $N \int_a^b \omega(f;\ I)v(I) = 0$. Suppose then $N \int_a^b \omega(f;\ I)v(I) = 0$. Then $(e,\ d_e,\ |\sigma| < d_e) : \Sigma_\sigma \omega(f;\ I)v(I) < e$. Let $|\sigma| < d_e/3$. Then if $x_{-1} = x_0 = a$, and $x_{n+1} = x_n = b$,

$$\begin{aligned}\sum_\sigma \omega(f, x_i')(v(x_i) - v(x_{i-1})) &\leqq \sum_\sigma \omega(f, x_i')\,(v(x_{i+1}) - v(x_{i-2})) \\ &\leqq \sum_\sigma \omega(f, [x_{i+1},\ x_{i-2}])\ v[x_{i+1},\ x_{i-2}],\end{aligned}$$

since x_i' is interior to $[x_{i+1},\ x_{i-2}]$. We can rearrange the points x_i into three subdivisions each with $|\sigma| < d_e$ as follows:

$\sigma_1 = (a, x_1, x_4, x_7, \ldots)$, $\sigma_2 = (a, x_2, x_5, x_8, \ldots)$ and $\sigma_3 = (a, x_3, x_6, \ldots)$, so that $\Sigma_\sigma = \Sigma_{\sigma_1} + \Sigma_{\sigma_2} + \Sigma_{\sigma_3}$. Now $\Sigma_{\sigma_i} \omega(f, I)v(I) < e$, $i = 1, 2, 3$. Then $\Sigma_\sigma \omega(f, x_i') (v(x_i) - v(x_{i-1})) < 3\,e$ provided $|\sigma| < d_e/3$, and consequently $N \int_a^b \omega(f, x)dv(x) = 0$.

On the other hand, assume $N \int_a^b \omega(f, x)dv(x) = 0$, or $(e, d_e, |\sigma| < d_e) : \Sigma_\sigma \omega(f, x_i') (v(x_i) - v(x_{i-1})) < e$. Now for each point x_0 of $[a, b]$ there exists an interval I_{x_0} containing x_0 as an interior point such that $\omega(f; I_{x_0}) < \omega(f, x_0) + e$. Consequently, $\omega(f; I_{x_0}) <$ l.u.b.$[\omega(f, x)$, for x in $I_{x_0}] + e$. By using the Borel theorem we find $(e, d_e', l(I) < d_e')$: $\omega(f; I) <$ l.u.b.$[\omega(f, x)$ for x in $I] + e$. If $|\sigma| < d_e$ and d_e', then

$$\sum\nolimits_\sigma \omega(f; I)v(I) < \sum\nolimits_\sigma (\text{l.u.b.}[\omega(f, x),\ x \text{ in } I] + e)v(I) < e + e \cdot v[a, b].$$

Consequently, $N \int_a^b \omega(f; I)v(I) = 0$.

We finally give the extension to Stietjes integrals of the existence theorem for Riemann integrals involving the measure of the points of discontinuity of $f(x)$. As we shall see later, this theorem follows easily from the Lebesgue integral theory, but it can be proved without invoking all of the ponderous measure theory which underlies the Lebesgue integral.

Let $g(x)$ be of bounded variation on $[a, b]$ and as usual $v(x) = \int_a^x |dg|$. For $I = [c, d]$, let $v(I) = v(d) - v(c)$, and for I open, let $v(I) = v(d - 0) - v(c + 0)$. Then we define:

13.12. Definition. A set E is of v-measure zero, if for every $e > 0$, there exists a finite or denumerable set of intervals $\{I_n\}$ covering E, in the sense that every point of E is an interior point of some I_n, such that $\Sigma_n v(I_n) < e$.

It is immaterial whether the intervals I_n are open or not in this definition. The only property of the class of sets of v-measure zero we shall use is:

13.13. THEOREM. If E_n are sets of v-measure zero, then the union $\Sigma_n E_n$ which contains all of the points in any E_n is also of v-measure zero.

For let I_{nm} be a set of intervals covering E_n such that $\Sigma_m v(I_{nm}) < e/2^n$. Then the intervals I_{nm} will be a denumerable set of intervals covering $\Sigma_n E_n$ with $\Sigma_{mn} v(I_{nm}) < e$.

If x_0 is a point of continuity of $g(x)$ and so of $v(x)$, then the v-measure of the set consisting only of x_0 is of v-measure zero. Consequently:

13.14. Corollary I. A denumerable set of points at each of which $g(x)$ is continuous is of v-measure zero.

13.15. Corollary II. A set of v-measure zero cannot contain a point of discontinuity of g.

In terms of set of v-measure zero, we now have:

13.16. THEOREM. *If $g(x)$ is of bounded variation, then necessary and sufficient conditions that $N \int_a^b f dg$ exist are*: (1) *f be bounded on the complements of a finite number of intervals on each of which $g(x)$ is constant and* (2) *the points of discontinuity of f form a set of v-measure zero.*

Observe that the theorem is restricted to the norm integral.

The necessity of condition (1) has been proved in II.10.10 for the case of any $g(x)$. To derive condition (2) we note that if $\omega(f, x)$ is the oscillation function for $f(x)$, then $f(x)$ is discontinuous at x_0 if and only if $\omega(f, x_0) > 0$. Let E_k be the set of points of $[a, b]$ for which $\omega(f, x) \geqq k > 0$. Then E_k is a closed set for all k. Since $N \int_a^b f dg$ exists, we have $(e, d_e, |\sigma| < d_e) : \Sigma_\sigma \omega(f, I) v(I) < e$. Take any σ_0 such that $|\sigma_0| < d_e$, and let $I_1, ..., I_m$ be the intervals of σ_0 containing points of E_k as interior points. Then $k \Sigma_i v(I_i) \leqq \Sigma_{\sigma_0} \omega(f, I) v(I) < e$. It might happen that some of the end points of I_i, $i = 1, ..., m$ are points of E_k. We can then find a subdivision σ_1 with $|\sigma_1| < d_e$, whose intervals contain the end points of σ_0 as interior points. If $I_1', ..., I_n'$ are the intervals of σ_1 containing points of E_k as interior points, then $k \Sigma_j v(I_j') < e$. Then all of the points of E_k will be interior to the intervals $I_1, ..., I_m, I_1', ..., I_n'$ and $\Sigma_i v(I_i) + \Sigma_j v(I_j') < 2\, e/k$. Since k is fixed and e is any, it follows that E_k is of zero v-measure. If now we let $k = 1/n$, then all of the points of discontinuity of $f(x)$ will belong to the union of $E_{1/n}$, and consequently this set of points is of v-measure zero.

For the sufficiency, assume first that $f(x)$ is bounded on $[a, b]$ with $|f(x)| < M$. Let E be the set of discontinuities of $f(x)$ and enclose E in a set of open intervals $\{I_n\}$ such that $\Sigma_n v(I_n) < e$. Since the I_n are open intervals, their union is an open set G consisting of the disjoint open intervals J_m. Consequently, J_m covers E and $\Sigma_m v(J_m) < \Sigma_n v(I_n) < e$. For any closed subinterval of an interval J_m can by the Borel theorem be covered by a finite number of the intervals I_n. Let F be the closed set complementary to G relative to $[a, b]$.

Then $f(x)$ is continuous for each point x_0 of F and consequently uniformly continuous, so that $(e, d_e, x_0 \text{ in } F, |x - x_0| < d_e): |f(x) -$

$f(x_0) \mid < e$, and so $\omega(f; [x_0 - d_e, x_0 + d_e]) < 2e$. Consider now any subdivision σ of $[a, b]$ such that $|\sigma| < d_e$. Let $I_1', \dots I_r'$ be the intervals of σ containing at least one point of F, and $I_1'', \dots I_s''$ be the complementary intervals, none of which contains a point of F. Then $\Sigma_i v(I_i'') < \Sigma_m v(J_m) < e$, and so $\Sigma_i \omega(f; I_i'')v(I_i'') < 2Me$. On the other hand, $\Sigma_j \omega(f; I_j')v(I_j') < e\,\Sigma_j v(I_j') < e(v(b) - v(a))$. Consequently, if $|\sigma| < d_e$, then $\Sigma_\sigma \omega(f; I)v(I) < e(2M + v(b) - v(a))$. Then by II.13.2: $N \int_a^b fdg$ exists.

In case $f(x)$ is unbounded, but bounded on the (closed) complements I' of a finite number of intervals of constancy of $g(x)$, then $\int_{I'} fdg$ exists for all such I'. For if $f(x)$ is discontinuous at any end point x_0 of an I', then the v-measure of x_0 must be zero, so that $g(x)$ is continuous at x_0, and f and g have no common discontinuities at the end points of the intervals I'. Consequently, by II.4.4N: $N \int_a^b fdg$ exists and is equal to $\Sigma_{I'} \int_{I'} fdg$.

The parallel existence theorem for $\int_a^b fdg$ offers some difficulty in elegant statement since the continuity conditions for the σ-integral on f are onesided at each point of discontinuity. Some concept of zero measure involving the fact that the points of x are two faced in this situation is needed. It is possible to bypass this difficulty as follows:

13.17. THEOREM. A necessary and sufficient condition that $\sigma \int_a^b fdg$ exist, f bounded and g of bounded variation on $[a, b]$ is that f and g have no common discontinuities on the same side of any points and $\int_a^b fdg_c$ exist, where g_c is the continuous part of g.

The previous theorem can then be applied to $\int_a^b fdg_c$.

Summarizing, we have the following necessary and sufficient conditions for the existence of the $N \int_a^b fdg$ and $\sigma \int_a^b fdg$, if g is of bounded variation and $f(x)$ is bounded on $[a, b]$:

(a) the Cauchy condition of convergence on the approximating sums $\Sigma_\sigma f\Delta g$ for both;

(b) $\int_a^b \omega(f; I) \cdot v(I) = 0$ in each case; $\text{g.l.b.}_\sigma \Sigma_\sigma \omega(f; I)v(I) = 0$ is necessary for N-integral, necessary and sufficient for σ-integral;

(c) $\int_a^b f(x)dv(x)$ exists for each case, where $v(x) = \int_a^x |dg|$;

(d) for the norm integral: $N \int_a^b \omega(f, x)dv(x) = 0$;

(e) for the norm integral: the set of discontinuities of $f(x)$ have v-measure zero.

EXERCISES

1. For each interior point x of $[a, b]$ define $\omega(f, x^+) = \text{g.l.b.}_{d>0}\ \omega(f; [x, x + d])$ and $\omega(f; x^-) = \text{g.l.b.}_{d>0}\ \omega(f; [x - d, x])$. Show that a necessary and sufficient condition that $\sigma \int_a^b dg$ exist is that $\sigma \int_a^b \omega(f, x^\pm)\, dv(x) = 0$, where in the approximating sum $\Sigma_\sigma \omega(f, x_i')\,(v(x_i) - v(x_{i-1}))$, the value x_i' may be x^+ or x^- if $x_{i-1} < x < x_i$, or x^+_{i-1} or x^-_i.

2. Modify the definition of a set of v-measure zero to a v^*-measure zero, so that $\sigma \int_a^b fdg$ exists for f bounded if and only if the discontinuities of f form a set of v^*-measure zero.

14. Properties of $\int_a^b$ fdg with g of Bounded Variation on (a, b)

The linearity and interval properties derived for the general Stieltjes integral, obviously apply also when $g(x)$ is of bounded variation. We consider properties when the assumption that $g(x)$ is of bounded variation is pertinent.

14.1. THEOREM. If $g(x)$ is of bounded variation on $[a, b]$ and $f_1(x)$, ..., $f_n(x)$ are bounded functions on $[a, b]$ such that the integrals $\int_a^b f_i dg$, $i = 1, \dots n$ exist; if $h(y_1, \dots y_n)$ is a continuous function in $(y_1, \dots y_n)$ on an n-dimensional rectangle containing the value set of $(f_1(x), \dots f_n(x))$ for x on $[a, b]$, then $\int_a^b h(f_1(x), \dots f_n(x))dg(x)$ exists also.

For the continuity points of $h(f_1(x), \dots f_n(x))$ will be those for which all of the functions $f_1, \dots f_n$ are continuous. Consequently, for the case of the norm integral, $h(f_1(x), \dots f_n(x))$ will be continuous excepting for a set of v-measure zero, the union of the sets for which one of the functions $f_1, \dots f_n$ is discontinuous. It follows that $h(f_1(x), \dots f_n(x))$ is integrable with respect to g on $[a, b]$.

For the case of the σ-integral, we note in addition that all of the functions $f_1, \dots f_n$ will be continuous on the side of a point where $g(x)$ is discontinuous, so that the same applies to $h(f_1(x), \dots f_n(x))$. So the theorem is valid for σ-integrals also.

Immediate consequences are:

14.2. THEOREM. If $f_1(x)$ and $f_2(x)$ are integrable on $[a, b]$ with respect to the function of bounded variation $g(x)$, so is $f_1(x) \cdot f_2(x)$.

14.3. THEOREM. If $f(x)$ is integrable on $[a, b]$ with respect to the function of bounded variation $g(x)$, then $|f(x)|$ is also. Moreover, $\int_a^b |f|\, dv$ exists and $\left| \int_a^b fdg \right| \leqq \int_a^b |f|\, dv$.

The second part of this statement follows from the existence theorem II.13.4 and from a comparison of the corresponding approximating sums. More generally, we have:

14.4. THEOREM. If g is of bounded variation and $\int_a^b f_1 dg$ and $\int_a^b f_2 dg$ exist; and if $|f_1(x)| \leqq |f_2(x)|$ for x on $[a, b]$, then $|\int_a^b f_1 dg| \leqq \int_a^b |f_2|\, dv$.

In particular then:

14.5. If $g(x)$ is monotonic nondecreasing on $[a, b]$ and $M =$ l.u.b. of $f(x)$ on $[a, b]$, and $m =$ g.l.b. of $f(x)$ on $[a, b]$, and if $\int_a^b fdg$ exists, then

$$m(g(b) - g(a)) \leqq \int_a^b fdg \leqq M(g(b) - g(a)).$$

From this we derive in the usual way the:

14.6. Mean Value Theorem. If $f(x)$ on $[a, b]$ takes on all values between two values [in particular, if $f(x)$ is continuous], if $g(x)$ is monotonic nondecreasing on $[a, b]$ and if $\int_a^b fdg$ exists, then there exists an x_0 on $[a, b]$ such that $\int_a^b fdg = f(x_0)\,(g(b) - g(a))$.

This mean value theorem leads to:

14.7. Second Mean Value Theorem of the Integral Calculus. If $f(x)$ is Riemann integrable, $g(x)$ monotonic nondecreasing on $[a, b]$, then there exists a point x_0 on $[a, b]$ such that

$$\int_a^b f(x)g(x)dx = g(a) \int_a^{x_0} f(x)dx + g(b) \int_{x_0}^b f(x)dx.$$

For any monotonic nondecreasing function is Riemann integrable so that $\int_a^b f(x)g(x)dx$ exists. If we set $h(x) = \int_a^x f(x)dx$, then by the substitution and integration by parts theorems we have:

$$\int_a^b f(x)g(x)dx = \int_a^b g(x)dh(x) = h(b)g(b) - \int_a^b h(x)dg(x).$$

Applying the mean value theorem gives an x_0 of $[a, b]$ such that

$$\int_a^b f(x)g(x)dx = g(b) \int_a^b f(x)dx - \int_a^{x_0} f(x)dx(g(b) - g(a))$$
$$= g(a) \int_a^{x_0} f(x)dx + g(b) \int_{x_0}^b f(x)dx.$$

Another application of the integration by parts and substitution theorems leads to:

14.8. THEOREM. If $g(x)$ is of bounded variation on $[a, b]$ and $\int_a^b fdg$ vanishes for every continuous function $f(x)$, then $g(x) = g(b)$ except for a denumerable set of points on $a < x < b$.

For set $f(x) = \int_a^x (g(b) - g(x))dx$. Then $f(x)$ is continuous and

$$0 = \int_a^b fdg = f(b)g(b) - f(a)g(a) - \int_a^b gdf$$

$$= f(b)g(b) - \int_a^b g(x)\,(g(b) - g(x))\,dx = \int_a^b (g(b) - g(x))^2 dx.$$

Now if a function $h(x)$ is Riemann integrable and positive or zero on $[a, b]$, and $\int_a^b h(x)dx = 0$, then $h(x)$ vanishes at all points of continuity of $h(x)$. Consequently, $g(x) = g(b)$, excepting at the points of discontinuity of $g(x)$ which are denumerable in number. The fact that $g(a) = g(b)$ follows from $\int_a^b f(x)dg(x) = 0$ by setting $f(x) \equiv 1$ on $[a, b]$.

This theorem is closely related to the fundamental lemma of the calculus of variations, which asserts that if $g(x)$ is continuous and $\int_a^b g(x)f'(x)dx = 0$ for every continuous function $f(x)$ which vanishes at a and b, and for which $f'(x)$ is Riemann integrable, then $g(x)$ is a constant.

An alternative proof of II.14.8 is as follows: Set $f(x) = x$ for $a \leqq x \leqq x_0$; $f(x) = x_0$ for $x_0 \leqq x \leqq b$. Then integration by parts leads to

$$0 = \int_a^b fdg = f(b)g(b) - f(a)g(a) - \int_a^b gdf = x_0 g(b) - ag(a) - \int_a^{x_0} g(x)dx.$$

Taking derivatives with respect to x_0 yields $g(x_0) = g(b)$ except for the points of discontinuity of g, with $a < x_0 \leqq b$. That $g(a) = g(b)$ follows as above.

Obviously if $g(x) = g(a)$ excepting for a denumerable set of points interior to $[a, b]$, then $\int_a^b fdg = 0$ for every continuous function. For the points of subdivision in the approximating sums can be chosen so as to avoid the points of discontinuity of g.

15. Convergence Theorems

As in the case of Riemann integrals we have:

15.1. THEOREM. If $g(x)$ is of bounded variation on $[a, b]$, $f_n(x)$ are such that $\int_a^b f_n dg$ exists for all n and $\lim_n f_n(x) = f(x)$ uniformly on $[a, b]$, then $\int_a^b fdg$ exists and $\lim_n \int_a^b f_n dg = \int_a^b fdg$.

This follows from the iterated limits theorem I.7.4. For

$$|\sum_\sigma f_n(x_i')\,(g(x_i)-g(x_{i-1}))-\sum_\sigma f(x_i')\,(g(x_i)-g(x_{i-1}))|$$
$$\leqq \underset{a\leqq x\leqq b}{\text{l.u.b.}}\,|\,f_n(x)-f(x)\,|\int_a^b|\,dg\,|\,.$$

If $\lim_n f_n(x) = f(x)$ uniformly on $[a, b]$, then it follows from this inequality that $\lim_n \Sigma_\sigma f_n \Delta g = \Sigma_\sigma f\Delta g$ uniformly as to σ. Consequently, $\lim_n \lim_\sigma \Sigma_\sigma f_n \Delta g = \lim_\sigma \lim_n \Sigma_\sigma f_n \Delta g$ or $\lim_n \int_a^b f_n dg = \int_a^b fdg$.

15.2. THEOREM. If g_n and g are of bounded variation on $[a, b]$ and such that $\lim_n \int_a^b |\,d(g_n - g)\,| = 0$; if $f(x)$ is bounded, and if $\int_a^b fdg_n$ exists for all n, then $\lim_n \int_a^b fdg_n$ and $\int_a^b fdg$ exist and are equal.

This also follows from the iterated limits theorem if we note that

$$|\sum_\sigma f\Delta g_n - \sum_\sigma f\Delta g\,| \leqq \underset{a\leqq x\leqq b}{\text{l.u.b.}}\ |f(x)\,|\int_a^b|\,d(g_n-g)\,|.$$

A slightly more sophisticated theorem is:

15.3. THEOREM. If $f(x)$ is continuous, if $g_n(x)$ are uniformly of bounded variation on $[a, b]$ with $\int_a^b |\,dg_n\,| \leqq M$ for all n, and if $\lim_n g_n(x) = g(x)$ for all x, then $\lim_n \int_a^b fdg_n = \int_a^b fdg$.

Since the g_n are uniformly of bounded variation, g is also of bounded variation so that $\int_a^b fdg$ exists. Now

$$|\int_a^b fdg_n - \sum_\sigma f\Delta g_n\,| \leqq \sum_\sigma \omega(f;I)\cdot\int_I|\,dg_n\,| \leqq \max_\sigma \omega(f;I)\int_a^b|\,dg_n\,|$$
$$\leqq \max_\sigma \omega(f;I)\cdot M.$$

Consequently, because of the uniform continuity of $f(x)$ on $[a, b]$ it follows that $\lim_{|\sigma|\to 0} \Sigma_\sigma f\Delta g_n = \int_a^b fdg_n$ uniformly as to n. The iterated limits theorem then gives the interchange of limits with integration.

It is, however, not necessary to assume that $g_n(x)$ converges to $g(x)$ for all x. It is sufficient to assume that the convergence holds on a denumerable dense set D on $[a, b]$, including a and b, and that $g(x)$ is of bounded variation on $[a, b]$. In the proof one can then limit the subdivisions to a sequence consisting of points of D such that $\lim_m |\,\sigma_m\,| = 0$.

It might be observed in this theorem that the continuity of $f(x)$ assures us of the existence of the limit integral $\int_a^b fdg$. This suggests:

15.4. THEOREM. If $g_n(x)$ are monotonic nondecreasing and $\lim_n g_n(x) = g(x)$ for all x of $[a, b]$, and if further $\int_a^b f dg_n$ and $\int_a^b f dg$ exist, then $\lim_n \int_a^b f dg_n = \int_a^b f dg$.

We prove the theorem for the σ-integral. It will then also hold for the norm integral. Since $\int_a^b f dg_n$ and $\int_a^b f dg$ exist, it follows from II.13.3 that $\lim_\sigma \Sigma_\sigma \omega(f; I) \cdot g_n(I) = 0$ and $\lim_\sigma \Sigma_\sigma \omega(f; I) \cdot g(I) = 0$. Now $\lim_n \Sigma_\sigma \omega(f; I) \cdot g_n(I) = \Sigma_\sigma \omega(f; I) \cdot g(I)$. Moreover, $\Sigma_\sigma \omega(f; I) \cdot g_n(I)$ is monotone in σ for every n. Since $\lim_n \lim_\sigma \Sigma_\sigma \omega(f; I) \cdot g_n(I) = \lim_\sigma \lim_n \Sigma_\sigma \omega(f; I) \cdot g_n(I)$, it follows from I.7.8 that $\lim_\sigma \Sigma_\sigma \omega(f; I) \cdot g_n(I) = 0$ uniformly in n. Hence $\int_a^b f dg_n$ exists uniformly in n, the iterated limits theorem I.7.4 applies and $\lim_n \int_a^b f dg_n$ exists and is equal to $\int_a^b f dg$.

This theorem can be extended to functions of bounded variation in the following form:

15.5. If $g_n(x)$ and $g(x)$ are of bounded variation such that $\lim_n g_n(x) = g(x)$ for every x, and $\lim_n \int_a^b | dg_n | = \int_a^b | dg |$; if further $\int_a^b f dg_n$ and $\int_a^b f dg$ exist, then $\lim_n \int_a^b f dg_n$ exists and is equal to $\int_a^b f dg$.

For the hypotheses of the theorem imply that $\lim_n \int_a^x | dg_n | = \int_a^x | dg |$ for all x [see II.8.7 (3)]. Consequently, if P and N stand for positive and negative variations, then $\lim_n P_n(x) = P(x)$ and $\lim_n N_n(x) = N(x)$. The rest is obvious.

A theorem for Riemann integrals not requiring the uniform convergence of the functions $f_n(x)$ is due to Arzela and Osgood, and is sometimes called *Osgood's theorem*. In the Stieltjes integral setting we have:

15.6. THEOREM. If the sequence of functions $f_n(x)$ is uniformly bounded on $[a, b]$; if $\lim_n f_n(x) = f(x)$ for every x; if $g(x)$ is of bounded variation on $[a, b]$; and if $\int_a^b f_n dg$ and $\int_a^b f dg$ exist for every n; then $\lim_n \int_a^b f_n dg = \int_a^b f dg$.

We prove this theorem more or less in reverse. We have

$$\left| \int_a^b f_n dg - \int_a^b f dg \right| = \left| \int_a^b (f_n - f) dg \right| \leqq \int_a^b | f_n - f | \, dv$$

where $v(x) = \int_a^x | dg |$. As a consequence, it is sufficient to prove that under the hypotheses of the theorem, the right-hand side of this inequality converges to zero. This will be accomplished by proving the following:

15.7. Lemma. If $f_n(x) \geqq 0$ on $[a, b]$ for all n; if $f_n(x) \leqq M$ for all x and n; if $\lim_n f_n(x) = 0$ for all x; and if $g(x)$ is monotonic nondecreasing then $\lim_n \underline{\int_a^b} f_n dg = 0$.

Note that the existence of $\int_a^b f_n dg$ is not assumed here.

We give a contrapositive proof. The assumption that $\underline{\int}_a^b f_n dg$ does not converge to zero gives rise to an $e > 0$, and a subsequence n_m such that for every m: $\underline{\int}_a^b f_{n_m} dg > e$. Since f_{n_m} would satisfy the same conditions as f_n, we can replace n_m by n. Then for each n there exists a subdivision σ_n such that $\Sigma_{\sigma_n} m_n(I) g(I) > e$, where

$$m_n(I) = \underset{x \text{ on } I}{\text{g.l.b.}} f_n(x).$$

For $\eta > 0$ let $I_{n1}, \ldots I_{nk_n}$ be the intervals of σ_n for which $m_n(I) > \eta$ and $I'_{n1}, \ldots, I'_{nk_n'}$ be the remaining intervals of σ_n. Then $M\,\Sigma_i g(I_{ni}) + \eta\,\Sigma_j g(I'_{nj}) > e$. Or since $\Sigma_j g(I'_{nj}) \leqq g(b) - g(a)$: $M\,\Sigma_i g(I_{ni}) > e - \eta(g(b) - g(a))$. If we select η small enough we can make the right-hand side of this inequality positive; for instance, if $\eta(g(b) - g(a)) < e/2$, then for each n: $\Sigma_i g(I_{ni}) > e/2M$. Then for each n, we have a finite number of intervals $I_{n1}, \ldots, I_{nk_n}$ on each of which $f_n(x) > \eta$, and such that $\Sigma_i g(I_{ni}) > e/2M$, a fixed number C independent of n.

Now the function $g(x)$ maps the interval $[a, b]$ on the interval $[g(a), g(b)]$ on the Y-axis. We shall assume the map is such that the closed interval $[g(c), g(d)]$ corresponds to the closed subinterval $[c, d]$. In case x_0 is a point of discontinuity of $g(x)$ this means that both $[g(x_0 - 0), g(x_0)]$ and $[g(x_0), g(x_0 + 0)]$ correspond to x_0 depending on the direction from which x_0 is approached. To any point y, between $g(a)$ and $g(b)$ there will be at least one x such that $g(x) = y$. As a result of this mapping, the intervals $[x_{n,\,i-1}, x_{ni}]$ are mapped into $J_{ni} = [g(x_{n,\,i-1}, g(x_{ni})]$. Then $\Sigma_i g(I_{ni}) > C$ becomes $\Sigma_i l(J_{ni}) > C$, where we can discard any J of length zero. If now we knew that there exists a sequence $n_m i_m$ such that the intervals $J_{n_m i_m}$ have a point y_0 in common, there would be a corresponding point x_0 in $I_{n_m i_m}$ for which $f_{n_m}(x_0) > \eta$ for all m. Then $\lim_m f_{n_m}(x_0) \neq 0$ contrary to the hypothesis of the lemma. Consequently our lemma and the theorem is proved if we prove a lemma due to Arzela:

15.8. Arzela's Lemma. If $\mathfrak{I}_n$ is a sequence of finite sets of intervals $I_{n1}, \ldots I_{nk_n}$, and there exists a constant C such that $\Sigma_i l(I_{ni}) > C$ for all n, then there exists at least one point x belonging to a subsequence of the $\mathfrak{I}_n$.

In terms of concepts used in the theory sets, this lemma asserts that

$\overline{\lim}_n \mathfrak{I}_n$ is not vacuous, where for a sequence of sets E_n, the set $E = \overline{\lim}_n E_n$, is the totality of all elements appearing in an infinite number of the sets E_n. This set E can be obtained by taking the union U_m of the sets E_n for $n \geqq m$, and then taking the intersection of the U_m.

For the proof of the Arzela lemma assume first that the intervals I_{ni} are closed, and that the set of points $\mathfrak{I}_n$ is contained in that of $\mathfrak{I}_{n-1}$. We then have a nonincreasing sequence of closed sets on $[a, b]$ none of which is vacuous. It is well known that there is a point common to these sets, so that the lemma holds for this case. The general case is reduced to this one.

For the general case, assume that the I_{ni} are open intervals, which will not affect the validity of the lemma. Let $\mathfrak{G}_m = \Sigma_{n=m}^{\infty} \mathfrak{I}_n$, that is, the union of the sets $\mathfrak{I}_n$ for $n \geqq m$. Then $\mathfrak{G}_m$ is an open set. If the intersection of the $\mathfrak{G}_m$ is not vacuous, i.e., if the $\mathfrak{G}_m$ have a point in common, then the lemma is proved. Note that $\mathfrak{G}_m$ is contained in $\mathfrak{G}_{m-1}$. $\mathfrak{G}_m$ being an open set it consists of a denumerable set of open intervals J_{mn}. Since $\mathfrak{G}_m$ contains $\mathfrak{I}_m$, we have $\Sigma_n l(J_{mn}) > C$ for all m. Let $e_1, \ldots, e_m, \ldots$ be a decreasing sequence of positive numbers such that $\Sigma_m e_m < C/2$. We then discard from $\mathfrak{G}_1$, a set of intervals J_{in}, $n = n_1 + 1, \ldots$, the sum of whose lengths is less than $e_1/2$. From the remaining intervals $J_{11}, \ldots, J_{1n_1}$, we lop off both ends totaling in length at most $e_1/2$ leaving the closed intervals $J'_{11}, \ldots, J'_{1n_1}$. Set $\Sigma_i J'_{1i} = \mathfrak{F}_1$. Then for the intervals in the intersection of $\mathfrak{G}_2$ with $\mathfrak{F}_1$, we have diminished the total length by at most e_1. Treat the common part of $\mathfrak{G}_2$ and $\mathfrak{F}_1$ the same as $\mathfrak{G}_1$ using e_2, resulting in closed intervals $J'_{21}, \ldots, J'_{2n_2}$ making up the closed set $\mathfrak{F}_2$ contained in $\mathfrak{F}_1$ with $l(\mathfrak{F}_2) = \Sigma_i l(J'_{2i}) > C - e_1 - e_2$. This process can be repeated and gives rise to a sequence of sets of closed intervals $\mathfrak{F}_1, \mathfrak{F}_2, \ldots$, each contained in the preceding with $l(\mathfrak{F}_m) = \Sigma_i l(J'_{mi}) > C/2$. Then each $\mathfrak{F}_m$ is not vacuous, and the intersection of the $\mathfrak{F}_m$ is not vacuous. The same holds for $\mathfrak{G}_m$, and there exists a point x_0 common to a sequence of intervals $I_{n_m i_m}$.

It might be noted that the intersection set $\mathfrak{F}$ of $\mathfrak{F}_m$, which is a closed set, is not of measure zero. For suppose $\{K_n\}$ is a set of open intervals enclosing $\mathfrak{F}$. Then by the Borel theorem a finite subset $K_{n_1}, \ldots K_{n_r}$, which we will denote by $\mathfrak{R}$, will cover $\mathfrak{F}$. We assert that there exists an m_0 such that for $m \geqq m_0$ the sets $\mathfrak{F}_m$ will be covered by $\mathfrak{R}$. If not, there exists for each m a point x_m in $\mathfrak{F}_m$ not in $\mathfrak{R}$. The sequence x_m will have a limiting point x_0 which because of the closure and monotoneity of the sequence $\mathfrak{F}_m$ will belong to $\mathfrak{F}$. But since x_m are not in $\mathfrak{R}$, and $\mathfrak{R}$ is open, x_0 is not in $\mathfrak{R}$ and so not in $\mathfrak{F}$. It follows that $l(\mathfrak{R}) = \Sigma_i l(K_{n_i}) > C$, so that the greatest lower bound of the sums of the lengths of any set of open intervals covering $\mathfrak{F}$ is positive, and not zero.

This completes the proof of II.15.6 which we shall call Osgood's theorem.

We can generalize our theorem as follows:

15.9. THEOREM. If $g(x)$ is of bounded variation with $v(x) = \int_a^x |dg|$: if the sequence of functions $f_n(x)$ is uniformly bounded on $[a, b]$; and if $\lim_n f_n(x) = f(x)$ excepting possibly at a set of v-measure zero; and if $\int_a^b f_n dg$ and $\int_a^b f dg$ exist for all n, then $\lim_n \int_a^b f_n dg = \int_a^b f dg$, even in the sense that $\lim_n \int_a^b |f_n - f| \, dv = 0$.

We note that the condition that $\int_a^b f dg$ exist cannot be dropped in this theorem. For suppose $g(x) = x$ on $[0, 1]$ and set $f_n(x) = 1$ for $x = p/q$, p and q integers with $0 \leqq p \leqq q \leqq n$, and $f_n(x) = 0$ elsewhere. Set $f(x) = 1$ for x rational, and $= 0$ for x irrational. Then $\lim_n f_n(x) = f(x)$ for all x, $\int_0^1 f_n(x)dx = 0$ for all n, but $\int_0^1 f(x)dx$ docs not cxist. Wc notc, howcvcr, that $\lim_n \int_0^1 f_n(x)dx$ exists, which as we shall show below always happens under the hypotheses of the theorem.

The convergence theorems developed are stated for sequences of functions. For some of them, the sequence of functions can be replaced by a directed set of functions and the proofs are still valid. We have:

15.10. If Q is a directed set; $f_q(x)$ a set of functions on $[a, b]$ such that $\lim_q f_q(x) = f(x)$ uniformly on $[a, b]$; if $g(x)$ is a function of bounded variation; and if $\int_a^b f_q(x)dg(x)$ exists for all q, then $\lim_q \int_a^b f_q(x)dg(x)$ and $\int_a^b f(x)dg(x)$ exist and are equal.

15.11. If Q is a directed set; $g_q(x)$ and $g(x)$ are of bounded variation on $[a, b]$ and such that $\lim_q \int_a^b | d(g_q - g) | = 0$; if $f(x)$ is bounded on $[a, b]$; and if $\int_a^b f dg_q$ exists for all q, then $\lim_q \int_a^b f dg_q$ and $\int_a^b f dg$ exist and are equal.

15.12. If Q is a directed set; if $g_q(x)$ and $g(x)$ are of bounded variation such that $\lim_q g_q(x) = g(x)$ on $[a, b]$, $\lim_q \int_a^b | dg_q | = \int_a^b | dg |$; and if $\int_a^b f dg$ exists and $\int_a^b f dg_q$ exists for all q, then $\lim_q \int_a^b f dg_q$ exists and is equal to $\int_a^b f dg$.

The proof of this last theorem for sequences requires some slight modifications for the directed set case.

The proof of the extension of Osgood's theorem depends on the fact that we are dealing with sequences of functions $f_n(x)$. To obtain a generalization to directed sets, we must limit our directed sets to those which have sequential character (see I.5) that is there exists a sequence $\{q_n\}$ of Q which is cofinal with Q. The resulting theorem reads:

15.13. If Q is a directed set of sequential character; if $g(x)$ is of bounded variation on $[a, b]$; if $f_q(x)$ is a uniformly bounded set of functions on $[a, b]$ such that $\lim_q f_q(x) = f(x)$ except at a set of v-measure zero, where $v(x) = \int_a^x | dg |$; and if $\int_a^b fdg$ exists and $\int_a^b f_q dg$ exists for all q, then $\lim_q \int_a^b f_q dg$ exists and is equal to $\int_a^b fdg$, even in the sense that $\lim_q \int_a^b | f_q - f | \, dv = 0$.

For then for every sequence $\{q_n'\}$ cofinal with Q we can apply the sequential form to show that $\lim_n \int_a^b f_{q_n'} dg = \int_a^b fdg$. It then follows by I.5.1 that $\lim_q \int_a^b f_q dg = \int_a^b fdg$.

This extended Osgood theorem gives us:

15.14. THEOREM. If $g(x)$ is of bounded variation on $[a, b]$; if $f_n(x)$ are uniformly bounded on $[a, b]$ and such that $\lim_n f_n(x) = f(x)$ except for a set of v-measure zero; and if $\int_a^b f_n dg$ exists for every n, then $\lim_n \int_a^b f_n dg$ exists even in the stronger sense that

$$\lim_{m,n} \int_a^b | f_m - f_n | \, dv = 0.$$

If we assume the double sequence (m, n) ordered by the condition that $(m_1, n_1) \geqq (m_2, n_2)$ if and only if $m_1 \geqq m_2$ and $n_1 \geqq n_2$, then $Q = (m, n)$ is a directed set of sequential character, (n, n) being cofinal with Q. If we set $h_{mn}(x) = | f_m(x) - f_n(x) |$, then $h_{mn}(x)$ form a directed set to which the preceding theorem applies so that $\lim_{m,n} \int_a^b | f_m - f_n | \, dv = 0$, so that $\lim_n \int_a^b f_n dg$ exists.

The extension to directed sets reads:

15.15. If Q is a directed set of sequential character; if $g(x)$ is of bounded variation on $[a, b]$; with $v(x) = \int_a^x | dg |$; if $f_q(x)$ is a set of functions uniformly bounded in q and x, such that $\lim_q f_q(x)$ exists except at most a set of v-measure zero, and if $\int_a^b f_q dg$ exists for all q, then $\lim_q \int_a^b f_q dg$ exists and $\lim_{q_1 q_2} \int_a^b | f_{q_1} - f_{q_2} | \, dv = 0$.

For if Q is sequential character, then $Q \times Q$ when ordered as above for sequences, is also of sequential character.

EXERCISES

1. Suppose $g(x)$ is monotonic nondecreasing on $[a, b]$ and $f(x) \geqq 0$ on $[a, b]$, and so that $\int_a^b fdg = 0$. Show that $f(x)$ vanishes excepting for a set of g-measure zero.

2. Suppose that $g(x)$ is of bounded variation and $\int_a^b fdg = 0$ for all continuous functions vanishing at both a and b. Show that $g(x)$ is a constant excepting for a denumerable set of points on $[a, b]$.

3. Show that if $g(x)$ is not of bounded variation on $[a, b]$, the uniform convergence of f_n to f on $[a, b]$ and the existence of $\int_a^b f_n dg$ for all n are not sufficient to ensure that $\lim_n \int_a^b f_n dg = \int_a^b fdg$.

4. If $g_n(x)$ are monotonic nondecreasing and $\lim_n g_n(x) = g(x)$ on a dense set of points of $[a, b]$ including a and b; if $\int_a^b fdg_n$ and $\int_a^b fdg$ exist, is $\lim_n \int_a^b fdg_n = \int_a^b fdg$?

5. Prove that if Q is a directed set; if $g_q(x)$ and $g(x)$ are monotonic nondecreasing and such that $\lim_q g_q(x) = g(x)$ for x on $[a, b]$; and if $\int_a^b fdg_q$ exist for all q, and $\int_a^b fdg$ exists, then $\lim_q \int_a^b fdg_q = \int_a^b fdg$.

6. Show that if $f(x) \geq 0$ for x on $[a, b]$ and $\int_a^b f(x)dx = 0$, then $f(x) > 0$ only if x is a point of discontinuity of f.

7. Construct an example of a directed set Q of elements q, and a set of uniformly bounded functions $f_q(x)$ on $[0, 1]$ such that $\lim_q f_q(x) = f(x)$ exists for each x and $\int_0^1 f_q(x)dx$ and $\int_0^1 f(x)dx$ exist for all q, but $\lim_q \int_0^1 f_q(x)dx \neq \int_0^1 f(x)dx$.

16. The Integral as a Function of the Upper Limit

We have already shown in II.11.3 that the continuity properties of the indefinite integral $\int_a^x fdg$ reflect those of $g(x)$. If $g(x)$ is of bounded variation on $[a, b]$, then $g(x + 0)$ and $g(x - 0)$ exist at all points. Then $h(x + 0)$ and $h(x - 0)$ exist for all x and $h(x + 0) - h(x) = f(x)\,(g(x+0) - g(x))$; $h(x) - h(x - 0) = f(x)\,(g(x) - g(x - 0))$. In addition, we have:

16.1. THEOREM. If $g(x)$ is of bounded variation on $[a, b]$, then $h(x) = \int_a^x fdg$ is also of bounded variation and $\int_a^b |\, dh \,| \leqq M \int_a^b |\, dg \,|$, where M is the least upper bounded of $|\, f(x) \,|$ on the intervals complementary to those for which $g(x)$ is constant.

This follows at once from the inequality $|\int_c^d f dg| \leqq M(f; [c, d]) \int_c^d |dg|$, for any interval $[c, d]$ on which f is bounded.

We cannot expect $h(x)$ to have a derivative with respect to x. However when $g(x)$ is monotone nondecreasing we have a kind of parallel theorem:

16.2. THEOREM. If $g(x)$ is monotonic nondecreasing on $[a, b]$, and $h(x) = \int_a^x f dg$, then $\lim_{\Delta x \to 0} (h(x + \Delta x) - h(x))/(g(x + \Delta x) - g(x)) = f(x)$ for all points where $f(x)$ is continuous which are not interior to an interval where $g(x)$ is constant.

For if $\Delta x > 0$, then

$$\begin{aligned} &| h(x_0 + \Delta x) - h(x_0) - f(x_0) (g(x_0 + \Delta x) - g(x_0)) | \\ &= \left| \int_{x_0}^{x_0 + \Delta x} (f(x) - f(x_0)) \, dg(x) \right| \\ &\leqq \underset{x_0 < x \leqq x_0 + \Delta x}{\text{l.u.b.}} | f(x) - f(x_0) | \, (g(x_0 + \Delta x) - g(x_0)) . \end{aligned}$$

Division of this inequality by the positive valued $g(x_0 + \Delta x) - g(x_0)$ yields the theorem for the limit on the right of x_0. A similar procedure works on the left.

The following theorem embodies a generalization of the fundamental theorem of the integral calculus:

16.3. THEOREM. If $g(x)$ is strictly monotone increasing ($x_1 < x_2$ implies $g(x_1) < g(x_2)$) on $[a, b]$; if the function $h(x)$ is such that $\lim_{\Delta x \to 0} (h(x + \Delta x) - h(x))/(g(x + \Delta x) - g(x)) = f(x)$ exists for all x on $[a, b]$ (with onesided limits at a and b); and if $N \int_a^b f dg$ exists; then $h(b) - h(a) = \int_a^b f dg$.

For the case of Riemann integrals with $g(x) = x$, the proof of this theorem is usually based on the mean value theorem of the differential calculus. Since we have derived no parallel to this theorem here (is there one?) we proceed differently. We have for every x of $[a, b]$ $(e, d_{ex}, | \Delta x | < d_{ex})$:

$$| h(x+\Delta x)-h(x)-f(x) (g(x+\Delta x)-g(x)) | \leqq e \, (g(x+\Delta x)-g(x)).$$

To the set of intervals $l_x = [x - \Delta x, x]$ and $r_x = [x, x + \Delta x]$ with $0 < \Delta x < d_{ex}$, attached to each x of $[a, b]$, we can either apply the Borel theorem or proceed directly to the right of $x = a$, and prove that there exists a finite number of intervals r_x, or/and l_x laid end to end reaching from a to b inclusive. These intervals can be chosen so that their maximum length is less than a predetermined d_1. The end points of this selection of intervals can then form a subdivision σ for $[a, b]$ with $|\sigma| < d_1$ such that for given e,

$$\left|\sum_\sigma f(x_i')\,(g(x_i) - g(x_{i-1})) - \int_a^b fdg\right| < e.$$

In $f(x_i')\,(g(x_i) - g(x_{i-1}))$ if $[x_{i-1}, x_i]$ is an r_x take $x_i' = x_{i-1}$, if $[x_{i-1}, x_i]$ is an l_x take $x_i' = x_i$. Then

$$\left|\sum_\sigma f(x_i')\,(g(x_i) - g(x_{i-1})) - \sum_\sigma (h(x_i) - h(x_{i-1}))\right|$$

$$\leqq \sum_\sigma |\, f(x_i')\,(g(x_i) - g(x_{i-1})) - (h(x_i) - h(x_{i-1}))\,|$$

$$\leqq e\sum_\sigma (g(x_i) - g(x_{i-1})) = e(g(b) - g(a)).$$

Then

$$\left|h(b) - h(a) - \int_a^b fdg\right| = \left|\sum\nolimits_\sigma (h(x_i) - h(x_{i-1})) - \int_a^b fdg\right|$$

$$\leqq e(1 + g(b) - g(a))$$

for all e. Then $h(b) - h(a) = \int_a^b fdg$.

Does the theorem also hold for σ-integrals?

17. The Integral as a Function of a Parameter

17.1. Continuity. The convergence theorems proved in II.15 can serve as a basis for obtaining properties of the integral, where $f(x)$ and/or $g(x)$ are functions of a parameter. As a matter of fact, we can think of the integers n as such a parameter. In the theorems below, we shall consider y as a parameter on the range $c \leqq y \leqq d$. The following continuity theorems are immediate consequences of Theorems II.15.6, II.15.3, and II.15.4 because of the sequential character of limits as to y.

17.1.1. THEOREM. If $g(x)$ is of bounded variation on $[a, b]$; if $f(x, y)$ is continuous in y for each x of $[a, b]$; if $|f(x, y)| \leqq M$ for $a \leqq x \leqq b$, $c \leqq y \leqq d$; and if $\int_a^b f(x, y)dg(x)$ exists for y on $[c, d]$; then $h(y) = \int_a^b f(x, y)dg(x)$ is continuous in y on $[c, d]$.

17.1.2. THEOREM. If $g(x, y)$ is of bounded variation in x on $[a, b]$ uniformly in y on $[c, d]$; if $g(x, y)$ is continuous at $y = y_0$ on a dense set D_{y_0} of $[a, b]$ including a and b; and if $f(x)$ is continuous in x; then $\int_a^b f(x)d_xg(x, y)$ is continuous in y at $y = y_0$.

17.1.3. THEOREM. If $g(x, y)$ is monotone nondecreasing in x for each y, and bounded on $a \leqq x \leqq b$, $c \leqq y \leqq d$; if $g(x, y)$ is continuous in y for each x of $[a, b]$; and if $\int_a^b f(x)d_x g(x, y)$ exists for each y, then $\int_a^b f(x)d_x g(x, y)$ is continuous in y.

17.2. Bounded Variation.

17.2.1. THEOREM. If $g(x)$ is of bounded variation on $[a, b]$; if $f(x, y)$ is defined on $[a, b]\times[c, d]$ with $\int_c^d | d_y f(x, y) | \leqq F(x)$ on $[a, b]$; if $\int_a^b f(x, y)dg(x)$ exists for each y; and if $\overline{\int}_a^b F(x)dv(x) < \infty$, where $v(x) = \int_a^x | dg |$, then $h(y) = \int_a^b f(x, y)dg(x)$ is of bounded variation on $[c, d]$ and $\int_c^d | dh | \leqq \overline{\int}_a^b F(x)dv(x)$.

For

$$| h(y_1) - h(y_2) | = | \int_a^b (f(x, y_1) - f(x, y_2))dg(x) |$$
$$\leqq \int_a^b | f(x, y_1) - f(x, y_2) | dv(x).$$

Consequently, if σ is a subdivision of $[c, d]$,

$$\sum_\sigma | h(y_i) - h(y_{i-1}) | \leqq \int_a^b \sum_\sigma | f(x, y_i) - f(x, y_{i-1}) | dv(x) \leqq \overline{\int}_a^b F(x)dv(x)$$

leading to the conclusion of the theorem. In particular, the theorem applies if $F(x)$ is bounded in x, that is, $f(x, y)$ is of bounded variation in y uniformly in x.

Another theorem guaranteeing that $\int_a^b f(x)dg(x, y)$ is of bounded variation in y is to be found below in connection with two-dimensional variation (see III.7.13).

17.3. Integrability. We have the following elegant theorem on integrability and interchange of order of iterated integrals:

17.3.1. THEOREM. If $g(x)$ is of bounded variation on $[a, b]$ and $h(y)$ on $[c, d]$; if $f(x, y)$ is bounded on $[a, b]\times[c, d]$; if $\int_c^d f(x, y)dh(y)$ exists for each x and $\int_a^b f(x, y)dg(x)$ exists for each y; then the iterated integrals $\int_a^b dg(x) \int_c^d f(x, y)dh(y)$ and $\int_c^d (\int_a^b dg(x)f(x, y))dh(y)$ both exist and are equal.

We prove this for the case when the integrals are all norm integrals. Set $G(y) = \int_a^b dg(x)f(x, y)$ and $H(x) = \int_c^d f(x, y)dh(y)$. Then the theorem states that $\int_c^d G(y)dh(y)$ and $\int_a^b H(x)dg(x)$ both exist and are equal. Let σ be any subdivision of $[a, b]$ and consider the approximating sum for $\int_a^b H(x)dg(x)$:

$$\sum_\sigma H(x_i')\,(g(x_i) - g(x_{i-1})) = \int_c^d \sum_\sigma (g(x_i) - g(x_{i-1}))f(x_i', y)dh(y).$$

Set $F_\sigma(y) = \Sigma_\sigma(g(x_i) - g(x_{i-1}))f(x_i', y)$. Then the functions $F_\sigma(y)$ are uniformly bounded in y and σ, since $|F_\sigma(y)| \leqq M \int_a^b |dg|$, where $|f(x, y)| \leqq M$ on $[a, b]\times[c, d]$. Further

$$\lim_{|\sigma|\to 0} F_\sigma(y) = \lim_{|\sigma|\to 0} \sum_\sigma (g(x_i) - g(x_{i-1}))f(x_i', y) = \int_a^b dg(x)f(x, y) = G(y)$$

for each y. Also for each σ: $\int_c^d F_\sigma(y)dh(y) = \Sigma_\sigma H(x_i')\,(g(x_i) - g(x_{i-1}))$ exists. Since the σ directed via $|\sigma|$ are of sequential character, it follows by II.15.15 that

$$\lim_{|\sigma|\to 0} \int_c^d F_\sigma(y)dh(y) = \lim_{|\sigma|\to 0} \sum_\sigma H(x_i')\Delta_i g$$

exists or, in other words, $\int_a^b H(x)dg(x)$ exists. By parity it follows that $\int_c^d G(y)dh(y)$ exists also, so that the Osgood theorem II.15.13 applies and we have

$$\lim_{|\sigma|\to 0} \int_c^d F_\sigma(y)dh(y) = \int_c^d G(y)dh(y) = \int_a^b H(x)dg(x).$$

Since $g(x)$ and $h(y)$ are of bounded variation, the σ-integrals exist if σ are ordered via R, i.e., as $|\sigma| \to 0$ and σ ultimately includes the points of discontinuity of g and h, respectively, and this ordering is of sequential character (see II.13.10). Consequently, the theorem also holds if σ-integrals are used instead of norm integrals.

A different type of iterated integral theorem is the following:

17.3.2. THEOREM. If $g(x, y)$ is defined on $[a, b]\times[c, d]$ and of bounded variation in x uniformly in y, or $\int_a^b |d_x g(x, y)| \leqq M$ for y on $[c, d]$; if $f(x)$ is continuous on $[a, b]$; if $h(y)$ is of bounded variation on $[c, d]$; if $\int_c^d g(x, y)dh(y)$ exists for each x of $[a, b]$; then

$$\int_a^b f(x)d_x \int_c^d g(x, y)dh(y) = \int_c^d \left(\int_a^b f(x)d_x g(x, y)\right)dh(y),$$

where all the integrals involved exist and are of the same type (norm or σ).

We prove the theorem for norm integrals, the proof for σ-integrals follows the same procedure.

By Theorem II.17.2.1, $\int_c^d g(x, y)dh(y)$ is of bounded variation in x, so that since $f(x)$ is continuous $\int_a^b f(x)d_x \int_c^d g(x, y)dh(y)$ exists.

On the other side, consider the approximating sums

$$\sum_\sigma \int_a^b f(x)d_x g(x, y_i') (h(y_i) - h(y_{i-1})) = \int_a^b f(x)dF_\sigma(x),$$

where we have set $F_\sigma(x) = \Sigma_\sigma g(x, y_i') (h(y_i) - h(y_{i-1}))$. The functions $F_\sigma(x)$ are of bounded variation in x uniformly as to σ, because

$$\begin{aligned}&\sum_j | F_\sigma(x_j) - F_\sigma(x_{j-1}) | \\ &\leqq \sum_j \sum_i | g(x_j, y_i') - g(x_{j-1}, y_i') | \; | h(y_i) - h(y_{i-1}) | \\ &\leqq \text{l.u.b.}_i \int_a^b | d_x g(x, y_i') | \int_c^d | dh | \leqq M \int_c^d | dh |.\end{aligned}$$

By hypothesis $\lim_{|\sigma| \to 0} F_\sigma(x) = \int_c^d g(x, y)dh(y)$ exists for all x. Consequently, since $f(x)$ is continuous, we have by II.15.3:

$$\begin{aligned}&\int_c^d (\int_a^b f(x)d_x g(x, y)dh(y) \\ &= \lim_{|\sigma| \to 0} \sum_\sigma \int_a^b f(x)d_x g(x, y_i') (h(y_i) - h(y_{i-1})) \\ &= \lim_{|\sigma| \to 0} \int_a^b f(x)dF_\sigma(x) = \int_a^b f(x)d_x \int_c^d g(x, y)dh(y).\end{aligned}$$

18. Linear Continuous Functionals on the Space of Continuous Functions

We have previously defined a linear normed space (I.9.2) and noticed that the space of continouus functions on $[a, b]$ is such a space if $||f|| = \text{l.u.b.} (| f(x) |; x \text{ on } [a, b])$. Then $\lim_n || f_n - f || = 0$ is equivalent to uniform convergence of f_n to f on $[a, b]$.

18.1. Definition. A *linear form* or *functional* on a linear space is a real valued function $L(f)$ on the space such that $L(c_1 f_1 + c_2 f_2) = c_1 L(f_1) + c_2 L(f_2)$, for all constants c_1 and c_2 and elements f_1 and f_2 of the space. A linear form on a linear normed space is *continuous* if $\lim_n || f_n - f || = 0$ implies $\lim_n L(f_n) = L(f)$. For a linear form $L(0) = 0$. A linear form on a linear normed space is obviously continuous if and only it is continuous at $f = 0$.

18.2. THEOREM. A linear form on a linear normed space is continuous if and only if it is bounded or limited, that is, if there exists a positive constant M such that for all f: $| L(f) | \leqq M || f ||$.

The fact that boundedness implies continuity follows from $| L(f_n) - L(f) | = | L(f_n - f) | \leqq M|| f_n - f ||$. On the other hand, assume $L(f)$ continuous and if possible not bounded. Then there exists a sequence $\{f_n\}$ with $\| f_n \| = 1$, such that $| L(f_n) | > n$. But $\| f_n/\sqrt{n} \| = 1/\sqrt{n}$, converges to zero in n while $| L(f_n/\sqrt{n}) | > \sqrt{n}$, which contradicts the continuity at $f = 0$. The l.u.b.[$| L(f) |$ for $\| f \| = 1$] is usually denoted by $\| L \|$, pointing the way to the fact that the space of all linear continuous forms on a linear normed space is again a linear normed space.

The problem of the most general linear continuous form on the normed space of continuous functions concerned analysts for some time. It was observed that $\int_a^b f(x)g(x)dx$ for any Riemann integrable function $g(x)$ is such a form. Also that $\Sigma_i c_i f(x_i)$, where $\Sigma_i | c_i | < \infty$ and x_i are any points of $[a, b]$ was a possibility. Borel proved that if $L(f)$ is such a form, then there exists a sequence of Riemann integrable functions $g_n(x)$ such that $L(f) = \lim_n \int_a^b f(x)g_n(x)dx$. The elegant solution of the problem by the use of Stieltjes integrals is due to F. Riesz who proved [see Sur les operations fonctionnelles lineaire, *Compt. rend. acad. sci. Paris* 149 (1909) 974-977]:

18.3. THEOREM. If $L(f)$ is a linear continuous form on the space of continuous functions on $[a, b]$ normed via $\| f \| = \text{l.u.b.}\ (| f(x) |;\ x \text{ on } [a, b])$, then there exists a function $g(x)$ of bounded variation on $[a, b]$ such that $L(f) = \int_a^b f(x)dg(x)$.

We shall prove the theorem for the interval [0, 1], the proof for the interval $[a, b]$ can be deduced by indulging in the linear transformation $x = (b - a)y + a$.

Our proof is based on the use of Bernstein polynomials in the proof of the *Weierstrass polynomial approximation theorem* for continuous functions: "for any continuous function $f(x)$ on the closed finite interval $[a, b]$, there exists a sequence of polynomials $P_n(x)$ such that $\lim_n P_n(x) = f(x)$ uniformly on $[a, b]$."

Since the proof is rather simple and elegant we repeat it here, limiting ourselves to the interval [0, 1], the necessary changes to any interval $[a, b]$ being simple.

18.4. Definition. *The Bernstein polynomials* for any function $f(x)$ on [0, 1] are defined

$$B_n(f; x) = \sum_{m=0}^{n} f(m/n)\ {}_nC_m x^m (1 - x)^{n-m},$$

where ${}_nC_m$ are the binomial coefficients $n!/(m!(n - m)!)$. The expression for $B_n(f; x)$ is reminiscent of the definition of an integral.

If we take $f(x) \equiv 1$ for all x, then

$$B_n(1; x) = \sum_{m=0}^{n} {}_nC_m x^m (1-x)^{n-m} \equiv 1.$$

If we take the derivative of this identity and multiply by $x(1-x)$ we obtain

$$\sum_{m=0}^{n} {}_nC_m (m - nx) x^m (1-x)^{n-m} = 0.$$

Taking a second derivative and multiplying by $x(1-x)$ we find

$$\sum_{m=0}^{n} {}_nC_m (m-nx)^2 x^m (1-x)^{n-m} = nx(1-x).$$

If we remember that the maximum value of $x(1-x)$ on [0, 1] is 1/4, and divide this expression by n^2, we conclude that

$$\sum_{m=0}^{n} {}_nC_m (x - m/n)^2 x^n (1-x)^{n-m} \leqq 1/4\,n.$$

Consequently, if m'' denotes values of m for which for a given x and d we have $|m/n - x| > d$, then

$$\sum_{m''} {}_nC_m x^m (1-x)^{n-m} \leqq 1/4\,nd^2.$$

Consider now for fixed x

$$f(x) - \sum_{m=0}^{n} f(m/n)\, {}_nC_m x^m (1-x)^{n-m}$$
$$= \sum_{m=0}^{n} (f(x) - f(m/n))\, {}_nC_m x^m (1-x)^{n-m}.$$

Then because of the continuity of $f(x)$ we have: $(e, d_e, |x' - x| < d_e)$: $|f(x') - f(x)| < e$. If m' are the m for which $|x - m/n| < d_e$ and m'' those for which $|x - m/n| \geqq d_e$, then

$$|f(x) - B_n(f; x)| \leqq \sum_{m'} |f(x) - f(m/n)|\, {}_nC_m x^m (1-x)^{n-m}$$
$$+ \sum_{m''} |f(x) - f(m/n)|\, {}_nC_m x^m (1-x)^{n-m}$$
$$\leqq e + M/2\,nd_e^2,$$

where $M = \text{l.u.b.}\ (|f(x)|;\ x \text{ on } [0, 1])$. Since, because of uniform continuity, d_e is independent of x, we will have $|f(x) - B_n(f; x)| < 2e$ provided $n > n_e$ and $n_e > M/2\,ed_e^2$. This is the desired uniform convergence. The demonstration shows incidentally that for any function $f(x)$ bounded on [0, 1], $B_n(f; x)$ converges to $f(x)$ at every point where f is continuous.

Returning to the proof of the Riesz theorem and to our linear continuous form $L(f)$, the continuity and linearity of L give:

$$L(f) = \lim_n L(B_n(f; x)) = \lim_n \sum_{m=0}^{n} f(m/n)\, L({}_nC_m x_m (1-x)^{n-m}).$$

We define a function $g_n(x)$ as follows: $g_n(0) = 0$; $g_n(x) = \Sigma_{m=0}^{p} L({}_nC_m x^m (1-x)^{n-m})$ for $p/n < x \leqq (p+1)/n$, $0 \leqq p < n$; $g_n(1) = L(1)$. Then

$$\int_0^1 f(x)\, dg_n(x) = \sum_{m=0}^{n} f(m/n) L({}_nC_m x^m (1-x)^{n-m}).$$

Whether $\lim_n g_n(x)$ exists is uncertain. But the $g_n(x)$ are uniformly of bounded variation, since

$$\int_0^1 | dg_n | = \sum_{m=0}^{n} | L({}_nC_m x^m (1-x)^{n-m}) |$$
$$= L(\sum_{m=0}^{n} \varepsilon_m \cdot {}_nC_m x^m (1-x)^{n-m}) \leqq \| L \| ,$$

where $\varepsilon_m = \operatorname{sgn} L({}_nC_m x^m (1-x)^{n-m})$ and obviously

$$|\sum_{m=0}^{n} \varepsilon_m \cdot {}_nC_m x^m (1-x)^{n-m} | \leqq \sum_{m=0}^{n} {}_nC_m x^m (1-x)^{n-m} = 1.$$

Using the Helly theorem II.8.9, there exists a subsequence $g_{n_k}(x)$ and a $g(x)$ of bounded variation such that $\lim_k g_{n_k}(x) = g(x)$ for all x. Consequently, by II.15.3, $L(f) = \lim_k \int_0^1 f(x) dg_{n_k}(x) = \int_0^1 f(x) dg(x)$. This completes the proof of the Riesz theorem.

Suppose a different subsequence of $g_n(x)$ leads to a different $g_1(x)$. Then $\int_0^1 f dg = \int_0^1 f dg_1$ for all continuous functions $f(x)$, and so $g(x) = g_1(x)$, excepting for a denumerable set of points on [0, 1]. It is customary to assume that $g(x)$ is chosen in such a way that for all x, $g(x)$ lies between $g(x-0)$ and $g(x+0)$, which does not affect the value of the integral. Such a function of bounded variation is said to be *regular*. Now if $g(x)$ is regular in this way, then the interval function $F(I) = | g(d) - g(c) |$ is pseudoadditive at every point since $| g(x+0) - g(x-0) | = | g(x+0) - g(x) | + | g(x) - g(x-0)|$. As a consequence $\int_0^1 | dg |$ exists as a norm integral. Moreover, we have:

18.5. THEOREM. If $g(x)$ is a regular function of bounded variation on $[a, b]$ and if $L(f) = \int_a^b fdg$ on the space of continuous functions, then $\| L \| = \int_a^b | dg |$, where $\| L \| =$ g.l.b. [M such that $| L(f) | \leqq M$ for $\| f \| = 1$].

Since $\int_a^b fdg \leqq \| f \| \int_a^b | dg |$, it follows that $\| L \| \leqq \int_a^b | dg |$. To show that $\| L \| \geqq \int_a^b | dg |$, we find a σ_0 such that for $\sigma \geqq \sigma_0$, we have $\int_a^b | dg | \geqq \Sigma_\sigma | \Delta_i g | - e$, and since $\int_a^b | dg |$ exists as a norm integral, we can assume that $g(x)$ is continuous at the points of subdivision x_i. Then for $i = 1, \ldots n - 1$, we can select points x_i', x_i'' such that $x_{i-1}'' < x_i' < x_i < x_i'' < x_{i+1}'$ and $\Sigma_i | g(x_i'') - g(x_i') | < e$. We then define $f(x) = \operatorname{sgn} (g(x_i') - g(x_{i-1}''))$ for $x_{i-1}'' \leqq x \leqq x_i'$, $i = 1, \ldots n - 1$; $f(x) = \operatorname{sgn} (g(x_1') - g(a))$ on $[a, x_1']$; $f(x) = \operatorname{sgn} (g(b) - g(x_{n-1}''))$ on $[x_{n-1}'', b]$; and $f(x)$ linear on $[x_i', x_i'']$. Then

$$\int_a^b fdg = | g(x_1') - g(a) | + \sum_i | g(x_i') - g(x_{i-1}'') |$$
$$+ | g(b) - g(x_{n-1}'') | + \sum_i \int_{x_i'}^{x_i''} fdg.$$

Since $\| f \| \leqq 1$ on $[x_i', x_i'']$ we have

$$\sum_i \left| \int_{x_i'}^{x_i''} fdg \right| \leqq \sum_i | g(x_i') - g(x_i'') |.$$

Consequently if σ consists of $a, x_1', \ldots, x_i', x_i, x_i'', \ldots, x''_{n-1}, b$, then

$$\left| \int_a^b fdg \right| \geqq \sum_\sigma | \Delta g | - 2 \sum_i | g(x_i'') - g(x_i') | \geqq \sum_\sigma | \Delta g | - 2 e$$
$$\geqq \int_a^b | dg | - 3 e.$$

Since $\| f \| = 1$, it follows that $\| L \| \geqq \int_a^b | dg |$.

EXERCISES

1. Show that for all n, the Bernstein polynomials of $f(x) = x$ are $B_n(x, x) = x$, while for $f(x) = x^2$, $B_n(x^2; x) = x^2 + x(1 - x)/n$.

2. In general show that if $P(x)$ is any polynomial in x, then $B_n(P(x); x) = P(x) + Q_n(x)$, where $Q_n(x)$ is a polynomial in x whose coefficients are polynomials in $1/n$, having $1/n$ as a factor.

3. Show that any function $f(x)$ on $[a, b]$ which has only discontinuities of the first kind (breaks), can be uniformly approximated by functions of the form $c_0 + \Sigma_{m=1}^n c_m \beta(x, x_m; d_m', d_m'')$ where as usual $\beta(x, x_0; d_1, d_2)$ is the simple break function with discontinuity at x_0.

19. Additional Definitions of Riemann Integrals of Stieltjes Type

The existence of the norm Stieltjes integral $N \int fdg$ we have considered imposes, among other things, the restriction that f and g have no common discontinuity, that of the σ-integral requires that f and g have no common discontinuity on the same side of a point. Modifications have been proposed which to some extent bypass these restrictions. Usually such modifications sacrifice some other desirable property of the Stieltjes integral.

19.1. The Mean Stieltjes Integral. One of the simplest modifications is that in which the basic function of intervals is $F[c, d] = \frac{1}{2}(f(c) + f(d))(g(d) - g(c))$. We define

19.1.1. Definition. *The Mean Stieltjes Integral* $M \int fdg$ of f with respect to g is the limit of $\Sigma_\sigma(f(x_i) + f(x_{i-1}))(g(x_i) - g(x_{i-1}))/2$, where we obtain the norm integral $NM \int fdg$ if the limit exists as $|\sigma| \to 0$ and the $\sigma M \int fdg$ if the limit exists as σ spreads.

If the ordinary integrals exist, so that both $\Sigma_\sigma f(x_i)(g(x_i) - g(x_{i-1}))$ and $\Sigma_\sigma f(x_{i-1})(g(x_i) - g(x_{i-1}))$ have the same limit, then obviously the corresponding mean integrals exist and give the same value for the integral.

Many of the usual properties of integrals, especially those based on the integrals of interval functions are valid, such as the bilinearity of $M \int fdg$ as a function of f and g, the existence of $\int_c^d fdg$ with $a \leqq c < d \leqq b$ if $\int_a^b fdg$ exists, and the additive property of the resulting interval function. The integration by parts theorem is almost trivial, since

$$\sum_i \tfrac{1}{2}(f(x_i) + f(x_{i-1}))(g(x_i) - g(x_{i-1}))$$
$$+ \sum_i \tfrac{1}{2}(g(x_i) + g(x_{i-1}))(f(x_i) - f(x_{i-1}))$$
$$= \sum_i (f(x_i)g(x_i) - f(x_{i-1})g(x_{i-1})) = f(b)g(b) - f(a)g(a)$$

for all subdivisions, so that we have:

19.1.2. THEOREM. If $M \int_a^b fdg$ exists, then $M \int_a^b gdf$ exists also and $M \int_a^b fdg + M \int_a^b gdf = f(b)g(b) - f(a)g(a)$.

Further, since $\Sigma_\sigma(f(x_i) + f(x_{i-1}))(f(x_i) - f(x_{i-1}) = \Sigma_\sigma((f(x_i))^2 - f(x_{i-1})^2) = (f(b))^2 - (f(a))^2$ for all σ, we have: if $f(x)$ is any finite valued function on $[a, b]$, then $M \int_a^b fdf$ exists and is equal to $\frac{1}{2}((f(b))^2$

$-(f(a))^2)$. This shows that f and g may have common points of discontinuity for this definition of integral, even under the norm limit.

On the other hand, the substitution theorem: " if $\int_a^b fdg$ exists and $h(x)$ is bounded on $[a, b]$, then $\int_a^b hfdg$ exists if and only if $\int_a^b h(x)d \int_a^x fdg$ exists and are equal," does not always hold. If we take for $f(x) = g(x)$ the break function $\beta(x, x_0; d_1, d_2)$ on $[a, b]$, and for $h(x)$ the break function $\beta(x, x_0; d_1', d_2')$, then $M \int_a^x fdg = M \int_a^x fdf = \frac{1}{2}(f(x))^2$. Then $NM \int_a^b hfdg$ exists if and only if $(d_1' - d_2')d_1 d_2 = 0$, while $NM \int_a^b h(x)d_x \int_a^x fdf$ exists if and only if $d_1'd_2^2 - d_2'd_1^2 = 0$. If $d_1' = d_2'$ but $d_1^2 \neq d_2^2$, then $NM \int_a^b hfdf$ and $NM \int_a^b h(x)d_x \int_a^x fdf$ do not exist simultaneously. If $d_1 = d_2$ and $d_1' = d_2'$, they do exist simultaneously, but the values might be different with $M \int_a^b hfdf = \frac{1}{2} d_1^2 d_1'$ and $M \int_a^b h(x)d_x \int_a^x fdf = \frac{1}{4} d_1^2 d_1'$.

If $g(x)$ is of bounded variation and $f(x)$ is bounded on $[a, b]$ then the inequality $| \int_a^b fdg | \leq K \int_a^b | dg |$, where K is the l.u.b. of $| f(x) |$ on $[a, b]$, leads to the uniform convergence theorems:

19.1.3. $\lim_n M \int_a^b f_n dg = M \int_a^b fdg$ for f_n approaching f uniformly on $[a, b]$ and

19.1.4. If f is bounded and $\lim_n \int_a^b | d(g_n - g) | = 0$, then

$$\lim_n M \int_a^b fdg_n = M \int_a^b fdg.$$

From the second of these two convergence theorems and the fact that $\sigma M \int_a^b f(x)d\beta(x, x_0; d_1, d_2)$ exists, if $f(x_0 + 0)$ and $f(x_0 - 0)$ exist at x_0, which can be easily verified, it follows that $\sigma M \int_a^b fdg$ exists if $f(x)$ has only discontinuities of the first kind.

For additional properties of these integrals the reader is referred to H. L. Smith: *Trans. Am. Math. Soc.* 27 (1925) 491-515; H.S. Kaltenborn: *Tokohu Math. J.* 44 (1938) 1-11; R.E. Lane: *Proc. Am. Math. Soc.* 5 (1954) 59-66; P. Porcelli: *Illinois J. Math.* 2 (1958) 124-128.

19.2. Cauchy Left and Right Integrals. Conceptually, the right and left Cauchy integrals based on the interval functions $F[c, d] = f(d)(g(d) - g(c))$ and $F[c, d] = f(c))(g(d) - g(c))$, respectively, are similar to the mean integrals. Obviously if both the right and left Cauchy integrals exist, then the mean integral exists and is the average of them. For the case where $g(x) = x$, D.C. Gillespie [*Ann. Math.* (2) 17 (1915) 61-63] has shown that the existence of the right or left Cauchy integral implies the existence of the Riemann integral and so equivalence. Modifications of this result if $g(x)$ is of bounded variation have been developed by G.B. Price. The reader is referred to the article by Price: *Bull. Am. Math. Soc.* 49 (1943) 625-630, for details. See also R.F. Deniston, *Koninkl. Ned. Akad. Wetenschap. Proc.* 52 (1949) 1111-1128 or *Indagationes Math.* 11 (1949) 385-402.

19.3. The Y-Integral. In case $g(x)$ in the integral $\int_a^b f dg$ has only discontinuities of the first kind, that is $g(x+0)$ and $g(x-0)$ exist finitely for every point, we can take account of this fact by including the discontinuities of g in the basic function of intervals. We assume that for any interval $I = [c, d]$

$$F(I) = F[c, d] = f(c)(g(c+0) - g(c)) + f(x')(g(d-0) - g(c+0)) + f(d)(g(d) - g(d-0))$$

with $c < x' < d$. Such a function of intervals was suggested by W.H. Young [*Proc. London Math. Soc.* (2) 13 (1914) 109-150] but the resulting integrals he considers are in the norm sense and it turns out that for the case when $g(x)$ is of bounded variation, this mode of convergence adds very little in integrability. We shall call Stieltjes integrals based on the above function of intervals Y-integrals.

Obviously, the existence and approximation theorems for integrals of functions of intervals apply. In particular, those involving $\omega(SF; I)$ prove useful, where it should be noted that for the interval function of the Y-integral, the oscillation function $\omega(SF; I)$ does not depend on the value of f or g at the end points of the interval I.

The reasoning used in II.10.10 shows that:

19.3.1. THEOREM. If $Y \int_a^b f dg$ exists, then $f(x)$ is bounded on a finite number of closed intervals, which are complementary to a finite number of open intervals on the interior of which $g(x)$ is constant.

For the pseudoadditive condition on $F(I)$ which links the norm and σ-integrals, substitution and rearrangement of terms shows that for $c < x_0 < d$, we have

$$F[c, d] - (F[c, x_0] + F[x_0, d]) = (f(x') - f(x''))(g(x_0 - 0) - g(c+0)) - (f(x_0) - f(x'))(g(x_0+0) - g(x_0-0)) + (f(x') - f(x'''))(g(d-0) - g(x_0+0))$$

where $c < x' < d$, $c < x'' < x_0$ and $x_0 < x''' < d$. For pseudoadditivity this expression must have limit zero as $c \to x_0 - 0$ and $d \to x_0 + 0$.

Now

$$\lim_{c \to x_0 - 0} g(c + 0) = g(x_0 - 0) \text{ and } \lim_{d \to x_0 + 0} g(d - 0) = g(x_0 + 0).$$

Consequently, if $f(x)$ is bounded, which we assume, we must have

$$\lim_{x' \to x_0} (f(x_0) - f(x'))(g(x_0 + 0) - g(x_0 - 0)) = 0,$$

or $f(x)$ is continuous if $g(x_0 + 0) \neq g(x_0 - 0)$. This condition is also obviously sufficient for pseudoadditivity of $F(I)$. We therefore have:

19.3.2. THEOREM. The interval function $F(I)$ for the Y-integral is pseudoadditive at x_0 if and only if f is continuous at x_0 when $g(x_0 + 0) \neq g(x_0 - 0)$. If $g(x)$ is regular at x_0 in the sense that $g(x_0)$ lies between $g(x_0 + 0)$ and $g(x_0 - 0)$, then $F(I)$ is pseudoadditive at x_0 if and only if f and g have no common discontinuities at x_0.

The $Y \int fdg$ is an extension of the ordinary Stieltjes integral $\int fdg$, for:

19.3.3. THEOREM. If $\int_a^b fdg$ exists in the ordinary sense, then $Y \int_a^b fdg$ exists and the two integrals are equal.

For consider the function of intervals $F(I)$ for the Y-integral:

$$F(I) = f(c)(g(c + 0) - g(c)) + f(x')(g(d - 0) - g(c + 0)) + f(d)(g(d) - g(d - 0))$$

with $|f(x)| \leq M$. Then for $e_0 > 0$ we can find points $c < c_1 < x' < d_1 < d$ such that $|g(c + 0) - g(c_1)| < e_0/3M$, and $|g(d - 0) - g(d_1)| < e_0/3M$. Then for

$$F_1(I) = f(c)(g(c_1) - g(c)) + f(x')(g(d_1) - g(c_1)) + f(d)(g(d) - g(d_1))$$

we have $|F(I) - F_1(I)| < e_0$, and moreover, $F_1(I)$ is a function of intervals for the ordinary integral. The validity of the theorem then follows from a comparison of $F(I)$ and $F_1(I)$ or rather $\Sigma_{\sigma_1} f\Delta g$, where σ_1 includes σ and points like c_1 and d_1 for each x_i of σ.

In the reverse direction we can assert:

19.3.4. THEOREM. If $Y \int_a^b fdg$ exists, and if $g(x)$ is continuous, then $\int_a^b fdg$ exists in the ordinary sense.

If $g(x)$ is continuous, then $F(I) = F[c, d] = f(x')(g(d) - g(c))$ x' is restricted to $c < x' < d$ for the Y-integral, while for the ordinary integral $c \leqq x' \leqq d$ is permitted. Suppose $(e, d_e, |\sigma| < d_e) : |\Sigma_\sigma f\Delta g - Y\int_a^b fdg| < e$. Select an arbitrary σ such that $|\sigma| < d_e/2$ and consider the ordinary sum $\Sigma_\sigma f(x_i')(g(x_i) - g(x_{i-1}))$, with n points of subdivision and $x_{i-1} \leqq x_i' \leqq x_i$. To compare with a sum for a Y-integral we need worry only about the points x_i' which are either x_{i-1} or x_i. If for a given i: $x_i' = x_i = x'_{i+1}$, then $f(x_i')(g(x_i) - g(x_{i-1})) + f(x'_{i+1})(g(x_{i+1}) - g(x_i)) = f(x_i)(g(x_{i+1}) - g(x_{i-1})$ where $x_{i-1} < x_i < x_{i+1}$ and $|x_{i-1} - x_{i-1}| < d_e$. If for a given i, we have $x_i' < x_i = x'_{i+1}$, the continuity of $g(x)$ at x_i gives us an x_i'' such that $x_i' < x_i'' < x_i < x_{i+1}$ so that $|g(x''_i) - g(x_i)| < e/2nM$, and so

$$|[f(x_i')(g(x_i) - g(x_{i-1})) + f(x_i)(g(x_{i+1}) - g(x_i))] - [f(x_i')(g(x_i'') - g(x_{i-1})) + f(x_i)(g(x_{i+1}) - g(x_i''))]| < e/n.$$

By considering each point of subdivision of σ in succession we arrive at a new subdivision σ' such that $|\sigma'| < d_e$ and such that

$$|\sum_{\sigma'} f(\bar{x}_i')(g(\bar{x}_i) - g(\bar{x}_{i-1})) - \sum_{\sigma} f(x_i')(g(x_i) - g(x_{i-1}))| < e$$

where $\bar{x}_{i-1} < \bar{x}_i' < \bar{x}_i$. From this it follows that

$$|\sum_{\sigma} f(x_i')(g(x_i) - g(x_{i-1})) - Y\int_a^b fdg| < e, \quad \text{for} \quad |\sigma| < d_e/2$$

and $x_{i-1} \leqq x_i' \leqq x_i$, for all i.

If $g(x)$ is the break function $\beta(x, x_0; d_1, d_2)$, then $\sigma Y \int fdg$ exists for any function f bounded in the vicinity of x_0 and $\sigma Y \int_a^b fdg = f(x_0)(g(x_0 + 0) - g(x_0 - 0))$, where $x_0 - 0$ is replaced by a if $x_0 = a$ and $x_0 + 0$ is replaced by b if $x_0 = b$. On the other hand, for $d_2 \neq 0$, $NY \int_a^b fdg$ exists if and only if $f(x)$ is continuous at x_0.

19.3.5. The Y-integrals have the usual linearity properties relative to f and g. Also if $Y\int_a^b fdg$ exists, then $Y\int_c^d fdg$ exists for $a \leqq c < d \leqq b$, and the resulting interval function is additive. Note that $Y\int_c^d$ does not depend on the behavior of f or g for $x < c$ and for $x > d$.

19.3.6. If $Y\int_a^b fdg$ exists, and f is bounded, then the function $h(x) = \int_a^x fdg$ reflects the continuity properties of $g(x)$ in that $h(x + 0) - h(x) = f(x)(g(x+0) - g(x))$ and $h(x) - h(x-0) = f(x)(g(x) - g(x - 0))$ for all x. For by II.4.7

$$\lim_{x \to x_0 + 0} |\int_{x_0}^{x} F(I) - F[x, x_0]| = 0.$$

Now for our $F(I)$ we have

$$F[x_0, x] = f(x_0)(g(x_0 + 0) - g(x_0)) + f(x')(g(x + 0) - g(x_0+0)) + f(x)(g(x - 0) - g(x)).$$

Also

$$\lim_{x \to x_0 + 0} g(x) = \lim_{x \to x_0 + 0} g(x - 0) = g(x_0 + 0),$$

so that

$$h(x_0 + 0) - h(x_0) = \lim_{x \to x_0 + 0} F[x_0, x] = f(x_0)(g(x_0 + 0) - g(x_0)).$$

Similarly for $x_0 - 0$.

The substitution theorem is valid in its usual form:

19.3.7. If $Y \int_a^b fdg$ exists, and $h(x)$ is bounded on $[a, b]$, then $Y \int_a^b h(x)d_x \int_a^x fdg$ exists if and only if $Y \int_a^b h(x)f(x)dg(x)$ exists, and then the two integrals are equal.

This follows in the usual way. For for any interval $[c, d]$ as a result of the discontinuity properties of $\int_a^x fdg$, we have

$$\begin{aligned} &| [h(c) \int_c^{c+0} fdg + h(x') \int_{c+0}^{d-0} fdg + h(d) \int_{d-0}^{d} fdg] \\ &- [h(c)f(c)(g(c + 0) - g(c)) + h(x')f(x')(g(d - 0) \\ &- g(c + 0)) + h(d)f(d)(g(d) - g(d - 0))] | \\ &= | h(x') (\int_{c+0}^{d-0} fdg - f(x')(g(d - 0) - g(c + 0)) | \\ &\leqq M \, \omega(Sf\Delta g; [c, d]) \end{aligned}$$

where $| h(x) | \leqq M$ for all x. The rest of the proof follows that given in II.11.6.

If $g(x)$ is of bounded variation on $[a, b]$ and $f(x)$ is bounded and if $Y \int_a^b fdg$ exists, then obviously $| Y \int_a^b fdg | \leqq M \int_a^b | dg |$, where $| f(x) | \leqq M$ on $[a, b]$. This inequality gives the usual convergence theorems based on uniform convergence:

19.3.8. If $\lim_n f_n(x) = f(x)$ uniformly on $[a, b]$, $g(x)$ is of bounded variation on $[a, b]$ and if $Y \int_a^b f_n dg$ exists for all n, then $Y \int_a^b fdg$ and $\lim_n Y \int_a^b f_n dg$ exist and are equal.

19.3.9. If $f(x)$ is bounded on $[a, b]$, $g_n(x)$ and $g(x)$ are of bounded variation with $\lim_n \int_a^b | d(g_n - g) | = 0$, and if $Y \int_a^b fdg_n$ exist for all n, then $Y \int_a^b fdg$ and $\lim_n Y \int_a^b fdg_n$ exist and are equal.

From this last theorem we deduce in the usual way that if $g(x)$ is a pure break function of bounded variation on $[a, b]$, that is, $g(x) = \Sigma_n \beta(x, x_n; d_n', d_n'')$ with $\Sigma_n (|d_n'| + |d_n'' - d_n'|) < \infty$; and if $f(x)$ is bounded on $[a, b]$, then $\sigma\ Y \int_a^b fdg$ exists and has as value

$$\sum_n f(x_n)d_n'' = \sum_n f(x_n)(g(x_n + 0) - g(x_n - 0))$$
$$= \sum_x f(x)(g(x + 0) - g(x - 0)).$$

Consequently:

19.3.10. THEOREM. If $\sigma\ Y \int_a^b fdg$ exists, then $\sigma\ Y \int_a^b fdg_b$ exists and so $\sigma\ Y \int_a^b fdg_c$ exists, where g_c and g_b are the continuous and break parts of g. It follows then that $\int_a^b fdg_c$ exists, so that

$$Y\int_a^b fdg = Y\int_a^b fdg_c + Y\int_a^b fdg_b = \int_a^b fdg_c + \sum_x f(x)(g(x+0) - g(x-0))$$

where $a - 0 = a$, and $b + 0 = b$.

From this theorem, we can conclude that if $f(x)$ is bounded, and $g(x)$ is of bounded variation on $[a, b]$, and if $\int_a^b fdg_c$ exists, then $Y \int_a^b fdg$ can be defined in two ways, viz.:

$$\lim_\sigma \sum_\sigma [(f(x_{i-1})(g(x_{i-1} + 0) - g(x_{i-1})) + f(x_i')(g(x_i - 0)$$
$$- g(x_{i-1} + 0)) + f(x_i)(g(x_i) - g(x_i - 0))]$$

or as $\int_a^b fdg_c + \Sigma_x f(x)(g(x + 0) - g(x - 0))$.

Since a function which is bounded and has only discontinuities of the first kind has at most a denumerable number of discontinuities, we have:

19.3.11. If $f(x)$ is bounded and has only discontinuities of the first kind, and if $g(x)$ is of bounded variation, then $\sigma\ Y \int_a^b fdg$ exists. In particular, $\sigma\ Y \int_a^b fdg$ exists if f and g are of bounded variation on $[a, b]$.

For the v_c-measure corresponding to g_c, the continuous part of g for a denumerable set of points is zero, so that $\int_a^b fdg_c$ exists.

If $NY \int_a^b fdg$ exists, then $f(x)$ is continuous at all points where $g(x + 0) \neq g(x - 0)$. If then $g(x)$ is regular, i.e., $g(x)$ lies between $g(x - 0)$ and $g(x + 0)$ for all x, then $f(x)$ is continuous at all points of discontinuity of $g(x)$. It follows that if $g_b(x)$ is the break function for the function $g(x)$ of bounded variation which is regular, then $NY \int_a^b fdg_b$ and $N \int_a^b fdg_b$ exist or do not exist simultaneously, so that we have:

19.3.12. If $g(x)$ is a regular function of bounded variation then $NY \int_a^b fdg$ exists if and only if $N \int_a^b fdg$ exists. This holds in partiuclar if $g(x)$ is monotone on $[a, b]$.

The $NY \int_a^b fdg$, with $g(x)$ of bounded variation is then essentially equal to the ordinary $N \int_a^b fdg$. However, the $\sigma\ Y \int_a^b fdg$ contributes something new in that it allows for common discontinuities of f and g, and gives a formal expression which is closely related to that of the Lebesgue-Stieltjes integral considered later.

19.3.13. Integration by Parts Theorem. If f and g are both of bounded variation on $[a, b]$ so that both $\sigma\ Y \int_a^b fdg$ and $\sigma\ Y \int_a^b gdf$ exist, then

$$\sigma\ Y \int_a^b fdg + \sigma\ Y \int_a^b gdf = f(b)g(b) - f(a)g(a)$$
$$- \sum_x [(f(x+0) - f(x))(g(x+0) - g(x))$$
$$- (f(x) - f(x-0))\ (g(x) - g(x-0))].$$

For the $\sigma\ Y$-integral then, the integration by parts formula involves corrective terms due to the common discontinuities of f and g, when f and g are both of bounded variation on $[a, b]$.

Suppose f and g have a finite number of discontinuities at the points $x_1 < x_2 < \ldots x_n$. Then on the open intervals $(x_{i-1} + 0, x_i - 0)$, f and g are both continuous, so that the Y integrals reduce to ordinary integrals, and the usual integration by parts formula applies. Then

$$Y \int_a^b fdg + Y \int_a^b gdf = \sum_{i=0}^{n+1} Y \int_{x_{i-1}+0}^{x_i - 0} (fdg + g\,df)$$
$$+ \sum_{i=0}^{n+1} Y \int_{x_i - 0}^{x_i + 0} (fdg + gdf)$$

where $x_0 - 0 = x_0 = a$, and $x_{n+1} + 0 = x_n = b$. To the first term on the right hand side we apply the ordinary integration by parts theorem, while for the second term we note that

$$Y \int_{x-0}^{x+0} (fdg + gdf) = f(x)(g(x+0) - g(x-0))$$
$$+ g(x)(f(x+0) - f(x-0)).$$

Then

$$Y \int_a^b fdg + Y \int_a^b gdf = \sum_{i=0}^{n+1} [f(x_i - 0)g(x_i - 0) - f(x_{i-1}+0)g(x_{i-1}+0)$$
$$+ f(x_i)(g(x_i + 0) - g(x_i - 0)) + g(x_i)(f(x_i + 0) - f(x_i - 0))]$$

$$= f(b)g(b) - f(a)g(a) + \sum_{i=0}^{n+1} [f(x_i - 0)g(x_i - 0)$$
$$- f(x_i + 0)g(x_i + 0) + f(x_i)(g(x_i + 0) - g(x_i - 0))$$
$$+ g(x_i)(f(x_i + 0) - f(x_i - 0))].$$

The expression under the summation sign can be arranged in various ways. It can be written for $x_i = x$ as $(f(x) - f(x - 0))(g(x) - g(x - 0)) - (f(x + 0) - f(x))(g(x + 0) - g(x))$, or as the determinant

$$\begin{vmatrix} f(x+0) & g(x-0) & 1 \\ f(x) & g(x) & 1 \\ f(x-0) & g(x+0) & 1 \end{vmatrix}$$

We have then shown that the formula of the theorem holds if f and g have a finite number of discontinuities. Since if f and g have an infinite number of discontinuities, they can be approximated by function f_n and g_n having only a finite number of discontinuities in such a way that $\int_a^b | d(f_n - f) |$ and $\int_a^b | d(g_n - g) |$ converge to zero, it follows easily that the formula is valid for any f and g of bounded variation on $[a, b]$.

If the ordinary integration by parts theorem is to hold for $[a, b]$, then the corrective term involving the discontinuities must vanish. If this is true for all intervals $[c, d]$ and so by continuity for all $(x - 0, x + 0)$ for all x, then $(f(x + 0) - f(x))(g(x + 0) - g(x)) - (f(x) - f(x - 0))(g(x) - g(x - 0)) = 0$ for all x. This happens for instance when f and g have no common discontinuities on the same side of a point. It also happens when there exist functions $A(x)$ and $B(x)$ such that $f(x) = A(x)f(x - 0) + B(x)f(x + 0)$ and $g(x) = B(x)g(x - 0) + A(x)g(x + 0)$ for all x, for instance, $A(x) = B(x) = \frac{1}{2}$ for all x.

The Osgood convergence theorem for integrals is valid for the Y-integral in the form:

19.3.14. If $f_n(x)$ are uniformly bounded on $[a, b]$, if $g(x)$ is of bounded variation on $[a, b]$, if $\lim_n f_n(x) = f(x)$ except for a set of v-measure zero $(v(x) = \int_a^x | dg |)$, and if $Y \int_a^b f_n dg$ and $Y \int_a^b f dg$ exist then $\lim_n Y \int_a^b f_n dg = Y \int_a^b f dg$.

From the corresponding theorem for ordinary integrals it follows that $\lim_n Y \int_a^b f_n dg_c = Y \int_a^b f dg_c$, since because of continuity of g_c

these are ordinary integrals and a set of v-measure zero will also be of v_c-measure zero. For the convergence of $Y \int_a^b f_n dg_b$ to $Y \int_a^b f dg_b$ we use the following theorem from the space l^1 of absolutely convergent series:

19.3.15. Lemma. If the double sequence a_{mn} is bounded and $\lim_n a_{mn} = a_m$ for all m, and if $\Sigma_m | b_m | < \infty$, then $\lim_n \Sigma_m a_{mn} b_m = \Sigma_m a_m b_m$.

Obviously, under the hypothesis of the theorem the sequence a_m is bounded so that $\Sigma_m a_m b_m$ is absolutely convergent. We then write

$$\sum_m a_{mn} b_m - \sum_m a_m b_m = \sum_{m=1}^{p} (a_{mn} - a_m) b_m + \sum_{p+1}^{\infty} (a_{mn} - a_m) b_m .$$

Since $\Sigma_m | b_m | < \infty$, and a_{mn} and a_m are uniformly bounded, for a given $e > 0$, we can find a p such that

$$| \sum_{m=p+1}^{\infty} (a_{mn} - a_m) b_m | < e/2 .$$

Since further

$$\lim_n \sum_{m=1}^{p} (a_{mn} - a_m) b_m = 0 ,$$

there exists n_e such that for $n > n_e$, we have

$$| \sum_{m=1}^{p} (a_{mn} - a_m) b_m | < e/2.$$

Consequently, $(e, n_e, n > n_e) : | \Sigma_m a_{mn} b_m - \Sigma_m a_m b_m | < e$.

Now $Y \int_a^b f_n dg_b = \Sigma_m f(x_m)(g(x_m + 0) - g(x_m - 0))$, where x_m are the points of discontinuity of g. Since $\lim_n f_n(x) = f(x)$ except for a set of v-measure zero, it follows that $\lim_n f_n(x_m) = f(x_m)$ if $g(x_m + 0) - g(x_m - 0) \neq 0$, since then x_m will not be of v-measure zero. If we set $a_{mn} = f_n(x_m)$, $a_m = f(x_m)$ and $b_m = g(x_m + 0) - g(x_m - 0)$, the lemma applies.

The Osgood theorem for Y-integrals then follows from the decomposition $Y \int_a^b f dg = \int_a^b f dg_c + Y \int_a^b f dg_b$.

Whether a theorem holds, relating $Y \int_a^b f dg_n$ to $Y \int_a^b f dg$ after the manner of II.15.4, we do not know. The fact that if $\lim_n g_n(x) = g(x)$ for all x, the discontinuities of $g(x)$ are not related to those of $g_n(x)$ is a source of trouble in deriving such a theorem.

EXERCISES

1. Prove the theorem that if $f(x)$ is bounded on $[a, b]$, and $g(x)$ is of bounded variation, then $\sigma\ Y \int_a^b fdg$ exists if and only if $\int_a^b fdg_c$ exists by applying the condition $\lim_\sigma \Sigma_\sigma\, \omega(Sf\Delta g,\ I) = 0$.

2. Show that for the Y-integral, the σ-convergence can be replaced by the R-convergence of II.13.10, where $\sigma_1 R \sigma_2$ if $|\sigma_1| < |\sigma_2|$ and σ_1 contains more points of discontinuity of $g(x)$ than σ_2.

3. Show that if $f(x, y)$ is bounded on $[a, b] \times [c, d]$; $g(x)$ is of bounded variation on $[a, b]$ and $h(y)$ on $[c, d]$; $\sigma\ Y \int_a^b dg(x) f(x, y)$ exists for each y of $[c, d]$ and $\sigma\ Y \int_c^d f(x, y) dh(y)$ exists for each x of $[a, b]$; then $Y \int_a^b dg(x)$ $\int_c^d f(x, y) dh(y)$ and $\int_c^d (\int_a^b dg(x) f(x, y)) dh(y)$ both exist and are equal, the integrals being σY-integrals throughout.

4. Let $g(x)$ be of bounded variation on $[a, b]$ and $f(x)$ bounded and suppose $\sigma Y \int_a^b fdg$ exists. Set $F(x) = f(x)$ for $a \leqq x \leqq x_0$ and $F(x) = 0$ for $x_0 < x \leqq b$. Show that

$$\sigma Y \int_a^b F(x) dg(x) = \sigma Y \int_a^{x_0} fdg + f(x_0)(g(x_0 + 0) - g(x_0)).$$

5. Under the hypotheses of Ex. 3 above, with $[c, d] = [a, b]$, show that if the integrals are σY-integrals, then

$$\int_a^b dg(x) \int_a^x f(x, y) dh(y) = \int_a^b (\int_y^b dg(x) f(x, y)) dh(y)$$
$$+ \textstyle\sum_x f(x, x)\, [(g(x) - g(x - 0))\ (h(x) - h(x - 0))$$
$$- (g(x + 0) - g(x))\ (h(x + 0) - h(x))].$$

6. A modified Stieltjes integral defined by B. Dushnik (University of Michigan, Ann Arbor, Michigan, Dissertation, 1931) is based on the interval function $F(I) = F[c, d] = f(x)(g(d) - g(c))$ with $c < x < d$. Determine which of the usual properties hold for the resulting norm and σ-integral and in what way it is related to other definitions of Stieltjes integrals. In particular show that if $g(a + 0)$ and $g(b - 0)$ exist and if the modified integral exists, then the corresponding mean integral exists.

7. Let $f(x)$ be of bounded variation, and $g(x)$ be bounded and have only discontinuities of the first kind on $[a, b]$. Does $Y \int_a^b fdg$ exist?

8. Let $g_n(x)$ and $g(x)$ be such that $\int_a^b |dg_n| \leqq M$ for all n and $\lim_n g_n(x) = g(x)$ for all x. Let $f(x)$ be also of bounded variation. Does it follow that $\lim_n \sigma Y \int_a^b fdg_n = \sigma Y \int_a^b fdg$?

20. Stieltjes Integrals on Infinite Intervals

For Stieltjes integrals on $(-\infty, +\infty)$, we can follow the usual procedure and define:

20.1. Definition. If $f(x)$ and $g(x)$ are defined for $-\infty < x < +\infty$, and $\int_a^b fdg$ exists for all a and b, then $\int_{-\infty}^{+\infty} fdg$ is defined as $\lim_{a\to-\infty, b\to+\infty} \int_a^b fdg$ provided this limit exists.

We note that the definition of $\int_{-\infty}^{+\infty} fdg$ involves an iterated limit, viz., $\lim_{a,b} \lim_\sigma \Sigma_{a\sigma}^b f\Delta g$. One might then consider the inverse order. In particular, if a norm integral is involved we start with a subdivision of $(-\infty, +\infty)$ of finite norm and set up $\Sigma_\sigma f(x_i')(g(x_i) - g(x_{i-1}))$. On the infinite interval this is an infinite series. It is then natural to assume that for all σ of finite norm and all choices of x_i' with $x_{i-1} \leqq x_i' \leqq x_i$, the expression $\Sigma_\sigma f(x_i')(g(x_i) - g(x_{i-1})$ is convergent, order being prescribed by $x_{i-1} < x_i$, i ranging over the positive and negative integers. Then $\int_{-\infty}^{+\infty} fdg$ could be defined as

$$\lim_{|\sigma|\to 0} \sum_\sigma f(x_i')(g(x_i) - g(x_{i-1})).$$

Sufficient conditions that the two iterated limits yield the same value can be obtained by applying the iterated limits theorem I.7.4. For instance, it is sufficient to have $\lim_{|\sigma|\to 0} \Sigma_{a\sigma} f\Delta g = \int_a^b fdg$ uniformly relative to a and b. Or to have the infinite series $\Sigma_\sigma f\Delta g$ converge uniformly in σ in the sense that for $e > 0$, there exist a_e and b_e such that if $a < a_e$ and $b > b_e$ then $|\Sigma_{\sigma'} f\Delta g| < e$ for all σ' of finite norm of $(-\infty, a]$ and $[b, +\infty)$. The second of these uniformities occurs if f is bounded and g is of bounded variation on $(-\infty, +\infty)$ in the sense that $\int_a^b |dg|$ is bounded in a and b.

20.2. Definition. If g is of bounded variation on every finite interval then f is said to be *absolutely integrable* on $(-\infty, +\infty)$ if $\int_a^b fdg$ exists for all finite intervals $[a, b]$ and $\int_{-\infty}^{+\infty} |f|\, dv$ exists, where $v(x) = \int_0^x |dg|$. Obviously if f is absolutely integrable on $(-\infty, +\infty)$, then f is integrable, and $|\int_{-\infty}^{+\infty} fdg| \leqq \int_{-\infty}^{+\infty} |f|\, dv$.

Stieltjes integrals with infinite limits play an important role in the theory of integral transforms, such as the La Place transform: $\int_{-\infty}^{+\infty} e^{-zx} dg(x)$; the Fourier transform: $\int_{-\infty}^{+\infty} e^{izx} dg(x)$; the Mellin transform: $\int_0^\infty z^{-x} dg(x)$; and the Stieltjes transform: $\int_{-\infty}^{+\infty} [dg(x)/(z+x)]$. The use of the Stieltjes integral permits simultaneous consideration of distributions such as $\int_{-\infty}^{+\infty} e^{-zx} g(x)dx$ and infinite series such as $\Sigma_n a_n e^{-zx_n} = \Sigma_n a_n b_n^{-z}$ with $b_n = e^{x_n}$.

Theorems concerning Stieltjes integrals with infinite limits can be deduced from the corresponding cases for finite limits by adding additional assumptions. We give two samples:

20.3. Osgood Theorem Generalized. If $g(x)$ is of bounded variation for all finite intervals $[a, b]$; if $f_n(x)$ are uniformly bounded on every $[a, b]$; if $\lim_n f_n(x) = f(x)$ for all x; if $\int_{-\infty}^{+\infty} f_n dg$ exist for all n in such a way that $\lim_{b\to\infty} \int_b^{+\infty} f_n dg = 0$ and $\lim_{a\to-\infty} \int_{-\infty}^{a} f_n dg = 0$ both uniformly as to n; and if $\int_a^b fdg$ exists for all a and b, then $\lim_n \int_{-\infty}^{+\infty} f_n dg$ and $\int_{-\infty}^{+\infty} fdg$ exist and are equal.

For by the Osgood theorem for finite intervals $\lim_n \int_a^b f_n dg = \int_a^b fdg$ for all n. Then by the iterated limits theorem I.7.4, $\lim_n \lim_{a,b} \int_a^b f_n dg = \lim_{a,b} \lim_n \int_a^b f_n dg$, or $\lim_n \int_{-\infty}^{+\infty} f_n dg = \int_{-\infty}^{+\infty} fdg$.

In a similar way we prove:

20.4. If $g_n(x)$ are uniformly of bounded variation on every $[a, b]$; if $\lim_n g_n(x) = g(x)$ for x dense on $-\infty < x < \infty$, and $g(x)$ is of bounded variation on every $[a, b]$; if $f(x)$ is continuous on $-\infty < x < \infty$; and if $\int_{-\infty}^{+\infty} fdg_n$ exist uniformly as to n, then $\lim_n \int_{-\infty}^{+\infty} f_n dg$ and $\int_{-\infty}^{+\infty} fdg$ exist and are equal.

Other theorems such as an iterated integral theorem can be proved from the case for finite limits by adding sufficient conditions for interchange of limits and integrals and iterated limits in general.

The integration by parts theorem in its usual form need not hold. However, the existence of $\int_{-\infty}^{+\infty} fdg$ will carry with it the existence of

$$\lim_{a\to-\infty,\, b\to+\infty} [f(b)g(b) - f(a)g(a) - \int_a^b gdf].$$

Consequently, we can state:

20.5. THEOREM. If $\int_{-\infty}^{+\infty} fdg$ exists, and if $\lim_{a\to-\infty} f(a)g(a)$ and $\lim_{b\to+\infty} f(b)g(b)$ exist, then $\int_{-\infty}^{+\infty} gdf$ exists and $\int_{-\infty}^{+\infty} (fdg + gdf) = \lim_{b\to+\infty} f(b)g(b) - \lim_{a\to-\infty} f(a)g(a)$.

21. A Linear Form on the Infinite Interval

In recent years considerable attention has been paid to linear forms on the class of continuous functions C_0 each of which vanishes outside of some closed bounded interval. This class of functions is obviously linear, and can be normed by defining $||f|| = \text{l.u.b.}_x |f(x)|$, since obviously $f(x)$ is bounded. However, the space is not complete under this norm. For if you set $f_n(x) = (\sin \pi x)/n$ for $n \leqq x \leqq n + 1$ and $-n-1 \leqq x \leqq -n$, and zero elsewhere, then for the sequence $F_m(x) = \Sigma_{n=1}^m f_n(x)$ we will have $\lim_{nm} \| F_n(x) - F_m(x) \| = 0$. But $F_m(x)$ converges in the norm to $\Sigma_{n=1}^\infty f_n(x)$ which is not in C_0.

21.1. Definition. A linear form $L(f)$ on C_0 will be said to be *continuous* if for every sequence $f_n(x)$ such that there exists a finite interval $[a, b]$ independent of n such that $f_n(x)$ vanishes outside of $[a, b]$, and $\lim_n f_n(x) = f(x)$ uniformly on $[a, b]$, then $\lim_n L(f_n) = L(f)$. For such a continuous linear form, the Riesz theorem reads:

21.2. THEOREM. There exists a function $g(x)$ of bounded variation on every finite interval, such that for every f of C_0 we have $L(f) = \int_{-\infty}^{+\infty} fdg$, where $L(f)$ is a linear continuous form on C_0.

By the Riesz theorem for a finite interval, there will exist a function of bounded variation $g_n(x)$ on $[-n, n]$ such that if $f(x)$ is continuous on $[-n, n]$ then $L(f) = \int_{-n}^{n} fdg_n$. This expression will be effective also if $f(x)$ vanishes for $x \leqq -n$ and for $x \geqq n$. Now for every $f(x)$ vanishing for $x \leqq -n + 1$ and for $x \geqq n - 1$, we will have $\int_{-n+1}^{n-1} fdg_{n-1} = \int_{-n+1}^{n-1} fdg_n$. Consequently, $g_n(x) = g_{n-1}(x)$ except for a denumerable set of points on $-n + 1 < x < n - 1$. If we alter $g_n(x)$ to agree with $g_{n-1}(x)$ on $-n + 1 \leqq x \leqq n - 1$, for all n, and set $g(x) = g_n(x)$ for $-n < x < n$, we obtain a function of bounded variation on every finite interval such that $L(f) = \int_{-\infty}^{+\infty} fdg$ for every f vanishing outside of a finite interval. This integral gives then the most general linear continuous form on C_0.

It should be mentioned in passing that if C is the class of bounded continuous functions on $-\infty < x < +\infty$, with $\| f \| = \text{l.u.b.}_x | f(x) |$, then the most general linear continuous form is not usually expressible as a simple Stieltjes integral $\int_{-\infty}^{+\infty} fdg$.

CHAPTER III

INTEGRALS OF RIEMANN TYPE OF FUNCTIONS OF INTERVALS IN TWO OR HIGHER DIMENSION

1. Interval Functions

We consider briefly integrals of interval functions on spaces of dimension greater than one. Their properties parallel in some respects those for the integral in the one-dimensional case. For convenience we shall limit ourselves to the two-dimensional case from which one can usually deduce the situation for the n-dimensional one.

Let J denote the basic rectangle or interval: $a_1 \leqq x_1 \leqq b_1$, $a_2 \leqq x_2 \leqq b_2$ or $[a_1, b_1; a_2, b_2]$. We shall denote by $I = [c_1, d_1; c_2, d_2]$, with $a_1 \leqq c_1 < d_1 \leqq b_1$, $a_2 \leqq c_2 < d_2 \leqq b_2$ any subrectangle or subinterval of J with sides parallel to those of J. A function of intervals $F(I)$ assigns one or more finite real numbers to every interval I of J. We shall not distinguish in this chapter between open and closed intervals, but in general the values of $F(I)$ for any I will depend only on the points interior to or on the boundary of I.

We give some instances of interval functions which to some extent parallel those of the one-dimensional case.

(1) $F(I) = (d_1 - c_1)(d_2 - c_2)$, that is, the area of I.

(2) $F(I) = (f(d_1) - f(c_1))(g(d_2) - g(c_2))$, where $f(x_1)$ and $g(x_2)$ are functions on $[a_1, b_1]$ and $[a_2, b_2]$, respectively.

(3) $F(I) = f(d_1, d_2) - f(c_1, c_2)$, where $f(x_1, x_2)$ is a function on J.

(4) $$F(I) = f(d_1, d_2) - f(c_1, d_2) - f(d_1, c_2) + f(c_1, c_2) = \Delta_{c_1}^{d_1} \Delta_{c_2}^{d_2} f(x_1, x_2),$$

where $f(x_1, x_2)$ is defined on J.

(5) $F(I) =$ l.u.b. $[|f(x_1'', x_2'') - f(x_1', x_2')|$ for all (x_1', x_2') and (x_1'', x_2'') of $I]$, that is, the oscillation $\omega(f; I)$ of the point function f on I.

(6) If $F(I)$ is any interval function on J, then $|F(I)|$ and l.u.b. $[F(I_0)$ for all I_0 in $I]$, or g.l.b. $[F(I_0)$ for all I_0 in $I]$ define additional interval functions. The last two are finite valued only if $F(I)$ is bounded on J.

(7) If $g(x_1, x_2)$ is a point function on J and $F(I)$ an interval function, then $g(x_1', x_2')F(I)$ defines a many-valued interval function, if (x_1', x_2') ranges over I.

1.1. Definition. A *subdivision* σ of an interval I consists of a finite number of intervals having at most edges or vertices in common, whose sum or union is I A subdivision of the fundamental interval J obviously induces a subdivision on any subinterval I. A subdivision will be called a *net* if it is determined by lines completely across I parallel to the coordinate axes, so that a net is determined by subdivision σ_{x_1} and σ_{x_2} of the projections of I on the coordinate axes. We shall denote a net by $\sigma_1 \times \sigma_2$.

1.2. Definition. A function of intervals $F(I)$ is *additive* if it is single-valued, and if for any subdivision σ of an interval I consisting of the intervals $I_1, \ldots, I_n$, we have $F(I) = \Sigma_i F(I_i)$.

To show that a given interval function $F(I)$ is additive it is obviously sufficient to verify additivity on subdivisions of net type since we can superimpose on any subdivision a net by extending the sides of the intervals of σ to the boundary of I, and then reassemble the net divided intervals $I_1, \ldots, I_n$ constituting σ. If $f(x_1, x_2)$ is a point function on J, then $F(I) = \Delta_{c_1}^{d_1} \Delta_{c_2}^{d_2} f = f(d_1, d_2) - f(c_1, d_2) - f(d_1, c_2) + f(c_1, d_1)$ is additive. Conversely, if $F(I)$ is additive, then the point function $f(x_1, x_2) = F[a_1, x_1; a_2, x_2]$ determines $F(I)$ in the sense that $F(I) = \Delta_{c_1}^{d_1} \Delta_{c_2}^{d_2} f(x_1, x_2)$.

1.3. Definition. A single-valued function $F(I)$ is *upper semiadditive*, if for any subdivision $\sigma = I_1, \ldots, I_n$ of any interval I we have $F(I) \leqq \Sigma_i F(I_i)$. The definition for lower semiadditivity reverses the inequality. If $F(I)$ is additive, than $|F(I)|$ is upper semiadditive.

2. Subdivisions

In dealing with Riemann type of integrals on a rectangle J, we note that we have available two types of subdivision: (a) a general subdivision σ, and (b) a net type of subdivisions $\sigma_1 \times \sigma_2$. Subdivisions can be ordered by the condition that $\sigma' \geqq \sigma''$ provided σ' consists of subdivisions of intervals of σ'', or if every interval of σ' is contained in some interval of σ''. Since any subdivision of J induces a subdivision of any interval I of J, it follows that the product of two subdivisions $\sigma' \cdot \sigma''$ is again a subdivision of J such that $\sigma'\sigma'' \geqq \sigma'$ and $\sigma'\sigma'' \geqq \sigma''$. So that subdivisions σ of J form a directed set under this ordering. If we define partial order on nets by the condition that $\sigma_1' \times \sigma_2' \geqq \sigma_1'' \times \sigma_2''$, provided $\sigma_{x_1} \geqq \sigma''_{x_1}$ and $\sigma'_{x_2} \geqq \sigma''_{x_2}$, then nets form a directed subset of subdivisions which is cofinal with the set of all subdivisions, as any subdivision contains the net obtained by extending the edges of all its intervals to the boundary of J. We can also order subdivisions by norm. At least two norms are available (a) if $|I|_A$ is the area of I, then $|\sigma|_A$ is the maximum $|I|_A$ for any I of σ; (b) if $|I|_S =$ maximum side length of I, then $|\sigma|_S$ is the maximum of $|I|_S$ for all I of σ. A limit taken as $|\sigma|_S \to 0$ is weaker than a limit as $|\sigma|_A \to 0$, since any statement true for all σ such that $|\sigma|_A < d$ will be true for all σ such that $|\sigma|_S < \sqrt{d}$. For nets we can take $|\sigma|_A = |\sigma_{x_1}| \cdot |\sigma_{x_2}|$ and $|\sigma|_S$ the greater of $|\sigma_{x_1}|$, $|\sigma_{x_2}|$.

3. Integrals

The interval function $F(I)$ will have a Riemann integral in case the expression $G(\sigma) = \Sigma_i F(I_i)$, where $\sigma = I_1, \ldots, I_n$ is a subdivision (or net) on J, has a limit in σ according to an ordering of σ of the type discussed in the preceding paragraph. In particular, we have the σ-integral, the net σ-integral, the area normed, and the side normed integrals, and the normed net integrals.

If $F(I)$ is an additive function of intervals, then all of these integrals exist and $\int_J F(I) = F(J)$. If $F(I)$ is upper semiadditive (lower semi additive) and if $G(\sigma)$ is bounded above (below) in σ, then $\sigma \int_J F(I)$ exists and agrees with the least upper bound (greatest lower bound) of $G(\sigma)$ as to σ. In this case it is sufficient to limit one's self to subdivisions of the net type.

Since the net subdivisions are cofinal with the general subdivisions, if an integral exists for general subdivisions, it also exists in the same sense if one limits one's self to nets, and yields the same value. However, the net integral $\sigma_1 \times \sigma_2 \int_J F(I)$ can exist without having the $\sigma \int_J F(I)$ exist. For example if $J = [0, 1; -1, 1]$ and for $I = [c_1, d_1; c_2, d_2]$ we define $F(I) = d_2 - c_2$ if $0 \leqq c_2 < d_2$; $= d_2 + c_2$ if $c_2 < 0 < d_2$ and $= c_2 - d_2$ if $c_2 < d_2 \leqq 0$. Then $\sigma_1 \times \sigma_2 \int_J F(I)$ exists and has value

0. But $\sigma \int_J F(I)$ does not exist, since by proper choice of σ any value can be approached by the approximating sums.

Unless otherwise indicated, we shall limit ourselves to integrals based on general sudivisions, and for the norm integral take as norm $|\sigma|_S$ the maximum side length of intervals of the subdivision.

Since any of the definitions of integrals depend on directed sets, the corresponding Cauchy conditions of convergence are applicable. For the integrals we are considering, the following theorem can be proved along the lines of II.3.6 for the space of one dimension:

3.1. THEOREM. A necessary and sufficient condition that the σ or norm integral exist is that $\int_J \omega(SF;\, I) = 0$ for the corresponding integral. Here $\omega(SF; I) = \text{l.u.b.}\ [|\Sigma_{\sigma_1} F - \Sigma_{\sigma_2} F|$ for all σ_1 and σ_2 of $I]$.

This theorem is not valid for net-convergence, as the example cited above shows. For if I is any interval entirely in $[0, 1; 0, 1]$ or entirely in $[0, 1; -1, 0]$, then $\omega(SF;\, I) = \infty$.

If the norm integral exists, so does the σ-integral. In one dimension, the condition to be added to the existence of the σ-integral in order to obtain the existence of the norm-integral was the pseudoadditive property at each point of J. Since in two dimensions, the boundaries of intervals I are lines and points, pseudoadditivity at points is not sufficient. We suggest the following more complicated notion:

3.2. Definition. $F(I)$ will be said to be *pseudoadditive* along a line l in J parallel to a coordinate axis, if for every $e > 0$, there exists a d_e such that if a finite number of nonoverlapping intervals $I_1, \ldots, I_n$ with $|I_i|_S < d_e$ are cut by the line l into intervals $I_1', I_1'', \ldots, I_n', I_n''$, respectively, then $|\Sigma_i F(I_i) - \Sigma_i (F(I_i') + F(I_i''))| < e$.

It is obvious that if $N \int_J F(I)$ exists, then $F(I)$ is pseudoadditive for all lines l parallel to the axes. We need only apply the Cauchy condition of convergence to a comparison of the subdivision σ' obtained from σ by replacing I_i by I_i' and I_i'' for $i = 1, \ldots, n$. Conversely, if $\sigma \int_J F(I)$ exists and $F(I)$ is pseudoadditive along all lines l of J parallel to an axis, then the norm integral $N \int_J F(I)$ exists and is equal to $\sigma \int_J F(I)$. The proof follows the procedure in one dimension, in that we determine a σ_e such that $\sigma \geqq \sigma_e$ implies $|\Sigma_\sigma F(I) - \sigma \int_J F(I)| < e$. We then determine d_e so that $|\sigma| < d_e$ implies that $|\Sigma_\sigma F(I) - \Sigma_{\sigma\sigma_e} F(I)| < e$, by using the pseudoadditive condition along the finite number of sides of intervals of σ_e. Combining statements gives: if $|\sigma| < d_e$, then $|\Sigma_\sigma F(I) - \sigma \int_J F(I)| < 2e$.

3.3. If $\int_J F(I)$ exists and I is contained in J then $\int_I F(I)$ exists in the same sense, so that $G(I) = \int_I F(I)$ defines an interval function on J, which turns out to be additive.

This follows in the usual way from the Cauchy condition of convergence by comparing the sums for subdivisions which vary only on I and remain the same on the complement of I relative to J. The theorem does not hold if convergence is only on nets as the above example shows. Here $\int_J F(I) = 0$. However if $I = [0, 1; 0, 1]$, then $\int_I F(I) = \infty$. The difficulty is traceable to the fact that in net subdivisions an alteration of the subdivision on I affects also the division of the complement of I.

The additivity of the function $\int_I F(I)$ follows in the usual way. The converse to additivity reads:

3.4. If $I_1, \ldots, I_n$ is a subdivision of J and $\sigma \int_{I_i} F(I)$ exist for $i = 1, \ldots, n$, then $\sigma \int_J F(I)$ exists and $\sigma \int_J F(I) = \Sigma_i \sigma \int_{I_i} F(I)$. For norm integrals, the condition that $F(I)$ be pseudoadditive along the sides of all I_i must be added.

In two dimensions we have:

3.5. Approximation Theorem. If $\sigma = I_1, \ldots, I_n$ is any subdivision of J and $\int_J F(I)$ exists, exists, then $| \int_J F(I) - \Sigma_\sigma F(I) | \leqq \Sigma_\sigma \omega(SF; I)$.

This leads at once to:

3.6. If $N \int_J F(I)$ exists, then $\lim_{|I| \to 0} | N \int_I F(I) - F(I) | = 0$. In particular, if I converges to the point $P = (x_1, x_2)$, then the convergence is uniform in (x_1, x_2) on J. If $\sigma \int_J F(I)$ exists then

$$\lim_{|I| \to 0;\ I \to P} | \sigma \int_I F(I) - F(I) | = 0 ,$$

if P is the same oriented vertex (lower right hand, upper right hand, etc.) for the intervals involved.

Because of the validity of the approximation theorem the following substitution theorem is available:

3.7. THEOREM. If $F(I)$ is an interval function such that $\int_J F(I)$ exists giving rise to the interval function $G(I) = \int_I F(I)$; if $h(x_1, x_2)$ is a bounded point function on J and $H(I) = h(x_1', x_2')G(I)$, (x_1', x_2') any point in I, then $\int_J H(I) = \int_J h(x_1, x_2)G(I)$ exists if and only if $\int_J h(x_1, x_2)F(I)$ exists and the two integrals are equal.

It is understood that in this theorem, the same convergence process using general subdivisions is used throughout. For $h(x_1, x_2) \equiv 1$ on J, this theorem asserts in effect the differential equivalence of the additive interval function $G(I)$ with that of $F(I)$.

Linearity and convergence properties of integrals of interval functions in two dimensions carry over without difficulty from the one-dimensional case.

4. Functions of Bounded Variation in Two Dimensions

4.1. Definition. In passing from functions of one variable to functions of two or more variables, that is, $f(x_1, x_2)$ defined on the rectangle or interval $J = [a_1, b_1; a_2, b_2]$, the choice of the interval function and its use in defining a function of bounded variation has taken different forms, depending on the objective of the investigator. If I is the rectangle $[c_1, d_1; c_2\ d_2]$, then a possible $F(I)$ is $|f(d_1, d_2) - f(c_1, c_2)| = |\Delta_{12} f|$, a first order difference. Closely associated with this is the oscillation function of f on the interval I:

$$\omega(f;I) = \text{l.u.b.}\ [|f(x_1', x_2') - f(x_1'', x_2'')| \text{ for } (x_1', x_2') \text{ and } (x_1'', x_2'') \text{ on } I].$$

A second possibility is the double difference which involves all four vertices of I, namely, $F(I) = |f(d_1, d_2) - f(c_1, d_2) - f(d_1, c_2) + f(c_1, c_2)| = |\Delta_1\Delta_2 f(I)| = |\Delta_2\Delta_1 f(I)|$. Since this second expression is more closely related to integration in two variables, we shall limit our discussion to bounded variation based on this interval or difference function. Bounded variation based on the interval function $\Delta_1\Delta_2 f(I)$ is due to Vitali, whose definition was later modified by Hardy and Krause. A full discussion of the interrelations between a variety of definitions of functions of bounded variation in two variables together with references will be found in the paper by J.A. Clarkson and C.R. Adams: On the definitions of bounded variation for functions of two variables, *Trans. Am. Math. Soc.* 35 (1933) 824-854.

4.2. Definition. The function $f(x_1, x_2)$ on the rectangle J:$[a_1, b_1; a_2, b_2]$ is of *bounded variation* on J if $\Sigma_\sigma F(I) = \Sigma_\sigma |\Delta_1\Delta_2 f(I)|$ is bounded as to subdivisions σ of J, where if $I = [c_1, d_1; c_2, d_2]$, then

$$F(I) = |\Delta_1\Delta_2 f(I)| = |f(d_1, d_2) - f(c_1, d_2) - f(d_1, c_2) + f(c_1, c_2)|.$$

Since the interval function $\Delta_1\Delta_2 f(I)$ is additive, the interval function $F(I) = | \Delta_1\Delta_2 f(I) |$ is upper semiadditive on J. Then $f(x_1, x_2)$ is of bounded variation on J if and only if $\sigma \int_J F(I) = \sigma \int_J | d_1 d_2 f |$ exists. Moreover, since the net subdivisions $\sigma_1 \times \sigma_2$ are cofinal with σ, it is sufficient to know that $\Sigma_\sigma F(I)$ is bounded on nets $\sigma_1 \times \sigma_2$. The total variation of f on J is expressible as

$$\lim_{\sigma_1 \sigma_2} \sum_{\sigma_1 \sigma_2} | \Delta_1\Delta_2 f(I) | = \sigma_1 \times \sigma_2 \int_J | d_1 d_2 f | .$$

We shall write $V(J) = \int_J | d_1 d_2 f |$.

From the properties of integrals we deduce that if $\int_J | d_1 d_2 f |$ exists, then for any I contained in J $\int_I | d_1 d_2 f | = V(I)$ exists. Further, $V(I)$ is an additive function of intervals, positive or zero for all I so that $V(I_1) \leqq V(I_2)$ for I_1 in I_2. As a consequence, $V(I)$ generates and is generated by the point function $v(x_1, x_2) = V[a_1, x_1; a_2, x_2]$.

If $f(x_1, x_2) = g(x_1) + h(x_2)$, then $\int_J | d_1 d_2 f | = \int_I | d_1 d_2 f | = 0$ for all I. Conversely, if $\int_J | d_1 d_2 f | = 0$, then $F(I) = | \Delta_1\Delta_2 f(I) | \leqq \int_I | d_1 d_2 f | = 0$ for all I, so that $f(x_1, x_2) = f(x_1, a_2) + f(a_1, x_2) - f(a_1, a_2)$, or $f(x_1, x_2)$ is the sum of a function of x_1 alone and a function of x_2 alone. This combination of functions replaces the constant function for functions of bounded variation in one variable. Because of the linearity of the operator $\Delta_1\Delta_2$, the addition of such a function to any function of two variables does not affect the bounded variation property of the function.

If $f(x_1, x_2) = g(x_1)h(x_2)$, then $\Delta_1\Delta_2 f = \Delta_1 g \Delta_2 h$, so that f is of bounded variation on J for nonconstant functions f and g if and only if $g(x_1)$ is of bounded variation in x_1 and $h(x_2)$ is of bounded variation in x_2, and then

$$\int_J | d_1 d_2 f | = \int_{a_1}^{b_1} | dg | \int_{a_2}^{b_2} | dh | .$$

If $\Delta_1\Delta_2 f(I) \geqq 0$ for all I, then $F(I) = | \Delta_1\Delta_2 f |$ is additive so that $\int_I F(I) = F(I)$. The functions $f(x_1, x_2)$ such that $f(x_1, a_2) = f(a_1, x_2) = 0$ and for which $\Delta_1\Delta_2 f(I) \geqq 0$ for every I have the additional property that $f(x_1, x_2)$ is monotone in x_1 for each x_2 and monotone in x_2 for each x_1. For

$$\begin{aligned} \Delta_{x_1'}^{x_1''} \Delta_{a_2}^{x_2} f &= f(x_1'', x_2) - f(x_1', x_2) - f(x_1', a_2) + f(x_1', a_2) \\ &= f(x_1'', x_2) - f(x_1', x_2) \end{aligned}$$

which is $\geqq 0$ for $x_1' < x_1''$. In the same way it can be shown that

$f(x_1, x_2'') - f(x_1, x_2')$ is positive or zero if $x_2' < x_2''$, and so $f(x_1, x_2)$ is monotone in x_2 for each x_1. The same monotone properties can be shown to hold if the vanishing of f for $x_1 = a_1$ and for $x_2 = a_2$ are replaced by the conditions that $f(a_1, x_2)$ and $f(x_1, a_2)$ are monotone nondecreasing in x_2 and x_1, respectively.

4.3. Definition. We shall call a function $f(x_1, x_2)$ *positively monotonely monotone if* $\Delta_1\Delta_2 f(I) \geqq 0$ for all I, and $f(x_1, a_2)$ and $f(a_1, x_2)$ are monotonic nondecreasing in x_1 and x_2, respectively.

The function $v\ (x_1, x_2)$ is positively monotonely monotone. Moreover, since $V(I) \pm \Delta_1\Delta_2 f(I) = \int_I | d_1 d_2 f | \pm \Delta_1\Delta_2 f(I) \geqq 0$ for all I and are additive functions of intervals, it follows that the interval functions $P(I) = \frac{1}{2}\,(V(I) + \Delta_1\Delta_2 f(I))$ and $N(I) = \frac{1}{2}\,(V(I) - \Delta_1\Delta_2 f(I))$ are additive and positive for all I, and consequently give rise to the two positively monotonely monotone functions:

$$p(x_1, x_2) = \tfrac{1}{2}\,[v(x_1, x_2) + (f(x_1, x_2) - f(a_1, x_2) - f(x_1, a_2) + f(a_1, a_2))]$$

$$n(x_1, x_2) = \tfrac{1}{2}\,[v(x_1, x_2) - (f(x_1, x_2) - f(a_1, x_2) - f(x_1, a_2) + f(a_1, a_2))].$$

4.4. THEOREM. The functions $p(x_1, x_2)$ and $n(x_1, x_2)$ effect a Jordan decomposition of the function $f(x_1, x_2) - f(x_1, a_2) - f(a_1, x_2) + f(a_1, a_2)$, as do $P(I)$ and $N(I)$ for $G(I) = \Delta_1\Delta_2 f(I)$.

We can duplicate some of the statements for functions of bounded variation in one variable; in particular,

4.5. $P(J)$ is equal to the l.u.b. as to σ of $\Sigma\, \Delta_1\Delta_2 f(I)$, the summation being extended over all intervals of σ for which $\Delta_1\Delta_2 f(I) \geqq 0$, while $N(J)$ is equal to the l.u.b. as to σ of $-\,\Sigma\, \Delta_1\Delta_2 f(I)$, the summation being extended over all intervals of σ for which $\Delta_1\Delta_2 f(I) \leqq 0$.

4.6. $P(J)$ is equal to the l.u.b. as to π of $\Sigma_\pi \Delta_1\Delta_2 f(I)$ for all π of J, where $\pi = I_1, \ldots, I_n$ is any finite set of nonoverlapping intervals of J, while $N(J)$ is the negative of the g.l.b. of $\Sigma_\pi \Delta_1\Delta_2 f(I)$ for all π of J.

4.7. If $f(x_1, x_2) - f(x_1, a_2) - f(a_1, x_2) + f(a_1, a_2) = p'(x_1, x_2) - n'(x_1, x_2)$ where $p'(x_1, x_2)$ and $n'(x_1, x_2)$ are positively monotonely monotone, vanishing on $x_1 = a_1$ and $x_2 = a_2$, then $\Delta_1\Delta_2(p' - p) \geqq 0$ and $\Delta_1\Delta_2(n' - n) \geqq 0$, that is $p(x_1, x_2)$ and $n(x_1, x_2)$ are minimal for functions having the properties of $p'(x_1, x_2)$ and $n'(x_1, x_2)$.

The Jordan decomposition and the monotone properties of $p(x_1, x_2)$ and $n(x_1, x_2)$ give us:

4.8. THEOREM. If $f(x_1, x_2)$ is of bounded variation on J and $f(x_1, a_2)$ and $f(a_1, x_2)$ are of bounded variation in x_1 and x_2, respectively, then $f(x_1, x_2)$ is of bounded variation in x_1 for each x_2 and in x_2 for each x_1.

5. Continuity Properties

We consider first, the continuity properties of the interval functions $F(I)$ defined on J, additive on intervals, with $F(I) \geqq 0$ for all I. Then if I_1 contains I_2, we have $F(I_1) \geqq F(I_2)$. Consequently if we have a monotone sequence of intervals I_n such that I_n contains I_{n+1}, with $\lim_n I_n = I$, then $\lim_n F(I_n)$ exists. In particular, if I reduces to a single point, $\lim_n F(I_n)$ exists. As a matter of fact, if we direct the intervals containing a fixed point (x_1, x_2) by inclusion, then $\lim_I F(I)$ exists and is equal to the g.l.b. of $F(I)$ for all I containing (x_1, x_2). Because of the additive and positive property of $F(I)$, for any fixed $e > 0$, the number of points (x_1, x_2) such that $\lim_{I \to (x_1, x_2)} F(I) > e$, is finite. If we take $e = 1/n$, we can conclude:

5.1. THEOREM. If $F(I)$ is a positive valued additive function of intervals on J, then the set of points such that $\lim_{I \to (x_1, x_2)} F(I) > 0$ is denumerable.

The conclusion of this theorem can also be stated that $F(I)$ is continuous as a function of I except at a denumerable set of points provided we define continuity of $F(I)$ at a point (x_1, x_2) by the condition $\lim_{I \to (x_1, x_2)} F(I) = 0$, intervals being directed by inclusion.

In the preceding considerations, we can assume that the point (x_1, x_2) is on the boundary of intervals I, in particular, it can be fixed as the lower left-hand corner (or any of the other three corners) of all I involved. If we consider the point function $f(x_1, x_2) = F[a_1, x_1; a_2, x_2]$ generated by such an $F(I)$ and if I is the interval $[x_1, x_1'; x_2, x_2']$ with $x_1' > x_1$ and $x_2' > x_2$, then

$$F(I) = f(x_1', x_2') - f(x_1, x_2') - f(x_1', x_2) + f(x_1, x_2),$$

and

$$\lim_{(x_1', x_2') \to (x_1+0, x_2+0)} F(I)$$

will exist. Since $f(x_1, x_2)$ is monotonely monotone, it follows that $f(x_1, x_2 + 0)$ and $f(x_1 + 0, x_2)$ exist for each x_1 and x_2, respectively. Consequently,

$$\lim_{(x_1', x_2') \to (x_1+0, x_2+0)} f(x_1', x_2')$$

will exist also. Similarly the other three quadrantal limits at $(x_1 - 0, x_2 + 0)$, $(x_1 + 0, x_2 - 0)$, and $(x_1 - 0, x_2 - 0)$ exist also. We can consequently state:

5.2. THEOREM. If $f(x_1, x_2)$ is positively monotonely monotone on J, then for each (x_1, x_2) of J, the four quadrantal limits: $f(x_1 + 0, x_2 + 0)$, $f(x_1 - 0, x_2 + 0)$, $f(x_1 + 0, x_2 - 0)$, and $f(x_1 - 0, x_2 - 0)$ exist.

For any positively monotonely monotone function gives rise to a positive additive interval function. This result can easily be extended to functions of bounded variation in the form:

5.3. THEOREM. If $f(x_1, x_2)$ is of bounded variation on J and $f(x_1, a_2)$ and $f(a_1, x_2)$ are of bounded variation in x_1 and x_2, respectively, then the four quadrantal limits of f at $(x_1 + 0, x_2 + 0)$, $(x_1 - 0, x_2 + 0)$, $(x_1 + 0, x_2 - 0)$ and $(x_1 - 0, x_2 - 0)$ exist at each point (x_1, x_2) of J.

It is to be noted that we assume that $(x_1', x_2') \to (x_1 + 0, x_2 + 0)$ includes the conditions $x_1' > x_1$ and $x_2' > x_2$ and similarly for the other three limits.

By way of proof, we need only apply the preceding theorem to the Jordan decomposition of $f(x_1, x_2)$, which gives us two monotonely monotone functions $p(x_1, x_2)$ and $n(x_1, x_2)$, such that

$$f(x_1, x_2) - f(x_1, a_2) - f(a_1, x_2) + f(a_1, a_2) = p(x_1, x_2) - n(x_1, x_2).$$

A consequence of this theorem is:

5.4. THEOREM. If $f(x_1, x_2)$ is of bounded variation on J, $f(x_1, a_2)$ and $f(a_1, x_2)$ of bounded variation in x_1 and x_2, respectively, then the set of discontinuities of $f(x_1, x_2)$ lie on a denumerable set of lines parallel to the coordinate axes.

Since $f(x_1, x_2)$ has double limits at every point of J if approach is limited to quadrants, it follows from the Cauchy condition of convergence that for each (x_1, x_2) of J and for a given $e > 0$, there exists a circle with (x_1, x_2) as center, such that if (x_1', x_2') is interior to this circle but not on the lines through (x_1, x_2) parallel to the coordinate axes, then $\omega(f; (x_1', x_2')) < e$, where $\omega(f; (x_1', x_2'))$ is the usual oscillation of f at (x_1', x_2'). By the Borel theorem, a finite number of these circles cover J. If the centers of these covering circles are the points $(x_1^{(k)}, x_2^{(k)})$, $k = 1, \ldots, n$, it follows that if (x_1', x_2') is not on the lines $x_1 = x_1^{(k)}$ or $x_2 = x_2^{(k)}$ for any k, then $\omega(f; (x_1', x_2') < e$, so that the points of J for which $\omega(f; (x_1, x_2)) \geqq e$ lie on the finite number of lines $x_1 = x_1^{(k)}$, $x_2 = x_2^{(k)}$, $k = 1, ..., n$. By setting $e = 1/m$, we obtain a method for counting the lines on which the discontinuities of $f(x_1, x_2)$ lie.

5.5. THEOREM. If $f(x_1, x_2)$ is of bounded variation on J, and $f(x_1, a_2)$ and $f(a_1, x_2)$ are of bounded variation in x_1 and x_2, respectively, and if $f(x_1, x_2)$ is continuous in x_2 for each x_1, then $f(x_1 + 0, x_2)$ and $f(x_1 - 0, x_2)$ are continuous in x_2 for each x_1.

Under the hypothesis of our theorem, $f(x_1, x_2)$ is of bounded variation in x_1 for each x_2 and in x_2 for each x_1, so that $f(x_1 + 0, x_2)$ and $f(x_1 - 0, x_2)$ exist for each x_2. Further, by Theorem III.5.3

$$\lim_{(x_1', x_2') \to (x_1+0, x_2+0)} f(x_1', x_2')$$

exists as a double limit. Because of the bounded variation properties of $f(x_1, x_2)$,

$$\lim_{x_1' \to x_1+0} f(x_1', x_2') \quad \text{and} \quad \lim_{x_2' \to x_2+0} f(x_1', x_2')$$

exist for all x_2' and x_1', respectively. Then by I.7.2 the iterated limits

$$\lim_{x_2' \to x_2'+0} \lim_{x_1' \to x_1'+0} f(x_1', x_2') \quad \text{and} \quad \lim_{x_1' \to x_1+0} \lim_{x_2' \to x_2+0} f(x_1', x_2')$$

both exist and are equal to the double limit. Because of the continuity of $f(x_1, x_2)$ in x_2, this tells us that

$$\lim_{x_2' \to x_2+0} f(x_1 + 0, x_2') = f(x_1 + 0, x_2),$$

that is, $f(x_1 + 0, x_2)$ is continuous on the right at x_2. The left-hand continuity at x_2, as well as the continuity of $f(x_1 - 0, x_2)$ in x_2 follow in a similar way.

5.6. THEOREM. If $f(x_1, x_2)$ is monotonely monotone with $f(a_1, x_2) = f(x_1, a_2) = 0$ and $\Delta_1\Delta_2 f(I) \geqq 0$ for all I, and if $f(x_1, x_2)$ is continuous in x_1 for each x_2 and in x_2 for each x_1, then $f(x_1, x_2)$ is continuous on J.

For then

$$\lim_{x'_1 \to x_1+0} \lim_{x'_2 \to x_2+0} f(x_1', x_2') = \lim_{x'_2 \to x_2+0} \lim_{x'_1 \to x_1+0} f(x_1', x_2') = f(x_1, x_2).$$

Since $f(x_1, x_2)$ is monotonic nondecreasing in x_1 for each x_2, it follows from I.7.8 that the double limit

$$\lim_{(x'_1, x'_2) \to (x_1+0, x_2+0)} f(x_1', x_2')$$

exists and is also equal to $f(x_1, x_2)$. The same procedure gives the same value for the other quadrantal limits. Because $f(x_1, x_2)$ is continuous along lines parallel to the coordinate axes, we can conclude from this that for the double limit we have

$$\lim_{(x'_1, x'_2) \to (x_1, x_2)} f(x_1', x_2') = f(x_1, x_2)$$

or f is continuous at (x_1, x_2).

For functions of bounded variation in one variable, we have a decomposition of the function into a continuous and a purely discontinuous part, the latter a sum of an absolutely and uniformly convergent sequence of simple break functions. For two variables, we consider first the case where $f(x_1, x_2)$ is positively monotonely monotone with $f(a_1, x_2) = f(x_1, a_2) = 0$. Then for each x_1 and fixed x_2, $f(x_1, x_2 - 0)$ and $f(x_1, x_2 + 0)$ exist so that we have the breaks $f(x_1, x_2) - f(x_1, x_2 - 0)$ and $f(x_1, x_2 + 0) - f(x_1, x_2 - 0)$. These will be monotonic nondecreasing functions in x_1. These suggest the simple break function

$$\begin{aligned} \beta(x_1, x_2; x_2'; g(x_1), h(x_1)) &= 0 \text{ for } x_2 < x_2' \\ &= g(x_1) \text{ for } x_2 = x_2' \\ &= h(x_1) \text{ for } x_2 > x_2'. \end{aligned}$$

Then the function

$$f(x_1, x_2) - \beta(x_1, x_2; x_2'; f(x_1, x_2') - f(x_1, x_2' - 0), \\ f(x_1, x_2' - 0) - f(x_1, x_2' + 0))$$

will be continuous at x_2', for every x_1. If $x_2 = x_2^{(n)}$ are the lines of discontinuity of f parallel to the x_1-axis, it follows as in the case of one variable that

$$f(x_1, x_2) - \sum_n \beta(x_1, x_2; x_2^{(n)}; f(x_1, x_2^{(n)}) - f(x_1, x_2^{(n)} - 0), \\ f(x_1, x_2^{(n)} + 0) - f(x_1, x_2^{(n)} - 0))$$

is continuous in x_2 for each x_1. The infinite series can be replaced by the single function

$$f_b(x_1, x_2) = \sum_{a_2 \leqq y_2 < x_2} (f(x_1, y_2 + 0) - f(x_1, y_2 - 0)) + f(x_1, x_2) - f(x_1, x_2 - 0).$$

Then if $f(x_1, x_2) = f_c(x_1, x_2) + f_b(x_1, x_2)$, $f_c(x_1, x_2)$ is continuous in x_2 for each x_1. It is possible to treat $f_c(x_1, x_2)$ relative to x_1 as we have $f(x_1, x_2)$ and write $f_c(x_1, x_2) = f_{cc}(x_1, x_2) + f_{bc}(x_1, x_2)$ where

$$f_{bc}(x_1, x_2) = \sum_{a_1 \leqq y_1 < x_1} (f_c(y_1 + 0, x_2) - f_c(y_1 - 0, x_2)) + f_c(x_1, x_2) - f_c(x_1 - 0, x_2)$$

so that $f_{cc}(x_1, x_2)$ is continuous in x_1 for each x_2. As a matter of fact, $f_{cc}(x_1, x_2)$ is also continuous in x_2 for each x_1. For as shown above in III.5.5, since $f_c(x_1, x_2)$ is continuous in x_2 for each x_1, $f_c(x_1 + 0, x_2) - f_c(x_1 - 0, x_2)$ and $f_c(x_1, x_2) - f(x_1 - 0, x_2)$ are continuous in x_2. Moreover, the series of positive monotone (in x_2) functions $\Sigma_{y_1}[f_c(y_1 + 0, x_2) - f_c(y_1 - 0, x_2)]$ is term by term less than the absolutely convergent series $\Sigma_{y_1}[f_c(y_1 + 0, b_2) - f_c(y_1 - 0, b_2)]$ and is consequently uniformly convergent in x_2. Then $f_{bc}(x_1, x_2)$ is continuous in x_2 for each x_1, and the same thing holds for $f_{cc}(x_1, x_2)$ as the difference of two continuous functions. Now $f_{cc}(x_1, x_2)$ is obviously a monotonely monotone function with $f_{cc}(x_1, a_2) = f_{cc}(a_1, x_2) = 0$, and is continuous in x_1 for each x_2 and in x_2 for each x_1. Consequently, by III.5.6, $f_{cc}(x_1, x_2)$ is continuous in (x_1, x_2) on J. We can then state:

5.7. THEOREM. If $f(x_1, x_2)$ is positively monotonely monotone on J with $f(a_1, x_2) = f(x_1, a_2) = 0$, then $f(x_1, x_2) = f_{cc}(x_1, x_2) + f_{bx_1}(x_1, x_2) + f_{bx_2}(x_1, x_2)$, where $f_{cc}(x_1, x_2)$ is continuous in (x_1, x_2), $f_{bx_1}(x_1, x_2)$ is the sum of a uniformly convergent sequence of break functions having breaks along the lines $x_1 = x_1^{(n)}$, and $f_{bx_2}(x_1, x_2)$ is a similar function with breaks along the lines $x_2 = x_2^{(n)}$, the lines of discontinuity of f.

From the Jordan decomposition of a function of bounded variation it now follows:

5.8. THEOREM. If $f(x_1, x_2)$ is of bounded variation on J, $f(a_1, x_2)$ and $f(x_1, a_2)$ are of bounded variation in x_2 and x_1, respectively, then

$f(x_1, x_2)$ can be decomposed into the sum of a continuous function and break functions of the kind described in Theorem III.5.7.

With respect to the continuity of the total variation function $v(x_1, x_2)$ of a continuous function of bounded variation $f(x_1, x_2)$ we have:

5.9. THEOREM. If $f(x_1, x_2)$ is of bounded variation and continuous in (x_1, x_2) on J, then the variation function $v(x_1, x_2) = V[a_1, x_1; a_2, x_2]$ is also continuous.

The continuity of $f(x_1, x_2)$ yields that $\lim_{|I|\to 0} V(I) = 0$, where $|I|$ is the maximum side length of I, since $\lim_{|I|\to 0} [V(I) - |\Delta_1\Delta_2 f(I)|] = 0$. This does not seem to be sufficient to prove that $v(x_1, x_2)$ is continuous. We use the Jordan decomposition of $f(x_1, x_2)$:

$$f(x_1, x_2) - f(x_1, a_2) - f(a_1, x_2) + f(a_1, a_2) = p(x_1, x_2) - n(x_1, x_2),$$
$$v(x_1, x_2) = p(x_1, x_2) + n(x_1, x_2).$$

If $v(x_1, x_2)$ is discontinuous, then since the right-hand side of the first equality is continuous, $p(x_1, x_2)$ and $n(x_1, x_2)$ are discontinuous at the same points and the discontinuities would cancel out in the difference $p(x_1, x_2) - n(x_1, x_2)$. But by virtue of the decomposition of p and n into their continuous and discontinuous portions, this would permit diminishing both p and n by a positively monotonely monotone function, which would contradict the minimal character of p and n. Then $p(x_1, x_2)$ and $n(x_1, x_2)$ and consequently $v(x_1, x_2)$ are continuous if $f(x_1, x_2)$ is.

6. The Space of Functions of Bounded Variation in Two Variables: BV2

The following statements are obvious or can be proved as in the one-dimensional case:

6.1. The space $BV2$ is linear, with $\int_J |cd_1d_2f| = |c| \int_J |d_1d_2f|$ and $\int_J |d_1d_2(f_1 + f_2)| \leqq \int_J |d_1d_2f_1| + \int_J |d_1d_2f_2|$.

6.2. The space $BV2$ is a lattice if partial order $f_1(\geqq)f_2$ is defined by the condition $\Delta_1\Delta_2(f_1 - f_2)(I) \geqq 0$ for all I, or if $f_1 = f_2 + p$, where $\Delta_1\Delta_2 p(I) \geqq 0$ for all I.

6.3. The subspace of functions of $BV2$ for which $f(a_1, x_2)$ and $f(x_1, a_2)$ are of bounded variation in x_2 and x_1, respectively, is also a linear space and can be normed by setting

$$\| f \| = | f(a_1, a_2) | + \int_{a_1}^{b_1} | d_1 f(x_1, a_2) | + \int_{a_2}^{b_2} | d_2 f(a_1, x_2) | + \int_J | d_1 d_2 f |.$$

$\mathrm{Lim}_n \| f_n \| = 0$ implies that $\lim_n f(x_1, x_2) = 0$ uniformly on J, $\lim_n \int_{a_1}^{x_1} | d_1 f_n(x_1, a_2) | = 0$ uniformly in x_1, $\lim_n \int_{a_2}^{x_2} | d_2 f_n(a_1, x_2) | = 0$ uniformly in x_2, and $\lim_n \int_{(a_1, a_2)}^{(x_1, x_2)} | d_1 d_2 f_n | = 0$ uniformly in (x_1, x_2) on J. But these conditions are not sufficient to yield $\lim_n \| f_n \| = 0$.

6.4. If $f_n(x_1, x_2)$ are in $BV2$ and $\lim_n f_n(x_1, x_2) = f(x_1, x_2)$ on J, then $\int_J | d_1 d_2 f | \leqq \underline{\lim}_n \int_J | d_1 d_2 f_n |$.

This follows from the upper semiadditive property of the interval function $F(I) = | \Delta_1 \Delta_2 f(I) |$ and an extension of II.5.4. In particular, if the functions f_n are uniformly of bounded variation in the sense that $\int_J | d_1 d_2 f_n | \leqq M$ for all n, then f is also in $BV2$.

6.5. Helly Theorem. If $f_n(x_1, x_2)$ is a sequence of functions in $BV2$, such that for some M, $\int_J | d_1 d_2 f_n | \leqq M$, $\int_{a_1}^{b_1} | d_1 f_n(x_1, a_2) | \leqq M$, $\int_{a_2}^{b_2} | d_2 f_n(a_1, x_2) | \leqq M$ and $| f_n(a_1, a_2) | \leqq M$, for all n, then we can find a subsequence f_{n_m} of f_n such that $\lim_m f_{n_m}(x_1, x_2)$ exists for all (x_1, x_2), and the variations of the limit function will satisfy the same inequalities as those for the variations of f_n.

The proof of this follows in the footsteps of the theorem for functions of bounded variation in one variable. It is proved first for a bounded sequence of monotonely monotone functions $f_n(x_1, x_2)$ with $f_n(x_1, a_2) = f_n(a_1, x_2) = 0$ and $\Delta_1 \Delta_2 f_n(I) \geqq 0$ for all n and I. By selecting a sequence of points P_k dense in J, one determines a subsequence f_{n_m} which converges at the points P_k. This determines a function f at points P_k subject to the condition $f(x_1, a_2) = f(a_1, x_2) = 0$ and $\Delta_1 \Delta_2 f \geqq 0$, the latter inequality limited to intervals all of whose vertices are points of P_k. The four quadrantal limits (x_1', x_2') approaching $(x_1 + 0, x_2 + 0)$, $(x_1 - 0, x_2 + 0)$, $(x_1 + 0, x_2 - 0)$, $(x_1 - 0, x_2 - 0)$ where (x_1', x_2') are limited to points of P_k, will exist at all points of J, and be equal except on a denumerable set of lines parallel to the coordinate axes defining a function $f(x_1, x_2)$ at such points. It turns out that $\lim_m f_{n_m}(x_1, x_2) = f(x_1, x_2)$ at all such points. The application of the Helly theorem in one variable to the lines of discontinuity of $f(x_1, x_2)$ produces a subsequence of f_{n_m} which converges for all points of J. The Jordan decomposition theorem together with the Helly theorem in one variable then yield the Helly theorem in two variables as stated.

EXERCISES

1. Show that the function $f(x_1, x_2) = 0$ for $0 \leqq x_1 \leqq x_2 \leqq 1$ and $= 1$ for $0 \leqq x_2 < x_1 \leqq 1$, is not of bounded variation on $[0, 1; 0, 1]$.

2. What theorems for functions of bounded variations in two variables (suitably modified) carry over to functions of bounded variation in three variables based on the interval function $F(I) = | \Delta_1\Delta_2\Delta_3 f|$, f being defined on a three-dimensional interval J.

7. Functions of Bounded Variation According to Fréchet

We devote a few pages to the discussion of a definition of bounded variation of functions in two variables, which is due to M. Fréchet [see M. Fréchet: Sur les fonctionelles bilineaires, *Trans. Am. Math. Soc.* 16 (1915) 215-234]. Fréchet found this form of bounded variation useful in extending the Stieltjes integral representation of the most general linear continuous functional on the normed space C of continuous functions on a finite interval to the determination of the most general bounded (and so continuous) bilinear functional on the product space $C_1 \times C_2$. [$B(f, g)$ is bilinear if for functions f_1, f_2 of C_1 and g_1, g_2 of C_2 and constants a_1, a_2, b_1, b_2 we have

$$B(a_1 f_1 + a_2 f_2, b_1 g_1 + b_2 g_2) = a_1 b_1 B(f_1, g_1) + a_1 b_2 B(f_1, g_2) + a_2 b_1 B(f_2, g_1) + a_2 b_2 B(f_2, g_2) ;$$

$B(f, g)$ is bounded if there exists a constant M such that $| B(f, g) | \leqq M \| f \| \cdot \| g \|$ for all f of C_1 and g of C_2].

For notational convenience, we shall replace the variables x_1 and x_2 of the preceding sections by x and y, and assume that J is the interval $[a, a'; b, b']$ defined by $a \leqq x \leqq a'$, $b \leqq y \leqq b'$.

The Fréchet bounded variation is based on net subdivisions of J. Let $\sigma_x = \sigma_1 = (a = x_0 < x_1 < \dots < x_i < \dots x_n = a')$ and $\sigma_y = \sigma_2 = (b = y_0 < y_1 < \dots < y_j < \dots < y_m = b')$ be subdivisions of $[a, a']$ and $[b, b']$, respectively; let $I_{ij} = [x_{i-1}, x_i; y_{j-1}, y_j]$; further let $\varepsilon_i = \pm 1$ and $\varepsilon_j' = \pm 1$ for all i and j. Then:

7.1. Definition. $f(x, y)$ on J is said to be of *Fréchet bounded variation* if the expression

$$\begin{aligned}&\textstyle\sum_{ij} \varepsilon_i \varepsilon_j' \Delta_1 \Delta_2 f(I_{ij})\\ &= \textstyle\sum_{ij} \varepsilon_i \varepsilon_j' [f(x_{i-1}, y_{j-1}) - f(x_i, y_{j-1}) - f(x_{i-1}, y_j) + f(x_i, y_j)]\end{aligned}$$

is bounded in σ_x and σ_y for all choices of $\varepsilon_i = \pm 1$, $\varepsilon_j' = \pm 1$. If $f(x, y)$ is of Fréchet bounded variation on J, then the Fréchet total variation $FV(J)$ is the l.u.b. $\Sigma_{\sigma_x \times \sigma_y} \varepsilon_i \varepsilon_j' \Delta_1 \Delta_2 f(I_{ij})$ for all $\varepsilon_i = \pm 1$, $\varepsilon_j' = \pm 1$ and $\sigma_x \times \sigma_y$ of J. We shall denote the class of functions of Fréchet bounded variation by *FBV*.

We note that $FV(J)$ is also $-$ g.l.b. $[\Sigma_{\sigma_x \times \sigma_y} \varepsilon_i \varepsilon_j' \Delta_1 \Delta_2 f(I_{ij})]$ since a change in the signs of all ε_i gives a negative value corresponding to any positive value of the sum.

If $f(x, y) = g(x) + h(y)$, then $\Delta_1 \Delta_2 f(I) = 0$ for all I so that $FV(J) = 0$. If $f(x, y) = g(x)h(y)$, then

$$\begin{aligned}&\sum_{ij} \varepsilon_i \varepsilon_j' \Delta_1 \Delta_2 f(I_{ij}) \\ &= [\sum_i \varepsilon_i (g(x_i) - g(x_{i-1}))] [\sum_j \varepsilon_j' (h(y_j) - h(y_{j-1}))].\end{aligned}$$

It follows that $f(x, y) = g(x)h(y)$ is of *FBV* if and only if $g(x)$ and $h(y)$ are of bounded variation on $[a, a']$ and $[b, b']$, respectively, provided f and g are not constant functions. Since

$$\sum_{ij} \varepsilon_i \varepsilon_j' \Delta_1 \Delta_2 f(I_{ij}) \leqq \sum_{ij} | \Delta_1 \Delta_2 f(I_{ij}) | ,$$

$f(x, y)$ will be of *FBV* if f is of bounded variation on J, and $FV(I) \leqq V(J)$. However, $f(x, y)$ can be of *FVB* without being of bounded variation on J. For an example of such a function, the reader is referred to C. R. Adams and J. Clarkson: On definitions of bounded variation for functions of two variables, *Trans. Am. Math. Soc.* 35 (1933) 837-841.

The total Fréchet variation $FV(J)$ is not expressible as an integral of an interval function, so theorems developed for such integrals do not apply.

If we define the functions of nets $F(\sigma_x \times \sigma_y) = \max [\Sigma_{ij} \varepsilon_i \varepsilon_j' \Delta_1 \Delta_2 f(I_{ij})$ for all $\varepsilon_i = \pm 1$ and $\varepsilon_j' = \pm 1]$, then $F(\sigma_x \times \sigma_y)$ is monotone nondecreasing in $\sigma_x \times \sigma_y$ ordered by $\sigma_x' \geqq \sigma_x$ and $\sigma_y' \geqq \sigma_y$. For if we add to σ_x the point x_0 with $x_{i-1} < x_0 < x_i$ and take $\varepsilon_{i1} = \varepsilon_{i2} = \varepsilon_i$ on $[x_{i-1}, x_i]$ for the new subdivision σ_x', then the sums for $\sigma_x' \times \sigma_y$ and for $\sigma_x \times \sigma_y$ will be the same. It follows then that

$$FV(J) = \operatorname*{l.u.b.}_{\sigma_x \times \sigma_y} F(\sigma_x \times \sigma_y) = \lim_{\sigma_x \times \sigma_y} F(\sigma_x \times \sigma_y).$$

7.2. THEOREM. If $f(x, y)$ is of *FBV* on J, and $I \leqq J$, then f is also of *FBV* on I and $FV(I) \leqq FV(J)$ or, more generally, if $I_1 \leqq I_2$, then

$FV(I_1) \leqq FV(I_2)$, so that $FV(I)$ is monotone nondecreasing in I, the intervals I being directed by inclusion.

Consider the case when $I = [a, c; b, b']$, with $a < c < a'$, and let σ_x be a subdivision of $[a, a']$ containing c. If σ_x' is the part of σ_x in $[a, c]$ and σ_x'' the part in $[c, a']$, then

$$\sum_{\sigma_x \times \sigma_y} \varepsilon_i \varepsilon_j' \Delta_1 \Delta_2 f(I_{ij}) = [\sum_{\sigma_x' \times \sigma_y} + \sum_{\sigma_x'' \times \sigma_y}] (\varepsilon_i \varepsilon_j' \Delta_1 \Delta_2 f(I_{ij}) \leqq FV(J).$$

Since subdivisions of $[a, c]$ and $[c, a']$ are independent of each other, we can select σ_x'' and the corresponding ε_i so that $\Sigma_{\sigma_x'' \times \sigma_y} \varepsilon_i \varepsilon_j' \Delta_1 \Delta_2 f(I_{ij})$ is positive or zero so that

$$\sum_{\sigma_x' \times \sigma_y} \varepsilon_i \varepsilon_j' \Delta_1 \Delta_2 f(I_{ij}) \leqq FV(J)$$

for all σ_x' of $[a, c]$ and σ_y of $[b, b']$. The extension of this result to any subinterval of J and to $I_1 \leqq I_2$, is a simple matter.

7.3. THEOREM. If $f(x, y)$ is of FBV on J, then the interval function $FV(I)$ is upper semiadditive, i.e., if $\sigma = (I_1 \ldots I_n)$ is any subdivision of I, then $FV(I) \leqq \Sigma_k FV(I_k)$.

For any $e > 0$, σ_x and σ_y can be selected so that the sides of $I_1 \ldots I_n$ are on lines determined by σ_x and σ_y, and so that

$$FV(I) - e \leqq \sum_{\sigma_x \times \sigma_y} \varepsilon_i \varepsilon_j' \Delta_1 \Delta_2 f(I_{ij}) = \sum_k \sum_{\sigma_x \times \sigma_y (I_k)} \varepsilon_i \varepsilon_j' \Delta_1 \Delta_2 f(I_{ij}).$$
$$\leqq \sum_k FV(I_k).$$

Then for all $e > 0$, $FV(I) - e \leqq \Sigma_k FV(I_k)$, which gives the upper semiadditivity of $FV(I)$.

7.4. THEOREM. If $FV(I)$ is additive, then $f(x, y)$ is of bounded variation on J.

For then the function of intervals $FV(I) \pm \Delta_1 \Delta_2 f(I)$ will be additive and positive or zero valued, since $FV(I) \geqq \Delta_1 \Delta_2 f(I)$ for all I. If we set $FV(I) + \Delta_1 \Delta_2 f(I) = P(I)$ and $FV(I) - \Delta_1 \Delta_2 f(I) = N(I)$, then $\Delta_1 \Delta_2 f(I) = \frac{1}{2} [P(I) - N(I)]$ and so

$$\sum_{\sigma_x \times \sigma_y} | \Delta_1 \Delta_2 f(I) | \leqq \tfrac{1}{2} \sum_{\sigma_x \times \sigma_y} (P(I) + N(I)) = \tfrac{1}{2} (P(J) + N(J)).$$

It follows that $FV(I)$ is not always additive; further, that a Jordan decomposition for a function in FBV may not exist.

As for the case of ordinary bounded variation we have:

7.5. THEOREM. If $f(x, y)$ is of FBV on J, and $f(x, b)$ is of bounded variation in x on $[a, a']$, then $f(x, y)$ is of bounded variation in x, uniformly for y on $[b, b']$. Similarly if $f(x, y)$ is of bounded variation in y on $[b, b']$ then $f(x, y)$ is of bounded variation in y, uniformly for x on $[a, a']$.

For

$$\sum_i \varepsilon_i [f(x_i, y) - f(x_i, b) - f(x_{i-1}, y) + f(x_{i-1}, b)] \leqq FV[a, a'; b, y] \leqq FV(J),$$

for all $\varepsilon_i = \pm 1$. Then

$$\sum_i \varepsilon_i [f(x_i, y) - f(x_{i-1}, y)] \leqq FV(J) + \sum_i \varepsilon_i [f(x_i, b) - f(x_{i-1}, b)] \leqq FV(J) + \int_a^{a'} | d_x f(x, b) |.$$

Consequently $\int_a^{a'} | d_x f(x, y) | \leqq FV(J) + \int_a^{a'} | d_x f(x, b) |$, for all y.

Since for a function $f(x, y)$ in FBV, $FV(I)$ is monotonic in I, it follows that $\lim_{I \to (x, y)} FV(I)$ exists when the intervals I contain (x, y) and are ordered by inclusion. If further we knew that $\lim_{I \to (x, y)} [FV(I) - \Delta_1 \Delta_2 f(I)]$ exists, which would be true if $FV(I) - \Delta_1 \Delta_2 f(I)$ were monotone nondecreasing in I, then we could conclude that

$$\lim_{(x', y') \to (x+0, y+0)} f(x', y')$$

exists, provided $f(x + 0, y)$ and $f(x, y + 0)$ exist for all (x, y). This latter condition is fulfilled if $f(x, b)$ and $f(a, y)$ are of bounded variation in x and y, respectively. Even though there seems to be no simple way of proving that $\lim_{I \to (x, y)} [FV(I) - \Delta_1 \Delta_2 f(I)]$ exists, we do have:

7.6. THEOREM. If $f(x, y)$ is of FBV on J, and if $f(x, b)$ and $f(a, y)$ are of bounded variation in x and y, respectively, then the four quadrantal limits of $f(x', y')$ exist at every point of J.

Since the proof which depends on showing that if, for instance, the

$$\lim_{(x', y') \to (x+0, y+0)} f(x', y')$$

does not exist, then $f(x, y)$ is not of FBV on J, is rather complicated, we refer the reader to the original demonstration by M. Morse and W. Transue in Functionals of bounded variation, *Can. Jour. of Math.* 1 (1949) 153-165. See also A Calculus for Fréchet Variations, *Jour. Ind. Math. Soc.* 14 (1950) 65-117 by the same authors.

As in the case of functions of bounded variation on J, it follows that:

7.7. THEOREM. The discontinuities of a function $f(x, y)$ of FBV on J, where $f(x, b)$ and $f(b, y)$ are of bounded variation in x and y, respectively, lie on a denumerable set of lines parallel to the coordinate axes.

The following statements are obvious:

7.8. If $f(x, y)$ is of FBV on J, then $cf(x, y)$ is also of FBV on J and $FV(cf; J) = |c| FV(f; J)$.

7.9. If $f_1(x, y)$ and $f_2(x, y)$ are of FBV on J, then so is $f_1(x, y) + f_2(x, y)$ and $FV(f_1 + f_2; J) \leqq FV(f_1; J) + V(f_2; J)$. Then the space FBV is linear.

7.10. The subspace of FBV for which $f(x, b)$ and $f(a, y)$ are of bounded variation in x and y, respectively, is also linear and can be normed by assuming that $\| f \| = | f(a, b) | + \int_a^{a'} | d_x f(x, b) | + \int_b^{b'} | d_y f(a, y) | + FV(f; J)$.

7.11. If $f_q(x, y)$ is a directed set of functions of FBV on J and $\lim_q f_q(x, y) = f(x, y)$ for all (x, y) of J, and if there exists an M such that $FV(f_q; J) \leqq M$ for all q, then f is also FBV and $FV(f; J) \leqq M$.

For if $FV(f_q; J) \leqq M$ for all q, then for all q, $\sigma_x \times \sigma_y$, and $\varepsilon_i = \pm 1$, $\varepsilon_j' = \pm 1$, we have

$$\sum_{\sigma_x \times \sigma_y} \varepsilon_i \varepsilon_j' \Delta_1 \Delta_2 f_q(I_{ij}) \leqq M.$$

From the linearity properties of limit it follows that

$$\sum_{\sigma_x \times \sigma_y} \varepsilon_i \varepsilon_j' \Delta_1 \Delta_2 f(I_{ij}) \leqq M$$

also.

We can replace III.7.11 by the more precise results:

7.12. If $f_q(x, y)$ is a directed set of functions of FBV on J, and $\lim_q f_q(x, y) = f(x, y)$ for all (x, y) of J, then $FV(f; J) \leqq \underline{\lim}_q FV(f_q; J)$.

For if $\underline{\lim}_q FV(f_q; J) = \infty$, there is nothing to prove. If $\underline{\lim}_q FV(f_q; J) = c < \infty$, then for $e > 0$ and q, there exists q_{eq} such that $q_{eq} R q$ and $FV(f_{q_{eq}}; J) < c + e$. The q_{eq} are cofinal with Q so that $\lim_q f_{q_{eq}}(x, y) =$

$f(x, y)$. Then by III.7.11, we have $FV(f; J) < c + e$ for all $e > 0$, so that $FV(f; J) \leqq c$.

As an application of III.7.11, we show:

7.13. THEOREM. If $g(x, y)$ is of FBV on $J = [a, a'; b, b']$; if $f(x)$ is bounded on $[a, a']$ and such that $h(y) = \int_a^{a'} f(x) d_x g(x, y)$ exists for all y of $[b, b']$, then $h(y)$ is of bounded variation on $[b, b']$.

For consider

$$\sum_{\sigma_y} | h(y_j) - h(y_{j-1}) | = \sum_{\sigma_y} \left| \int_a^{a'} f(x)(d_x g(x, y_j) - d_x g(x, y_{j-1})) \right|$$
$$= \sum_{\sigma_y} \left| \lim_{\sigma_x} \sum_i f(x_i')(g(x_i, y_j) - g(x_{i-1}, y_j) - g(x_i, y_{j-1}) + g(x_{i-1}, y_{j-1})) \right|.$$

If we can show that the function $G_{\sigma_x}(y) = \Sigma_i f(x_i')(g(x_i, y) - g(x_{i-1}, y))$ is of bounded variation in y, uniformly relative to σ_x, then by III.7.11,

$$\lim_{\sigma_x} \sum_i f(x_i')(g(x_i, y) - g(x_{i-1}, y)) = \int_a^{a'} f(x) d_x g(x, y)$$

will be of bounded variation in y.

Let $\sigma_y = (b = y_0 < y_1 < \dots < y_j < \dots < y_m = b')$, and let

$$\varepsilon_j' = \operatorname{sgn} \sum_i f(x_i')(g(x_i, y_j) - g(x_{i-1}, y_j) - g(x_i, y_{j-1}) + g(x_{i-1}, y_{j-1}))$$
$$= \operatorname{sgn} \sum_i f(x_i') \Delta_1 \Delta_2 g(I_{ij}).$$

Then

$$\sum_{\sigma_y} | G_{\sigma_x}(y_j) - G_{\sigma_x}(y_{j-1}) | = \sum_j \left| \sum_i f(x_i') \Delta_1 \Delta_2 g(I_{ij}) \right|$$
$$= \sum_j \varepsilon_j' \sum_i f(x_i') \Delta_1 \Delta_2 g(I_{ij})$$
$$= \sum_i \sum_j f(x_i') \varepsilon_j' \Delta_1 \Delta_2 g(I_{ij}).$$

Take $\varepsilon_i = \operatorname{sgn} \Sigma_j \varepsilon_j' \Delta_1 \Delta_2 g(I_{ij})$. Then

$$0 \leqq \sum_{\sigma_y} | G_{\sigma_x}(y_j) - G_{\sigma_x}(y_{j-1}) | \leqq \sum_i | f(x_i') | \varepsilon_i \sum_j \varepsilon_j' \Delta_1 \Delta_2 g(I_{ij})$$
$$\leqq | M | \sum_{ij} \varepsilon_i \varepsilon_j' \Delta_1 \Delta_2 g(I_{ij}) \leqq MFV(g; J)$$

where $| f(x) | \leqq M$ for $a \leqq x \leqq a'$. This gives us the uniform bounded variation of the functions $G_{\sigma_x}(y)$ and consequently that of their limit $\int_a^{a'} f(x) d_x g(x, y)$.

A consequence of this theorem is the following iterated integrals theorem:

7.14. THEOREM. If $f(x)$ is continuous on $[a, a']$; if $g(y)$ is bounded on $[b, b']$; if $h(x, y)$ is of *FBV* on $[a, a'; b, b']$ and of bounded variation in x for $y = b$ (and so for all y); and if $\int_b^{b'} g(y)d_x h(x, y)$ exists for all x, then $\int_a^{a'} f(x)d_x \int_b^{b'} g(y)d_y h(x, y)$ and $\int_b^{b'} g(y)d_y \int_a^{a'} f(x)d_x h(x, y)$ both exist and are equal.

The existence of the first two of these integrals is a consequence of the continuity of $f(x)$ and the bounded variation of $\int_b^{b'} g(y)d_y h(x, y)$ proved in the preceding theorem. Also, $\int_a^{a'} f(x)d_x h(x, y)$ exists for each y, since $f(x)$ is continuous and $h(x, y)$ is of bounded variation in x for each y. To prove the existence of the second integral, we consider:

$$\sum_{\sigma_y} g(y_i') \int_a^{a'} f(x)d_x[h(x, y_i) - h(x, y_{i-1})]$$
$$= \int_a^{a'} f(x)d_x[\sum_{\sigma_y} g(y_i')(h(x, y_i) - h(x, y_{i-1}))]$$

where $y_{i-1} \leqq y_i' \leqq y_i$. By the proof of III.7.13, the functions $G_{\sigma_y}(x) = \Sigma_{\sigma_y} g(y_i')\ [h(x, y_i) - h(x, y_{i-1})]$ are uniformly of bounded variation in x relative to σ_y. Further, by hypothesis

$$\lim_{\sigma_y} G_{\sigma_y}(x) = \sum_{\sigma_y} g(y_i')\ [h(x, y_i) - h(x, y_{i-1})] = \int_b^{b'} g(y)d_y h(x, y)$$

for every x. Consequently, since $f(x)$ is continuous, the convergence theorems II.15.3 and II.15.12 give us that $\int_b^{b'} g(y)d_y \int_a^{a'} f(x)d_x h(x, y)$ exists and is equal to $\int_a^{a'} f(x)d_x \int_b^{b'} g(y)d_y h(x, y)$.

EXERCISES

1. Show that if $f(x, y)$ on J is such that $FV(f,; J) = 0$, then $f(x, y) = f(x, b) + f(a, y) - f(a, b)$.

2. If $f(x, y)$ is of bounded variation on J, is $FV(I)$ an additive function of intervals?

3. Is it possible to weaken the hypotheses of the last theorem by replacing the condition that $f(x)$ be continuous on $[a, a']$ by the conditions that $f(x)$ be bounded on $[a, a']$ and $\int_a^{a'} f(x)d_x h(x, y)$ exist for every y of $[b, b']$?

4. Is there a theorem of Helly's theorem type which is valid for functions in *FBV* on J?

8. Riemann-Stieltjes Integrals in Two Variables

Riemann-Stieltjes integrals in two variables are integrals of the interval functions based on two point functions $f(x, y)$ and $g(x, y)$ defined on an interval $J = [a, a'; b, b']$, where $F(I) = f(x', y')\Delta_1\Delta_2 g(I)$. Here (x', y') is any point of the interval $[x_1, x_2; y_1, y_2]$ and $\Delta_1\Delta_2 g(I) = g(x_1, y_1) - g(x_1, y_2) - g(x_2, y_1) + g(x_2, y_2)$. Such an $F(I)$ is of the form $f(x', y')G(I)$ where $G(I)$ is an additive function of intervals. The value of $\Delta_1\Delta_2 g(I)$ is obviously unchanged if we add to $g(x, y)$ a function of the form $h_1(x) + h_2(y)$. If we replace $g(x, y)$ by $\bar{g}(x, y) = g(x, y) - g(x, b) - g(a, y) + g(a, b)$, then for all intervals I $f(x', y')\Delta_1\Delta_2 g(I) = f(x', y')\Delta_1\Delta_2 \bar{g}(I)$, so that for the properties of integrals we can usually assume that $g(x, b) = g(a, y) = 0$ for all x and y.

We recall that there there is some variety in the definitions of integrals of interval functions which are based on the limits of functions of subdivisions σ of J: $G(\sigma) = \Sigma_\sigma F(I)$.

We have a choice of subdivisions σ of the interval J, either σ is general $= [I_1 \dots I_n]$, where the I_i have at most parts of a side in common and $\Sigma_n I_n = J$; or σ is a net, where σ is determined by subdivisions σ_x of $[a, a']$ and σ_y of $[b, b']$ by drawing lines parallel to the coordinate axes through the points of σ_x and σ_y.

The limits of the approximating sums $G(\sigma) = \Sigma_\sigma F(I)$ depend upon the partial order. We have either: the σ are ordered by inclusion $\sigma_1 \geq \sigma_2$, if every interval of σ_1 is a subinterval of some interval of σ_2, or σ_1 is obtained from σ_2 by redividing the intervals of σ_2. Similarly for nets $\sigma_x' \times \sigma_y' \geqq \sigma_x'' \times \sigma_y''$ if $\sigma_x' \geqq \sigma_x''$ and $\sigma_y' \geqq \sigma_y''$. Or: the σ can be ordered by some metric or norm. The usual norm $|\sigma|$ is the maximum of the length of the sides of the intervals constituting σ. For nets this norm becomes the larger of $|\sigma_x|$ and $|\sigma_y|$.

In addition, conditions may be made on the choice of the points (x', y') in I. We shall usually assume that (x', y') is any point of I (interior or boundary), depending only on I. For net subdivisions one obtains a weak type of integral by assuming that the points (x', y') in the intervals I are chosen so that they form a net also, that is, in $I_{ij} = [x_{i-1}, x_i; y_{j-1}, y_j]$ we assume for (x'_{ij}, y'_{ij}) that $x'_{ij} = x_i'$ for all j and $y'_{ij} = y_j'$ for all i.

Corresponding to these choices we have σ-integrals $(\sigma \int)$ and norm integrals $(N \int)$ based on general subdivisions, σ-net integrals $(\sigma_x \times \sigma_y \int)$ and norm net integrals $(N \sigma_x \times \sigma_y \int)$, based on net subdivisions, and weak σ-integrals (weak σ-$\int$) and weak norm integrals (weak $N \int$) based on net convergence with the points (x'_{ij}, y'_{ij}) forming a net. We shall usually denote integrals by $\int_J f d_1 d_2 g$, omitting the variables (x, y) and sometimes the interval J where no confusion results. Also, we shall be concerned largely with the σ and norm integrals based on general subdivisions.

If $f(x, y) = 1$ on J, then obviously all of these integrals exist with value $\Delta_1\Delta_2 g(J)$. If $g(x, y) = xy$, then $\Delta_1\Delta_2 g(I) = (x_2 - x_1)(y_2 - y_1)$, leading to double Riemann integrals. If $g(x, y) = h_1(x)h_2(y)$, then $\Delta_1\Delta_2 g(I) = (h_1(x_2) - h_1(x_1))(h_2(y_2) - h_2(y_1))$, leading to double Stieltjes integrals.

In the matter of existence theorems, Cauchy conditions of convergence formulated for the type of limit involved are necessary and sufficient for the existence of the corresponding integrals. The finiteness and equality of upper and lower integrals, defined as greatest and least of limits, is also available. When it comes to more specialized conditions the corresponding theorem for integrals of interval functions III.3.1 gives us:

8.1. A necessary and sufficient condition that the $\sigma \int_J f d_1 d_2 g$ (or $N \int_J f d_1 d_2 g$) exist when based on general subdivisions is that $\sigma \int_J \omega(Sf\Delta g; I) = 0$ (or $N \int_J \omega(Sf\Delta g; I) = 0$).

For the case of net integrals there is no difficulty in showing that $\int_J \omega(Sf\Delta g; I) = 0$ (where the S extends over nets of I) has the corresponding Cauchy condition of convergence as a consequence, so that it gives a sufficient condition for the existence of net $\int_J f d_1 d_2 g$. The proof of the necessity of this condition for unrestricted $g(x, y)$ runs into difficulty, since a net subdivision of an interval I_{ij} induces subdivisions of $I_{i'j}$ for $i' = 1 \dots n$ and $I_{ij'}$ for $j' = 1 \dots m$.

A simple necessary condition for the existence of the integral $\int_J f d_1 d_2 g$ emerges from the observation that for any given subdivision σ of J and for all $e > 0$, there exist points (x', y') and (x'', y'') in I such that

$$\begin{aligned} &\left| \sum\nolimits_\sigma (f(x', y')\Delta_1\Delta_2 g(I) - f(x'', y'')\Delta_1\Delta_2 g(I)) \right| \\ &\geqq \sum\nolimits_\sigma \omega(f; I) \left| \Delta_1\Delta_2 g(I) \right| - e. \end{aligned}$$

For if $\Sigma_\sigma | \Delta_1\Delta_2 g(I) | = M$, we need only determine (x', y') and (x'', y'') in each I so that $\operatorname{sgn}(f(x', y') - f(x'', y'')) = \operatorname{sgn} \Delta_1\Delta_2 g(I)$ and $| f(x', y') - f(x'', y'') | > \omega(f : I) - e/M$. Using the Cauchy condition of convergence we obtain:

8.2. A necessary condition that $\int_J fd_1d_2g$ exist is that correspondingly $\int_J\omega(f;\ I)\mid \Delta_1\Delta_2 g(I)\mid = 0$.

This result is valid for integrals based on general and net subdivisions but not for weak integrals.

It follows that if $N\int_J fd_1d_2g$ exists then $\lim_{|I|\to 0}\omega(f,;\ I)\mid \Delta_1\Delta_2 g(I)\mid = 0$ uniformly on J, where $\mid I\mid =$ the maximum side length of I. Consequently, $\lim_{I\to(x,y)}\omega(f;\ I)\Delta_1\Delta_2 g(I) = 0$ for all (x, y) in J. If $f(x, y)$ is discontinuous at (x, y) so that $\omega(f;\ x, y) > 0$, then $\lim_{I\to(x,y)}\Delta_1\Delta_2 g(I) = 0$, if $\lim_{I\to(x,y)}\Delta_1\Delta_2 g(I) \neq 0$, then $f(x, y)$ must be continuous at (x, y). In an extended sense then, if $N\int_J fd_1d_2g$ exists, then f and g have no common discontinuities. For the σ-integral, similar necessary conditions can be developed involving quadrantal convergence at the points (x, y) of J.

It is obvious that if $N\int_J fd_1d_2g$ exists, then the corresponding $\sigma\int_J fd_1d_2g$ exists also. No simple condition added to the existence of $\sigma\int_J fd_1d_2g$ which yields the existence of the norm integral seems to be available. The pseudoadditive condition defined for interval functions when applied to the function $f(x', y')\Delta_1\Delta_2 g(I)$ does not seem to produce a simple relation between the behavior of $f(x, y)$ and $\Delta_1\Delta_2 g(I)$.

8.3. THEOREM. If $\int_J fd_1d_2g$ exists, then for any I in J, the corresponding $\int_I fd_1d_2g$ exists, provided the integrals are based on general subdivisions. Further, the resulting function of intervals is additive.

This follows from III.3.3. This does not seem to be true for net integrals unless g is restricted. It is not always true for weak integrals based on net convergence. For let $J = [0, 1;\ -1, 1]$: let $f(x, y)$ be independent of y, equal to $f(x)$, and set $g(x, y) = x\mid y\mid$. Then

$$\sum_{\sigma_x\times\sigma_y} f(x_i')\,(x_i - x_{i-1})\,(\mid y_j\mid - \mid y_{j-1}\mid) = 0$$

for all $\sigma_x \times \sigma_y$ of J since $\Sigma_{\sigma_y}(\mid y_j\mid - \mid y_{j-1}\mid) = 0$ for all subdivisions σ_y of $[-1, 1]$. Consequently weak $\int_J f(x)d_1d_2g(x, y) = 0$. If $I = [0, 1;\ 0, 1]$ then

$$\sum_{\sigma_x\times\sigma_y} f(x_i')\,(x_i - x_{i-1})\,(\mid y_i\mid - \mid y_{j-1}\mid) = \sum_{\sigma_x} f(x_i')\,(x_i - x_{i-1}),$$

so that $\int_I f(x)d_1d_2g(x, y)$ will exist only if $f(x)$ is Riemann integrable on $[0, 1]$.

There is the usual converse theorem:

8.4. THEOREM. If $I_1 \dots I_n$ are a subdivision of J and $\sigma \int_{I_i} f d_1 d_2 g$ exists for each i, then $\sigma \int_J f d_1 d_2 g$ exists and is equal to the sum of these integrals.

For norm integrals this theorem does not hold without additional conditions on the behavior of $f(x, y)$ and $g(x, y)$ on the boundaries of the I_i.

On the boundedness of the function $f(x, y)$, when the integrals exist we have:

8.5. THEOREM. If either $N \int_J f d_1 d_2 g$ or $\sigma \int_J f d_1 d_2 g$ exists, then there exists a subdivision σ_0 of J such that the subintervals of σ_0 fall into two categories: I', I'' such that f is bounded on each I', f is unbounded on each I'', but $\Delta_1\Delta_2 g(I) = 0$ for every I in any I''. Then $\int_J f d_1 d_2 g = \Sigma_{I'} \int_{I'} f d_1 d_2 g$, that is the integral $\int_J f d_1 d_2 g$ depends only on the values of f and g on the intervals I' where f is bounded.

Since the integrals exist, there exists a subdivision σ_0 such that if $\sigma \geqq \sigma_0$, then $\Sigma_\sigma f(x', y')\Delta_1\Delta_2 g(I)$ is bounded for all choices of (x', y') in the corresponding intervals I. If then $f(x, y)$ is unbounded on the interval $I = [x_1, x_2; y_1, y_2]$ of σ_0, then $\Delta_1\Delta_2 g(I) = 0$. Divide I into intervals $I_1 = [x_1, x; y_1, y_2]$ and $I_2 = [x, x_2; y_1, y_2]$. Then $f(x, y)$ is unbounded on either I_1 or I_2 and consequently $\Delta_1\Delta_2 g(I_1) = 0$ or $\Delta_1\Delta_2 g(I_2) = 0$. Since $0 = \Delta_1\Delta_2 g(I) = \Delta_1\Delta_2 g(I_1) + \Delta_1\Delta_2 g(I_2)$, it follows that both $\Delta_1\Delta_2 g(I_1) = 0$ and $\Delta_1\Delta_2 g(I_2) = 0$. Similarly, if I is divided into the intervals $I_1' = [x_1, x_2; y_1, y]$ and $I_2' = [x_1, x_2; y, y_2]$, then $\Delta_1\Delta_2 g(I_1') = \Delta_1\Delta_2 g(I_2') = 0$. If I is divided into four rectangles by lines through the point (x, y) parallel to the coordinate axes, it follows that $f(x, y)$ is unbounded on one of these rectangles, say I_0, and $\Delta_1\Delta_2 g(I_0) = 0$. From the additive character of $\Delta_1\Delta_2 g$, and the preceding considerations, we conclude that $\Delta_1\Delta_2 g(I') = 0$ for all four I' having (x, y) as common vertex, so that in particular $\Delta_1\Delta_2 g(I')$ vanishes for $I' = [x_1, x; y_1, y]$. Consequently, $g(x, y) - g(x, y_1) - g(x_1, y) + g(x_1, y_1) = 0$ for all (x, y) in I and $\Delta_1\Delta_2 g(I'') = 0$ for any interval I'' in I.

This theorem is valid for the integrals based on general subdivisions and the net integrals, but does not need to hold for weak integrals as the example in the preceding paragraph shows.

The proof of the following *substitution theorem* follows the usual lines:

8.6. THEOREM. If $f(x, y)$ is bounded on J, and $g(x, y)$ and $h(x, y)$ are such that $\int_J g(x, y) d_1 d_2 h(x, y)$ exists and if $k(x, y) = \int_{a,b}^{x,y} g d_1 d_2 h$, then $\int_J f(x, y)g(x, y)d_1d_2h(x, y)$ exists if and only if $\int_J f(x, y)d_1d_2 k(x, y)$ exists and the two integrals are equal.

Here the same integral (norm or σ) based on general subdivisions is used throughout. The theorem is limited to these since we do not have assurance that $k(x, y)$ exists for net type integrals.

8.7. Integration by Parts. There is difficulty in proving any integration by parts theorem for the general subdivision or net integrals since in the interval function $f(x', y')\Delta_1\Delta_2 g(I)$, the points (x', y') do not determine a subdivision of J into rectangles. The proof of the following integration by parts theorem is valid *only for weak net integrals*, where both subdivisions and the points (x', y') form nets.

8.8. THEOREM. If $f(x, y)$ and $g(x, y)$ on $J = [a, a'; b, b']$ are such that weak $\int_J [f(x, y) - f(x, b) - f(a, y) + f(a, b)]d_1d_2g(x, y)$ exists, then weak $\int_J [g(x, y) - g(x, b') - g(a', y) + g(a', b')]d_1d_2f(x, y)$ exists and the two integrals are equal.

This could be expressed:

$$\int_J \left[\int_{(a,b)}^{(x,y)} d_1d_2f(u, v)\right] d_1d_2g(x, y) = \int_J \left[\int_{(x,y)}^{(a',b')} d_1d_2g(u, v)\right] d_1d_2f(x, y).$$

It is sufficient to prove this theorem for the case when $f(x, y)$ vanishes on $x = a$, and $y = b$, and $g(x, y)$ vanishes on $x = a'$, and $y = b'$. To obtain the theorem for any two functions $f(x, y)$ and $g(x, y)$ we set $\bar{f}(x, y) = f(x, y) - f(x, b) - f(a, y) + f(a, b)$ and $\bar{g}(x, y) = g(x, y) - g(x, b') - g(a', y) + g(a', b')$.

As in the case of one variable we rearrange the approximating sum

$$\sum_{i=1}^{n} \sum_{j=1}^{n} f(x_i', y_j')\,(g(x_i, y_j) - g(x_{i-1}, y_j) - g(x_i, x_{j-1}) + g(x_{i-1}, y_{j-1}))$$

with $a = x_0 \leqq x_1' \leqq x_1 \ldots \leqq x_{m-1} \leqq x_m' \leqq x_m = a'$ and $b = y_0 \leqq y_1' \leqq y_1 \leqq \ldots \leqq y_{n-1} \leqq y_n' \leqq y_n = b'$, so as to collect the multipliers of $g(x_i, y_j)$. In general, these will be of the form $f(x'_{i+1}, y'_{j+1}) - f(x_i', y'_{j+1}) - f(x'_{i+1}, y_j') + f(x_i', y_j') = \Delta_1\Delta_2 f(I')$, where $I' = [x_i', x'_{i+1}; y_j', y'_{j+1}]$. The exceptions are the terms $g(a, y_j)$, $g(a', y_j)$, $g(x_i, b)$, and $g(x_i, b')$. For instance, the coefficient of $g(a, y_j)$ with $0 < j < n$ will be $f(x_1', y'_{j+1}) - f(x_1', y_j')$. But since $f(a, y) = 0$ for all y, we can write this term: $g(a, y_j)\ [f(x_1', y'_{j+1}) - f(x_1', y_j') - f(a, y'_{j+1}) + f(a, y_j')]$. The term involving $g(x_i, b)$ can be treated in the same way. Since $g(a', y) = 0$, the term involving $g(a', y_j)$

can be written $g(a', y_j)\,[f(a', y'_{j+1}) - f(a', y_j') - f(x_m', y'_{j+1}) + f(x_m', y_j')]$ and similarly for $g(x_i', b)$. In the same way the values of g at the vertices of J, for instance, $g(a, b)$, can be provided with a factor of the form $\Delta_1\Delta_2 f$, since $g(a, b)f(x_1', y_1')$ can be written $g(a, b)\,(f(x_1', y_1') - f(x_1', b) - f(a, y_1') + f(a, b))$. It follows that

$$\sum_{i=1}^{m}\sum_{j=1}^{n} f(x_i', y_j')\,[g(x_i, y_j) - g(x_{i-1}, y_j) - g(x_i, y_{j-1}) + g(x_{i-1}, y_{j-1})]$$
$$= \sum_{i=0}^{m}\sum_{j=0}^{n} g(x_i, y_j)\,[f(x'_{i+1}, y'_{j+1}) - f(x_i', y'_{j+1}) - f(x'_{i+1}, y_j') + f(x_i', y_j')]$$

where $x_0' = a$, $y_0' = b$, $x'_{m+1} = a'$ and $y'_{n+1} = b'$. The same type of formula holds if f and g are interchanged.

The remainder of the proof proceeds as in the case of one variable. If $N\int_J f d_1 d_2 g$ exists, then $(e, d_e, |\sigma_x| \leqq d_e, |\sigma_y| \leqq d_e) : |\Sigma_{ij} f(x_i', y_j')\,\Delta_1\Delta_2 g(I_{ij}) - \int_J f d_1 d_2 g| < e$. Select $\sigma_x \equiv (a = x_0 < x_1 < \dots < x_m = a')$ and $\sigma_y \equiv (b = y_0 < y_1 < \dots < y_n = b')$ such that $|\sigma_x| < d_e/2$ and $|\sigma_y| < d_e/2$. Then

$$\sum_{i=1}^{m}\sum_{j=1}^{n} g(x_i', y_j')\Delta_1\Delta_2 f(I_{ij}) = \sum_{i=0}^{m}\sum_{j=0}^{n} f(x_i, y_j)\Delta_1\Delta_2 g(I'_{i+1,\,j+1}).$$

If we set $\sigma_x' \equiv (a = x_0' \leqq x_1' < \dots \leqq x'_{m+1} = a')$ and $\sigma_y' \equiv (b = y_0' \leqq y_1' < \dots \leqq y'_{n+1} = b')$, then $|\sigma_x'| < d_e$ and $|\sigma_y'| < d_e$, so that

$$(e, d_e, |\sigma_x| < d_e/2, |\sigma_y| < d_e/2) :$$
$$\left|\sum_{i=1}^{m}\sum_{j=1}^{n} g(x_i', y_j')\Delta_1\Delta_2 f(I_{ij}) - \int_J f d_1 d_2 g\right| < e,$$

from which the theorem follows at once.

The proof for the corresponding σ-integral situation for the one variable case can also be adapted here, by using the trick of dividing the rectangle $[x_i', x'_{i+1}; y_j', y'_{j+1}]$ into four rectangles having the point (x_i, y_j) as common vertex and applying the additivity of the interval function $\Delta_1\Delta_2 f(I)$.

9. Stieltjes Integrals in Two Dimensions with Respect to Functions of Bounded Variation

In the theorems of the preceding paragraphs, the function $g(x, y)$ with respect to which the integrals are taken does not belong to any special class of functions. We obtain additional properties of the integrals when we assume $g(x, y)$ to be of bounded variation on J. Since the value for $g(x, y)$ for $x = a$, or for $y = b$ do not affect the existence nor the values of the integrals, we shall usually assume that $g(x, y)$ is normalized so that $g(a, y) = g(x, b) = 0$ for all x and y. We denote by $v(I)$ the function of intervals determined by $\int_I | d_1 d_2 g |$ and by $v(x, y)$ the corresponding point function $\int_{(a,b)}^{(x,y)} | d_1 d_2 g |$. We have at once:

9.1. THEOREM. If $g(x, y)$ is of bounded variation on J, then a necessary condition that $\int_J f d_1 d_2 g$ exist is that $\int_J \omega(f,; I) \mid d_1 d_2 g(I) \mid = 0$ and a sufficient condition that $\int_J \omega(f; I) v(I) = 0$.

Here the integrals involved are assumed to be of the same type throughout, norm, σ, norm-net, or σ-net integrals. The theorem is not valid for weak net integrals.

The necessity part of the theorem has been demonstrated in III.8.2. For the sufficiency, we note that if σ and σ_1 are such that $\sigma_1 \geqq \sigma$, then $| \Sigma_\sigma f \Delta_1 \Delta_2 g - \Sigma_{\sigma_1} f \Delta_1 \Delta_2 g | \leqq \Sigma_\sigma \omega(f; I) v(I)$. For if I is any interval of σ, then

$$| f(x', y') \Delta_1 \Delta_2 g(I) - \sum_{\sigma_1 \cdot I} f \Delta_1 \Delta_2 g | \leqq | \sum_{\sigma_1 \cdot I} (f(x', y') - f(x_i', y_i')) \Delta_1 \Delta_2 g |$$
$$\leqq \omega(f; I) \sum_{\sigma_1 \cdot I} | \Delta_1 \Delta_2 g | \leqq \omega(f; I) v(I).$$

If, then, $\int_J \omega(f; I) v(I) = 0$, and for $e > 0$, σ_1 and σ_2 are such that $\Sigma_{\sigma_1} \omega(f; I) v(I) < e$, for $i = 1, 2$, then for $\sigma' \geqq \sigma_1$ and σ_2 we have

$$| \sum_{\sigma_1} f \Delta_1 \Delta_2 g - \sum_{\sigma_2} f \Delta_1 \Delta_2 g | \leqq | (\sum_{\sigma_1} - \sum_{\sigma'}) f \Delta_1 \Delta_2 g |$$
$$+ | (\sum_{\sigma_2} - \sum_{\sigma'}) f \Delta_1 \Delta_2 g | \leqq 2 e.$$

Then $\int_J \omega(f; I) v(I) = 0$ implies the corresponding Cauchy condition of convergence and the existence of the corresponding integral.

As an immediate corollary we have:

9.2. THEOREM. If $g(x, y)$ is monotone on J in the sense that for each I of J: $\Delta_1 \Delta_2 g(I) \geqq 0$, then $\int_J f d_1 d_2 g$ exists if and only if for the corresponding integral $\int_J \omega(f; I) d_1 d_2 g(I) = 0$.

Further:

9.3. If $f(x, y)$ is continuous on J and $g(x, y)$ is of bounded variation, then $\int_J f d_1 d_2 g$ exists for all definitions of integral considered.

As in the case of one variable we can show by a contrapositive procedure that if $\int_J fd_1d_2g$ exists for every continuous function $f(x, y)$ on J, then $g(x, y)$ is necessarily of bounded variation on J. The demonstration can be made on the assumption that the integral is of the σ-net type, and will then hold also for the three other types of integrals which are stronger. As a matter of fact, one can even limit $f(x, y)$ to be of the form $f_1(x)f_2(y)$ where $f_1(x)$ and $f_2(y)$ are any continuous functions on $[a, a']$ and $[b, b']$, respectively.

On the matter of existence of integrals, we can prove the stronger theorem:

9.4. If $f(x, y)$ is bounded on J, and $g(x, y)$ is of bounded variation then a necessary and sufficient condition that $\sigma \int_J fd_1d_2g$ exist is that $\sigma \int_J \omega(f; I) v(I) = 0$.

The sufficiency has already been shown. For the necessity, we note that if $\sigma \int fd_1d_2g$ exists, then $\sigma \int \omega(f; I) \mid \Delta_1\Delta_2 g(I) \mid = 0$, so that $(e, \sigma_e, \sigma \geqq \sigma_e) : \Sigma_\sigma \omega(f; I) \mid \Delta_1\Delta_2 g(I) \mid < e$. If g is of bounded variation, then $(e, \sigma_e', \sigma \geqq \sigma_e') : \mid v(J) - \Sigma_\sigma \mid \Delta_1\Delta_2 g(I) \mid\mid < e$, or $\Sigma_\sigma (v(I) - \mid \Delta_1\Delta_2 g\ (I) \mid) < e$, since $v(I)$ is additive and $v(I) \geqq \mid \Delta_1\Delta_2 g(I) \mid$ for all I. Consequently, if $\sigma \geqq \sigma_e$ and σ_e', then

$$\left|\sum\nolimits_\sigma \omega(f; I) v(I) - \sum\nolimits_\sigma \omega(f\,; I) \mid \Delta_1\Delta_2 g(I) \mid \right.$$
$$= \sum\nolimits_\sigma \omega(f; I)\ (v(I) - \mid \Delta_1\Delta_2 g(I) \mid) < 2\,Me,$$

where $\mid f(x, y) \mid \leqq M$ on J. Consequently, $\sigma \int_J \omega(f; I) v(I) = 0$.

Since the variation function $v(x, y)$ is monotone, we can assert:

9.5. THEOREM. If $f(x, y)$ is bounded on J and $g(x, y)$ of bounded variation, then a necessary and sufficient condition that $\sigma \int_J fd_1d_2g$ exist is that $\sigma \int_J fd_1d_2v$ exist. Consequently, if $p(x, y)$ and $n(x, y)$ are the positive and negative variation functions of $g(x, y)$, then $\sigma \int_J fd_1d_2g$ exists if and only if $\sigma \int_J fd_1d_2p$ and $\sigma \int_J fd_1d_2n$ both exist.

It is probable that the same theorem holds for norm integrals but simple proofs of the necessity condition, in particular: if $N \int_J fd_1d_2g$ exists, then $N \int_J fd_1d_2v$ exists also, are lacking. The method of proof given for the σ-integral extends to the norm integral if we know that the total variation $v(J) = \int_J \mid d_1d_2g \mid$ exists as a norm integral.

The boundedness conditions on f in the above theorems can be dropped if we add the convention that $\omega(f; I) v(I) = 0$, when $v(I) = 0$. Also although the proof has been made for the σ-integrals based on general subdivisions, it is also valid for the σ-integrals based on net subdivisions, since the total variation exists as a net integral.

Since for given f and g, the function $\Sigma_\sigma \omega(f; I)v(I)$ is a monotone nonincreasing function of σ, and the net subdivisions are cofinal with general subdivisions, we conclude:

9.6. THEOREM. A necessary and sufficient condition that $\sigma \int_J f d_1 d_2 g$ exist is that net $\sigma \int_J \omega(f; I)v(I) = 0$, or that net $\sigma \int_J f d_1 d_2 v$ exist.

We also note:

9.7. THEOREM. If $g_1(x, y)$ and $g_2(x, y)$ are of bounded variation on J and such that $\int_I |d_1 d_2 g_1| \leqq \int_I |d_1 d_2 g_2|$ for all I of J, and if $\sigma \int_J f d_1 d_2 g_2$ exists, then $\sigma \int_J f d_1 d_2 g_1$ exists also. The same statement holds for norm integrals if g_1 and g_2 are monotone.

Further we conclude that if net-σ $\int_J f d_1 d_2 g$ exists and if I is any interval of J, then net-σ $\int_I f d_1 d_2 g$ exists for all I of J, and the resulting interval function is additive. The corresponding result for norm net integrals is valid if $g(x, y)$ is monotone in the sense that $\Delta_1 \Delta_2 g(I) \geqq 0$ for all I, but it is an open question whether it holds when g is any function of bounded variation.

The following theorems are proved in the usual way:

9.8. Approximation Theorem. If $g(x, y)$ is of bounded variation on J, and $f(x, y)$ is such that $\int_J f d_1 d_2 g$ exists, then for every subdivision σ, we have $| \int_J f d_1 d_2 g - \Sigma_\sigma f \Delta_1 \Delta_2 g | \leqq \Sigma_\sigma \omega(f; I)v(I)$.

This holds for general or net, norm or σ-integrals, the σ being correspondingly restricted, but not for weak integrals. The same remark applies also to the following convergence theorems:

9.9. THEOREM. If $f_q(x, y)$ with q on directed Q, converge uniformly to $f(x, y)$ on J; if $g(x, y)$ is of bounded variation on J, and if $\int_J f_q d_1 d_2 g$ exists for all q, then $\lim_q \int_J f_q d_1 d_2 g$ exists and is equal to $\int_J f d_1 d_2 g$.

9.10. THEOREM. If $g_q(x, y)$ with q on directed Q and $g(x, y)$ are of bounded variation on J; if $\lim_q \int_J | d_1 d_2 (g_q - g) | = 0$; if $f(x, y)$ is bounded on J; and if $\int_J f d_1 d_2 g_q$ exists for all q, then $\lim_q \int_J f d_1 d_2 g_q$ exists and is equal to $\int_J f(x, y) d_1 d_2 g$.

9.11. THEOREM. If $g_q(x, y)$ with q on directed Q and $g(x, y)$ are positively monotonely monotone on J, if $\lim_q g_q(x, y) = g(x, y)$ for all (x, y) of J; if $f(x, y)$ is bounded and such that $\int_J f d_1 d_2 g_q$ and $\int_J f d_1 d_2 g$ exist for all q of Q, then $\lim_q \int_J f d_1 d_2 g_q = \int_J f d_1 d_2 g$.

The last theorem is a generalization to functions of two variables of Ex. 5 at the close of II.15.

10. Relation between Double and Iterated Integrals

A reduction of double integrals to iterated integrals is possible in the case when the function $g(x, y)$ of bounded variation with respect to which the integration is taken, is a product of a function of x by a function of y, that is $g(x, y) = \alpha(x)\beta(y)$. We shall assume in this section that $\alpha(x)$ is of bounded variation in x on $[a, a']$ and $\beta(x)$ in y on $[b, b']$. The basic inequality is contained in:

10.1. THEOREM. If $f(x, y)$ is bounded on $J = [a, a'; b, b']$ and $\alpha(x)$ and $\beta(y)$ are of bounded variation on $[a, a']$ and $[b, b']$, respectively, then

$$\overline{\int_a^{a'}} d\alpha(x) \overline{\int_b^{b'}} f(x, y)d\beta(y) \leqq \overline{\int_J} f(x, y)d_1d_2\alpha(x)\beta(y).$$

Here the upper integrals are the greatest of the corresponding limits and the double integrals are based on general subdivisions.

We give the proof for the norm integrals, for the σ-integrals the procedure is similar. We have:

$$(e, d_e, |\sigma| \leqq d_e): \textstyle\sum_\sigma f(x', y')\Delta_x\Delta_y\alpha(x)\beta(y)$$
$$\leqq \overline{\int_J} f(x, y)d_1d_2\alpha(x)\beta(y) + e.$$

For the same e and d_e, there exists a σ_x such that $|\sigma_x| < d_e$ and x_i' with $x_{i-1} \leqq x_i' \leqq x_i$, such that

$$\sum_i (\alpha(x_i) - \alpha(x_{i-1})) \overline{\int_b^{b'}} f(x_i', y)d\beta(y)$$
$$\geqq \overline{\int_a^{a'}} d\alpha(x) \overline{\int_b^{b'}} f(x, y)d\beta(y) - e.$$

If $\alpha(x_i) - \alpha(x_{i-1}) \geqq 0$, we can find σ_{iy} such that $|\sigma_{iy}| < d_e$ and y'_{ij} with $y_{i,j-1} \leqq y'_{ij} \leqq y_{ij}$, $j = 1 \ldots n_i$, such that

$$\sum_j f(x_i', y'_{ij})\,(\beta(y_{ij}) - \beta(y_{i,j-1})) \geqq \overline{\int_b^{b'}} f(x_i', y)d\beta(y) - e.$$

If $\alpha(x_i) - \alpha(x_{i-1}) < 0$, there exists a $d_e' \leqq d_e$ such that for $|\sigma_{iy}| < d_e'$ we have:

$$\sum_j f(x_i', y'_{ij})\,(\beta(y_{ij}) - \beta(y_{i,j-1})) \leqq \overline{\int_b^{b'}} f(x_i', y)d\beta(y) + e.$$

As a consequence,

$$\sum_i (\alpha(x_i) - \alpha(x_{i-1})) \overline{\int_b^{b'}} f(x_i', y)\, d\beta(y)$$
$$\leqq \sum_i \sum_{j=1}^{n_i} f(x_i', y'_{ij})\, (\beta(y_{ij}) - \beta(y_{i,j-1}))$$
$$(\alpha(x_i) - \alpha(x_{i-1})) + e \sum_i |\alpha(x_i) - \alpha(x_{i-1})|.$$

Consequently, if σ consists of the intervals $[x_{i-1}, x_i; y_{ij}, y_{i,j-1}]$, $i = 1 \dots m$, $j = 1 \dots n_i$, then

$$\overline{\int_a^{a'}} d\alpha(x) \overline{\int_b^{b'}} f(x, y) d\beta(y) \leqq \sum_i (\alpha(x_i) - \alpha(x_{i-1})) \overline{\int_b^{b'}} f(x_i', y) dy + e$$
$$\leqq \sum_i (\alpha(x_i) - \alpha(x_{i-1})) \sum_{j=1}^{n_i} f(x_i', y'_{ij})\, (\beta(y_{ij}) - \beta(y_{i,j-1}))$$
$$+ e(1 + V\alpha)$$
$$\leqq \overline{\int_J} f(x, y) d\alpha(x) d\beta(y) + e(2 + V\alpha).$$

Since this holds for all $e > 0$, the inequality of the theorem follows.

In a similar way (or by replacing $f(x, y)$ by $-f(x, y)$), we prove that

$$\underline{\int_a^{a'}} d\alpha(x) \underline{\int_b^{b'}} f(x, y) d\beta(y) \geqq \underline{\int_J} f(x, y) d\alpha(x) d\beta(y).$$

As an immediate corollary we have:

10.2. If $\alpha(x)$ is monotonic nondecreasing on $[a, a']$ if $\beta(y)$ is of bounded variation on $[b, b']$ and if $f(x, y)$ is bounded on J, then

$$\underline{\int_J} f d\alpha d\beta \leqq \underline{\int_a^{a'}} d\alpha \underline{\int_b^{b'}} f d\beta \leqq \left\{ \begin{matrix} \underline{\int_a^{a'}} d\alpha \overline{\int_b^{b'}} f d\beta \\ \overline{\int_a^{a'}} d\alpha \underline{\int_b^{b'}} f d\beta \end{matrix} \right\} \leqq \overline{\int_a^{a'}} d\alpha \overline{\int_b^{b'}} f d\beta \leqq \overline{\int_J} f d\alpha d\beta.$$

The monotoneity condition is needed for the inner inequalities:

$$\underline{\int_a^{a'}} d\alpha \underline{\int_b^{b'}} f d\beta \leqq \underline{\int_a^{a'}} d\alpha \overline{\int_b^{b'}} f d\beta, \text{ and } \overline{\int_a^{a'}} d\alpha \underline{\int_b^{b'}} f d\beta \leqq \overline{\int_a^{a'}} d\alpha \overline{\int_b^{b'}} f d\beta.$$

An immediate consequence of these inequalities is:

10.3. If $N \int_J f(x, y) d\alpha(x) d\beta(y)$ exists, with $\alpha(x)$ monotonic nondecreasing and $\beta(y)$ of bounded variation, then $\int_b^{b'} f(x, y) d\alpha(y)$ exists except for a set of α-measure zero, and $\int_J f(x, y)d\alpha(x)d\beta(y) = \int_a^{a'} d\alpha(x) \int_b^{b'} f(x, y)d\beta(y)$.

For if $\int_J f(x, y)d\alpha(x)d\beta(y)$ exists, the end terms of the inequalities of the preceding theorem are equal so that all of the inequalities become equalities. Then

$$\underline{\int}_a^{a'} d\alpha(x) \underline{\int}_b^{b'} f(x, y)d\beta(y) = \overline{\int}_a^{a'} d\alpha(x) \underline{\int}_b^{b'} f(x, y)d\beta(y)$$

and

$$\underline{\int}_a^{a'} d\alpha(x) \overline{\int}_b^{b'} f(x, y)d\beta(y) = \overline{\int}_a^{a'} d\alpha(x) \overline{\int}_b^{b'} f(x, y)d\beta(y).$$

This means that $\int_a^{a'} d\alpha(x) \underline{\int}_b^{b'} f(x, y)d\beta(y)$ and $\int_a^{a'} d\alpha(x) \overline{\int}_b^{b'} f(x,y)d\beta(y)$ both exist and are equal. Then

$$\int_a^{a'} d\alpha(x) \left(\overline{\int}_b^{b'} f(x, y)d\beta(y) - \underline{\int}_b^{b'} f(x, y)d\beta(y)\right) = 0,$$

so that

$$h(x) = \overline{\int}_b^{b'} f(x, y)d\beta(y) - \underline{\int}_b^{b'} f(x, y)d\beta(y)$$

is a positive or zero function of x such that $N \int_a^{a'} d\alpha(x)h(x) = 0$. But by Ex. 1 at end of II.15 such a function $h(x)$ vanishes excepting possibly at a set of α-measure zero. Then $\int_b^{b'} f(x, y)d\beta(y)$ exists for all x excepting at most a set of α-measure zero and we can write $\int_J f(x, y)d\alpha(x)d\beta(y) = \int_a^{a'} d\alpha(x) \int_b^{b'} f(x, y)d\beta(y)$, where $\int_b^{b'} f(x, y) d\beta(y)$ can be either $\overline{\int}_b^{b'} f(x, y)d\beta(y)$ or $\underline{\int}_b^{b'} f(x, y)d\beta(y)$, and is defined except for a set of α-measure zero.

By interchanging x and y, we obtain:

10.4. If $\alpha(x)$ and $\beta(y)$ are monotone on $[a, a']$ and $[b, b']$, respectively, if $f(x, y)$ is bounded on J, and $N \int_J f(x, y)d\alpha(x)d\beta(y)$ exists, then $N \int_a^{a'} f(x, y)d\alpha(x)$ exists for all y except for a set of β-measure zero and $N \int_b^{b'} f(x, y)\, d\beta(y)$ exists for all x except for a set of α-measure zero, and

$$\int_J f(x, y)d\alpha(x)d\beta(y) = \int_a^{a'} d\alpha(x) \int_b^{b'} f(x, y)d\beta(y)$$
$$= \int_b^{b'} d\beta(y) \int_a^{a'} f(x, y)d\alpha(x)$$

provided we interpret the inner integrals properly.

The same type of theorem is possible for σ-integrals. The modifications necessary are due to the fact that the condition $\int_a^{a'} h(x)d\alpha(x) = 0$ for $h(x) \geqq 0$, and $\alpha(x)$ monotone yields only that $h(x)$ vanishes except for a set of α^*-measure zero, where the α^*-measure takes into account the right and left hand approach to points of $[a, a']$. For the points for which $h(x) \neq 0$ will be either those for which $h(x)$ is discontinuous, or those for which $h(x)$ is continuous but which are interior to an interval of constancy of $\alpha(x)$.

Our theorem can be extended to the case when $\alpha(x)$ and $\beta(y)$ are of bounded variation in the following form:

10.5. If $\alpha(x)$ and $\beta(y)$ are of bounded variation on $[a, a']$ and $[b, b']$, respectively, if $f(x, y)$ is bounded on $J = [a, a'; b, b']$, and if $N\int_J f(x, y)dV\alpha(x)dV\beta(y)$ exists, then the iterated integrals $N\int_a^{a'} d\alpha(x) \int_b^{b'} f(x, y)d\beta(y)$ and $N \int_b^{b'} d\beta(y) \int_a^{a'} f(x, y)d\alpha(x)$ exist and are equal to $N \int_J f(x, y)d\alpha(x)d\beta(y)$.

Here $V\alpha(x)$ and $V\beta(y)$ are the variation functions corresponding to α and β, respectively, and the inner iterated integrals exist except for sets of $V\alpha$-measure zero and $V\beta$-measure zero, respectively.

If $p_1(x)$ and $n_1(x)$ are the positive and negative variations of $\alpha(x)$ and $p_2(y)$ and $n_2(y)$ of $\beta(y)$, then

$$(\alpha(x) - \alpha(a)) (\beta(y) - \beta(b)) = (p_1(x) - n_1(x)) (p_2(y) - n_2(y))$$
$$= p_1(x)p_2(y) + n_1(x)n_2(y) - (p_1(x)n_2(y) + n_1(x)p_2(y)).$$

But we also have

$$\int_{(a,b)}^{(x,y)} |d_1d_2(\alpha(x)\beta(y))| = V\alpha(x)V\beta(y) = p_1(x)p_2(y) + n_1(x)n_2(y)$$
$$+ p_1(x)n_2(y) + n_1(x)p_2(y).$$

Then the functions $p_1(x)p_2(y) + n_1(x)n_2(y)$ and $p_1(x)n_2(y) + n_1(x)p_2(y)$ are the positive and negative two-dimensional variation functions of the function $\alpha(x)\beta(y)$. Since $N \int_J fdV\alpha dV\beta$ exists, it follows that $N \int_J fd\alpha d\beta$ also exists. Further, since $\Delta_1\Delta_2 p_1 p_2(I) \leqq \Delta_1\Delta_2 V\alpha V\beta(I)$ for every interval I, it follows that $\int_J fdp_1dp_2$ exists. In the same way $\int_J fdn_1dn_2$, $\int_J fdp_1dn_2$, and $\int_J fdn_1dp_2$ exist also. Each of these four integrals can be expressed as an iterated integral. Then $\int_b^{b'} f(x, y)dp_2(y)$ and $\int_b^{b'} f(x, y)dn_2(y)$ each exist except for a set of p_1-measure zero. Since the sum of two sets of p_1-measure zero is also of p_1-measure zero, it follows that $\int_b^{b'} f(x, y)d\beta(y)$ exists excepting for a set E_1 of p_1-measure zero. Similarly, the same integral will exist excepting for a set E_2 of n_1 measure zero and so $\int_b^{b'} f(x, y)d\beta(y)$ exists excepting perhaps for the points of a set E common to E_1 and E_2 which will be of p_1 as well as n_1-measure zero. Then since for any interval I: $V\alpha(I) = p_1(I) + n_1(I)$ it follows that E is also of $V\alpha$-measure zero. It follows that $\int_b^{b'} f(x, y)d\beta(y)$ exists except for a set of $V\alpha$-measure zero and by combining parts we can write

$$\int_J f(x, y)d\alpha(x)d\beta(y) = \int_a^{a'} d\alpha(x) \int_b^{b'} f(x,y)d\beta(y) ,$$

where $\int_b^{b'} f(x, y)d\beta(y)$ is defined except for a set of $V\alpha$-measure zero. To ensure integrability it can be taken as the function $\overline{\int}_b^{b'} f(x, y)dp_2(y) - \overline{\int}_b^{b'} f(x, y)dn_2(y)$ on the exceptional set. Since $\alpha(x)$ and $\beta(x)$ enter symmetrically, the reduction to an iterated integral in which the order is reversed is also possible.

For the case of the σ-integrals, it is sufficient to assume that $\sigma \int_J f(x, y)d\alpha(x)d\beta(y)$ exists, since the variation function corresponding to $\alpha(x)\beta(y)$ is $V\alpha(x)V\beta(y)$, so that by Theorem III.9.5 we know that $\sigma \int_J f(x, y)dV\alpha(x)dV\beta(y)$ exists also.

11. Double Integrals with Respect to Functions of Fréchet Bounded Variation

In connection with the expression for the most general continuous bilinear form on the space $C_x \times C_y$ of products of functions continuous in x on $[a, a']$ by functions continuous in y on $[b, b']$, the following theorem is important:

11.1. THEOREM. If $\alpha(x, y)$ is of Fréchet bounded variation on $J = [a, a'; b, b']$, then the weak norm double integral $wk \int_J f(x)g(y) d_1d_2\alpha(x, y)$ exists for all function $f(x)$ continuous on $[a, a']$ and $g(y)$ continuous on $[b, b']$.

The proof depends on showing that the sums

$$\sum_{\sigma_x\sigma_y} f(x_i')g(y_j')\Delta_1\Delta_2(I_{ij})$$

satisfy the Cauchy condition of convergence. Here σ_x is the subdivision $a = x_0 < x_1 < \dots < x_m = a'$ with $x_{i-1} \leq x_i' \leq x_i$, and σ_y and y_j' similarly for $[b, b']$, while $I_{ij} = [x_{i-1}, x_i; y_{j-1}, y_j]$. It is sufficient to show that the difference $|\Sigma_{\sigma_x\sigma_y} - \Sigma_{\sigma_x'\sigma_y'}|$ approaches zero as $|\sigma_x| \to 0$ and $|\sigma_y| \to 0$, if $\sigma_x' \geqq \sigma_x$ and $\sigma_y' \geqq \sigma_y$, since the sums for any two subdivisions $\sigma_x\sigma_y$ and $\sigma_x'\sigma_y'$ can be compared with a sum involving $\sigma_x''\sigma_y''$, where $\sigma_x'' \geqq \sigma_x$ and σ_x', and $\sigma_y'' \geqq \sigma_y$ and σ_y'. Suppose that σ_x' results from σ_x by redividing the interval $[x_{i-1}, x_i]$ by the points x_{ik}, $k = 0 \ldots m_i$ and σ_y' by dividing $[y_{j-1}, y_j]$ by the points y_{jl}, $l = 0, 1, \ldots, n_j$. Then:

$$
\begin{aligned}
&\Big|\sum_{ij} f(x_i')g(y_j')\Delta_1\Delta_2\alpha(I_{ij}) - \sum_{ik,jl} f(x'_{ik})g(y'_{jl})\Delta_1\Delta_2\alpha(I_{ik,jl})\Big| \\
&\quad = \Big|\sum_{ik,jl} (f(x_i')g(y_j') - f(x'_{ik})g(y'_{jl}))\Delta_1\Delta_2\alpha(I_{ik,jl})\Big| \\
&\quad = \Big|\sum_{ik,jl} [f(x_i')(g(y_j') - g(y'_{jl})) \\
&\quad + g(y'_{jl})(f(x_i') - f(x'_{ik}))]\Delta_1\Delta_2\alpha(I_{ik,jl})\Big| \\
&\quad \leqq M_1\omega(g;\sigma_y)\Big|\sum_{ik,jl} A_iB_{jl}\,\Delta_1\Delta_2\alpha(I_{ik,jl})\Big| + M_2\omega(f;\sigma_x) \\
&\quad \cdot\Big|\sum_{ik,jl} C_{ik}D_{jl}\,\Delta_1\Delta_2\alpha(I_{ik,jl})\Big|.
\end{aligned}
$$

Here $\omega(g;\sigma_x)$ and $\omega(f;\sigma_y)$ are the maximum oscillation of g and f on the intervals of σ_x and σ_y, respectively, M_1 is the maximum of $|f(x)|$ on $[a, a']$, and M_2 that of $|g(y)|$ on $[b, b']$, while $A_i, B_{jl}, C_{ik}, D_{jl}$ are numbers whose absolute value is less than or equal to unity. For the next step in the proof, we use a lemma on the maximum value of bilinear forms which we shall prove below:

11.2. Lemma. The maximum value of the bilinear form $\Sigma_{i=1}^m \Sigma_{j-1}^n a_{ij}x_iy_j$ for $|x_i| \leqq 1$ and $|y_j| \leqq 1$ is attained for $|x_i| = 1$ and $|y_j| = 1$. Since this maximum is necessarily positive, there exist $\varepsilon_i = \pm 1$, and $\varepsilon_j' = \pm 1$, such that $|\Sigma_{ij}a_{ij}x_iy_j| \leqq \Sigma_{ij}a_{ij}\,\varepsilon_i\varepsilon_j'$ for $|x_i| \leqq 1$ and $|y_j| \leqq 1$.

Applying this lemma to

$$\sum_{ik,jl} A_iB_{jl}\Delta_1\Delta_2\alpha(I_{ik,jl})$$

and

$$\sum_{ik,jl} G_{ik}D_{jl}\Delta_1\Delta_2\alpha(I_{ik,jl}),$$

there exist ε_{ik}, ε_{jl}', ε_{ik}'', ε_{jl}''', with values ± 1, such that

$$\Big|\sum_{ik,jl} A_iB_{jl}\Delta_1\Delta_2\alpha(I_{ik,jl})\Big| \leqq \sum_{ik,jl} \varepsilon_{ik}\varepsilon_{jl}'\Delta_1\Delta_2\alpha(I_{ik,jl})$$

and

$$\left| \sum_{ik,jl} C_{ik} D_{jl} \Delta_1 \Delta_2 \alpha(I_{ik,jl}) \right| \leqq \sum_{ik,jl} \varepsilon_{ik}'' \; \varepsilon_{jl}''' \Delta_1 \Delta_2 \alpha(I_{ik,jl}).$$

Now the right-hand sides of these inequalities are each less than or equal to $FV\alpha(J)$. We therefore have if $\sigma_x' \geqq \sigma_x$ and $\sigma_y' \geqq \sigma_y$, then

$$\left| \sum_{\sigma_x \sigma_y} fg\Delta_1 \Delta_2 \alpha - \sum_{\sigma_x' \sigma_y'} fg\Delta_1 \Delta_2 \alpha \right| \leqq [M_1 \omega(g; \sigma_y) + M_2 \omega(f; \sigma_x)] \, FV\alpha(J).$$

Since f and g are uniformly continuous, this inequality leads to the existence of the weak net integral $wk \int_J f(x)g(y)d_1d_2\alpha(x, y)$.

[Proof of lemma. Suppose that the maximum of $\Sigma_{ij} a_{ij} x_i y_j$ is attained for $x_i = x_i'$ and $y_j = y_j'$. This maximum is positive unless $a_{ij} = 0$ for all i and j. Since $|\Sigma_{ij} a_{ij} x_i' y_j'| \leqq \Sigma_j |\Sigma_i a_{ij} x_i'| \, |y_j'|$ it follows that the maximum is attained if we set $y_j' = \varepsilon_j' = \text{sgn}\,(\Sigma_i a_{ij} x_i')$. Now

$$\sum_{ij} a_{ij} x_i' \varepsilon_j' = \sum_i (\sum_j a_{ij} \varepsilon_j') x_i' \leqq \sum_i \left| \sum_j a_{ij} \varepsilon_j' \right| |x_i'|,$$

and so the maximum is attained for $x_i' = \varepsilon_i = \text{sgn}\,(\Sigma_j a_{ij} \varepsilon_j')$. In other words, there exist $\varepsilon_i = \pm 1$ and $\varepsilon_j' = \pm 1$, such that $|\Sigma_{ij} a_{ij} x_i y_j| \leqq \Sigma_{ij} a_{ij} \varepsilon_i \varepsilon_j'$ for all $|x_i| \leq 1$ and $|y_j| \leq 1$].

It is possible to show that this theorem is reversible in the form: If $wk \int_J f(x)g(y)d_1d_2\alpha(x, y)$ exists for all continuous functions $f(x)$ on $[a, a']$ and $g(y)$ on $[b, b']$, then $\alpha(x, y)$ is of Fréchet bounded variation on J. For a proof see J. A. Clarkson: On double Riemann-Stieltjes integrals, *Bull. Am. Math. Soc.*, 39 (1933) 929-936.

As suggested in the opening sentence of this section, Fréchet has shown that the most general linear continuous functional on the product space of functions continuous in x on $[a, a']$ by those in y on $[b, b']$ is $wk \int_J f(x)g(y)d\alpha(x, y)$, where $\alpha(x, y)$ is of Fréchet bounded variation. For a proof see M. Fréchet: Sur les fonctionelles bilineaires, *Trans. Am. Math. Soc.* 16 (1915) 215-234. It would be interesting to know whether the Weierstrass polynomial approximation theorem based on Bernstein polynomials could be used for the proof.

EXERCISES

1. Show that if $f(x, y)$ and $g(x, y)$ on $J = [a, a'; b, b']$ are such that $\int_J fdg$ exists, and $f(x, y) = f(x)$, independent of y, then $\int_J fdg = \int_a^{a'} f(x) d_x(g(x, b') - g(x, b))$. Is this reversible, that is, if $f(x, y)$ is independent of y

and $\int_a^{a'} f(x)d_x(g(x, b') - g(x, b))$ exists, can one conclude that $\int_J fdg$ exists?

2. If $g(x, y)$ is of bounded variation on J, under what conditions on g does the total variation $v(J) = \int_J |d_1 d_2 g(I)|$ exist as a norm integral?

3. If $g(x, y)$ is continuous and of bounded variation on J, is it true that if $\sigma \int_J f d_1 d_2 g$ exists, then $N \int_J f d_1 d_2 g$ exists and has the same value?

4. Let $g(x, y)$ be of bounded variation on J, and $f(x, y)$ be bounded. Let $p(x, y)$ and $n(x, y)$ be, respectively, the positive and negative variations of $g(x, y)$. If $M(I) =$ l.u.b. of $f(x, y)$ on I and $m(I) =$ g.l.b. of $f(x, y)$ on I define $\overline{F}(\sigma) = \Sigma_\sigma[M(I)\Delta_1\Delta_2 p(I) - m(I)\Delta_1\Delta_2 n(I)]$ and $\underline{F}(\sigma) = \Sigma_\sigma [m(I)\Delta_1\Delta_2 p(I) - M(I)\Delta_1\Delta_2 n(I)]$. Show that $\sigma \overline{\int} fdg = \text{g.l.b.}_\sigma \overline{F}(\sigma) = \lim_\sigma \overline{F}(\sigma)$ and $\sigma \underline{\int} fdg = \text{l.u.b.}_\sigma \underline{F}(\sigma) = \lim_\sigma \underline{F}(\sigma)$.

5. Show that if $g(x, y)$ is the break function $\beta(x, y; x_0; h_1(y), h_2(y))$ defined: $g(x, y) = 0$ for $a \leqq x < x_0$, $g(x_0, y) = h_1(y)$, $g(x, y) = h_2(y)$ for $x_0 < x \leqq a'$, all for y on $[b, b']$, and if $\int_J f(x, y)dg(x, y)$ exists, then $\int_b^{b'} f(x_0, y)dh_2(y)$ exists and gives the value of the integral.

6. Show that if $g(x, y)$ is monotonely monotone, if $f(x, y)$ is bounded on J and $\int_J f(x, y)d_1 d_2 g(x, y)$ exists, then

$$\begin{aligned}\int_J f(x, y)d_1 d_2 g(x, y) &= \int_J f(x, y)d_1 d_2 g_c(x, y)\\ &+ \sum_x \int_b^{b'} f(x, y)d_y\,[g(x+0, y) - g(x-0, y)]\\ &+ \sum_y \int_a^{a'} f(x, y)d_x[g(x, y+0) - g(x, y-0)]\\ &- \sum_{xy} f(x, y)\,[g(x+0, y+0) - g(x-0, y+0)\\ &- g(x+0, y-0) + g(x-0, y-0)]\end{aligned}$$

where $g_c(x, y)$ is the continuous part of $g(x, y)$. The same type of integral (norm or σ) appears on both sides of the equality. Can the result be extended to any function of bounded variation such that $g(x, b)$ and $g(a, y)$ are of bounded variation?

7. Show that if the net integral $\int_J f(x)g(y)d_1 d_2 \alpha(x, y)$ exists for every continuous function $f(x)$ on $[a, a']$ and every continuous function $g(y)$ on $[b, b']$, then $\alpha(x, y)$ is of bounded variation on J.

REFERENCES

The following articles may be consulted in connection with material covered in the preceding paragraphs relating to multiple Riemann-Stieltjes integrals:

J. Burkill, Functions of intervals, *Proc. London Math. Soc.* (2) **22** (1924) 275-310.

J.A. Clarkson, Double Riemann-Stieltjes integrals, *Bull. Am. Math. Soc.* **39** (1933) 929-936.

M. Fréchet, Extension du cas des integrales multiples d'une definition d'integrale due à Stieltjes, *Nouv. Ann. de Math.* (4) **10** (1910) 241-256.

M. Fréchet, Sur les fonctionelles bilineaires, *Trans. Am. Math. Soc.* **16** (1915) 215-234.

H. Luikens, Riemann Stieltjes Integratie dij Functies van tree of meer Veranderlichem, Doctoral Dissertation, Groningen, 1937.

R.C. Young, On Riemann integrals with respect to a continuous increment, *Math. Z.* **29** (1929) 217-233.

W.H. Young, On multiple integrals, *Proc. Roy. Soc.* **A93** (1917) 27-41.

W.H. Young, Multiple integration by parts and the second mean value theorem, *Proc. London Math. Soc.* (2) **16** (1917) 273-293.

CHAPTER IV

SETS

1. Fundamental Operations

For convenience, we collect in this chapter nomenclature, operations, and manipulations of sets and classes of sets, some of which have been used in the earlier sections. The concepts presented are basic in connection with the theory of measure and Lebesgue integration.

We postulate a basic set W, and concern ourselves with subsets E of W. We assume that there is a way of distinguishing between elements of W and consequently between subsets of W. The empty or null set will be denoted by O.

1.1. Order. The concept of inclusion, where all elements of a set E_1 belong to E_2, sets up a natural order in subsets and in classes of subsets of W. $E_1 \leqq E_2$ shall mean that E_1 is a subset of, or contained in E_2 (other notations in use are $E_1 \subset E_2$, and $E_1 \in E_2$).

1.2. Addition. For two or more sets E_α, the sum (or union or join) is the set E consisting of all elements in any E_α. For two sets we write $E = E_1 + E_2$, for a collection of sets E_α, $E = \Sigma_\alpha E_\alpha$. Alternate notations are $E = E_1 \cup E_2$ for two sets and $E = \cup_\alpha E_\alpha$, for a collection. (The symbol $\cup$ can be associated with the initial letter of union.) Addition of sets is obviously commutative $(E_1 + E_2 = E_2 + E_1)$ and associative $[(E_1 + E_2) + E_3 = E_1 + (E_2 + E_3) = E_1 + E_2 + E_3]$. Further, $E + E = E$ for all E, i.e., addition is idempotent, and the relation $E_1 \leqq E_2$ is equivalent to $E_1 + E_2 = E_2$.

1.3. Multiplication. For two or more sets E_α, the product (or intersection or meet) is the set of all elements common to all E_α. For two sets we write $E = E_1 \cdot E_2$ or E_1E_2, for a collection $E = \Pi_\alpha E_\alpha$. Alternate notations are: $E = E_1 \cap E_2$ for two sets, and $E = \cap_\alpha E_\alpha$ for a collection of sets. (The symbol $\cap$ can be thought of as a rounded off Π.) Multiplication is commutative and associative. It is also distributive with respect to addition in both ways: $E_1(E_2 + E_3) = E_1E_2 + E_1E_3$, and $E_1 + E_2E_3 = (E_1 + E_2)(E_1 + E_3)$. The second of these follows if the right-hand side is "multiplied out." We also have $EE = E$ for all E, and $E_1 \leqq E_2$ is equivalent to $E_1E_2 = E_1$. Further $E_1E_2 = O$ is equivalent to the fact that E_1 and E_2 are disjoint.

1.4. Complementation. To every set E in W, there corresponds uniquely its complement in W, the set of all elements of W not in E. We shall denote the complement of E by CE. Another acceptable notation is $\neg E$ (read: not E). Then for any set E, CE is the set for which $E + CE = W$ and $E \cdot CE = O$. If we apply the operator C to order, addition and multiplication we find:

1.4.1. If $E_1 \leqq E_2$, then $CE_1 \geqq CE_2$,

1.4.2. $C(\Sigma_\alpha E_\alpha) = \Pi_\alpha CE_\alpha$,

1.4.3. $C(\Pi E_\alpha) = \Sigma_\alpha CE_\alpha$,

that is, under complementation order is reversed, and sums and products interchanged.

Under the definitions of addition, multiplication, and complementation given, the set of all subsets of a set W form a Boolean algebra.

1.5. Definition. *A Boolean algebra* is a class X of elements: x, y, z ... consisting of at least two elements, on which there are defined two binary operations: $x \oplus y$ and $x \odot y$ on all pairs of elements (x, y) of X to X.

These operations are both commutative and mutually distributive $(x \odot (y \oplus z) = x \odot y \oplus x \odot z$ and $x \oplus y \odot z = (x \oplus y) \odot (x \oplus z))$. Further, there exist two elements 0 and 1 such that $x \oplus 0 = x$ and $x \odot 1 = x$ for all x; and for each x there exists an x^* in X such that $x \oplus x^* = 1$ and $x \odot x^* = 0$. Then it can be shown that $\oplus$ and $\odot$ are also associative, that $x \oplus x = x$ and $x \odot x = x$ for all x, and $x \oplus x \odot y = x$, $x \odot (x \oplus y) = x$ for all x and y. See E. V. Huntington: Sets of independent postulates for the algebra of logic, *Trans. Am. Math. Soc.* 5 (1904) 288-309

1.6. Difference. If E_2 is a subset of E_1, then $E_1 - E_2$ is the set of all elements of E_1 which are not in E_2. Since this statement also makes sense even when E_2 does not belong to E_1, we use it to define $E_1 - E_2$ in any case. Equivalent definitions are: $E_1 - E_2 = E_1 - E_1E_2 = E_1CE_2$.

We note that we do not in general have $E_2 + (E_1 - E_2) = E_1$. For two sets E_1 and E_2, there exists an E such that $E_1 + E = E_2$ only if $E_1 \leqq E_2$, and in that case there are many sets E which will serve. We do have $E_1 - (E_2 + E_3) = (E_1 - E_2) - E_3 = (E_1 - E_3) - E_2 = ECE_2CE_3$ and $E_3(E_1 - E_2) = E_3E_1 - E_3E_2$.

1.6.1. THEOREM. The product of two sets can be expressed in terms of differences.

We have $E_1E_2 = E_1 - (E_1 - E_2)$. For: $E_1 - (E_1 - E_2) = E_1C(E_1CE_2) = E_1(CE_1 + E_2) = E_1E_2$. If E_n is a sequence of sets then:

$$\prod_n E_n = (E_1 - (E_1 - E_2)) - (E_2 - E_3) \ldots = E_1 - \sum_{n=1}^{\infty} (E_n - E_{n+1}).$$

For the right-hand side can be written $E_1C(E_1CE_2)C(E_2CE_3)$ .... This is equal to

$$\begin{aligned} &E_1(CE_1 + E_2)\,(CE_2 + E_3) \ldots \\ &\quad = E_1E_2(CE_2 + E_3)\,(CE_3 + E_4) \ldots \\ &\quad = E_1E_2E_3(CE_3 + E_4) \ldots = \ldots = \prod_n E_n. \end{aligned}$$

This formula depends on an order of the sets, but the ultimate set is independent of the ordering. If E_α is any collection of sets, then

$$\prod_\alpha E_\alpha = E_{\alpha_0} - \sum_{\alpha \neq \beta} [E_\alpha - E_\beta].$$

An alternative expression relating products to sums and differences is

$$\prod_\alpha E_\alpha = \sum_\alpha E_\alpha - \sum_\beta (\sum_\alpha E_\alpha - E_\beta) = E - \sum_\beta (E - E_\beta)$$

where $E = \Sigma_\alpha E_\alpha$. This is equivalent to complimentation relative to the set $E = \Sigma_\alpha E_\alpha$.

1.7. Symmetric Difference. The symmetric difference of two sets E_1 and E_2 and denoted by $E_1 \Delta E_2$ is defined:

$$E_1 \Delta E_2 = (E_1 - E_2) + (E_2 - E_1) = E_1CE_2 + E_2CE_1.$$

1.7.1. Obviously: If E_1 and E_2 are disjoint, then $E_1 \Delta E_2 = E_1 + E_2$; if $E_1 = E_2 = E$, then $E \Delta E = O$; for any E, $E \Delta O = E$ and $E \Delta W = CE$; and for any E_1 and E_2, $(CE_1) \Delta (CE_2) = E_1 \Delta E_2$.

1.7.2. As its name implies the operation Δ is symmetric: $E_1 \Delta E_2 = E_2 \Delta E_1$. It is also associative: $(E_1 \Delta E_2) \Delta E_3 = E_1 \Delta (E_2 \Delta E_3)$.

For:

$$
\begin{aligned}
(E_1 \Delta E_2) \Delta E_3 &= (E_1 CE_2 + E_2 CE_1) \Delta E_3 \\
&= (E_1 CE_2 + E_2 CE_1) CE_3 + C(E_1 CE_2 + E_2 CE_1) E_3 \\
&= E_1 CE_2 CE_3 + E_2 CE_1 CE_3 + E_3 CE_1 CE_2 + E_1 E_2 E_3,
\end{aligned}
$$

which is symmetric in E_1, E_2, and E_3.

1.7.3. Further, for any E_1 and E_2, there exists a unique E such that $E \Delta E_1 = E_2$.

For if E is such that $E \Delta E_1 = E_2$, then $(E \Delta E_1) \Delta E_1 = E_2 \Delta E_1$. But $(E \Delta E_1) \Delta E_1 = E \Delta (E_1 \Delta E_1) = E \Delta O = E$, so that E must be $E_2 \Delta E_1$. Conversely if $E = E_2 \Delta E_1$, then $(E_2 \Delta E_1) \Delta E_1 = E_2$. Consequently, $E \Delta E_1 = E_2$ is equivalent to $E = E_2 \Delta E_1$.

1.7.4. Summarizing, we can say that the class of all subsets of W form a commutative group under the operation Δ between sets, the operation Δ being nilpotent.

1.7.5. Multiplication of sets is distributive relative to symmetric difference in the sense that for three sets: E_1, E_2 and E_3, we have $E_1(E_2 \Delta E_3) = (E_1 E_2) \Delta (E_1 E_3)$.

For:

$$
\begin{aligned}
(E_1 E_2) \Delta (E_1 E_3) &= E_1 E_2 C(E_1 E_3) + E_1 E_3 C(E_1 E_2) \\
&= E_1 E_2 (CE_1 + CE_3) + E_1 E_3 (CE_1 + CE_2) \\
&= E_1 (E_2 \Delta E_3).
\end{aligned}
$$

1.7.6. Under the combined operations of symmetric difference (Δ) and multiplication $(\cdot)$, the class of all subsets of a set W form then a Boolean ring. *

1.7.7. Addition of a finite number of sets can be expressed in terms of multiplication and symmetric differences.

* A Boolean ring of a set of elements X involves two binary operations $\oplus$ and $\odot$. Under $\oplus$, X is a commutative group. Multiplication $\odot$ is associative and distributive relative to $\oplus$, and is idempotent ($x \odot x = x$ for all x). It can then be proved that $\oplus$ is nilpotent ($x \oplus x = 0$, where 0 is the identity element of $\oplus$), and multiplication is commutative. See: C. Caratheodory, Mass und Integral und ihre Algebraisierung, pp. 18-20; M.H. Stone, Theory of representations of Boolean algebras, *Trans. Am. Math. Soc.* 40 (1936) 37-111.

For:

$$E_1 + E_2 = E_1 \Delta E_2 + E_1E_2 = (E_1 \Delta E_2) \Delta (E_1E_2) = E_1E_2 \Delta (E_1 \Delta E_2).$$

For three sets $E_1 + E_2 + E_3$, we first obtain an expression for $E_1 + E_2$ which in turn yields an expression for $(E_1 + E_2) + E_3$, and so on.

1.7.8. Similarly multiplication of a finite number of sets can be expressed in terms of addition and symmetric difference.

We have: $E_1E_2 = (E_1 + E_2) \Delta (E_1 \Delta E_2)$, the result of solving $E_1 + E_2 = E_1E_2 \Delta (E_1 \Delta E_2)$ for E_1E_2.

1.8. Limits of Sequences of Sets. In terms of addition and multiplication, it is possible to define the notions of limits of sequences of sets. If E_n is any sequence of subsets of W, then

$$\overline{\lim_n}\, E_n = \prod_{m=1}^{\infty} (\sum_{n=m}^{\infty} E_n) \text{ and } \underline{\lim_n}\, E_n = \sum_{m=1}^{\infty} (\prod_{n=m}^{\infty} E_n).$$

These definitions are analogous to the following definitions of greatest and least of the limits of a sequence of real numbers $\{x_n\}$:

$$\overline{\lim_n}\, x_n = \underset{m}{\text{g.l.b.}}\, (\underset{n \geqq m}{\text{l.u.b.}}\, x_n) \quad ; \quad \underline{\lim_n}\, x_n = \underset{m}{\text{l.u.b.}}\, (\underset{n \geqq m}{\text{g.l.b.}}\, x_n).$$

Alternate definitions are:

1.8.1. For any sequence of sets E_n, $\overline{\lim}_n E_n$ is the set which consists of the elements in an infinite number of E_n, while $\underline{\lim}_n E_n$ is the set which consists of the elements in E_n for n greater than some n_0, depending on the element.

For if the element x is in an infinite number of the sets E_n, then it belongs to $\Sigma_{n=m}^{\infty} E_n$ for all m and so to $\overline{\lim}_n E_n$. Conversely, if x is in $\overline{\lim}_n E_n$, then it is in $\Sigma_{n=m}^{\infty} E_n$ for all m, and so in E_n for an infinity of n's. Similar reasoning applies to $\underline{\lim}_n E_n$.

As an example, if E_{2m} is the set of x such that $-\frac{1}{2} \leqq x \leqq 1 - 1/m$ and E_{2m+1}, the x such that $-1 + 1/m \leqq x \leqq \frac{1}{2}$, then $\overline{\lim}_n E_n$ is the set of x such that $-1 < x < 1$, and $\underline{\lim}_n E_n$ the x such that $-\frac{1}{2} \leqq x \leqq \frac{1}{2}$.

1.8.2. Obviously $C(\overline{\lim}_n E_n) = \underline{\lim}_n CE_n$.

1.8.3. The sequence E_n is said to have a limit if $\overline{\lim}\, E_n = \underline{\lim}\, E_n$. If the sequence E_n is monotone nondecreasing, that is, $E_{n+1} \geqq E_n$

for all n, then $\lim_n E_n = \Sigma_n E_n$; if E_n is monotone nonincreasing, then $\lim_n E_n = \Pi_n E_n$. If for any sequence E_n, we write $E_m{}' = \Sigma_m^\infty E_n$, then $\overline{\lim}_n E_n = \lim_m E_m{}'$, while if $E_m{}'' = \Pi_m^\infty E_n$, then $\underline{\lim}\, E_n = \lim_m E_m{}''$.

2. Characteristic Functions

To every set E of a set W, there corresponds a point function, the characteristic function of the set E defined $\chi(E; x) = 1$ for x in E and $\chi(E, x) = 0$ for x in CE or not in E. Characteristic functions set up a one to one map of the subsets of W on the class of real valued functions on W taking only the values 0 and 1.

We note the following:

2.1. $\chi(O; x) = 0$ and $\chi(W; x) = 1$ for all x.

2.2. If E_1 and E_2 are any two sets, then
$$\chi(E_1; x) + \chi(E_2; x) = \chi(E_1 + E_2; x) + \chi(E_1E_2; x).$$

2.3. If the sets E_a are disjoint, then $\chi(\Sigma_a E_a; x) = \Sigma_a \chi(E_a; x)$.

2.4. If E is any set, then $\chi(E; x) = 1 - \chi(CE; x)$.

2.5. If E_1 and E_2 are any sets, then $\chi(E_1E_2; x) = \chi(E_1; x)\chi(E_2; x)$. If E_a is any collection of sets, then $\chi(\Pi_a E_a; x) = \Pi_a \chi(E_a; x)$.

2.6. If E_1 and E_2 are any sets, then
$$\chi(E_1 - E_2; x) = \chi(E_1; x)\,(1 - \chi(E_2; x)).$$

2.7. If E_1 and E_2 are any sets, then
$$\chi(E_1 \Delta E_2; x) = \chi(E_1 + E_2; x) - \chi(E_1E_2; x) = |\,\chi(E_1; x) - \chi(E_2; x)\,|.$$

2.8. If E_n is any sequence of sets, then
$$\chi(\overline{\lim}_n E_n; x) = \overline{\lim}_n\, \chi(E_n; x) \quad \text{and} \quad \chi(\underline{\lim}_n E_n; x) = \underline{\lim}_n\, \chi(E_n; x).$$

2.9. If E_n is a sequence of sets, then $\lim_n E_n$ exists if and only if $\lim_n \chi(E_n; x)$ exists for all x of W, and this limit is $\chi(\lim_n E_n; x)$.

The relations of 2.8. above give additional justification for the definitions of $\overline{\lim}_n E_n$ and $\underline{\lim}_n E_n$.

3. Properties of Classes of Sets

Each of the operations on sets of the preceding sections suggest a closure property of classes $\mathfrak{E}$ of subsets of W. Thus we have:

3.1. Definition. A class $\mathfrak{E}$ of sets E is *additive*: A, if the sum of any finite number of sets of $\mathfrak{E}$ belongs to $\mathfrak{E}$; $\mathfrak{E}$ is *sequentially additive*: *s-A*, if the sum of any denumerable number of sets of $\mathfrak{E}$ belongs to $\mathfrak{E}$; $\mathfrak{E}$ is *totally additive*: *t-A*, if the sum of any collection of sets of $\mathfrak{E}$ belongs to $\mathfrak{E}$.

The class of closed sets of points on a straight line or of a topological space is additive but not *s*-additive. The class of open sets is totally additive. If the function $\alpha(x)$ is monotonic on $[a, b]$ then the class of sets of points of α-measure zero is *s*-additive.

3.2. In the same way, the class $\mathfrak{E}$ is *multiplicative*: *M*, if the product of any finite number of sets of any $\mathfrak{E}$ belongs to $\mathfrak{E}$, *sequentially multiplicative*: *s-M*, if the product of a denumerable number of sets of $\mathfrak{E}$ belongs to $\mathfrak{E}$; and *totally multiplicative*: *t-M*, if the product of any collection of sets of $\mathfrak{E}$ belongs to $\mathfrak{E}$.

The class of closed sets on a straight line is totally multiplicative.

3.3. A class $\mathfrak{E}$ of sets E has the *complementary* property (C) if with the set E, $\mathfrak{E}$ also contains its complement CE.

3.4. A class of sets $\mathfrak{E}$ has the *subtractive* property (S) if the difference of any two sets of $\mathfrak{E}$ belongs to $\mathfrak{E}$.

3.5. A class of sets $\mathfrak{E}$ has the *symmetric difference* property (Δ) if the symmetric difference of two and so of any finite number of sets of $\mathfrak{E}$ belongs to $\mathfrak{E}$.

These properties are not independent. We have, for instance:

3.6. If $\mathfrak{E}$ has the complementary property then additive properties are equivalent to the corresponding multiplicative properties. If $\mathfrak{E}$ is subtractive, then it is multiplicative, which follows from the identity $E_1E_2 = E_1 - (E_1 - E_2)$. If $\mathfrak{E}$ is subtractive and sequentially (totally) additive, then it is sequentially (totally) multiplicative, a result of the formula $\Pi_\alpha E_\alpha = \Sigma_\alpha E_\alpha - \Sigma_\beta(\Sigma_\alpha E_\alpha - E_\beta)$.

3.7. Definition. Certain combinations of these properties have proved to be of interest especially in the theory of measure.

A class $\mathfrak{E}$ of sets is said to be a *ring* of sets if it is additive, multiplicative, subtractive and has the symmetric difference property. It is said to be an *s-ring* if it is also *s*-additive and *s*-multiplicative. A class of sets $\mathfrak{E}$ is called an *algebra* if it is a ring which has the complementary property, an *s-algebra* if it is an *s-ring* with the complementary property.

Since the properties of classes of sets are not independent we can reduce the ring conditions as follows:

3.8. THEOREM. The class $\mathfrak{E}$ of sets is a ring if it has any of the following four pairs of properties:

(1) additive and subtractive

(2) additive and symmetric difference

(3) multiplicative and symmetric difference

(4) symmetric difference and subtractive.

Since each of the properties of a ring is involved in one of these four combinations, it is sufficient to show that (1) $\rightarrow$ (2) $\rightarrow$ (3) $\rightarrow$ (4) $\rightarrow$ (1). (1) $\rightarrow$ (2), since $E_1 \Delta E_2 = (E_1 - E_2) + (E_2 - E_1)$; (2) $\rightarrow$ (3) since $E_1 E_2 = (E_1 + E_2) \Delta E_1 \Delta E_2$; (3) $\rightarrow$ (4) since $E_1 - E_2 = E_1 - E_1 E_2 = E_1 \Delta (E_1 E_2)$; and (4) $\rightarrow$ (1) since $E_1 + E_2 = (E_1 E_2) \Delta E_1 \Delta E_2$.

3.9. The class $\mathfrak{E}$ of sets is an s-ring if it is s-additive and subtractive since these two properties imply also that $\mathfrak{E}$ is s-multiplicative and has the symmetric difference property.

3.10. Similarly the class $\mathfrak{E}$ of sets is an algebra if it has the complementary property and is either additive or multiplicative, it is an s-algebra if it has the complementary property and is either s-additive or s-multiplicative.

4. Extensions of Classes of Sets Relative to Properties

In general, a class $\mathfrak{E}$ of sets of a fundamental space W will not have a given property P. In such a case, it may however be possible to extend $\mathfrak{E}$ by the adjoining of additional sets so that *the extended class has the property P and is the smallest class containing $\mathfrak{E}$ which has the property P.* The resulting class will be called the class $\mathfrak{E}$ extended to have property P and be denoted by $\mathfrak{E}_P$, when it exists. In a way, the class $\mathfrak{E}$ and the property P might be said to generate the class $\mathfrak{E}_P$ which has property P.

4.1. Definition. A property of classes of sets of W is said to be *extensionally attainable*, if for every such class $\mathfrak{E}$, there exists the extension $\mathfrak{E}_P$ having property P.

4.2. Necessary and sufficient conditions that a property P be extensionally attainable are: (1) that the class $\overline{\mathfrak{E}}$ of all subsets of W have the property P, and (2) the product class or greatest common subclass of any collection of classes having the property P also have property P.

For the necessity we note that if P is extensionally attainable then since there is no class $\mathfrak{E}$ larger than $\overline{\mathfrak{E}}$, $\overline{\mathfrak{E}}$ itself must have property P. Further if for some set of classes, each of which has property P, the product of these classes $\mathfrak{E}_0$ does not have the property P, then there is no smallest class having property P and containing $\mathfrak{E}_0$. That the two conditions are sufficient follows from the observation that for any $\mathfrak{E}$ an extension $\mathfrak{E}_P$ having property P exists if there exists a class $\mathfrak{E}_0$ containing $\mathfrak{E}$ which has property P, and the product of any set of classes having property P also has property P.

4.3. We note that if a collection of properties P_α are each extensionally attainable, then any property which is a combination of these properties is also extensionally attainable.

4.4. For the properties A, s-A, t-A, M, s-M, t-M, S, C and Δ discussed in IV.3, it is a simple matter to verify the conditions for extensionally attainability of the above theorem. It follows then that any combination of these properties, in particular, ring, s-ring, algebra, s-algebra are also extensionally attainable.

The actual construction of extensions relative to given properties may involve difficulties. For the properties: additive, multiplicative, symmetric difference, the extensions $\mathfrak{E}_P$ of any class $\mathfrak{E}$ of sets is obtained by adjoining to $\mathfrak{E}$ all finite combinations of subsets $E_1 \circ E_2 \circ \ldots \circ E_n$, where $\circ$ stands for $+$, $\cdot$, and Δ, respectively. To secure the complementary extension of a class $\mathfrak{E}$, we adjoin to $\mathfrak{E}$ all sets CE which are complements of sets of $\mathfrak{E}$.

The subtractive extension of a class involves complications. For instance, if $\mathfrak{E}$ consists of two sets E_1 and E_2, then the class $\mathfrak{E}_S$ consists of E_1, E_2, $E_1 - E_2$, $E_2 - E_1$, E_1E_2, and O. If $\mathfrak{E}$ consists of three sets E_1, E_2, E_3, then by analogy, $\mathfrak{E}_S$ will need to contain additionally at least $E_1E_2CE_3$, $E_1CE_2E_3$, $CE_1E_2E_3$, $E_1CE_2CE_3$, $CE_1E_2CE_3$, $CE_1CE_2E_3$, and $E_1E_2E_3$, seven mutually disjoint sets. These sets can be obtained by multiplying out $(E_1 + CE_1)(E_2 + CE_2)(E_3 + CE_3) = W$, which gives the totality of disjoint sets of W determined by E_1, E_2, E_3, and discarding $CE_1CE_2CE_3 = C(E_1 + E_2 + E_3)$. If we set $A_1 = E_1E_2CE_3$, $A_2 = E_1CE_2E_3$, $A_3 = CE_1E_2E_3$, $A_4 = E_1CE_2CE_3$, $A_5 = CE_1E_2CE_3$, $A_6 = CE_1CE_2E_3$, and $A_7 = E_1E_2E_3$, then $E_1 = E_1(E_2 + CE_2)(E_3 + CE_3) = A_7 + A_1 + A_2 + A_4$. Similarly, $E_2 = A_7 + A_1 + A_3 + A_5$ and $E_3 = A_7 + A_2 + A_3 + A_6$, that is, E_1, E_2, E_3 are each expressible in terms of four of the disjoint sets $A_1 \ldots A_7$. It follows that the other sets belonging to $\mathfrak{E}_S$ can be obtained by dropping out one or two sets in the expressions for E_1, E_2, and E_3. In this way we find that $\mathfrak{E}_S$ consists of: O, E_1, E_2, E_3, A_1, A_2, A_3, A_4, A_5, A_6, A_7, $A_7 + A_1 + A_2$, $A_7 + A_1 + A_4$, $A_7 + A_2 + A_4$, $A_1 + A_2 + A_4$, $A_7 + A_1 + A_3$, $A_7 + A_1 + A_5$, $A_7 + A_3 + A_5$, $A_1 + A_3 + A_5$, $A_7 + A_2 + A_3$, $A_7 + A_2 + A_6$, $A_7 + A_3 + A_6$, $A_2 + A_3 + A_6$, $A_7 + A_1$, $A_7 + A_2$, $A_7 + A_4$, $A_1 + A_2$, $A_1 + A_4$, $A_2 + A_4$, $A_7 + A_3$, $A_7 + A_5$, $A_1 + A_3$, $A_1 + A_5$, $A_3 + A_5$, $A_7 + A_6$, $A_2 + A_3$, $A_2 + A_6$, $A_3 + A_6$, a total of 38 sets. Obviously any one of these sets can be written as a combination of E_1, E_2, and E_3. The same procedure can be set up for any finite number of sets: $E_1, E_2, \ldots, E_n$. We determine first a basic block of sets by expanding $(E_1 + CE_1) \ldots (E_n + CE_n)$ and dropping $CE_1 \ldots CE_n$ from this expansion. We then express $E_1 \ldots E_n$ each in terms of these new sets, each expression containing 2^{n-1} sets, and then discard successively all collections of one, two, ..., $2^{n-1} - 1$ sets from these expressions. All sets so obtained together with the null set: O, will constitute $\mathfrak{E}_S$ for $\mathfrak{E} = (E_1 \ldots E_n)$. The number of sets resulting increases very rapidly with n.

To obtain $\mathfrak{E}_S$ for any collection of sets, it is necessary to collect all extensions of any finite number of subsets of $\mathfrak{E}$.

To extend $\mathfrak{E}$ to be s-additive, we adjoin to $\mathfrak{E}$, all sums of a denumerable number of subsets of $\mathfrak{E}$. For instance if $\mathfrak{E}$ consists of all open subintervals of the open interval $a < x < b$, then $\mathfrak{E}_{s-A}$ is the set of all sums of a finite or denumerable number of open intervals that is, the set of all open subsets of $a < x < b$. The s-multiplicative extension of a class can be obtained in a similar way.

In general, if a class $\mathfrak{E}$ has the property P_1, the extension $\mathfrak{E}_{P_2}$ relative to a property P_2 need not have the property P_1, in other words the extension $\mathfrak{E}_{P_1P_2}$ may differ from $(\mathfrak{E}_{P_1})_{P_2}$. This observation is important in connection with the problem of extending a class of sets to be a ring. As we have seen in IV.3.8 this can be done by extending $\mathfrak{E}$ by any of the four double extensions (AS), $(A\Delta)$, $(M\Delta)$, $(S\Delta)$. We note the following instances where $\mathfrak{E}_{(P_1P_2)} = (\mathfrak{E}_{P_1})_{P_2}$:

4.5. If the class of sets $\mathfrak{E}$ is multiplicative, then the extension $\mathfrak{E}_A$ is also multiplicative, and so $\mathfrak{E}_{MA} = (\mathfrak{E}_M)_A$.

For if $E_1 + E_2 + \ldots + E_k$ and $E_1' + E_2' + \ldots + E_m'$ are two sets from $\mathfrak{E}_A$, then $(\Sigma_i E_i)(\Sigma_j E_j') = \Sigma_{ij} E_i E_j'$ belongs to $\mathfrak{E}_A$, since $E_i E_j'$ belongs to $\mathfrak{E}$ for all i and j.

Similarly by interchanging addition and multiplication, we have:

4.6. If the class of sets $\mathfrak{E}$ is additive, then the extension $\mathfrak{E}_M$ is also additive and so $\mathfrak{E}_{AM} = (\mathfrak{E}_A)_M$.

4.7. If the class of sets $\mathfrak{E}$ is subtractive, then the extension $\mathfrak{E}_A$ is also subtractive, so that $\mathfrak{E}_{AS} = (\mathfrak{E}_S)_A$.

For

$$(\sum_i E_i - \sum_j E_j') = (\sum_i E_i)C(\sum_j E_j')$$
$$= (\sum_i E_i) \prod_j CE_j' = \sum_i (E_i \prod_j CE_j')$$

Now the sets $E_i \Pi_j CE_j'$ are formed from elements of $\mathfrak{E}$ by subtraction and so belong to $\mathfrak{E}$, so that $\Sigma_i E_i(\Pi_j CE_j')$ is in $\mathfrak{E}_A$.

4.8. If the class of sets $\mathfrak{E}$ is multiplicative, then the extension $\mathfrak{E}_\Delta$ is also multiplicative so that $\mathfrak{E}_{M\Delta} = (\mathfrak{E}_M)_\Delta$.

For because of the associativity and distributivity of Δ, $(E_1 \Delta E_2 \dots \Delta E_k)(E_1' \Delta E_2' \dots \Delta E_m') = E_1E_1' \Delta E_1E_2' \Delta E_1E_3' \dots \Delta E_kE_m'$, and so belongs to $\mathfrak{E}_\Delta$.

4.9. If the class of sets $\mathfrak{E}$ is additive, then $\mathfrak{E}_\Delta$ is multiplicative.

For any two sets E_1 and E_2, the set $E_1E_2 = (E_1 + E_2)\Delta E_1 \Delta E_2$ will belong to $\mathfrak{E}_\Delta$. Application of the reasoning in the preceding theorem IV.4.8 yields the multiplicativity of $\mathfrak{E}_\Delta$.

From the preceding theorems and the fact that if $\mathfrak{E}$ is subtractive then it is also multiplicative, we have the following four ways of obtaining a ring extension of a class of sets:

4.10. $\mathfrak{E}_{ring} = (\mathfrak{E}_S)_A = (\mathfrak{E}_M)_\Delta = (\mathfrak{E}_A)_\Delta = (\mathfrak{E}_S)_\Delta$.

Note that the order of extension is important.

In order to extend a class of sets $\mathfrak{E}$ to be an algebra, we note that any algebra contains the whole space W as well as the empty set O. Consequently, to obtain the extension of $\mathfrak{E}$ to be an algebra, we adjoin W and apply the methods of ring extension to the resulting class.

When it comes to the setting up of a constructive procedure for extending a given class of sets $\mathfrak{E}$ to be an s-ring or an s-algebra we run into some difficulty. We start by extending $\mathfrak{E}$ to be s-additive, and then the resulting class to be subtractive. Call the resulting class $\mathfrak{S}_1$. Extending $\mathfrak{S}_1$ to be s-additive, and the resulting class to be subtractive leads to $\mathfrak{S}_2$. And so on, $\mathfrak{S}_{n+1}$ being $((\mathfrak{S}_n)_{s-A})_S$. If after a sequence of such extensions the resulting total class $\mathfrak{S}_\omega = \Sigma_n \mathfrak{S}_n$ is not an s-ring, we repeat the same operations on $\mathfrak{S}_\omega$. By using the Cantor set of transfinite ordinals, we can in this way obtain an ordered set of classes $\mathfrak{S}_\alpha$ for all transfinite ordinals α of the second class. The class of sets γ consisting of all sets in any $\mathfrak{S}_\alpha$: $\mathfrak{S} = \Sigma_\alpha \mathfrak{S}_\alpha$ is then the class $\mathfrak{E}$ extended to be an s-ring. For every $\mathfrak{S}_\alpha$ is contained in the existent s-ring extension of $\mathfrak{E}$. On the other hand, $\mathfrak{S}$ is an s-ring. For if $E_1, \ldots, E_n, \ldots$ is a sequence of sets belonging to $\mathfrak{S}$, there will be a minimal α_n such that E_n belongs to $\mathfrak{S}_{\alpha_n}$. Since α_n is denumerable, there exists an ordinal β greater than or equal to α_n for all n, so that $\Sigma_n E_n$ will belong to $\mathfrak{S}_\beta$, and then $\mathfrak{S}$ is s-additive. Similarly, for two sets E_1 and E_2 in $\mathfrak{S}$, there exist α_1 and α_2 such that E_1 is in $\mathfrak{S}_{\alpha_1}$ and E_2 in $\mathfrak{S}_{\alpha_2}$, so that $E_1 - E_2$ is in the $\mathfrak{S}_\alpha$ for α the greater of α_1 and α_2. This gives the subtractivity of $\mathfrak{S}$. A loose way of describing the class $\mathfrak{S} = \Sigma_\alpha \mathfrak{S}_\alpha$, is to say that it consists of all sets which can be obtained from $\mathfrak{E}$ by applying the operations of sequential addition and taking differences a denumerable number of times.

The same class $\mathfrak{S}$ also emerges, if we replace the subtractive extension by the ring extension throughout. This means considering the class $\mathfrak{R}_\alpha$, where $\mathfrak{R}_{\alpha+1}$ is obtained from $\mathfrak{R}_\alpha$ by extending $\mathfrak{R}_\alpha$ to be s-additive and then extending the resulting class to be a ring. For $\mathfrak{S}_\alpha \leqq \mathfrak{R}_\alpha \leqq (\mathfrak{S}_\alpha)_{s-A} \leqq \mathfrak{S}_{\alpha+1}$.

In a similar way, the s-algebra extension of $\mathfrak{E}$ involves adjoining the fundamental set W to $\mathfrak{E}$ and then applying successively the pair of operations of s-additive extension followed by complementation.

The procedure outlined above for the s-ring and s-algebra extensions of a class of sets is the basis of the Borel theory of measure (see E. Borel, "Leçons sur la Théorie des Fonctions," Gauthier-Villars, Paris, 1914, pp. 228-230). His fundamental set W is the closed interval $0 \leqq x \leqq 1$. The initial class of sets $\mathfrak{E}$ consists of all open subintervals of (0, 1).

4.11. The measurable sets according to Borel consist of all sets belonging to the s-algebra extension of $\mathfrak{E}$.

As a consequence in any space in which the topology is defined in terms of open sets, the Borel measurable sets consist of all sets in the s-algebra extension of the class of open sets.

EXERCISES

1. Express all of the sets in the subtractive extension of $\mathfrak{E} = (E_1, E_2, E_3)$ in terms of E_1, E_2, and E_3.

2. Show that if $\mathfrak{E}$ is any class of sets, then the algebra extension of $\mathfrak{E}$ can be constructed as $(((\mathfrak{E}, W)_C)_M)_A$.

3. What is the ring extension of the class $\mathfrak{E}$ if $\mathfrak{E}$ consists of the closed subintervals of the closed interval $a \leqq x \leqq b$? Same question for two-dimensional closed intervals of $[a, a'; b, b']$.

4. What are the ring and algebra extensions of the class $\mathfrak{E}$ if $\mathfrak{E}$ consists of all closed subintervals of $-\infty < x < \infty$?

5. What is the algebra extension of $\mathfrak{E}$ if $\mathfrak{E}$ consists of all half open intervals $a \leqq x < b$ of $-\infty < x < \infty$? What is the s-algebra extension of the same class $\mathfrak{E}$?

CHAPTER V

CONTENT AND MEASURE

1. Content of a Linear Bounded Set

For sets of points on a bounded linear interval: $a \leqq x \leqq b$, we are accustomed to attach to subintervals $[a_1, b_1]$, the length of the interval $l(I) = b_1 - a_1$ as a measure or content. No distinction is made between closed, open, or half-open intervals. By a natural extension we attach as a measure to a set E consisting of a finite number of disjoint intervals $I_1 \ldots I_n$ the sum of the lengths of the intervals: $\Sigma_k l(I_k)$. The problem of attaching a measure to some subsets E of $[a, b]$ can then be formulated as follows: To determine a function $\mu(E)$ of some subsets E of $[a, b]$ having the following properties: (1) for every E for which $\mu(E)$ is defined $\mu(E) \geqq 0$; (2) if $E_1 \leqq E_2$ and $\mu(E_1)$ and $\mu(E_2)$ exist, then $\mu(E_1) \leqq \mu(E_2)$; (3) if E_1 and E_2 are disjoint and $\mu(E_1)$ and $\mu(E_2)$ are defined, then $\mu(E_1 + E_2)$ is defined also and $\mu(E_1 + E_2) = \mu(E_1) + \mu(E_2)$; (4) if E is an interval I (open, closed, or half-open), then $\mu(I) = l(I)$.

One line of procedure is suggested by the observation that if I is a subinterval of $[a, b]$, then the characteristic function $\chi(I; x)$, which is equal to unity for x on I and zero for x not on I, is Riemann integrable and $\int_a^b \chi(I; x)\, dx = l(I)$. Further, if E consists of a finite number of disjoint intervals $I_1 \ldots I_n$, then $\int_a^b \chi(E; x) dx = \Sigma_k l(I_k)$. We consequently consider the class of subsets E of $[a, b]$ for which the characteristic function $\chi(E; x)$ are Riemann integrable and the properties of the set function defined by $\int_a^b \chi(E; x) dx$. We define:

1.1. Definition. A subset E of $[a, b]$ has *content* if and only if the characteristic funtion $\chi(E; x)$ is Riemann integrable on $[a, b]$. The corresponding integral $\int_a^b \chi(E; x)\, dx$ will be called the content of E and denoted by cont E. The class of subsets E of $[a, b]$ which have content will be denoted by $\mathfrak{C}$.

Since for any set E of $[a, b]$ the function $\chi(E; x)$ is bounded, it is logical to define for any subset E:

1.2. upper content: $\overline{\text{cont}}\, E = \overline{\int_a^b} \chi(E; x)dx$ and

1.3. lower content: $\underline{\text{cont}}\, E = \underline{\int_a^b} \chi(E; x)dx$.

1.4. Then a set E has content if and only if $\overline{\text{cont}}\, E = \underline{\text{cont}}\, E$.

An application of the definition of upper integral to the special function $\chi(E; x)$ yields the following definitions of upper content in terms of lengths of intervals:

1.2 a. (a) $\overline{\text{cont}}\, E =$ g.l.b. as to subdivisions σ of $[a, b]$ of $\Sigma_\sigma l(I')$ for all I' of σ containing points of E.

1.2 b. (b) $\overline{\text{cont}}\, E =$ g.l.b. of $\Sigma_k l(I_k)$ for all finite sets of intervals $I_1 \dots I_n$ such that $\Sigma_k I_k \geqq E$. Here we could restrict ourselves to sets of intervals which are disjoint.

In the same way, we see that

1.3 a. (a) $\underline{\text{cont}}\, E =$ l.u.b. as to subdivisions σ of $[a, b]$ of $\Sigma_\sigma l(I'')$ for all I'' of σ consisting entirely of points of E.

1.3 b. (b) $\underline{\text{cont}}\, E = b - a - \overline{\text{cont}}\, CE$.

For if CE is covered by a finite set of intervals $I_1 \dots I_n$ then each interval complementary to $\Sigma_k I_k$ consists entirely of points of E.

As a consequence of definition (b) of $\underline{\text{cont}}\, E$, we can say:

1.4 b. A set E has content if and only if $\overline{\text{cont}}\, E + \overline{\text{cont}}\, CE = b - a$.

Obviously any subinterval of $[a, b]$ has content and cont $I = l(I)$. A set consisting of a finite number of points has content zero. On the other hand, the upper content of the points of $[a, b]$ with rational coordinates is $b - a$, while the lower content is zero. As a consequence, the set of rationals on $[a, b]$ (or any denumerable dense subset of $[a, b]$) does not have content.

Sets consisting of a finite number of nonoverlapping intervals $J \equiv I_1 \dots I_n$ have content with cont $J = \Sigma_k l(I_k)$. We shall find use for the following:

1.5. THEOREM. If $J_1 \equiv I_{11} \dots I_{1m}$ and $J_2 \equiv I_{21} \dots I_{2n}$, each consisting of a finite number of nonoverlapping intervals, then

$$\text{cont}\, J_1 + \text{cont}\, J_2 = \text{cont}\, (J_1 + J_2) + \text{cont}\, J_1 J_2.$$

The set $J_1 + J_2$ can be expressed as the sum of a finite number of intervals and is of the same character as J_1 and J_2. The set J_1J_2 will consist of a finite number of intervals and perhaps a finite number of separate points and so will also have content. Now

$$\chi(J_1; x) + \chi(J_2; x) = \chi(J_1 + J_2; x) + \chi(J_1J_2; x)$$

If we apply Riemann integration to this identity, we get the relation involving content.

2. Properties of the Content Functions

We have:

2.1. For any set E: $0 \leqq \underline{\text{cont}}\, E \leqq \overline{\text{cont}}\, E$;

2.2. If $E_1 \leqq E_2$, then $\underline{\text{cont}}\, E_1 \leqq \underline{\text{cont}}\, E_2$ and $\overline{\text{cont}}\, E_1 \leqq \overline{\text{cont}}\, E_2$;

2.3. For every E_1 and E_2: $\overline{\text{cont}}\,(E_1 + E_2) + \overline{\text{cont}}\, E_1E_2 \leqq \overline{\text{cont}}\, E_1 + \overline{\text{cont}}\, E_2$ and $\underline{\text{cont}}\,(E_1 + E_2) + \underline{\text{cont}}\, E_1E_2 \geqq \underline{\text{cont}}\, E_1 + \underline{\text{cont}}\, E_2$.

2.1 and 2.2 follow directly from the definitions. For 2.3 we find for $e > 0$, interval sets $J_1 \geqq E_1$ and $J_2 \geqq E_2$ such that cont $J_1 \leqq \overline{\text{cont}}\, E_1 + e$ and cont $J_2 \leqq \overline{\text{cont}}\, E_2 + e$. Then since $J_1 + J_2 \geqq E_1 + E_2$ and $J_1J_2 \geqq E_1E_2$:

$$\begin{aligned}\overline{\text{cont}}\,(E_1 + E_2) + \overline{\text{cont}}\, E_1E_2 &\leqq \text{cont}\,(J_1 + J_2) + \text{cont}\, J_1J_2 \\ &= \text{cont}\, J_1 + \text{cont}\, J_2 \leqq \overline{\text{cont}}\, E_1 + \overline{\text{cont}}\, E_2 + 2e.\end{aligned}$$

Consequently, $\overline{\text{cont}}\,(E_1 + E_2) + \overline{\text{cont}}\, E_1E_2 \leqq \overline{\text{cont}}\, E_1 + \overline{\text{cont}}\, E_2$. If we replace E_1 by CE_1 and E_2 by CE_2 we get:

$$\overline{\text{cont}}\,(CE_1 + CE_2) + \overline{\text{cont}}\,(CE_1 \cdot CE_2) \leqq \overline{\text{cont}}\, CE_1 + \overline{\text{cont}}\, CE_2$$

and so

$$\begin{aligned}b - a - \overline{\text{cont}}\,(CE_1 + CE_2) + b - a - \overline{\text{cont}}\,(CE_1 \cdot CE_2) \\ \geqq b - a - \overline{\text{cont}}\, CE_1 + b - a - \overline{\text{cont}}\, CE_2\end{aligned}$$

or

$$\underline{\text{cont}}\, E_1E_2 + \underline{\text{cont}}\,(E_1 + E_2) \geqq \underline{\text{cont}}\, E_1 + \underline{\text{cont}}\, E_2.$$

As an immediate consequence of 2.3 above we have:

2.4. If E_1 and E_2 are subsets of $[a, b]$ with content, then $E_1 + E_2$ and E_1E_2 also have content, and cont $E_1 +$ cont $E_2 =$ cont $(E_1 + E_2) +$ cont E_1E_2.

As a result of 2.1 and 2.3 above we have

$$\text{cont}\, E_1 + \text{cont}\, E_2 \leqq \underline{\text{cont}}\,(E_1 + E_2) + \underline{\text{cont}}\, E_1E_2 \leqq \overline{\text{cont}}\,(E_1 + E_2) + \overline{\text{cont}}\, E_1E_2 \leqq \text{cont}\, E_1 + \text{cont}\, E_2.$$

Consequently, the inequalities become equalities and we have

$$\underline{\text{cont}}\,(E_1 + E_2) - \overline{\text{cont}}\,(E_1 + E_2) = \overline{\text{cont}}\, E_1E_2 - \underline{\text{cont}}\, E_1E_2.$$

Since the right-hand side of this equality is $\leqq 0$ and the left $\geqq 0$, it follows that they are both zero which proves the theorem.

Since the condition that a set E have content is symmetric in E and CE [since $C(CE) = E$] we also have:

2.5. If the set E has content, so does CE and cont $E +$ cont $CE = b - a$.

Combining these results we obtain:

2.6. THEOREM. The class $\mathfrak{C}$ of subsets of $[a, b]$, which have content, is an algebra of sets (additive, multiplicative, and complementary). Moreover, the content function on sets of $\mathfrak{C}$ is additive in the sense that if E_1 and E_2 belong to $\mathfrak{C}$ and are disjoint, then

$$\text{cont}\, E_1 + \text{cont}\, E_2 = \text{cont}\,(E_1 + E_2).$$

The additive-multiplicative part of this theorem could also have been demonstrated as follows: If E_1 and E_2 are in $\mathfrak{C}$, then $\chi(E_1; x)$ and $\chi(E_2; x)$ are Riemann integrable. Consequently, $\chi(E_1E_2; x) = \chi(E_1; x)\, \chi(E_2; x)$ is R-integrable and so $\chi(E_1 + E_2; x) = \chi(E_1; x) + \chi(E_2, x) - \chi(E_1E_2; x)$ is also R-integrable. The relation between the contents of the sets involved follows from the last relation between the characteristic functions and the linearity properties of integration.

If we remember that $\overline{\text{cont}}\, E$ and $\underline{\text{cont}}\, E$ as upper and lower integrals of the characteristic functions, are limits in the σ-sense, the basic set of inequalities between greatest and least of limits of sums in I.4.6 give us in the case when $E_1E_2 = 0$, that is, when

$$\chi(E_1 + E_2; x) = \chi(E_1; x) + \chi(E_2; x):$$

$$\underline{\int_a^b} \chi(E_1; x)dx + \underline{\int_a^b} \chi(E_2; x)dx \leq \underline{\int_a^b} \chi(E_1 + E_2; x)dx$$

$$\leq \underline{\int_a^b} \chi(E_1; x)dx + \overline{\int_a^b} \chi(E_2; x)dx \leq \overline{\int_a^b} \chi(E_1 + E_2; x)dx$$

$$\leq \overline{\int_a^b} \chi(E_1; x)dx + \overline{\int_a^b} \chi(E_2; x)dx.$$

Rewritten in terms of upper and lower content, we have:

2.7. If the sets E_1 and E_2 are disjoint then:

$$\underline{\mathrm{cont}}\, E_1 + \underline{\mathrm{cont}}\, E_2 \leq \underline{\mathrm{cont}}\,(E_1 + E_2) \leq \underline{\mathrm{cont}}\, E_1 + \overline{\mathrm{cont}}\, E_2$$
$$\leq \overline{\mathrm{cont}}\,(E_1 + E_2) \leq \overline{\mathrm{cont}}\, E_1 + \overline{\mathrm{cont}}\, E_2.$$

Suppose now that M is a set which has content, and E is any set. Then

$$\overline{\mathrm{cont}}\, E + \mathrm{cont}\, M \geq \overline{\mathrm{cont}}\,(E + M) + \overline{\mathrm{cont}}\, EM$$
$$\geq \overline{\mathrm{cont}}\,(E - EM) + \underline{\mathrm{cont}}\, M + \overline{\mathrm{cont}}\, EM,$$

since $E - EM$ and M are disjoint sets whose sum is $E + M$. Since $\underline{\mathrm{cont}}\, M = \mathrm{cont}\, M$, we obtain

$$\overline{\mathrm{cont}}\, E \geqq \overline{\mathrm{cont}}\,(E - EM) + \overline{\mathrm{cont}}\, EM.$$

On the other hand,

$$\overline{\mathrm{cont}}\, E \leqq \overline{\mathrm{cont}}\,(E - EM) + \overline{\mathrm{cont}}\, EM.$$

Hence:

2.8. THEOREM. If M is a set having content and E is any set, then

$$\overline{\mathrm{cont}}\, E = \overline{\mathrm{cont}}\, EM + \overline{\mathrm{cont}}\,(E - EM).$$

If E is the basic interval $[a, b]$ in this identity, we have the condition on a set M that it have content. The validity of this identity for all E is then a necessary and sufficient condition that a set M have content. The identity also asserts that if we divide a set E into two sets by means of a set M with content and its complement CM, then $\overline{\mathrm{cont}}$ is an additive function on this division. It follows that if the sets $M_1 \ldots M_n$ each have content and E is any set then $\overline{\mathrm{cont}}\, E(\Sigma_k M_k) = \Sigma_k\, \overline{\mathrm{cont}}\, EM_k$.

In terms of content, necessary and sufficient conditions that a function $f(x)$ on $[a, b]$ be Riemann integrable can be expressed as follows:

2.9. THEOREM. A function $f(x)$ is Riemann integrable on $[a, b]$ if and only if (a) $f(x)$ is bounded on $[a, b]$ and (b) the points of discontinuity of $f(x)$ can be expressed as the sum of a denumerable number of closed sets E_n, each of content zero.

In view of II.13.16 we need only show that condition (b) is equivalent to the statement that the set of discontinuities of $f(x)$ has measure zero based on $\alpha(x) = x$ on $[a, b]$. The set of points of discontinuity of any function $f(x)$ is then sum of the sets E_n consisting of the x's for which $\omega(f, x) \geqq 1/n$, each of which is closed. If the set of discontinuities of $f(x)$ is of zero measure, then the E_n are also of zero measure. Since by the Borel theorem, any covering by intervals of a bounded closed set can be replaced by a covering consisting of a finite number of these intervals, it follows that any closed set of zero measure also has zero content. Then cont $E_n = 0$ for all n. Conversely, we note that a set of zero content is also of zero measure. If then the set of discontinuities of $f(x)$ is the sum of a denumerable number of sets of zero content, the total set of discontinuities of $f(x)$ will be of zero measure.

As a means for assigning a measure to sets, the notion of content has a number of drawbacks. For instance, we have:

2.10. If E is any subset of $[a, b]$, and E' is its derived set, then $\overline{\text{cont}}\, E = \overline{\text{cont}}\, (E + E')$.

For if E is covered by a finite number of closed intervals $I_1 \ldots I_n$, then no point of E' can lie in the intervals which form the complement of $J = \Sigma_k I_k$. Since $\overline{\text{cont}}$ of a set does not depend on whether the covering is by open or closed intervals, we have $\overline{\text{cont}}\, (E + E') \leqq \overline{\text{cont}}\, E$ and so equality holds. It follows at once that:

2.11. If E is any set on $[a, b]$ which has content, then $E + E'$ also has content and cont $(E + E') =$ cont E.

The inequalities

$$\underline{\text{cont}}\, E \leqq \underline{\text{cont}}\, (E + E') \leqq \overline{\text{cont}}\, (E + E') = \overline{\text{cont}}\, E$$

lead at once to the conclusion of the theorem.

In effect, a set can have content only if its closure $E + E'$ as a closed set also has content, which is rather restrictive. This is particularly unfortunate because a large class of closed sets do not have content. For instance, a nondense perfect set has content if and only if it has content zero. For if a set is nondense on $[a, b]$, then $\underline{\text{cont}}\, E = 0$, since E contains no intervals. On the other hand, if E is perfect, then $\overline{\text{cont}}\, E = b - a - \Sigma_n(b_n - a_n)$, where (a_n, b_n) are the open intervals which make up the open set complementary to E. These bits of awkwardness are due among other things to the fact that the class $\mathfrak{C}$ of sets is not sequentially additive. For if E consists of the single point

x, then cont $E = 0$. But a sequence of points dense in $[a, b]$ does not have content.

The extension of Riemann integrals to Stieltjes integrals, particularly with respect to a function of bounded variation $\alpha(x)$ suggest consideration of the following set functions:

$$\alpha_N(E) = N\int_a^b \chi(E; x)d\alpha(x)$$

$$\alpha_\sigma(E) = \sigma\int_a^b \chi(E; x)d\alpha(x)$$

$$\alpha_Y(E) = Y\int_a^b \chi(E; x)d\alpha(x)$$

$$= \int_a^b \chi(E; x)d\alpha_c(x) + \sum_x \chi(E; x)\ (\alpha(x+0) - \alpha(x-0))$$

where $\alpha_c(x)$ is the continuous part of $\alpha(x)$ and it is assumed that the integrals exist. Each integral gives rise to a class of sets, on which a corresponding set function is defined. We have:

2.12. The class of sets for which $\alpha(E)$ is defined is an algebra (additive, complementary) of sets of $[a, b]$. For each class, the corresponding set function is finitely additive in the sense that if E_1 and E_2 are in the class, then

$$\alpha(E_1) + \alpha(E_2) = \alpha(E_1 + E_2) + \alpha(E_1E_2).$$

These integrals lead to a positive valued function of sets, if and only if $\alpha(x)$ is monotone nondecreasing.

EXERCISES

1. Show that if E consists of a single point x, then E belongs to the class determined by $\alpha_Y(E)$ and $\alpha_Y(E) = \alpha(x+0) - \alpha(x-0)$, but that $\alpha_N(E)$ and $\alpha_\sigma(E)$ are defined only if $\alpha(x)$ is continuous at x.

2. When does an open interval $a_1 < x < b_1$, a half-open interval $a_1 \leqq x < b_1$, or a closed interval $a_1 \leqq x \leqq b_1$ belong to the class of sets defined by $\alpha_N(E)$ or $\alpha_\sigma(E)$ or $\alpha_Y(E)$? Determine the values of these functions when they are defined.

3. Suppose $\alpha(x)$ is monotonic nondecreasing on $[a, b]$. Is it possible to define upper and lower functions $\overline{\alpha}_\sigma(E)$ and $\underline{\alpha}_\sigma(E)$ by the use of enclosing intervals as in the case of upper and lower content?

3. Borel Measurability

It seems sensible to assume that if we define the length of an open interval (a, b) as $b - a$, then a proper length or measure for an open set G consisting of the open subintervals (a_n, b_n) of a finite interval $[a, b]$ would be $\Sigma_n(b_n - a_n)$. Further, it seems sensible to attach to a closed set F the complement of G relative to $[a, b]$ the measure $b - a - \Sigma_n(b_n - a_n)$. These considerations involve two principles: (a) if E_n is a sequence of disjoint sets, each of which has a measure $\mu(E_n)$, then $\Sigma_n E_n$ also has measure (or is measurable) and $\mu(\Sigma_n E_n) = \Sigma_n \mu(E_n)$; (b) if E has measure, then the complement of E relative to the fundamental set $[a, b]$ also has measure and $\mu(CE) = b - a - \mu(E)$. These principles applied to subsets of the linear interval and the assumption that an open subinterval is measurable, yield that the minimal class of such measurable sets is the s-algebra extension of the class of open subintervals of $[a, b]$. The same procedure can be applied to open subintervals of $-\infty < x < +\infty$ to yield a class of "measurable" subsets. In either case the s-algebra so obtained is called the class of *Borel measurable* subsets, or *Borel sets* (see IV.4.11). A finite measure can be attached to sets of this class only if the basic interval $[a, b]$ is bounded, and then one can presumably proceed according to the second part of each principle stated above. For open and closed sets, such measure is easily computed, but for sets determined after a number of steps, the computation may become rather complex. However, as so often happens in the case of good mathematical notions, H. Lebesgue by a different approach derived a simple procedure which not only assigns a measure to Borel measurable sets, but a measure for an s-algebra which contains the s-algebra of Borel measurable sets. The Borel sets occupy an important position in this theory in that every Lebesgue measurable set is essentially a Borel measurable set of low order.

The derivation of Lebesgue measurability is similar to that of content, based on the enclosure of a set by intervals. The main difference in the two theories is that in defining upper content of a set E, E is covered by a finite number of intervals, while for upper measure coverings by a denumerably infinite set of intervals is allowed. We have already encountered such enclosures in the definition of sets of measure zero relative to a monotonic function (see II.13.12).

4. General Lebesgue Measure of Linear Sets

Linear measure is based on the interval function $l(I) = b - a$, for I the interval $[a, b]$ with or without end points. This interval function is obtained from differences of the point function $y = x$. In the following considerations with Stieltjes integrals in mind, we replace $y = x$ by $y = \alpha(x)$, where $\alpha(x)$ is a bounded monotonic non-decreasing function on $X = -\infty < x < +\infty$. Then linear measure considerations for a finite interval $[a, b]$ are based on the monotone function $\alpha(x) = a$, for $x \leqq a$, $\alpha(x) = x$ for $a \leqq x \leqq b$, and $\alpha(x) = b$ for $x \geqq b$. We shall set $\alpha(-\infty) = \lim_{x\to-\infty} \alpha(x)$ and $\alpha(+\infty) = \lim_{x\to+\infty} \alpha(x)$. The case where $\alpha(x)$ is unbounded will be taken up later.

The basic class of sets will be taken as the open intervals I: $a < x < b$ or (a, b) and we shall define $\alpha(I) = \alpha(b-0) - \alpha(a+0)$, with $\alpha(b-0) = \alpha(+\infty)$, if $b = +\infty$ and $\alpha(a+0) = \alpha(-\infty)$ if $a = -\infty$. Then $\alpha(X) = \alpha(+\infty) - \alpha(-\infty)$.

In order to obtain an upper measure function on sets E, we take as covering of a set E, a finite or denumerable number of open intervals. Now for linear sets, the sum of the points in a denumerable number of open intervals is a general open set and this in turn is equivalent to a sequence of disjoint open intervals. If $\{I_n\}$ is the original set of covering intervals and $\{J_k\}$ are the intervals defined by $\Sigma_n I_n$, then $\Sigma_k \alpha(J_k) \leq \Sigma_n \alpha(I_n)$. Consequently, if we are interested in greatest lower bounds of sums of the form $\Sigma_n \alpha(I_n)$, we can replace the sequences of open intervals by general open sets. For any open set G, consisting of the open intervals: $J_k = (a_k, b_k)$, we define:

4.1. $$\alpha(G) = \Sigma_k \alpha(J_k) = \Sigma_k(\alpha(b_k - 0) - \alpha(a_k + 0)).$$

In terms of the function $\alpha(G)$ on open sets, we can in turn define an upper (or outer) measure $\alpha^*(E)$ for any set E in X by the statement:

4.2. Definition. The *upper measure* $\alpha^*(E)$ of a set E is the greatest lower bound of $\alpha(G)$ for all open sets G covering E in the sense that all points of E are in G; or,

$$\alpha^*(E) = \text{g.l.b.}[\alpha(G) \text{ for } G \geq E].$$

We have already indicated that one gets the same value for $\alpha^*(E)$ if we replace this definition by:

4.2.1. $\alpha^*(E) =$ g.l.b. $[\Sigma_n \alpha(I_n)$ for all $\{I_n\}$ such that $\Sigma_n I_n \geq E]$, the I_n being open intervals.

Further, we note that if we order open sets $G \geq E$ by inclusion, then since $\alpha(G)$ is monotone on this directed set of G, we also have:

4.2.2. $$\alpha^*(E) = \lim_{G \geq E} \alpha(G).$$

In order to obtain properties of $\alpha^*(E)$, we first note:

4.3. The function $\alpha(G)$ on open subsets G of X has the following properties:

(1) $0 \leq \alpha(G) \leq \alpha(X) < \infty$ for all G.

(2) If $G_1 \leq G_2$, then $\alpha(G_1) \leq \alpha(G_2)$.

(3) For any two open sets G_1 and G_2, we have:

$$\alpha(G_1) + \alpha(G_2) = \alpha(G_1 + G_2) + \alpha(G_1 \cdot G_2)$$

where $G_1 + G_2$, the sum of two open sets, and $G_1 \cdot G_2$, their product, each is again an open set.

(4) If $\{G_n\}$ is any sequence of open sets, then

$$\alpha(\textstyle\sum_n G_n) \leqq \textstyle\sum_n \alpha(G_n).$$

Property (1) is obvious.

Property (2) follows from the fact that if (a_n, b_n) is any sequence of disjoint open intervals on (a, b), then

$$\textstyle\sum_n (\alpha(b_n + 0) - \alpha(a_n - 0)) \leqq \alpha(b - 0) - \alpha(a + 0).$$

For the monotone function $y = \alpha(x)$ maps the open intervals (a_n, b_n) onto the nonoverlapping intervals $(\alpha(a_n + 0), \alpha(b_n - 0))$ on the Y-axis, which are subintervals of $(\alpha(a + 0), \alpha(b - 0))$.

For property (3), we assume first that G_1 and G_2 each consist of a finite number of open intervals. Then the mapping $y = \alpha(x)$ yields two sets J_1 and J_2, each consisting of a finite number of disjoint intervals on the Y-axis: $J_1 = \Sigma_n(\alpha(a_{1n} + 0), \alpha(b_{1n} - 0)$, and $J_2 = \Sigma_m(\alpha(a_{2m} + 0), \alpha(b_{2m} - 0)$. Then $G_1 + G_2$ maps into $J_1 + J_2$ and $G_1 \cdot G_2$ into $J_1 \cdot J_2$, while the statement

$$\text{cont } J_1 + \text{cont } J_2 = \text{cont } (J_1 J_2) + \text{cont } (J_1 + J_2)$$

translates into

$$\alpha(G_1) + \alpha(G_2) = \alpha(G_1 \cdot G_2) + \alpha(G_1 + G_2).$$

If G_1 consists of a denumerable set of intervals, while G_2 of a finite number, then for any $e > 0$, we can divide G_1 into two disjoint sets G_{11} and G_{12}, where G_{11} consist of a finite number of intervals while $\alpha(G_{12}) < e$. Then $\alpha(G_1 + G_2) - \alpha(G_{11} + G_2) \leqq \alpha(G_{12}) < e$, since in passing from $G_{11} + G_2$ to $G_1 + G_2$ the increase is confined to the intervals and parts of intervals of G_{12}. Similarly, $\alpha(G_1G_2) + \alpha(G_{11}G_2) \leqq \alpha(G_{12}) < e$. Then

$$\begin{aligned}
&[\alpha(G_1 + G_2) + \alpha(G_1 \cdot G_2) - \alpha(G_1) - \alpha(G_2)] \\
&\quad - [\alpha(G_{11} + G_2) + \alpha(G_{11}G_2) - \alpha(G_{11}) - \alpha(G_2)] \\
&\quad \leqq |\alpha(G_1 + G_2) - \alpha(G_{11} + G_2)| \\
&\quad + |\alpha(G_1 \cdot G_2) - \alpha(G_{11} \cdot G_2)| + |\alpha(G_1) - \alpha(G_{11})| \leqq 3e.
\end{aligned}$$

But since G_{11} and G_2 each consist of a finite numbers of intervals $\alpha(G_{11} + G_2) + \alpha(G_{11} \cdot G_2) - \alpha(G_{11}) - \alpha(G_2) = 0$, so that $|\alpha(G_1 + G_2) + \alpha(G_1 \cdot G_2) - (\alpha(G_1) + \alpha(G_2))| \leqq 3e$. Since this inequality holds for all e, we obtain $\alpha(G_1 + G_2) + \alpha(G_1G_2) = \alpha(G_1) + \alpha(G_2)$, for the case when G_1 consists of an infinite set of intervals, while G_2 consists of a finite set.

A repetition of this reasoning leads at once to the validity of the formula when G_1 and G_2 are any two open subsets of X.

For property (4), let us assume that the open set $\Sigma_n G_n$ consists of the open intervals (a_m, b_m). Then for fixed m and for any $e > 0$, it is possible to find points $a_m < a_m' < b_m' < b_m$ such that $\alpha(a_m') - \alpha(a_m + 0) < e/2^m$, and $\alpha(b_m - 0) - \alpha(b_m') < e/2^m$. Now the closed interval $[a_m', b_m']$ is covered by intervals from the sets G_n, and by the Borel theorem a finite number of these $I_{m1} \dots I_{mk_m}$ will suffice. Then

$$\begin{aligned}
\alpha(b_m - 0) - \alpha(a_m + 0) &\leqq \alpha(b_m') - \alpha(a_m') + e/2^{m-1} \\
&\leqq \textstyle\sum_k \alpha(I_{mk}) + e/2^{m-1}.
\end{aligned}$$

Consequently,

$$\begin{aligned}
\alpha(\textstyle\sum_n G_n) = \sum_m (\alpha(b_m - 0) - \alpha(a_m + 0)) &\leqq \textstyle\sum_m \sum_k \alpha(I_{mk}) + \sum_m e/2^{m-1} \\
&\leqq \textstyle\sum_n \alpha(G_n) + 2e,
\end{aligned}$$

since the I_{mk} are only part of the intervals which occur in the various G_n. Since the inequality holds for all e, we have $\alpha(\Sigma_n G_n) \leqq \Sigma_n \alpha(G_n)$.

The properties of $\alpha(G)$ lead at once to:

4.4. THEOREM. The upper measure $\alpha^*(E)$ has the following properties:

(1*) For all $E : 0 \leqq \alpha^*(E) \leqq \alpha(X) = \alpha(+\infty) - \alpha(-\infty); \alpha^*(O) = 0$.

(2*) If $E_1 \leqq E_2$, then $\alpha^*(E_1) \leqq \alpha^*(E_2)$.

(3*) For any two sets E_1 and E_2

$$\alpha^*(E_1) + \alpha^*(E_2) \geqq \alpha^*(E_1 + E_2) + \alpha^*(E_1 E_2).$$

(4*) For any sequence of sets $\{E_n\}$

$$\alpha^*(\sum_n E_n) \leqq \sum_n \alpha^*(E_n).$$

Properties (1*) and (2*) follow from the definition of α^* and the corresponding properties of $\alpha(G)$.

For property (3*), to any $e > 0$, there exist sets $G_1 \geqq E_2$ and $G_2 \geqq E_2$, such that $\alpha^*(E_1) \geqq \alpha(G_1) - e$, and $\alpha^*(E_2) \geqq \alpha(G_2) - e$. Then for every $e > 0$,

$$\alpha^*(E_1) + \alpha^*(E_2) \geqq \alpha(G_1) + \alpha(G_2) - 2e = \alpha(G_1 + G_2)$$
$$+ \alpha(G_1 \cdot G_2) - 2e \geqq \alpha^*(E_1 + E_2) + \alpha^*(E_1 E_2) - 2e,$$

since $G_1 + G_2 \geqq E_1 + E_2$ and $G_1 G_2 \geqq E_1 E_2$. This leads at once to (3*).

For property (4*), to $e > 0$ and E_n there exist $G_n \geqq E_n$ such that $\alpha^*(E_n) \geqq \alpha(G_n) - e/2^n$. Then for all $e > 0$:

$$\sum_n \alpha^*(E_n) \geqq \sum_n \alpha(G_n) - e \geqq \alpha(\sum_n G_n) - e \geqq \alpha^*(\sum_n E_n) - e,$$

from which (4*) follows at once.

5. Lower Measure

As in the case of content, we introduce a *lower measure* (or inner measure) $\alpha_*(E)$ by means of the equality:

5.1. $\alpha_*(E) = \alpha(X) - \alpha^*(CE) = \alpha(+\infty) - \alpha(-\infty) - \alpha^*(CE)$.

For $\alpha_*(E)$ we have a set of properties analogous to those for $\alpha^*(E)$:

5.2. THEOREM. The lower measure $\alpha_*(E)$ defined on all subsets of X has the following properties:

(0) $\alpha^*(E) \geqq \alpha_*(E)$ for all E.

(1_*) $0 \leqq \alpha_*(E) \leqq \alpha(X)$ for all E.

(2_*) If $E_1 \leqq E_2$, then $\alpha_*(E_1) \leqq \alpha_*(E_2)$.

(3_*) For any E_1 and E_2: $\alpha_*(E_1) + \alpha_*(E_2) \leqq \alpha_*(E_1 + E_2) + \alpha_*(E_1E_2)$.

(4_*) If the sets E_n are disjoint, then $\alpha_*(\Sigma_n E_n) \geqq \Sigma_n \alpha_*(E_n)$.

Property (0) follows from the inequality $\alpha(X) \leqq \alpha^*(E) + \alpha^*(CE)$, a consequence of ($3^*$).

Property (1_*) is obvious.

Property (2_*) follows from the definition of $\alpha_*(E)$, and the fact that $E_1 \leqq E_2$ implies $CE_1 \geqq CE_2$.

Property (3_*) follows from (3^*). For if E_1 and E_2 are any sets then for CE_1 and CE_2, we have

$$\alpha^*(CE_1) + \alpha^*(CE_2) \geqq \alpha^*(CE_1 + CE_2) + \alpha^*(CE_1 \cdot CE_2).$$

Consequently,

$$\alpha(X) - \alpha^*(CE_1) + \alpha(X) - \alpha^*(CE_2) \leqq \alpha(X) - \alpha^*(CE_1 + CE_2) + \alpha(X) - \alpha^*(CE_1 \cdot CE_2).$$

The use of the definition of $\alpha_*(E)$ then yields (3_*).

Property (4_*) follows from (3_*). For if $E_1, \ldots, E_n, \ldots$ are disjoint, then

$$\alpha_* (\sum_n E_n) \geqq \alpha_* (\sum_{n=1}^{m} E_n) \geqq \sum_{n=1}^{m} \alpha_* E_n.$$

Since this holds for all m, we have $\alpha_*(\Sigma_n E_n) \geqq \Sigma_n \alpha_*(E_n)$. We call attention to the fact that (4^*) is not deducible from (3^*), but depends on the property (4) of $\alpha(G)$ for G open.

It is possible to deduce some additional inequalities from (3^*). If we rewrite (3^*) in the form:

$$\alpha^*(E_1E_2) - \alpha^*(E_2) \leqq \alpha^*(E_1) - \alpha^*(E_1 + E_2)$$

and add $\alpha(X)$ to both sides we obtain:

(3^{**}) $\alpha^*(E_1E_2) + \alpha_*(CE_2) \leqq \alpha^*(E_1) + \alpha_*(C(E_1 + E_2)) = \alpha^*(E_1) + \alpha_*(CE_1 \cdot CE_2)$. Let E_1' and E_2' be any two sets and set $E_1 = E_1' + E_2'$, $CE_2 = E_2'$. Then $CE_1 \cdot CE_2 = O$, $E_1E_2 = E_1'CE_2'$ and

$$\alpha^*(E_1'CE_2') + \alpha_*(E_2') \leqq \alpha^*(E_1' + E_2').$$

If we drop the primes, we can say that for any two sets E_1 and E_2:

$$\alpha^*(E_1 - E_2) + \alpha_*(E_2) \leqq \alpha^*(E_1 + E_2).$$

If in addition E_1 and E_2 are disjoint, then this inequality becomes:

$$\alpha^*(E_1) + \alpha_*(E_2) \leqq \alpha^*(E_1 + E_2).$$

On the other hand, if we set $CE_2 = E_1' + E_2'$ and $E_1 = E_1'$ in (3^{**}), then $E_1E_2 = O$, $CE_1 \cdot CE_2 = E_2'CE_1'$ and

$$\alpha_*(E_1' + E_2') \leqq \alpha^*(E_1') + \alpha_*(E_2'CE_1') \leqq \alpha^*(E_1') + \alpha_*(E_2').$$

Consequently, if E_1 and E_2 are disjoint, then these inequalities together with (3^*) and (3_*) give

5.3. $$\alpha_*(E_1) + \alpha_*(E_2) \leqq \alpha_*(E_1 + E_2) \leqq \alpha^*(E_1) + \alpha_*(E_2) \leqq \alpha^*(E_1 + E_2) \leqq \alpha^*(E_1) + \alpha^*(E_2).$$

We note that only the first and third inequalities require that $E_1 \cdot E_2 = O$, the second and fourth are true for all E_1 and E_2.

6. Measurability

We now define:

6.1. Definition. A set E of X is *α-measurable* if and only if $\alpha^*(E) = \alpha_*(E)$.

We will denote the class of measurable subsets of X by $\mathfrak{M}$. The common value of $\alpha^*(E)$ and $\alpha_*(E)$ will be denoted by $\alpha(E)$.

The condition $\alpha^*(E) = \alpha_*(E)$ is equivalent to $\alpha^*(E) + \alpha^*(CE) = \alpha(X)$. This is symmetrical in E and CE since $C(CE) = E$. Hence:

6.2. If E is α-measurable, so is CE, the complement of E and $\alpha(E) + \alpha(CE) = \alpha(X)$.

Properties (1^*) and (2^*) of $\alpha^*(E)$ lead to corresponding properties of $\alpha(E)$.

Applying (3^*) and (3_*) to the case when E_1 and E_2 are α-measurable gives us

$$\alpha(E_1) + \alpha(E_2) \leqq \alpha_*(E_1 + E_2) + \alpha_*(E_1E_2) \leqq \alpha^*(E_1 + E_2) + \alpha^*(E_1E_2) \leqq \alpha(E_1) + \alpha(E_2).$$

Or $\alpha_*(E_1E_2) - \alpha_1{}^*(E_1E_2) = \alpha^*(E_1 + E_2) - \alpha_*(E_1 + E_2)$. Then each of these expressions is zero, since $\alpha^*(E) - \alpha_*(E) \geqq 0$ for all E. It follows that $E_1 + E_2$ are measurable. Then:

6.3. If E_1 and E_2 are measurable so are $E_1 + E_2$ and E_1E_2 and

$$\alpha(E_1) + \alpha(E_2) = \alpha(E_1 + E_2) + \alpha(E_1E_2).$$

Consequently:

6.4. THEOREM. The class $\mathfrak{M}$ of α-measurable subsets of X is additive, multiplicative and complementary and consequently an algebra. The function α on $\mathfrak{M}$ is additive.

We note that:

6.5. Definition. A set function β on a class $\mathfrak{E}$ of sets is *additive*, if for E_1 and E_2 disjoint in $\mathfrak{E}$, such that $E_1 + E_2$ belongs to $\mathfrak{E}$ we have

$$\beta(E_1 + E_2) = \beta(E_1) + \beta(E_2).$$

It follows that if β is additive on $\mathfrak{E}$, and E_1 and E_2 of $\mathfrak{E}$ are such that $E_2 \leqq E_1$ and $E_1 - E_2$ is in $\mathfrak{E}$, then $\beta(E_1) - \beta(E_2) = \beta(E_1 - E_2)$. If $\mathfrak{E}$ is an algebra of sets, then β is additive on $\mathfrak{E}$ if and only if for all E_1 and E_2 of $\mathfrak{E}$ we have $\beta(E_1 + E_2) + \beta(E_1E_2) = \beta(E_1) + \beta(E_2)$.

Properties (4*) and (4_*) of α^* and α_* applied to a sequence $\{E_n\}$ of disjoint α-measurable sets gives

$$\sum_n \alpha(E_n) \leqq \alpha_*(\sum_n E_n) \leqq \alpha^*(\sum_n E_n) \leqq \sum_n \alpha(E_n).$$

Since the end terms of this series of inequalities are equal, it follows that the inequalities become equalities, that is $\Sigma_n E_n$ is α-measurable and $\alpha(\Sigma_n E_n) = \Sigma_n \alpha(E_n)$. Now the sum of any sequence of sets can be expressed as the sum of a denumerable number of disjoint sets by the formula $\Sigma_n E_n = E_1 + (E_2 - E_1) + (E_3 - (E_1 + E_2)) + \ldots$. If the sets E_n are α-measurable, then $E_2 - E_1$, $E_3 - (E_1 + E_2)$, ... are also α-measurable and disjoint. Then:

6.6. THEOREM. If $\{E_n\}$ is any sequence of α measurable sets, then $\Sigma_n E_n$ is measurable, or the class $\mathfrak{M}$ is s-additive. In view of the complementary character of $\mathfrak{M}$, the class $\mathfrak{M}$ of α-measurable sets forms an s-algebra. Moreover the measure function $\alpha(E)$ on $\mathfrak{M}$, is s-additive.

We define:

6.7. Definition. A set function β on a class of sets $\mathfrak{E}$ in *s-additive* if for any sequence of disjoint sets E_n of $\mathfrak{E}$ such that $\Sigma_n E_n$ belongs to $\mathfrak{E}$, we have $\beta(\Sigma_n E_n) = \Sigma_n \beta(E_n)$.

Since we assume here that β is finite valued on $\mathfrak{E}$, and any reordering of E_n leads to the same set $\Sigma_n E_n$, it follows that if β is s-additive, then the series $\Sigma_n \beta(E_n)$ is absolutely convergent. The terms completely additive, or totally additive are sometimes used in place of s-additive.

Since $\overline{\lim}_n E_n$ and $\underline{\lim}_n E_n$ are each expressible in terms of s-sums and s-products, it follows that:

6.8. If $\{E_n\}$ is a sequence of α-measurable sets, then $\overline{\lim}_n E_n$ and $\underline{\lim}_n E_n$ are also α-measurable, and so is $\lim_n E_n$ when it exists.

6.9. If E_n is any monotonic nondecreasing sequence of α-measurable sets $(E_n \leqq E_{n+1})$, then $\Sigma_n E_n = \lim_n E_n$ is α-measurable and $\alpha(\lim_n E_n) = \lim_n \alpha(E_n)$. For

$$\lim_n E_n = E_1 + (E_2 - E_1) + (E_3 - E_2) + \ldots,$$

a sum of disjoint measurable sets. The s-additivity of α gives

$$\alpha(\textstyle\sum_n E_n) = \alpha(E_1) + \alpha(E_2 - E_1) + \alpha(E_3 - E_2) + \ldots = \lim_m \alpha(E_n).$$

Similarly:

6.10. If $\{E_n\}$ is a monotonic nonincreasing sequence of α-measurable sets $(E_n \geqq E_{n+1})$, then $\Pi_n E_n = \lim_n E_n$ is measurable and $\lim_n \alpha(E_n) = \alpha(\Pi_n E_n) = \alpha(\lim_n E_n)$.

This follows from the identity $\Pi_n E_n = E_1 - ((E_1 - E_2) + (E_2 - E_3) + \ldots)$. The fact that $\alpha(E)$ is finite valued plays a role in this theorem.

Assuming that the sets E_n are α-measurable, consider

$$\overline{\lim_n}\, E_n = \prod_{m=1}^{\infty} \sum_{n=m}^{\infty} E_n.$$

Then

$$\alpha(\overline{\lim_n}\, E_n) = \lim_m \alpha(\sum_{n=m}^{\infty} E_n).$$

Then $(e > 0,\ m_e,\ m \geqq m_e)$:

$$\alpha(\overline{\lim_n}\, E_n) \geqq \alpha(\sum_{n=m}^{\infty} E_n) - e \geqq \alpha(E_m) - e.$$

It follows that $\alpha(\overline{\lim}_n E_n) \geqq \overline{\lim}_n \alpha(E_n)$. So:

6.11. If E_n is any sequence of α-measurable sets, then $\alpha(\overline{\lim}_n E_n) \geqq \overline{\lim}_n \alpha(E_n)$.

This theorem contains the Arzéla lemma (II.15.8) as a special case, where E_n consists of a finite number of disjoint intervals and $\alpha(I)=l(I)$.

By taking complements with respect to X, or by similar reasoning it follows that:

6.12. If E_n are α-measurable sets, then $\alpha(\underline{\lim}_n E_n) \leq \underline{\lim}_n \alpha(E_n)$.

Combining these results gives:

6.13. THEOREM. If $\alpha(x)$ is a monotonic nondecreasing bounded function on X, and the sets E_n are α-measurable and such that $\lim_n E_n$ exists, then $\alpha(\lim_n E_n) = \lim_n \alpha(E_n)$.

7. Examples of Measurable Sets

The null set O and the basic interval X are each measurable since $\alpha^*(O) = 0$.

A set E consisting of a single point x is measurable and $\alpha(E) = \alpha(x+0) - \alpha(x-0)$. For if E consists of x, then $\alpha^*(E) = \alpha(x+0) - \alpha(x-0)$. On the other hand, CE consists of the open intervals $(-\infty, x)$ and $(x, +\infty)$, so that $\alpha^*(CE) = \alpha(x-0) - \alpha(-\infty) + \alpha(+\infty) - \alpha(x+0)$. Since $\mathfrak{M}$ is s-additive, it follows that:

7.1. If E consists of a denumerable set of points $\{x_n\}$, then E is α-measurable, and $\alpha(E) = \Sigma_n(\alpha(x_n+0) - \alpha(x_n-0))$.

If E is an open interval $(a, b) \equiv a < x < b$, then E is α-measurable and $\alpha((a, b)) = \alpha(b-0) - \alpha(a+0)$. For $\alpha^*(E) = \alpha(b-0) - \alpha(a+0)$ while $\alpha^*(CE) = \alpha(a+0) - \alpha(-\infty) + \alpha(+\infty) - \alpha(b-0)$. Consequently, if G is any open set consisting of the open intervals (a_n, b_n), then G is α-measurable and $\alpha(G) = \Sigma_n(\alpha(b_n-0) - \alpha(a_n+0))$; in other words, $\alpha(G)$ has the same value with which we started. If F is any closed set, then F is α-measurable, and $\alpha(F) = \alpha(X) - \alpha(G)$ where G is the set complementary to F relative to X. Moreover, any Borel measurable set E is α-measurable.

We call attention to the fact that:

7.2. THEOREM. The class of α-measurable sets relative to any bounded monotonic function α on $X \equiv -\infty < x < +\infty$ always includes the s-algebra extension of the open subintervals of X, that is, the class of Borel measurable subsets of X. In particular, every open subset G and every closed subset F of X is measurable relative to any bounded monotonic α.

8. Sets of Zero Measure

If $\alpha^*(E) = 0$, then $\alpha_*(E) = 0$ also, so that E is α-measurable, and its α-measure is zero. A set of α-measure zero (or α-null set) can then be defined by the condition that for every $e > 0$, there exists a sequence of open intervals I_n such that $\Sigma_n I_n \geqq E$ and $\Sigma_n \alpha(I_n) < e$. Here $\alpha(I_n) = \alpha(b_n - 0) - \alpha(a_n + 0)$.

8.1. THEOREM. The class $\mathfrak{N}$ of sets of α-measure zero is an s-ring.

For if E_n are such that $\alpha(E_n) = 0$, then $\alpha(\Sigma_n E_n) \leq \Sigma_n \alpha(E_n) = 0$, so that $\Sigma_n E_n$ belongs to $\mathfrak{N}$ also. Also if E belongs to $\mathfrak{N}$ and $E_1 \leq E$, then $\alpha(E_1) \leq \alpha(E) = 0$, so that E_1 belongs to $\mathfrak{N}$ also. Consequently, if $\alpha(E) = 0$, and E_1 is any set then $\alpha(E - E_1) = 0$, or $E - E_1$ is in $\mathfrak{N}$. Then $\mathfrak{N}$ is s-additive and subtractive, i.e., $\mathfrak{N}$ is an s-ring.

We note that we have shown that if E is of α-measure zero, then every subset of E is also of α-measure zero. From another angle, we can say, that if E is is in $\mathfrak{N}$, and E_1 is in X, then $E \cdot E_1$ is in $\mathfrak{N}$. Following algebraic terminology, a class $\mathfrak{E}$ of sets which is a ring and closed under multiplication by subsets of W can be called an *ideal* relative to W. The class $\mathfrak{N}$ of sets of α-measure zero is an ideal relative to X.

8.2. THEOREM. If E_1 is α-measurable and E_2 differs from E_1 by a set of α-measure zero in the sense that $E_1 \Delta E_2$ is of α-measure zero, then E_2 is also α-measurable and $\alpha(E_1) = \alpha(E_2)$.

For if $\alpha(E_1 \Delta E_2) = 0$, then $\alpha^*(E_1 - E_2) = \alpha^*(E_2 - E_1) = 0$ also. Then $E_2 = (E_1 + (E_2 - E_1)) - (E_1 - E_2)$ expresses E_2 as sum and differences of α-measurable sets and is consequently also α-measurable. The equality $\alpha(E_1) = \alpha(E_2)$ follows immediately from the additive properties of α.

EXERCISES

1. In II.13.12 a set E on a finite interval $[a, b]$ was defined to be of α-measure zero, if for any $e > 0$, there exists a sequence of intervals $I_n = [a_n, b_n]$ enclosing or covering E, such that $\Sigma_n \alpha(I_n) = \Sigma_n(\alpha(b_n) - \alpha(a_n)) < e$. Show that this definition yields the same class of sets of α-measure zero as the class $\mathfrak{N}$ above.

2. Show that if for any pair of subsets E of X we define a distance function by the condition $\delta(E_1, E_2) = \alpha^*(E_1 \Delta E_2) = \alpha^*(E_1 C E_2 + E_2 C E_1)$, then δ satisfies the metric conditions: $\delta(E_1, E_2) \geq 0$ for all E_1 and E_2; $\delta(E, E) = 0$ for all E; $\delta(E_1, E_2) = \delta(E_2, E_1)$ for all E_1 and E_2; and $\delta(E_1, E_3) \leq \delta(E_1, E_2) + \delta(E_2, E_3)$ for all E_1, E_2 and E_3; but $\delta(E_1, E_2) = 0$ is equivalent to the statement: E_1 and E_2 differ by a set of α-measure zero.

9. Additional Properties of Upper and Lower Measure

By definition, $\alpha^*(E) =$ g.l.b.$[\alpha(G)$ for $G \geqq E]$, G being open. Consequently, there exists a sequence of open sets G_n such that $\alpha(G_n) \geqq \alpha^*(E) \geqq \alpha(G_n) - 1/n$. Then $\Pi_n G_n \geqq E$ so that $\alpha(\Pi_n G_n) \geqq \alpha^*(E) \geqq \alpha(G_n) - 1/n \geqq \alpha(\Pi_m G_m) - 1/n$. It follows that for $G_\delta = \Pi_n G_n$ we have $\alpha^*(E) = \alpha(G_\delta)$. Then:

9.1. For every set E, there exists a G_δ set, the product of a denumerable number of open sets, containing E such that $\alpha(G_\delta) = \alpha^*(E)$.

Since the complement of an open set is a closed set, and a closed set is α-measurable, we can revise the definition of $\alpha_*(E) = \alpha(X) - \alpha^*(CE)$ to read as follows: For any set E the lower measure $\alpha_*(E) =$ l.u.b. $[\alpha(F)$ for F contained in $E]$, where F stands for a closed set. This definition contrasts with that of upper and lower content, where both of these concepts were defined by using the same class of sets: a finite number of intervals. Following through as in the case of upper measure we have:

9.2. For every E, there exists an F_σ the sum of a denumerable number of closed sets, such that F_σ is contained in E and $\alpha(F_\sigma) = \alpha_*(E)$.

10. Additional Conditions for Measurability

We have defined E to be α-measurable if $\alpha^*(E) = \alpha_*(E) = \alpha(X) - \alpha^*(CE)$, or $\alpha^*(E) + \alpha^*(CE) = \alpha(X)$. Since we always have $\alpha^*(E) + \alpha^*(CE) \geqq \alpha(X)$, for measurability, we need only prove that $\alpha^*(E) + \alpha^*(CE) \leqq \alpha(X)$. We give in this paragraph additional necessary and sufficient conditions for measurability.

From the preceding section we have:

10.1. The set E is α-measurable if and only if there exists a G_δ and an F_σ such that $G_\delta \geqq E \geqq F_\sigma$ and $\alpha(G_\delta - F_\sigma) = 0$.

For if E is α-measurable, there exist $G_\delta \geqq E$ and $F_\sigma \leqq E$ such that $\alpha(G_\delta) = \alpha(E) = \alpha(F_\sigma)$, and so $\alpha(G_\delta - F_\sigma) = 0$. On the other hand, from $\alpha(G_\delta - F_\sigma) = 0$ and $G_\delta \geqq E \geqq F_\sigma$ it follows that $\alpha^*(G_\delta - E) = 0$ and $\alpha^*(E - F_\sigma) = 0$, so that E differs from the (Borel) measurable sets G_δ and F_σ by a set of α-measure zero, and is consequently α-measurable. We can strengthen this theorem as follows:

10.2. A necessary and sufficient condition that the set E be α-measurable is that for every $e > 0$, there exists an open set $G_e \geqq E$ such that

$\alpha^*(G_e - E) < e$. Also E is α-measurable if and only if for all $e > 0$ there exists a closed set $F_e \leqq E$ such that $\alpha^*(E - F_e) < e$.

We prove the first part only, the second part being proved in a similar way. If E is measurable, then for $e > 0$, there exists G_e such that $\alpha(G_e) \geqq \alpha(E) > \alpha(G_e) - e$, so that $\alpha^*(G_e - E) = \alpha(G_e - E) < e$. For the sufficiency take $e = 1/n$, and let G_n be such that $\alpha^*(G_n - E) < 1/n$. If $G_\delta = \Pi_n G_n$, then $\alpha^*(G_\delta - E) \leqq \alpha^*(G_n - E) < 1/n$ for all n, so that $\alpha^*(G_\delta - E) = 0$. Then E agrees with the α-measurable set G_δ except for a set of α-measure zero, and is by V.8.2 α-measurable.

10.3. The set E is α-measurable if and only if for every $e > 0$ there exist open sets G_1 containing E and G_2 containing CE such that $\alpha(G_1 G_2) < e$.

This is essentially a reformulation of the preceding theorem. If E is measurable, then for $e > 0$ there exists open $G_e \geqq E$ and closed $F_e \leqq E$ such that $\alpha^*(G_e - E) < e/2$ and $\alpha^*(E - F_e) < e/2$. Then $\alpha(G_e - F_e) = \alpha^*(G_e - F_e) \leqq \alpha^*(G_e - E) + \alpha^*(E - F_e) < e$. The open set $\overline{G}_e = CF_e$ will enclose CE and $\alpha(G_e \cdot \overline{G}_e) < e$. Conversely, if for $G_1 \geqq E$ and $G_2 \geqq CE$ we have $\alpha(G_1 G_2) < e$, and if $F = CG_2$ then $F \leqq E$ and $\alpha(G_1 - F) < e$. Then $\alpha^*(G_1 - F) < e$ and E is α-measurable by the preceding theorem.

10.4. A necessary and sufficient condition that a set M be α-measurable is that for every E, we have $\alpha^*(E) = \alpha^*(ME) + \alpha^*(E - ME)$.

This condition is sufficient since for $E = X$ we would have $\alpha^*(X) = \alpha(X) = \alpha^*(M) + \alpha^*(CM)$, the definition of measurability. To prove the necessity we note that since for all E: $\alpha^*(E) \leqq \alpha^*(ME) + \alpha^*(E - ME)$, it is only necessary to show that if M is α-measurable then $\alpha^*(E) \geqq \alpha^*(ME) + \alpha^*(E - ME)$. Now

$$\alpha^*(E) + \alpha(M) \geqq \alpha^*(E + M) + \alpha^*(ME) = \alpha^*(M + (E - ME)) + \alpha^*(ME) \geqq \alpha(M) + \alpha^*(E - ME) + \alpha^*(ME),$$

where we use the inequality $\alpha^*(E_1 + E_2) \geqq \alpha_*(E_1) + \alpha^*(E_2)$ from V.5.3 for E_1 and E_2 disjoint and take $E_1 = M$ and $E_2 = E - ME$. Since $\alpha(M)$ is finite, we have $\alpha^*(E) \geqq \alpha^*(ME) + \alpha^*(E - ME)$.

The equality $\alpha^*(E) = \alpha^*(ME) + \alpha^*(E - ME)$ virtually says that if we cross any set E by a measurable set M, then α^* is additive on the portions of E: EM and $E - EM$. Then if M_1 and M_2 are disjoint measurable sets, we have $\alpha^*((M_1 + M_2)E) = \alpha^*(M_1 E) + \alpha^*(M_2 E)$.

This extends at once to a finite number of disjoint α-measurable sets. We even have:

10.5. If $\{M_n\}$ is a sequence of disjoint α-measurable sets, then for any set E: $\alpha^*(E\Sigma_n M_n) = \Sigma_n \alpha^*(EM_n)$.

This means that α^* is s-additive if you cut across any set E by a sequence of disjoint α-measurable sets. By way of proof set $M = \Sigma_n M_n$. Then since $\Sigma_1^m M_n$ and $M - \Sigma_1^m M_n$ are α-measurable,

$$\alpha^*(EM) = \alpha^*(E\sum_1^m M_n) + \alpha^* E(M - \sum_1^m M_n) = \sum_1^m \alpha^*(EM_n) + \alpha^*(E(M - \sum_1^m M_n))$$

Now $\lim_m \alpha^*(E(M - \Sigma_1^m M_n)) \leq \lim_m \alpha(M - \Sigma_1^m M_n) = 0$. Hence

$$\alpha^*(EM) = \alpha^*(E\sum_n M_n) = \sum_n \alpha^*(EM_n).$$

EXERCISES

1. Suppose E_1 and E_2 are disjoint and such that $\alpha^*(E_1) + \alpha^*(E_2) = \alpha^*(E_1 + E_2)$. Show that there exist disjoint α-measurable sets M_1 and M_2 such that $(E_1 + E_2)M_1 = E_1$ and $(E_1 + E_2)M_2 = E_2$. More generally, if E_n is a sequence of disjoint sets such that $\alpha^*(\Sigma_n E_n) = \Sigma_n \alpha^*(E_n)$, then there exist disjoint measurable sets M_n such that $(\Sigma_n E_n)M_m = E_m$, for each m.

2. Prove that if M is α-measurable, then $\alpha_*(E) = \alpha_*(EM) + \alpha_*(E - EM)$ for all E.

3. Prove that if M_n are disjoint measurable sets, then for any E: $\alpha_*(E\Sigma_n M_n) = \Sigma_n \alpha_*(EM_n)$.

4. Is a theorem corresponding to exercise (1) true for lower measures $\alpha_*(E)$?

11. The Function $\alpha(x)$ Is Unbounded

Up to the present time, we have assumed that $\alpha(X)$ is finite, that is the monotone function $\alpha(x)$ giving rise to our interval function is bounded on $-\infty < x < +\infty$. We now consider the changes in our theory of measure if the boundedness condition is dropped and we allow $\alpha(X) = \infty$. We assume that $\alpha(x)$ is finite valued on $-\infty < x < +\infty$, but it may happen that $\lim_{x\to-\infty} \alpha(x) = -\infty$ and/or

$\lim_{x \to +\infty} \alpha(x) = +\infty$. For any finite open interval $I = (a, b)$ we still have $\alpha(I) = \alpha(b-0) - \alpha(a+0)$, but if I is $(-\infty, a)$ or $(b, +\infty)$ or $(-\infty, +\infty)$, then $\alpha(I)$ may be $+\infty$. Obviously if G is any open set on X, then $+\infty$ is a permissible value for $\alpha(G)$.

11.1. The fundamental properties of α on open sets G are still valid, to wit: (1) $0 \leqq \alpha(G) \leqq +\infty$; (2) if $G_1 \leqq G_2$, then $\alpha(G_1) \leqq \alpha(G_2)$; (3) $\alpha(G_1 + G_2) + \alpha(G_1 \cdot G_2) = \alpha(G_1) + \alpha(G_2)$; and (4) $\alpha(\Sigma_n G_n) \leqq \Sigma_n \alpha(G_n)$.

For (3) we note that if either $\alpha(G_1)$ or $\alpha(G_2)$ is $+\infty$, then $\alpha(G_1 + G_2) = +\infty$ also. If both $\alpha(G_1)$ and $\alpha(G_2)$ are finite, then the former reasoning is valid. Similarly, if $\Sigma_n \alpha(G_n) = +\infty$, there is nothing to prove; if $\Sigma_n \alpha(G_n) < +\infty$, the reasoning for the case when $\alpha(X) < \infty$ applies.

There is no change in the definition of upper measure, that is: $\alpha^*(E) = \text{g.l.b.}[\alpha(G) \text{ for } G \geqq E]$. Moreover, the properties (1*), (2*), (3*), and (4*) of V.4.4. continue to hold. The reasoning involved is the same as for $\alpha(G)$ above.

The definition of $\alpha_*(E)$ in terms of $\alpha(X)$ and $\alpha^*(CE)$ is no longer usable. Consequently, the definition of measurability must be discarded also. We then have a choice of definitions of measurability which do not involve lower measure $\alpha_*(E)$ or $\alpha(X)$. We shall use the condition of V.10.4 as our basis of measurability:

11.2. Definition. A set M is α-measurable if for every set E of X, we have

$$\alpha^*(E) = \alpha^*(EM) + \alpha^*(E - EM).$$

The objectionable feature in this definition of measurability is that it requires the verification of an equality for a large group of sets: all subsets of X, while measurability for $\alpha(X) < \infty$ requires validity of the equality only for the single set X. It is, however, possible to reduce the number of verifications involved. In the first place because of the inequality $\alpha^*(E) \leqq \alpha^*(EM) + \alpha^*(E - ME)$, we need consider only those E for which $\alpha^*(E) < \infty$. Further, we have:

11.3. THEOREM. A set M is measurable if and only if for all open intervals $I_n = (-n, n)$, we have $\alpha(I_n) = \alpha^*(I_n M) + \alpha^*(I_n - I_n M)$.

If we let $\alpha_n(x) = \alpha(x)$ for $-n < x < n$, $\alpha_n(x) = \alpha(-n+0)$ for $x \leqq -n$ and $\alpha_n(x) = \alpha(n-0)$ for $x \geqq n$, then $\alpha^*(I_n E) = \alpha_n^*(E)$ for all E, and the theorem asserts that M is measurable if and only if M is measurable relative to α_n for all n, that is relative to α restricted to the open intervals $(-n, n)$.

The condition of the theorem is obviously necessary. To prove the sufficiency, we demonstrate first the following:

11.4. Lemma. For any set E:

$$\begin{aligned}\alpha^*(E) &= \sum_m \alpha^*(I_m - I_{m-1})E \\ &= \sum_m (\alpha^*(I_m E) - \alpha^*(I_{m-1})E)) = \lim_n \alpha^*(I_n E).\end{aligned}$$

It is assumed that $I_0 = O$. If we use the functions $\alpha_n(x)$, then since the sets $I_m - I_{m-1}$ are α_n-measurable we have by V.10.5:

$$\alpha^*(I_n E) = \alpha_n{}^*(E) = \sum_{m=1}^{n} \alpha_n{}^*(I_m - I_{m-1})E = \sum_{m=1}^{n} \alpha^*(I_m - I_{m-1})E.$$

Consequently, for all n

$$\sum_{m=1}^{n} \alpha^*((I_m - I_{m-1})E) = \alpha^*(I_n E) \leqq \alpha^*(E) \leqq \sum_{m=1}^{\infty} \alpha^*((I_m - I_{m-1})E).$$

These inequalities lead at once to the lemma.

If M satisfies the condition $\alpha(I_n) = \alpha^*(I_n M) + \alpha^*(I_n - I_n M)$ for all n, then as already indicated, M is measurable relative to each α_n. Consequently if E is any set then

$$\begin{aligned}\alpha^*(I_n E) &= \alpha_n{}^*(E) = \alpha_n{}^*(EM) + \alpha_n{}^*(E - EM) \\ &= \alpha^*(I_n EM) + \alpha^*(I_n(E - EM)).\end{aligned}$$

The fact that $\lim_n \alpha^*(I_n E) = \alpha^*(E)$ for all E now gives $\alpha^*(E) = \alpha^*(EM) + \alpha^*(E - EM)$, or the α-measurability of M.

Obviously the open intervals I_n can be replaced by any monotone sequence of open intervals (a_n, b_n) with $a_{n+1} < a_n$, $b_{n+1} > b_n$, $\lim_n a_n = -\infty$, and $\lim_n b_n = +\infty$.

11.5. As a result of this lemma and theorem, most of the properties of α-measurable sets can be extended to the case when $\alpha(X) = +\infty$. In particular: (a) if E is measurable so is CE, follows from the definition of measurability, (b) if E_1 and E_2 are measurable then $E_1 + E_2$ and $E_1 E_2$ are measurable and $\alpha(E_1 + E_2) + \alpha(E_1 E_2) = \alpha(E_1) + \alpha(E_2)$, follow at once from the theorem and the corresponding finite case; if E_n are α-measurable, then $\Sigma_n E_n$ is measurable, follows from the theorem; to show that if in addition E_n are disjoint then $\alpha(\Sigma E_n) = \Sigma_n \alpha(E_n)$, we note that for the open intervals $I_m = (-m, m)$

$$\alpha(\sum_n E_n) = \sum_m \alpha((I_m - I_{m-1}) \sum_n E_n) = \sum_m \sum_n \alpha((I_m - I_{m-1})E_n)$$
$$= \sum_n \sum_m \alpha((I_m - I_{m-1})E_n) = \sum_n \alpha(E_n).$$

We use here that $\alpha((I_m - I_{m-1})E_n) = \alpha_m((I_m - I_{m-1})E_n)$ and since $\alpha_m(X)$ is finite that

$$\alpha((I_m - I_{m-1}) \sum_n E_n) = \alpha_m((I_m - I_{m-1}) \sum_n E_n)$$
$$= \sum_n \alpha_m((I_m - I_{m-1})E_n) = \sum_n \alpha((I_m - I_{m-1})E_n.$$

Other theorems on α-measurability and α-measure based on these theorems are immediately available. In particular, since every open interval is α-measurable, every open, closed, or Borel measurable set is measurable relative to every monotonic $\alpha(x)$. We can then define lower measure in terms of closed sets:

11.6. $\alpha_*(E) =$ l.u.b. $[\alpha(F)$ for all closed $F \leqq E]$. However, the condition $\alpha^*(E) = \alpha_*(E)$ guarantees measurability of E only if $\alpha^*(E) < \infty$.

The theorems relating to limits of sequences of sets need some modifications. As before, if E_n is a monotonic increasing sequence of measurable sets, then $\alpha(\Sigma_n E_n) = \alpha(\lim_n E_n) = \lim_n \alpha(E_n)$. But the proof for the same theorem when E_n is a monotonic decreasing sequence involves the identity

$$\prod_n E_n = E_1 - ((E_1 - E_2) + (E_2 - E_3) + \ldots)$$
$$= E_m - (\sum_m^\infty (E_n - E_{n-1})).$$

As a consequence the additional assumption: there exists an m such that $\alpha(E_m) < \infty$ is indicated. That this assumption is essential follows from the instance: $\alpha(x) = x$, $E_n \equiv [x > n]$, for which $\Pi_n E_n = O$, but $\alpha(E_n) = \infty$ for all n. Similarly the theorem: if E_n are measurable, then $\alpha(\overline{\lim}_n E_n) \geqq \overline{\lim}\, \alpha(E_n)$ requires the additional condition: for some m: $(\Sigma_{n=m}^\infty E_n) < \infty$, while $\alpha(\underline{\lim}_n E_n) \leqq \underline{\lim}_n \alpha(E_n)$ is valid for all sequences of measurable E_n. We note that if $\alpha(x) = x$, $E_n \equiv [n < x < n+1]$, then $\overline{\lim}_n E_n = \lim_n E_n = O$, but $\alpha(E_n) = 1$ for all n. We conclude then:

11.7. THEOREM. If E_n is a sequence of measurable sets such that $\lim_n E_n$ exists, and if for some m: $\alpha(\Sigma_{n=m}^{\infty} E_n) < \infty$, then $\lim_n \alpha(E_n) = \alpha(\lim_n E_n)$.

By slight changes, the theory presented in this section can be adapted to the case when X is an open interval (a, b) and α is finite valued monotone but unbounded on (a, b).

EXERCISES

1. What properties of lower measure $\alpha_*(E)$, defined as the l.u.b. of $\alpha(F)$ for all closed $F \leqq E$, are valid if $\alpha(X) = \infty$?

2. Show that the condition $\alpha^*(E) < \infty$ is essential in using the equality $\alpha^*(E) = \alpha_*(E)$ as a condition for measurability.

3. Show that even when $\alpha(X) = \infty$, the following three conditions are each necessary and sufficient for α-measurability of a set E:

(A) There exist G_δ and F_σ such that $G_\delta \geqq E \geqq F_\sigma$ and $\alpha(G_\delta - F_\sigma) = 0$.

(B) For every $e > 0$, there exists an open set $G_e \geqq E$ such that $\alpha^*(G_e - E) < e$.

(C) For every $e > 0$, there exist open sets $G_1 \geqq E$ and $G_2 \geqq CE$ such that $\alpha(G_1 G_2) < e$.

4. Show that if M_n is a sequence of α-measurable disjoint sets and E is any set then $\alpha^*(\Sigma_n M_n E) = \Sigma_n \alpha^*(M_n E)$, even if $\alpha(X) = \infty$.

12. Lebesgue Measure

For the case when $\alpha(x) = x$, the value of $\alpha(I)$ reduces to the length of the interval I and the resulting measure function and measurable sets are then generalizations of the length or measure of intervals and their measurability. The process by which we have deduced a measure function from an interval function defined by differences of a monotonic point function is an adaptation of that used by Lebesgue for the special case when $\alpha(I) = l(I)$. We shall consequently call a set of points E on an interval Lebesgue measurable, or L-measurable or simply measurable if it is measurable relative to $\alpha(x) = x$. We obtain Lebesgue measurable subsets of a finite interval $[a, b]$ if we set $\alpha(x) = a$ for $x \leqq a$; $\alpha(x) = x$ for $a \leqq x \leqq b$, and $\alpha(x) = b$ for $x \geqq b$.

If $\mu^*(E)$ and $\mu_*(E)$ are the upper and lower L-measure of E on $[a, b]$ then $\underline{\text{cont}}\, E \leqq \mu_*(E) \leqq \mu^*(E) \leqq \overline{\text{cont}}\, E$. Consequently, if a set E has content it is also L-measurable and cont $E = \mu(E)$.

We recall that any L-measurable set differs from a Borel measurable set by a set of zero measure, in particular, that for any measurable set E, there exist G_δ and F_σ such that $G_\delta \geqq E \geqq F_\sigma$ and $\mu(G_\delta - E) = 0$ and $\mu(E - F_\sigma) = 0$. Since the class $\mathfrak{N}$ of sets of measure zero has the property that if E belongs to $\mathfrak{N}$, then for every $E_1 \leqq E$, E_1 also belongs to $\mathfrak{N}$, the class of sets of measure zero consists of the totality of subsets of G_δ sets in $\mathfrak{N}$. The totality of L-measurable sets can be obtained by adjoining to the class of Borel measurable sets any set which is the sum of a G_δ and a subset of $\mathfrak{N}$. Since in Lebesgue integration many situations involve the statement "except for a set of measure zero," the Borel measurable sets are important.

The definition of measurability on a finite interval depends on the equality of upper and lower measure. This suggests the question: do there exist sets which are not measurable, where the upper and lower measure are unequal. For the case of L-measurability, this question is answered in the affirmative, provided we allow ourselves the validity of the well ordering theorem for points on a linear interval (or the axiom of choice). We note that the measure function in L-measure has an invariant property: if the interval I is translated, the length function $l(I)$ remains unchanged, or if $E + x$ represents the set obtained from E by adding x to each point of E, then $l(I + x) = l(I)$. Since upper and lower measure depend on interval lengths, it follows that $\mu^*(E + x) = \mu^*(E)$ and $\mu_*(E + x) = \mu_*(E)$ for all E and x. If we think of the set of real numbers as a group under addition, then Lebesgue measure is an instance of measure invariant under this group.

We give the construction due to G. Vitali of sets which are not Lebesgue measurable (see F. Hausdorff: "Grundzuege der Mengenlehre," Veit, Leipzig, 1914, pp. 401-2). The invariance of measure under translation plays an important role. The points of the interval $0 \leqq x < 1$ are divided into a denumerable number of disjoint sets. To obtain the basic set E_0, assume that the points $0 \leqq x < 1$ are well ordered. Retain 0 in E_0 and delete all rational points from the well ordered set. Let x_1 be the first remaining point and add it to E_0. Delete all points of the form $x_1 + r$, where r is any rational. Add x_2, the first remaining point to E_0 and delete all points of the form $x_2 + r$. Continuing in this way, we obtain a set E_0 such that if x' and x'' belong to

E_0, then $x' - x''$ is not rational. We define $E_n = E_0 + r_n$ (mod 1), where r_n is the nth rational in some denumeration of the rationals with $0 < r_n < 1$, and $x + r_n - 1$ belongs to E_n if $x + r_n > 1$. If we think of the interval $0 \leqq x < 1$ wound on the circle of radius $1/2\,\pi$, then E_n will be obtained from E_0 by translation by a length r_n on this circle. Consequently, $\mu^* E_n = \mu^* E_0$ and $\mu_* E_n = \mu_* E_0$. Moreover, $\Sigma_n E_n \equiv [0 \leqq x < 1]$. Consequently, $1 = \mu^*(\Sigma_n E_n) \leqq \Sigma_n \mu^* E_n$, so that $\mu^* E_n > 0$. On the other hand, since the E_n are disjoint $1 = \mu_*(\Sigma_n E_n) \geqq \Sigma_n \mu_* E_n$. Since $\mu_* E_n$ are all equal it follows that $\mu_* E_n = 0$. Then the sets E_n are not measurable.

The problem of existence of nonmeasurable sets for a general monotonic nondecreasing function $\alpha(x)$ is somewhat more complicated. As a matter of fact, there exist monotone functions relative to which every set is measurable. We take $\alpha(x)$ as a monotone bounded pure break function on [0, 1], namely:

$$\alpha(x) = \sum_{0 \leqq y < x} (\alpha(y+0) - \alpha(y-0)$$

where $\alpha(y+0) - \alpha(y-0) \geqq 0$ and zero except for a denumerable set of points x_n, at which $\alpha(x)$ is discontinuous. It is assumed that

$$\sum_{0 \leqq x \leqq 1} (\alpha(x+0) - \alpha(x-0)) < \infty.$$

Then every subset of [0, 1] is measurable and if $\{x_n\}$ are the points of discontinuity of α, then

$$\alpha^*(E) = \alpha_*(E) = \sum_{x_n \text{ in } E} (\alpha(x_n + 0) - \alpha(x_n - 0)).$$

For if E contains no points of discontinuiy of α, then $\alpha(E) = 0$. To see this, for $e > 0$ we select m so that $\Sigma_{n=m}^{\infty} (\alpha(x_n + 0) - \alpha(x_n - 0)) < e$. Then G, the open set which is complementary to the set of points consisting of $(x_1 \ldots x_{m-1})$ will enclose E and $\alpha(G) = \Sigma_{n=m}^{\infty} (\alpha(x_n + 0) - \alpha(x_n - 0)) < e$, so that $\alpha(E) = 0$. Since any sequence of points is α-measurable, it follows that all subsets of [0, 1] are α-measurable.

Essentially, the Vitali example shows that there does not exist a s-additive measure function on $X = [0, 1]$, such that $\mu(X) = 1$, which is invariant under translation. S. Banach ("Theorie des Operations Lineaires," Warsaw, 1932, p. 32; reprint, Chelsea, New York, 1955, p. 32) has shown that there exists a function μ defined for all subsets E of the circumference X of the circle of radius $1/2\pi$, which satisfies the conditions: (1) $\mu(E) \geqq 0$ for all E; (2) if E_1 and E_2 are disjoint then $\mu(E_1 + E_2) = \mu(E_1) + \mu(E_2)$; (3) $\mu(E)$ is invariant under translation of E on the circle; (4) $\mu(X) = 1$; that is, a finitely additive measure function invariant under translation. The same result is not valid on a spherical surface. (See F. Hausdorff: "Grundzuege der Mengenlehre," Veit, Leipzig, 1914, p. 469.)

EXERCISES

1. Show that there exists a monotone decreasing sequence of sets E_n of [0, 1] such that $\Pi_n E_n = 0$, but $\lim_n \mu^*(E_n) \neq 0$, where μ^* is upper Lebesgue measure.

2. Suppose E_q is a collection of sets defined for q on the directed set Q. Define

$$\overline{\lim_q} E_q = \prod_{q_1} \sum_{qRq_1} E_q \text{ and } \underline{\lim_q} E_q = \sum_{q_1} \prod_{qRq_1} E_q .$$

Show that $\overline{\lim}_q E_q$ and $\underline{\lim}_q E_q$ may be nonmeasurable, even though E_q are measurable for all q. If, however, Q has sequential character, then measurability of E_q for all q implies measurability of $\overline{\lim}_q E_q$ and $\underline{\lim}_q E_q$.

13. Relation between α-Measure and Lebesgue Measure

If $\alpha(x)$ is a monotonic nondecreasing function on $-\infty < x < +\infty$, then α maps the X-axis on the portion of the Y-axis between $\alpha(-\infty)$ and $\alpha(+\infty)$, if we agree that to any point of discontinuity x_0 of α, there corresponds the closed interval $[\alpha(x_0 + 0), \alpha(x_0 - 0)]$ on the Y-axis, while an interval of constancy of α will map into a single point on the Y-axis. Open intervals on the X-axis will map into a point, or an interval (open, half-open, or closed) on the Y-axis, so that an open set on X will map into a sequence of nonoverlapping intervals together with a sequence of separate points on the Y-axis. We denote by $\alpha^{-1}(y)$ the inverse map to $\alpha(x)$. It is of the same character as $\alpha(x)$. We assert:

13.1. THEOREM. If E_x is any set on the X-axis, and E_y the map of E_x on the Y-axis induced by the monotonic function $\alpha(x)$, then $\alpha^*(E_x) = \mu^*(E_y)$, where $\mu^*(E_y)$ is the upper Lebesgue measure of E_y.

Suppose that $\alpha^*(E_x) < \infty$. Then for any $e > 0$, let G_x, be an open set such that $\alpha^*(E_x) \geqq \alpha(G_x) - e$. Under $\alpha(x)$, G_x maps into $\overline{G}_y$, consisting of a sequence of nonoverlapping intervals and points on the Y-axis, containing E_y. If I_n denotes the nth interval or point of this sequence, then for the same $e > 0$, we can extend I_n at the ends by an amount at most $e/2^{n+1}$ to an interval I_n' so that $\Sigma_n l(I_n) \geqq \Sigma_n l(I_n') - e$, and the open set $\Sigma_n I_n' \geqq \Sigma_n I_n = G_y$. Consequently, $\alpha^*(E_x) \geqq \alpha(G_x) - e = \Sigma_n l(I_n) - e \geqq \Sigma_n l(I_n') - 2e \geqq \mu^*(E_y) - 2e$, for all e. Then $\alpha^*(E_x) \geqq \mu^*(E_y)$. On the other hand, let G_y be an open set containing E_y such that $\mu(G_y) \leqq \mu^*(E_y) + e$. Under the mapping by the inverse function $\alpha^{-1}(y)$, G_y will be mapped into a sequence of nonoverlapping intervals and separate points: $\overline{G}_x$ containing E. We discard from $\overline{G}_x$ any separate point or end point of an interval which is not in E. The end points of intervals of $\overline{G}_x$ belonging to $\overline{G}_x$ and E will be a denumerable set. Let b_n be such a right-hand end point of the nth interval I_n of $\overline{G}_x$. Then extend I_n to a point of continuity $b_n + d$ of α so that $\alpha(b_n + d - 0) - \alpha(b_n + 0) = \alpha(b_n + d) - \alpha(b_n + 0) < e/2^{n+1}$. For a left-hand end point we proceed similarly. If x_n is the nth separate point belonging to $\overline{G}_x$ and E, we find points of continuity of α: $x_n + d'$, $x_n - d''$, to the right and left of x_n such that $(\alpha(x_n + d') - \alpha(x_n - d'')) - (\alpha(x_n + 0) - \alpha(x_n - 0)) < e/2^n$. The sum of the open intervals so obtained will be equivalent to an open set G_x which contains $\overline{G}_x$ and such that $\alpha(G_x) - 2e \leqq \alpha(\overline{G}_x)$. Consequently,

$$\mu^*(E_y) \geqq \mu(G_y) - e = \alpha(\overline{G}_x) - e \geqq \alpha(G_x) - 3e \geqq \alpha^*(E) - 3e,$$

for all $e > 0$. Then $\mu^*(E_y) \geqq \alpha^*(E_x)$ and so $\mu^*(E_y) = \alpha^*(E_x)$.

If $\alpha^*(E_x) = \infty$, and if $I_{xn} = (-n, n)$, then

$$\alpha^*(E_x) = \lim_n \alpha^*(E_x \cdot I_{nx}) = \lim_n \mu^*(E_y(\alpha(n-0), \alpha(-n+0)) = \mu^* E_y.$$

Then for all E_x we have $\alpha^*(E_x) = \mu^*(E_y)$. This leads to:

13.2. THEOREM. A set E_y is α-measurable if and only if its map E_y via $\alpha(x)$ on the Y-axis is Lebesgue measurable and $\alpha(E_x) = \mu(E_y)$.

Note that an arbitrary set E_y on the Y-axis may be not-L-measurable and still have its map on the X-axis via α^{-1} measurable relative to α. This is shown by the case where $\alpha(x)$ is a pure break function relative to which every set E_x is α-measurable.

14. Relations between Classes of α-Measurable Sets

The class $\mathfrak{M}$ of α-measurable sets depends on the particular function $\alpha(x)$ on which measurability is based. As we have already noted, every such class $\mathfrak{M}_\alpha$ contains the class of Borel measurable sets, the s-algebra extension of the class of open subintervals of X. We consider relations between the classes $\mathfrak{M}_\alpha$ depending on relations between the corresponding α.

Let $\alpha_1(x)$, $\alpha_2(x)$ be two monotone nondecreasing functions on X such that for every finite interval $[a, b]$: $\alpha_1(b) - \alpha_1(a) \geqq \alpha_2(b) - \alpha_2(a)$. Then we also have for all (a, b): $\alpha_1(b - 0) - \alpha_1(a + 0) \geqq \alpha_2(b - 0) - \alpha_2(a + 0)$. Consequently, for any set E and open interval $I_n = (-n, n)$ we have $\alpha_1{}^*(I_nE) \geqq \alpha_2{}^*(I_nE)$, and so $\alpha_1{}^*(E) = \lim_n \alpha_1{}^*(I_nE) \geqq \lim_n \alpha_2{}^*(I_nE) = \alpha_2{}^*(E)$. From this we derive:

14.1. THEOREM. If $\alpha_1(x)$ and $\alpha_2(x)$ are monotonic nondecreasing on X, and if for every finite interval (a, b): $\alpha_1(b) - \alpha_1(a) \geqq \alpha_2(b) - \alpha_2(a)$, than any α_1-measurable set is also α_2-measurable.

For if E is α_1-measurable, there exists for every $I_n = (-n, n)$ and $e > 0$, open sets $G_1 \geqq I_nE$ and $G_2 \geqq I_n - I_nE$ such that $\alpha_1(G_1G_2) < e$. Consequently, $\alpha_2(G_1G_2) \leqq e$ also, so that by V.10.3 E is α_2-measurable on I_n and so on X.

If we order monotone functions by the condition that $\alpha_1 (\geqq) \alpha_2$ if and only if for every finite interval $I = (a, b)$: $\alpha_1(b) - \alpha_1(a) \geqq \alpha_2(b) - \alpha_2(a)$, this will induce the same ordering on the corresponding upper measure functions. If we consider the corresponding classes of α-measurable sets $\mathfrak{M}_\alpha$, then $\alpha_1 (\geqq) \alpha_2$ implies $\mathfrak{M}_{\alpha_1} \leqq \mathfrak{M}_{\alpha_2}$.

14.2. THEOREM. If $\alpha_1(x)$ and $\alpha_2(x)$ are monotonic nondecreasing on X, then E is measurable relative to $\alpha_1 + \alpha_2$ if and only if E is both α_1-measurable and α_2-measurable, or $\mathfrak{M}_{\alpha_1+\alpha_2} = \mathfrak{M}_{\alpha_1} \cdot \mathfrak{M}_{\alpha_2}$.

Since $\alpha_1 + \alpha_2 (\geqq) \alpha_1$ and $\alpha_1 + \alpha_2 (\geqq) \alpha_2$, it follows from the preceding theorem that if E is measurable relative to $\alpha_1 + \alpha_2$ it is also α_1-measurable and α_2-measurable. For the converse we note that for any E: $(\alpha_1 + \alpha_2)^* (E) = \alpha_1{}^*(E) + \alpha_2{}^*(E)$. For if G is any open set, then $(\alpha_1 + \alpha_2) (G) = \alpha_1(G) + \alpha_2(G)$. Further from the definition of upper measure it follows that $\alpha^*(E) = \lim_{G \geqq E} \alpha(G)$, where the class of open sets $G \geqq E$ is a directed set ordered by inclusion. Then by the additive property of directed limits:

$$(\alpha_1 + \alpha_2)^*(E) = \lim_{G \geqq E} (\alpha_1 + \alpha_2)(G) = \lim_{G \geqq E} \alpha_1(G) + \lim_{G \geqq E} \alpha_2(G)$$
$$= \alpha_1{}^*(E) + \alpha_2{}^*(E).$$

Applying the condition for measurability to this equality gives us the result desired: if E is measurable relative to α_1 and α_2, then it is measurable relative to $\alpha_1 + \alpha_2$.

In this connection it is desirable to consider briefly *measurability relative to functions of bounded variation.* We shall assume that the functions considered are of bounded variation on every finite interval (B.V.F.I.) of $X = -\infty < x < +\infty$. Then $V(x) = \int_0^x |\, d\alpha \,|$ determines a monotone point function on X. It is customary to define:

14.3. Definition. A set E is measurable relative to an α of B.V.F.I. if and only if it is measurable relative to the monotone function $V(\alpha)$. If we define

$$P(x) = \tfrac{1}{2} \left(\int_0^x |\, d\alpha \,| + \alpha(x) \right) \quad \text{and} \quad N(x) = \tfrac{1}{2} \left(\int_0^x |\, d\alpha \,| - \alpha(x) \right),$$

then $P(x)$ and $N(x)$ will both be monotonic nondecreasing on X with $V(x) = P(x) + N(x)$ and $\alpha(x) = P(x) - N(x)$. Moreover, $V(I) = P(I) + N(I)$ where $I = [a, b]$ and $V(I) = \int_a^b |\, d\alpha \,|$. It follows that a necessary and sufficient condition that E be measurable relative to the function $\alpha(x)$ of B.V.F.I. is that E be measurable relative to both $P(x)$ and $N(x)$.

The class of functions of bounded variation on every finite interval is linear. We have

14.4. If $\alpha_1(x)$ and $\alpha_2(x)$ are in B.V.F.I. and E is measurable relative to both α_1 and α_2 then it is also measurable relative to $c_1\alpha_1 + c_2\alpha_2$, where c_1 and c_2 are any two constants.

For if E is measurable relative to α, then it is also measurable relative to $c\alpha$ for any c. From the inequality

$$\int_a^b |\, d(\alpha_1 + \alpha_2) \,| \leqq \int_a^b |\, d\alpha_1 \,| + \int_a^b |\, d\alpha_2 \,|$$

it follows that if E is measurable relative to α_1 and α_2 it is also measurable relative to $\alpha_1 + \alpha_2$.

The converse does not need to hold. For instance, let α by a monotone pure break function on $[a, b]$, and set $\alpha_1(x) = \alpha(x) + x$ and $\alpha_2(x) = x$, then any subset E of $[a, b]$ is measurable relative to $\alpha_1(x) - \alpha_2(x)$, but need not be measurable relative to $\alpha_2(x)$.

14.5. If $\alpha_n(x)$ is any sequence of monotone nondecreasing functions on X, and if $\alpha(x)$ is such that for every E of X: $\lim_n \alpha_n^*(E) = \alpha^*(E)$, then any set E measurable relative to all α_n is also measurable relative to α, or $\mathfrak{M}_\alpha \geqq \Pi_n \mathfrak{M}_{\alpha_n}$.

For if M is measurable relative to α_n, then for all E

$$\alpha_n^* (E) = \alpha_n^* (EM) + \alpha_n^* (E - EM).$$

Taking limits as to n yields $\alpha^*(E) = \alpha^*(EM) + \alpha^*(E - EM)$ for all E, the measurability of M relative to α.

A stronger condition under which the conclusion of the preceding theorem is valid is:

14.6. If $\alpha_n(x)$ and $\alpha(x)$ are monotone nondecreasing functions on X such that $\lim_n \int_{-\infty}^{+\infty} | d(\alpha_n - \alpha) | = 0$, then for any set E we have $\lim_n \alpha_n{}^*(E) = \alpha^*(E)$ and so any set measurable relative to all α_n is also measurable relative to α.

For for any interval $I = [a, b]$ we have

$$| \alpha_n(I) - \alpha(I) | \leqq \int_a^b | d(\alpha_n - \alpha) |.$$

Then for any open set $| \alpha_n(G) - \alpha(G) | \leqq \int_X | d(\alpha_n - \alpha)|$, and by taking limits as to $G \geqq E$, $| \alpha_n^*(E) - \alpha^*(E) | \leqq \int_X | d(\alpha_n - \alpha) |$.

On the other hand, in case $\alpha_n(x)$ and $\alpha(x)$ are bounded on X we can state:

14.7. If $\alpha_n(x)$ and $\alpha(x)$ are bounded on X and such that $\lim_n \alpha_n(G_\delta) = \alpha(G_\delta)$ for all G_δ subsets of X, products of denumerable open sets, then $\lim_n \alpha_n^*(E) = \alpha^*(E)$ for all E and so any set measurable relative to all α_n is also measurable relative to α.

For if E_n is any subset of X, then $\alpha_n^*(E)$ and $\alpha^*(E)$ will be finite and so there exists for each n an open set $G_n \geqq E$ such that

$$\alpha_n(G_n) - 1/n \leqq \alpha_n^*(E) \leqq \alpha_n(G_n) \text{ and } \alpha(G_n) - 1/n \leqq \alpha^*(E) \leqq \alpha(G_n).$$

The sets G_n can be taken to be the same for α_n and α, since if G_{1n} serves for α_n and G_{2n} for α, then $G_{1n} \cdot G_{2n}$ will serve for both. Let $G_\delta = \Pi_n G_n$. Then for all n: $\alpha_n(G_\delta) - 1/n \leqq \alpha_n^*(E) \leqq \alpha_n(G_\delta)$, and and $\alpha(G_\delta) - 1/n \leqq \alpha^*(E) \leqq \alpha(G_\delta)$. Then $\alpha(G_\delta) = \alpha^*(E)$ and

$$\lim_n \alpha_n^* (E) = \lim_n \alpha_n(G_\delta) = \alpha(G_\delta) = \alpha^*(E).$$

The question arises what conditions does the hypothesis $\lim_n \alpha_n(G_\delta) = \alpha(G_\delta)$ for every G_δ impose on α_n and α. For any G_δ there exists a sequence of open sets G_m monotonic nonincreasing in m, such that $\lim_m G_m = G_\delta$. Then $\lim_m \alpha_n(G_m) = \alpha_n(G_\delta)$ for each n. Since any open set is also a G_δ, it follows that the condition $\lim_n \alpha_n(G_\delta) = \alpha(G_\delta)$

for all G is equivalent to $\lim_n \lim_m \alpha_n(G_m) = \lim_m \lim_n \alpha_n(G_m)$ for all monotone decreasing sequences G_m, all limits indicated existing. Since the double sequence $\alpha_n(G_m)$ is monotone in m for each n, it follows from the converse I.7.8 of the iterated limits theorem I.7.4 that $\lim_m \alpha_n(G_m) = \alpha_n(\Pi_m G_m)$ uniformly in n and $\lim_n \alpha_n(G_m) = \alpha(G_m)$ uniformly in m. By the iterated limits theorem either of these conditions is also sufficient to guarantee that $\lim_n \alpha_n(G_\delta) = \alpha(G_\delta)$ for all G_δ. Then:

14.8. If $\alpha_n(x)$ and $\alpha(x)$ are bounded monotonic functions on X, then a necessary and sufficient condition that $\lim_n \alpha_n^*(E) = \alpha^*(E)$ for all E of X is that for any monotone decreasing sequence of open sets G_m either $\lim_n \alpha_n(G_m) = \alpha(G_m)$ uniformly in m, or $\lim_m \alpha_n(G_m) = \alpha_n(\Pi_m G_m)$ uniformly in n.

We note that the condition $\lim_m \alpha_n(G_m) = \alpha_n(\Pi_m G_m)$ uniformly in n for any decreasing sequence of open sets carries with it the condition $\lim_m \alpha_n(\Sigma_m^\infty I_k) = 0$ uniformly in n for any sequence I_k of disjoint open intervals. This condition in addition to the condition that $\lim_n \alpha_n(I) = \alpha(I)$ for any open I is sufficient to ensure that $\lim_n \alpha_n(G) = \alpha(G)$ for all G.

In these theorems, there is nothing assumed explicitly concerning the convergence of $\alpha_n(x)$ to $\alpha(x)$, since upper measures depend on difference. We could then assume, for instance, that the $\alpha_n(x)$ are normalized in such a way that for some point of continuity x_0 of all α_n and α, $\lim_n \alpha_n(x_0) = \alpha(x_0)$. Then from the condition $\lim_n \alpha_n(I) = \alpha(I)$ applied to open intervals $x_0 < x < x_1 + 0$ and $x_1 - 0 < x < x_0$, it follows that $\lim_n \alpha_n(x_1 + 0) = \alpha(x_1 + 0)$ and $\lim_n \alpha_n(x_1 - 0) = \alpha(x_1 - 0)$ for all x_1.

EXERCISES

1. Which of the theorems on the measurability of E relative to $\alpha(x)$ on the basis of its measurability relative to the each of the sequence of functions $\alpha_n(x)$ are valid if the sequence α_n is replaced by a set of functions $\alpha_q(x)$ with q on a directed set Q?

2. Show that if for a sequence of monotone functions $\alpha_n(x)$ on a finite closed interval $[a, b]$, and $\alpha(x)$ on $[a, b]$, we have $\lim_n \alpha_n(x) = \alpha(x)$, $\lim_n \alpha_n(x + 0) = \alpha(x + 0)$, and $\lim_n \alpha_n(x - 0) = \alpha(x - 0)$ for all x, then α_n converges to α uniformly on $[a, b]$. Is the same theorem true if the sequence α_n is replaced by a set α_q, q on directed Q?

15. Measurability of Sets in Euclidean Space of Higher Dimension

A theory of measurable sets and measure can be formulated for higher dimensions along the lines carried through in the one-dimensional case in V.4-V.10. An examination of the procedure shows that the theorems for the one-dimensional case are based on the definition of an α-measure for open sets G satisfying the following conditions:

(1) For all G we have $\alpha(G) \geqq 0$;

(2) $G_1 \leqq G_2$ implies $\alpha(G_1) \leqq \alpha(G_2)$;

(3) $\alpha(G_1 + G_2) + \alpha(G_1 \cdot G_2) = \alpha(G_1) + \alpha(G_2)$ for all G_1 and G_2;

(4) $\alpha(\Sigma_n G_n) \leqq \Sigma_n \alpha(G_n)$ for every sequence of open sets G_n.

We shall indicate how functions on open sets having these four properties can be defined for the two-dimensional space: $-\infty < x, y < +\infty$. The theory for n-dimensions: $-\infty < x_1, x_2, \ldots, x_n < +\infty$ follows through at once by proper change of terminology.

The main difficulty in this program for higher dimensions is that of finding a suitable definition of α-measure for an open set G, which in two or higher dimensions does not have the simple structure it does in one dimension. We make the following observation. If for the monotone function $\alpha(x)$ we define $\alpha(I)$ for the interval $[a, b]$ as $\alpha(b) - \alpha(a)$, then for the open set G, $\alpha(G)$ is the l.u.b. $\Sigma_n \alpha(I_n)$ for all finite collections of (closed) nonoverlapping intervals $I_1, \ldots, I_k$ such that $\Sigma_n I_n$ is contained in G. In particular, if I_0 is the open interval $a < x < b$, then $\alpha(I_0) = \alpha(b - 0) - \alpha(a + 0)$.

In two dimensions we start with a function of two variables $\beta(x, y)$ which satisfies the monotoneity condition of Vitali,

$$\Delta_x \Delta_y \beta = \beta(x+\Delta x, y+\Delta y) - \beta(x+\Delta x, y) - \beta(x, y+\Delta y) + \beta(x, y) \geqq 0$$

for all (x, y) and $\Delta x \geqq 0$, $\Delta y \geqq 0$, and in addition the condition that $\beta(0, y) = \beta(x, 0) = 0$ for all x and y. Such a function gives rise to a positive function of rectangles $I = [a, b; c, d] = [a \leqq x \leqq b; c \leqq y \leqq d]$, namely, $\beta(I) = \beta(b, d) - \beta(b, c) - \beta(a, d) + \beta(a, b)$. In terms of this function of intervals we can define a function of interval sets.

15.1. Definition. An interval set J will be assumed to consists of a finite number of intervals $I_1 \ldots I_n$ having at most edges or parts of edges in common. Then:

15.2. The class $\mathfrak{J}$ of J is finitely additive and finitely multiplicative.

To see this, we observe that every interval I is equivalent to the interval set obtained by any subdivision of I into subintervals. If then for the interval sets J_1 and J_2, we cut across any interval of J_1 by lines which are extensions of sides of intervals of J_2, and any interval of J_2 by lines which are extensions of sides of rectangles of J_1, then $J_1 + J_2$ will consist of the resulting finite set of nonoverlapping intervals, each of which is a subinterval of J_1 or J_2, while $J_1 \cdot J_2$ consists of those subintervals which belong to both J_1 and J_2.

We now extend the interval function $\beta(I)$ to interval sets J by the condition that if $J = I_1 \dots I_n$, then $\beta(J) = \Sigma_k \beta(I_k)$. If $I_1 \dots I_n$ is a subdivision of the interval I, then because of the additive character of $\beta(I)$ it follows that $\beta(I) = \Sigma_k \beta(I_k)$. Further, if J_1 and J_2 are equivalent in the sense that there exists a set of subdivisions of the intervals constituting J_1 and one of the intervals of J_2 which yield the same collection of intervals, then the additivity of $\beta(I)$ assures us that $\beta(J_1) = \beta(J_2)$.

15.3. As a function of interval sets J, β has the following properties:

(1) $\beta(J) \geqq 0$ for all J.

(2) $J_1 \leqq J_2$ implies $\beta(J_1) \leqq \beta(J_2)$.

(3) $\beta(J_1 + J_2) + \beta(J_1 J_2) = \beta(J_1) + \beta(J_2)$.

Property (1) is obvious. For (2), we note that $J_1 \leqq J_2$ means that every interval of J_1 is a subinterval of some interval of J_2, and use the monotone character of β. For (3) we follow out the above construction leading to interval sets equivalent to J_1, J_2, $J_1 + J_2$, $J_1 J_2$. If we express $\beta(J_1)$, $\beta(J_2)$, $\beta(J_1 + J_2)$, and $\beta(J_1 \cdot J_2)$ in terms of this particular group of interval sets, the identity $\beta(J_1) + \beta(J_2) = \beta(J_1 + J_2) + \beta(J_1 J_2)$ emerges since $\beta(J_1 J_2)$ covers the terms which appear in both $\beta(J_1)$ and $\beta(J_2)$.

In order to define a function of open sets, we notice that any open set G can be expressed as the sum of a monotone sequence of interval sets J_n (with $J_n \geqq J_{n-1}$). This leads to the definition:

15.4. $\alpha(G) = \text{l.u.b.}\ [\alpha(J)$ for all $J \leqq G]$.

If we think of the interval sets $J \leqq G$ ordered by inclusion, then these interval sets $J \leqq G$ are a directed set, and we can also define:

15.5. $\alpha(G) = \lim_{J \leqq G} \beta(J)$ since $\beta(J)$ is monotone in J.

We show that $\alpha(G)$ has the four properties (1), (2), (3), (4) listed at the beginning of this section.

Properties (1) and (2) are immediate consequences of the corresponding properties of $\beta(J)$. For property (3) we note that if either $\alpha(G_1)$ or $\alpha(G_2) = \infty$, then $\alpha(G_1 + G_2) = \infty$ and then (3) is valid. Assume then that both $\alpha(G_1)$ and $\alpha(G_2)$ are finite. Then for $e > 0$ there exist interval sets $J_1 \leqq G_1$ and $J_2 \leqq G_2$, such that $\alpha(G_1) \leqq \beta(J_1) + e$, and $\alpha(G_2) = \beta(J_2) + e$, so that

$$\alpha(G_1)+\alpha(G_2) \leqq \beta(J_1)+\beta(J_2)+2e = \beta(J_1+J_2)+\beta(J_1 \cdot J_2)+2e$$
$$\leqq \alpha(G_1+G_2)+\alpha(G_1 \cdot G_2)+2e.$$

since $J_1 + J_2 \leqq G_1 + G_2$ and $J_1 \cdot J_2 \leqq G_1 \cdot G_2$. Then $\alpha(G_1) + \alpha(G_2) \leqq \alpha(G_1 + G_2) + \alpha(G_1 \cdot G_2)$. On the other hand, for any $e > 0$ there exist interval sets J' and J'' such that $J' \leqq G_1 + G_2$ and $J'' \leqq G_1 \cdot G_2$, and $\alpha(G_1 + G_2) \leqq \beta(J') + e$ and $\alpha(G_1 \cdot G_2) \leqq \beta(J'') + e$. Here we can assume that $J' \geqq J''$ since otherwise we need only replace J' by $J' + J''$. Unfortunately, the intervals in J' will usually not belong entirely either to G_1 or to G_2. Consider an arbitrary interval I of J'. Then since I is contained in $G_1 + G_2$, for each point P of I, including the boundary there will exist an interval I_P lying entirely in G_1 or G_2. Since I is a closed bounded set, a finite number of these intervals I_P will cover I and each of them will lie either in G_1 or G_2. The sides of this finite number of intervals extended across I will determine a subdivision of I, such that each interval I' of this subdivision σ will be interior either to G_1 or G_2, and such that $\beta(I) = \Sigma_\sigma \beta(I')$. This procedure can be extended to all intervals in J'. In this way we replace the interval set J' by an equivalent interval set J_1' such that each interval of J_1' is interior either to G_1 or G_2. It follows that J_1' can be expressed as the sum of two interval sets $J^{(1)}$ and $J^{(2)}$, where $J^{(1)}$ is the set of intervals of J_1' lying in G_1 and $J^{(2)}$ the set of intervals of J_1' lying in G_2, so that $J' = J^{(1)} + J^{(2)}$ and $J^{(1)} \cdot J^{(2)} \geqq J''$.

Consequently,

$$\alpha(G_1 + G_2) + \alpha(G_1 \cdot G_2) \leqq \beta(J') + \beta(J'') + 2e$$
$$\leqq \beta(J^{(1)} + J^{(2)}) + \beta(J^{(1)} \cdot J^{(2)}) + 2e = \beta(J^{(1)}) + \beta(J^{(2)}) + 2e$$
$$\leqq \alpha(G_1) + \alpha(G_2) + 2e.$$

We can conclude that $\alpha(G_1 + G_2) + \alpha(G_1 \cdot G_2) = \alpha(G_1) + \alpha(G_2)$.

It follows that if $G_1 \ldots G_n$ is any finite collection of open sets, then $\alpha(\Sigma_1^n G_k) \leqq \Sigma_1^n \alpha(G_k)$.

The procedure for property (4) is much as in the one-dimensional case. Suppose $\alpha(\Sigma_1^\infty G_n) < \infty$. Consider for $e > 0$ any J set such that $J \leq \Sigma_n G_n$ and $\alpha(\Sigma_n G_n) \leqq \beta(J) + e$. Now J is a bounded closed set of points covered by the denumerable set of open sets $\{G_n\}$. Consequently, by the Borel theorem a finite number of the G_n: $G_{n_1}, G_{n_2} \ldots G_{n_k}$ will suffice to cover J. Consequently,

$$\beta(J) \leqq \alpha(\sum_1^k G_{n_i}) \leqq \sum_1^k \alpha(G_{n_i}) \leqq \sum_1^\infty \alpha(G_n).$$

Then $\alpha(\Sigma_n G_n) \leqq \Sigma_n \alpha(G_n)$. If $\alpha(\Sigma_n G_n) = \infty$, then for every N there exists a $J \leqq \Sigma_n G_n$ such that $\beta(J) \geqq N$. Applying the Borel theorem again, we have $N \leqq \beta(J) \leqq \Sigma_n \alpha(G_n)$ for all N, which implies that $\Sigma_n \alpha(G_n) = \infty$. Consequently the inequality of (4) always holds.

If X is the total set $-\infty < x, y < +\infty$, then X is a G and consequently $\alpha(X)$ is defined. It is equal to $\lim_n \beta(I_n)$ where $I_n = [-n, n; -n, n]$.

On the basis of the function $\alpha(G)$ defined on open sets G we can now proceed as in the one-dimensional case, define an upper measure $\alpha^*(E) =$ g.l.b. $[\alpha(G)$ for all $G \geqq E]$, and develop a theory of α-measurability, so far as this theory uses the properties (1), (2), (3), and (4) of $\alpha(G)$.

We note that in general for a closed interval I: $\alpha(I)$ will not agree with $\beta(I)$ but be larger. This is also true in the one-dimensional case since the same procedure applied to the function $\alpha(I) = \alpha(b) - \alpha(a)$ gives $\alpha(b+0) - \alpha(a-0)$ as the value for $\alpha(\bar{I})$ where $\bar{I} \equiv [a \leqq x \leqq b]$.

EXERCISE

Show that if I is any open interval $\equiv (a < x < b;\ c < y < d)$ where a, b, c, d may be infinite, then I is measurable relative to the α function on open sets defined above from the monotone function $\beta(x, y)$.

16. Some Abstract Measure Theory

The preceding constructions of measure functions and measurable sets suggest some lines along which an abstract theory of measure can be developed, the advantage of which would be to establish certain theorems on the basis of few postulates, so as to avoid proofs for individual cases. We outline such an abstract theory, with the usual reservation that it is valid in a particular case only if the case conforms to the general situation in both postulates and definitions.

The measure theories developed for the one and two dimensional Euclidean spaces, center in an "upper measure" function, which is defined and positive valued for all subsets of a fundamental set. We consequently assume a basic set X together with the class $\mathfrak{E}$ of all of its subsets E. We then assume:

16.1. Postulate (A). The function $\mu^*(E)$ is defined for all E of $\mathfrak{E}$ with $0 \leqq \mu^*(E) \leqq +\infty$.

We select from the class $\mathfrak{E}$ a subclass $\mathfrak{M}$ of sets M which satisfy the "measurability" condition:

16.2. $\mathfrak{M}$ = [class of sets M such that for all E:

$$\mu^*(E) = \mu^*(EM) + \mu^*(E - M) = \mu^*(EM) + \mu^*(ECM)\,].$$

We note that the class $\mathfrak{M}$ may be vacuous or consist of all of $\mathfrak{E}$ as in the case when $\mu^*(E) = 0$ or $+\infty$ for all E. We proceed to determine properties of the class $\mathfrak{M}$. In case M belongs to $\mathfrak{M}$, we shall write $\mu^*(M) = \mu(M)$.

If we assume that $\mathfrak{M}$ contains at least one set M, and put $E = O$ in the measurability condition, then

$$\mu^*(O) = \mu^*(O \cdot M) + \mu^*(O \cdot CM) = \mu^*(O) + \mu^*(O).$$

Then $\mu^*(O) = 0$ or $+\infty$. If we put $E = M$ in the same condition, then

$$\mu^*(M) = \mu^*(M \cdot M) + \mu^*(M \cdot CM) = \mu^*(M) + \mu^*(O).$$

If $\mu^*(O) = +\infty$, then for every M of $\mathfrak{M}$: $\mu^*(M) = +\infty$. It then seems sensible to add the additional postulate:

16.3. Postulate (B). If E is the null set O, then $\mu^*(O) = 0$.

As an immediate consequence we have:

16.4. If $\mu^*(O) = 0$, then $\mathfrak{M}$ contains at least the null set O.

For then $\mu^*(E) = \mu^*(E \cdot O) + \mu^*(E \cdot X) = 0 + \mu^*(E)$ for all E.

Further because of the relation $C(CM) = M$, the measurability condition is symmetric in M and CM, so that:

16.5. The class $\mathfrak{M}$ has the complementary property, i.e., with M it also contains CM. Consequently, if $\mu^*(O) = 0$, then O and X both belong to $\mathfrak{M}$.

Suppose next that M_1 and M_2 belong to $\mathfrak{M}$, and consider $M_1 + M_2$. By applying the measurability condition to M_1 and M_2, we find:

$$\mu^*E(M_1 + M_2) + \mu^*EC(M_1 + M_2) = \mu^*(E(M_1 + M_2)M_1)$$
$$+ \mu^*(E(M_1 + M_2)CM_1) + \mu^*(ECM_1CM_2)$$
$$= \mu^*(EM_1) + \mu^*(EM_2CM_1) + \mu^*(ECM_1CM_2)$$
$$= \mu^*(EM_1) + \mu^*(ECM_1) = \mu^*(E).$$

Consequently:

16.6. If M_1 and M_2 are in $\mathfrak{M}$, then $M_1 + M_2$ is also in $\mathfrak{M}$, and because of the complementary property $M_1 - M_2$ is also in $\mathfrak{M}$. It follows that the class $\mathfrak{M}$ is an algebra of sets.

Moreover, if M_1 and M_2 are in $\mathfrak{M}$, then for any E

$$\mu^*(E(M_1 + M_2)) + \mu^*(EM_1M_2) = \mu^*(E(M_1 + M_2)M_1)$$
$$+ \mu^*(E(M_1 + M_2)CM_1 + \mu^*(EM_1M_2)$$
$$= \mu^*(EM_1) + \mu^*(EM_2CM_1) + \mu^*(EM_2M_1)$$
$$= \mu^*(EM_1) + \mu^*(EM_2).$$

If in particular we take $E = X$, then:

16.7. $\mu(M_1 + M_2) + \mu(M_1M_2) = \mu(M_1) + \mu(M_2)$. As a consequence, the function μ on the class $\mathfrak{M}$ is additive. If $M_1 \ldots M_n$ are disjoint, then $\mu(\Sigma_1^n M_k) = \Sigma_1^n \mu(M_k)$. Further, we note that if M_1 and M_2 are in $\mathfrak{M}$, and if $M_1 \geqq M_2$, then $M_1 - M_2$ is in $\mathfrak{M}$ also and $\mu^*(EM_1) \geqq \mu^*(EM_2)$ for all E. If further $\mu^*(EM_2) < +\infty$, then $\mu^*(EM_1 - EM_2) = \mu^*(EM_1) - \mu^*(EM_2)$.

These results may seem somewhat surprising until one realizes that the measurability condition is rather strong so that the class $\mathfrak{M}$ is limited, and may if $\mu^*(O) = 0$, consist only of O and X.

In order to obtain the s-additive property for the class $\mathfrak{M}$, the function μ^* must be restricted further. The following upper semiadditive condition is suggested by the properties of upper measure:

16.8. Postulate (C). For all sequences of sets E_n we have $\mu^*(\Sigma_n E_n) \leqq \Sigma_n \mu^*(E_n)$.

Since this also holds for a finite number of sets, we obtain at once the monotoneity property of μ^* on $\mathfrak{E}$, namely:

16.8.1. If $E_1 \leqq E_2$, then $\mu^*(E_1) \leqq \mu^*(E_2)$, and if $\mu^*(E_2) < +\infty$, then $\mu^*(E_1 - E_2) \geqq \mu^*(E_1) - \mu^*(E_2)$.

We note in passing that postulate (C) is equivalent to the condition:

16.8.2. (C′). If $E \leqq \Sigma_n E_n$, then $\mu^*(E) \leqq \Sigma_n \mu^*(E_n)$.

To show that the class $\mathfrak{M}$ has the *s*-additive property, we derive first two lemmas:

16.9. Lemma I. If $\{M_n\}$ is a sequence of disjoint subsets of $\mathfrak{M}$, and E is any set, then $\mu^*(E\Sigma_n M_n) = \Sigma_n \mu^*(EM_n)$.

Note that we do not assume that $\Sigma_n M_n$ is in $\mathfrak{M}$. Since $E\Sigma_1^m M_n \leqq E\Sigma_1^\infty M_n$, we have

$$\sum_1^m \mu^*(EM_n) = \mu^*(E\sum_1^m M_n) \leqq \mu^*(E\sum_1^\infty M_n) \leqq \sum_1^\infty \mu^*(EM_n).$$

Since this holds for all m, it follows that $\mu^*(E\Sigma_1^\infty M_n) = \Sigma_1^\infty \mu^*(EM_n)$.

16.10. Lemma II. If M_n and M are in $\mathfrak{M}$, M_n are disjoint, and $\Sigma_n M_n \leqq M$, and if $\mu^*(EM) < +\infty$, then $\mu^*(E(M - \Sigma_1^\infty M_n)) = \mu^*(EM) - \Sigma_1^\infty \mu^*(EM_n)$.

We have $\Sigma_1^m \mu^*(EM_n) = \mu^*(\Sigma_1^m EM_n) \leqq \mu^*(EM)$. Since $\mu^*(EM) < +\infty$, it follows that $\Sigma_n \mu^*(EM_n)$ converges. Then

$$\mu^*(E(M - \sum_1^\infty M_n)) \leqq \mu^*(E(M - \sum_1^m M_n)) = \mu^*(EM) - \sum_1^m \mu^*(E_n)$$

for all m. Consequently,

$$\mu^*(E(M - \sum_1^\infty M_n)) \leqq \mu^*(EM) - \sum_1^\infty \mu^*(EM_n).$$

On the other hand, by Lemma I

$$\mu^*((E(M - \sum_1^\infty M_n)) + \sum_1^\infty \mu^*(EM_n)$$
$$= \mu^*((E(M - \sum_1^\infty M_n)) + \mu^*(E(\sum_1^\infty M_n)) \geqq \mu^*(EM).$$

Then $\mu^*(E(M - \Sigma_1^\infty M_n)) = \mu^*(EM) - \Sigma_1^\infty \mu^*(EM_n)$.

As an immediate corollary we have:

16.10.1. If $\{M_n\}$ are in $\mathfrak{M}$ and such that $M_1 \geqq M_2 \geqq \ldots \geqq M_n \geqq \ldots$, then for all E such that $\mu^*(EM_1) < \infty$, we have

$$\mu^*(E\prod_n M_n) = \mu^*(E\lim_n M_n) = \lim_n \mu^*(EM_n).$$

For $\Pi_n M_n = M_1 - (\Sigma_1^\infty (M_n - M_{n+1}))$ with M_1 in $\mathfrak{M}$ and $M_n - M_{n+1}$ disjoint in $\mathfrak{M}$ since $\mathfrak{M}$ is an algebra. Obviously the condition $\mu^*(EM_1) < \infty$ can be replaced by the condition there exists an m such that $\mu^*(EM_m) < \infty$. We now prove:

16.11. If $\{M_n\}$ is a sequence of disjoint subsets of $\mathfrak{M}$, then $\Sigma_n M_n$ is also in $\mathfrak{M}$, $\mathfrak{M}$ is s-additive, and so an s-algebra. Moreover, the function μ on $\mathfrak{M}$ is additive, that is if M_n are disjoint then $\mu(\Sigma_n M_n) = \Sigma_n \mu(M_n)$.

Since by postulate C we have $\mu^*(E) \leqq \mu^*(EM) + \mu^*(ECM)$, we need only show that the measurability condition holds for $\Sigma_n M_n$ in the case when $\mu^*(E) < \infty$. We have by Lemma I:

$$\mu^*(E(\sum_n M_n)) + \mu^*(EC(\sum_n M_n)) = \sum_n \mu^*(EM_n) + \mu^*(E(\prod_n CM_n))$$
$$= \sum_n \mu^*(EM_n) + \mu^*(E(CM_1 - \sum_2^\infty M_n)),$$

since the M_n are disjoint and so $CM_1 \geqq M_n$ for $n \geqq 2$. But since $\mu^*(ECM) \leqq \mu^*(E) < \infty$, Lemma II applies and

$$\mu^*(E(CM_1 - \sum_2^\infty M_n)) = \mu^*(ECM_1) - \sum_2^\infty \mu^*(EM_n).$$

Then

$$\mu^*(E(\sum_1^\infty M_n)) + \mu^*(EC(\sum_1^\infty M_n)) = \mu^*(EM_1) + \mu^*(ECM_1) = \mu^*(E),$$

so that $\Sigma_1^\infty M_n$ is in $\mathfrak{M}$.

To show that $\Sigma_n M_n$ is still in $\mathfrak{M}$ even when M_n are not disjoint, we use the fact that $\mathfrak{M}$ is subtractive to express $\Sigma_n M_n$ as the sum of a sequence of disjoint sets of $\mathfrak{M}$, namely $\Sigma_n M_n = M_1 + (M_2 - M_1) + (M_3 - (M_1 + M_2)) + \dots$.

The identity $\mu(\Sigma_n M_n) = \Sigma_n \mu(M_n)$ for M_n disjoint follows from Lemma I by setting $E = X$.

We summarize our results in the theorem:

16.12. THEOREM. If $\mu^*(E)$ is a function on the subsets of a set X, which satisfies the conditions: (A) $0 \leqq \mu^*(E) \leqq \infty$ for all E; (B) $\mu^*(O) = 0$; and (C) $\mu^*(\Sigma_n E_n) \leqq \Sigma_n \mu^*(E_n)$, then the class of subsets M of X for which $\mu^*(E) = \mu^*(EM) + \mu^*(ECM)$ for all E is an s-algebra of sets, and the function μ is s-additive on $\mathfrak{M}$.

EXERCISE

Show that if the function $\mu^*(E)$ on the subsets of X satisfies the conditions (A), (B) and (C), then any set N such that $\mu^*(N) = 0$ belongs to $\mathfrak{M}$, the class $\mathfrak{N}$ of sets N for which $\mu^*(N) = 0$ is an s-ring which has the property that if for some N, the set E is contained in N, then E is in $\mathfrak{N}$ also; if the set M is in $\mathfrak{M}$ and E is such that $M \Delta E = MCE + ECM$ is in $\mathfrak{N}$, then E is in $\mathfrak{M}$ also and $\mu(E) = \mu(M)$.

17. Upper Semiadditive Functions

The assumption of the upper semiadditivity property for the function $\mu^*(E)$ on all subsets E of X, suggests the problem of determining such a function. In the study of measurability in the one-dimensional case, this property was induced by the values of and properties of the function $\alpha(G)$ on open sets, and these in turn depended on the value of $\alpha(G)$ on open intervals. In terms of $\alpha(G)$ we defined $\alpha^*(E)$ for any set as the greatest lower bound of $\alpha(G)$ for $G \geqq E$. However, we would have obtained the same value for $\alpha^*(E)$ if we had defined $\alpha^*(E)$ as the greatest lower bound of $\Sigma_n \alpha(I_n)$ for all sequences $\{I_n\}$ of open intervals such that $\Sigma_n I_n$ contains or covers E. Guided by these remarks, we assume a class $\mathfrak{G}$ of subsets G of X, which contains the null set O, and is such that for any E of X, there exists a sequence of sets $\{G_n\}$ such that $\Sigma_n G_n \geqq E$. Further, we assume given the function $\alpha(G)$ on $\mathfrak{G}$ to $0 \leqq y \leqq +\infty$, such that $\alpha(O) = 0$. We define then

17.1. $\mu^*(E) = \text{g.l.b.}\ [\Sigma_n \alpha(G_n)$ for all $\{G_n\}$ such that $\Sigma_n G_n \geqq E]$.

We could drop the condition that for every E there exists $\{G_n\}$ such that $\Sigma_n G_n \geqq E$, if we define $\mu^*(E) = +\infty$, for all sets E for which no such sequence exists. Then:

17.2. THEOREM. The function $\mu^*(E)$ satisfies the conditions (A): $0 \leqq \mu^*(E) \leqq +\infty$; (B): $\mu^*(O) = 0$; and (C): if $E \leqq \Sigma_n E_n$, then $\mu^*(E) \leqq \Sigma_n \mu^*(E_n)$.

That (A) and (B) hold is obvious. As for (C) we need only consider the case when $\Sigma_n \mu^*(E_n) < \infty$, so that $\mu^*(E_n)$ are all finite. Then for $e > 0$, and n, there exists a sequence $\{G_{nm}\}$ in $\mathfrak{G}$, such that $\Sigma_m G_{nm} \geqq E_n$, and $\mu^*(E_n) \geqq \Sigma_m \alpha(G_{nm}) - e/2^n$. Then

$$\sum_n \mu^*(E_n) \geqq \sum_n \sum_m \alpha(G_{nm}) - e \geqq \mu^*(E) - e,$$

since $\Sigma_n \Sigma_m G_{nm} \geqq E$. Since this holds for all e, property (C) holds for $\mu^*(E)$.

It follows that the function $\mu^*(E)$ defines a class $\mathfrak{M}$ which is an s-algebra of sets.

There are at least two difficulties with this construction: (a) it is not certain that for any set G of $\mathfrak{G}$, we have $\alpha(G) = \mu^*(G)$; and (b) the sets G may not belong to the class $\mathfrak{M}$ of measurable sets.

With respect to (a) we note that for any G $\mu^*(G) \leqq \alpha(G)$. That the inequality is possible is illustrated by points on the linear interval [0, 1], where $\mathfrak{G}$ is the class of all subsets of [0, 1] and $\alpha(G) = \overline{\text{cont}}\, E$. In this case $\mu^*(E)$ is the upper Lebesgue measure of E. For a denumerable dense set on [0, 1] we would have $\alpha(G) = 1$, but $\mu^*(E) = 0$. By using the definition of $\mu^*(G)$, we see that a necessary and sufficient condition that $\mu^*(G) = \alpha(G)$ for all G of $\mathfrak{G}$, is that α satisfy the condition:

17.3. For all sequences $\{G_n\}$ and G of $\mathfrak{G}$, such that $\Sigma_n G_n \geqq G$, we have $\Sigma_n \alpha(G_n) \geqq \alpha(G)$.

Such a condition might be called *cover-additive*. In case $\mathfrak{G}$ is s-additive, it is equivalent to upper semiadditivity.

To ensure that any set G of $\mathfrak{G}$ belongs to the class $\mathfrak{M}$ determined by $\mu^*(E)$ it would be necessary that for all G_1 of $\mathfrak{G}$, we have $\mu^*(G_1) = \mu^*(G_1 G) + \mu^*(G_1 CG)$. If $\mathfrak{G}$ is multiplicative and subtractive and $\mu^*(G) = \alpha(G)$ for all G, this condition becomes $\alpha(G_1) = \alpha(G_1 G) + \alpha(G_1 CG)$, that is any G is α-measurable relative to $\mathfrak{G}$. Sufficient conditions to cover this situation are (1) $\mathfrak{G}$ is a ring of sets and (2) α is (finitely) additive on $\mathfrak{G}$. We can then prove:

17.4. If $\mathfrak{G}$ is a ring, and α is finitely additive on $\mathfrak{G}$, then any set G of $\mathfrak{G}$ is in the class $\mathfrak{M}$ determined by $\mu^*(E)$.

We need to show that for any E of $\mathfrak{E}$ and G of $\mathfrak{G}$, we have $\mu^*(E) = \mu^*(EG) + \mu^*(ECG)$. In view of the upper semiadditivity property of μ^* we can limit ourselves to the case when $\mu^*(E) < \infty$. Then for $e > 0$ there exists $\{G_n\}$ such that $\Sigma_n G_n \geqq E$, and $\mu^*(E) \geqq \Sigma_n \alpha(G_n) - e$. Now $\alpha(G_n) = \alpha(G_n G) + \alpha(G_n CG)$ for all n. Then for all $e > 0$

$$\begin{aligned}\mu^*(E) &\geqq \textstyle\sum_n \alpha(G_n) - e \geqq \sum_n [\alpha(G_n G) + \alpha(G_n CG)] - e \\ &\geqq \mu^*(EG) + \mu^*(ECG) - e.\end{aligned}$$

Since for all E: $\mu^*(E) \leqq \mu^*(EG) + \mu^*(ECG)$, it follows that equality holds.

We note that if $\mathfrak{G}$ is a ring of sets and α is additive on $\mathfrak{G}$, then the cover-additive condition: for any sequence $\{G_n\}$ and G of $\mathfrak{G}$ such that $G \leqq \Sigma_n G_n$, we have $\alpha(G) \leqq \Sigma_n \alpha(G_n)$ is equivalent to s-additivity: if $\overline{G}_n$ are disjoint and $\Sigma_n \overline{G}_n$ is in $\mathfrak{G}$, then $\Sigma_n \alpha(\overline{G}_n) = \alpha(\Sigma_n \overline{G}_n)$.

For from the additive and cover additivity condition on α, we have for all m:

$$\sum_1^m \alpha(\overline{G}_n) = \alpha(\sum_1^m \overline{G}_n) \leqq \alpha(\sum_1^\infty \overline{G}_n) \leqq \sum_1^\infty \alpha(\overline{G}_n),$$

and so $\alpha(\Sigma_1^\infty \overline{G}_n) = \Sigma_1^\infty \alpha(\overline{G}_n)$.

On the other hand, if $\{G_n\}$ is a sequence of sets of $\mathfrak{G}$ with $G \leqq \Sigma_n G_n$, and if we set $\overline{G}_n = G(G_n - \Sigma_1^{n-1} G_m)$, then $\overline{G}_n$ are disjoint in $\mathfrak{G}$ and $G = \Sigma_n \overline{G}_n$, so that

$$\alpha(G) \leqq \sum_n \alpha(\overline{G}_n) \leqq \sum_n \alpha(G_n).$$

We can summarize:

17.5. THEOREM. If $\mathfrak{G}$ is a ring of subsets of X, and $\alpha(G)$ on $\mathfrak{G}$ to $0 \leqq y \leqq +\infty$ is s-additive on $\mathfrak{G}$, then there exists an upper measure $\mu^*(E)$ on $\mathfrak{E}$ to $0 \leqq y \leqq +\infty$, which is upper semiadditive, and such that the class $\mathfrak{M}$ of measurable sets M is an s-algebra, which contains $\mathfrak{G}$ with $\mu(G) = \alpha(G)$ for all G.

The class $\mathfrak{M}$ is then an s-algebra extension $\mathfrak{G}$ preserving measure.

More detailed expositions of abstract measure theory can be found, for instance, in:

C. Caratheodory, "Reelle Funktionen," Teubner, Leipzig, 1918, Chapter V.

C. Caratheodory, "Mass und Integral und ihre Algebraisierung," Birkhaeuser, Basel, 1956 Chapter V.

H. Hahn and A. Rosenthal, "Set Functions," Univ. of New Mexico Press, Albuquerque, 1948, Chapter II.

P. Halmos, "Measure Theory," Van Nostrand, New York, 1950, Chapters II and III.

J. v. Neumann, "Functional Operators," Princeton Univ. Press, Princeton, New Jersey, 1960, Chapters II-IV.

CHAPTER VI

MEASURABLE FUNCTIONS

1. Semicontinuous Functions

Before discussing measurable functions, we make a slight detour and treat briefly semicontinuous functions and some of their properties. We shall limit ourselves to functions $f(x)$ on $X = [a, b]$ to finite reals, although many results carry over to metric spaces.

The continuity of $f(x)$ at a point x_0 requires

$$(e > 0,\ d_{ex_0},\ |x - x_0| < d_{ex_0}) : |f(x) - f(x_0)| < e,$$

or

$$f(x_0) - e < f(x) < f(x_0) + e.$$

If only the inequality: $f(x) < f(x_0) + e$ holds for $|x - x_0| < d_{ex_0}$, then $f(x)$ is said to be *upper semicontinuous* at x_0, if $f(x_0) - e < f(x)$, then $f(x)$ is *lower semicontinuous* at x_0. Now the statement $(e > 0,\ d_{ex_0},\ |x - x_0| < d_{ex_0}) : f(x) < f(x_0) + e$, is equivalent to $\overline{\lim}_{x \to x_0} f(x) \leqq f(x_0)$. Then alternatively we can say:

1.1. Definition. The function $f(x)$ is *upper semicontinuous* at x_0 if and only if $\overline{\lim}_{x \to x_0} f(x) \leqq f(x_0)$ and $f(x)$ is *lower semicontinuous* at x_0, if and only if $\underline{\lim}_{x \to x_0} f(x) \geqq f(x_0)$. If $f(x)$ is both upper and lower semicontinuous at a point, then it is continuous. A function is upper (lower) semicontinuous on an interval $[a, b]$ if it is upper (lower) semicontinuous at every point of the interval.

A function all of whose discontinuities are of the first kind (breaks) is upper semicontinuous if $f(x) \geqq f(x + 0)$ and $f(x - 0)$ for all x. In particular, $f(x)$ on $[0, 1]$ with $f(x) = 0$ for x irrational and $f(x) = 1/q$ for $x = p/q$, p and q relatively prime, is upper semicontinuous on $[0, 1]$. A monotone nondecreasing function on $[a, b]$ is upper semicontinuous if $f(x + 0) = f(x)$ for all x, that is $f(x)$ is continuous on the right.

The negative of an upper semicontinuous function is lower semicontinuous since $\overline{\lim} f(x) = - \underline{\lim} (-f(x))$. The sum of two upper semicontinuous functions is again upper semicontinuous since $\overline{\lim} (f_1(x) + f_2(x)) \leqq \overline{\lim} f_1(x) + \overline{\lim} f_2(x)$. The space of upper semicontinuous functions is positively linear.

A function upper semicontinuous on a closed interval $[a, b]$ can also be characterized as follows:

1.2. THEOREM. A function $f(x)$ is upper semicontinuous on $[a, b]$ if and only if for every constant c, the set E of x for which $f(x) \geqq c$, is closed.

We denote by $E[f(x) \geqq c]$ the set x for which $f(x) \geqq c$. Let $f(x)$ be upper semicontinuous on $[a, b]$ and let x_0 be a limiting point of $E[f(x) \geqq c]$. Let $\{x_n\}$ in $E[f(x) \geqq c]$ be such that $\lim_n x_n = x_0$. Then $c \leqq \overline{\lim}_n f(x_n) \leqq \overline{\lim}_{x \to x_0} f(x) \leqq f(x_0)$, so that x_0 is in $E[f(x) \geqq c]$. Conversely suppose that for all c: $E[f(x) \geqq c]$ is closed. Let x_0 by any point of $[a, b]$ and the sequence $\{x_n\}$ such that $\lim_n x_n = x_0$ and $\lim_n f(x_n) = \overline{\lim}_{x \to x_0} f(x)$. Now for each m, the set $E[f(x) \geqq \overline{\lim}_{x \to x_0} f(x) - 1/m]$ is closed, and contains the points x_n for n large enough. Hence it contains x_0, so that $f(x_0) \geqq \overline{\lim}_{x \to x_0} f(x) - 1/m$ for all m, and so independently of m.

The interesting thing about this characterisation is that it makes the property of semicontinuity on an interval depend on the fact that the set of x's for which $f(x) \geqq c$ belongs to a certain class of sets for all c. By taking complements, we can also characterize upper semicontinuous functions on an interval by the condition that $E[f(x) < c]$ is open for all c. For a lower semicontinuous function $E[f(x) \leqq c]$ is closed and $E[f(x) > c]$ is open for all c. Since a continuous function is both upper and lower semicontinuous, it follows that $f(x)$ is continuous on $[a, b]$ if and only if the sets $E[f(x) \geqq c]$ and $E[f(x) \leqq c]$ are closed for all c or the sets $E[f(x) > c]$ and $E[f(x) < c]$ are open for all c. Since the product of two open sets is open and a continuous function is bounded on a closed interval, the latter condition is equivalent to the statement that for all c_1 and c_2, the set $E[c_1 < f(x) < c_2]$ is open. This leads to the further statement that a function is continuous on $[a, b]$ to Y if and only if, the inverse by $f(x)$ of an open set on Y is an open set in X. This condition is the basis of definition of continuity of a function on a topological space X to a topological space Y, topology being defined in terms of open set.

It is possible to replace the condition: "$E[f(x) \geqq c]$ is closed for all c," by the condition "$E[f(x) \geqq c_n]$ is closed for a denumerable dense set c_n on the real line." For for any c not in $\{c_n\}$, the set $E[f(x) \geqq c]$ will be the product of the closed sets $F_n = E[f(x) \geqq c_n]$ for $c_n < c$, and will consequently be closed also.

A similar type of reasoning leads to:

1.3. If $f(x)$ is finite valued and upper (lower) semicontinuous on $[a, b]$ then $f(x)$ is bounded above (below) and assumes it least upper bound (greatest lower bound).

If $F_n = E[f(x) \geqq n]$, then the product $\Pi_n F_n$ is vacuous. Consequently there exists an m such that for $n > m$, F_m is vacuous, and so $f(x)$ is bounded above. If $B =$ l.u.b. $[f(x)$ for x on $[a, b]]$, then $E[f(x) > B]$ is vacuous but $F_n = E[f(x) \geqq B - 1/n]$ contains elements x for each n so that $E[f(x) \geqq B] = \Pi_n F_n$ is not vacuous, and B is the maximum value of $f(x)$ on $[a, b]$. It follows from this theorem that a sufficient condition that a function $f(x)$ have a maximum on $[a, b]$ is that $f(x)$ be upper semicontinuous on $[a, b]$.

1.4. If $f_n(x)$ is a monotone nonincreasing sequence of upper semicontinuous functions, then $f(x) = \lim_n f_n(x)$ is also upper semicontinuous.

For all c, the set $E[f(x) \geqq c] = \Pi_n E[f_n(x) \geqq c]$. For if $f(x) \geqq c$, then $f_n(x) \geqq f(x) \geqq c$. And if $f_n(x) \geqq c$ for all n, then $f(x) = \lim_n f_n(x) \geqq c$. Then $E[f(x) \geqq c]$ as a product of closed sets is also closed.

Similarly a monotone nondecreasing sequence of lower semicontinuous functions converges to a lower semicontinuous function. As a consequence:

1.5. A nonincreasing sequence of continuous functions converges to an upper semicontinuous function and a nondecreasing sequence of continuous functions to a lower semicontinuous function. The last statement is reversible in the form:

1.6. If $f(x)$ is a finite valued upper semicontinuous function on $[a, b]$, then there exist nonincreasing sequences of continuous functions $f_n(x) \geqq f_{n+1}(x) \geqq f(x)$ such that $\lim_n f_n(x) = f(x)$ for all x.

For any function $f(x)$ bounded above we can define the functions

$$f_n(x) = \text{l.u.b. } [f(x_1) - n\,|x - x_1| \text{ for } x_1 \text{ on } [a, b]].$$

Obviously $f_n(x) \geqq f_{n+1}(x) \geqq f(x)$ for all x and n. Further if x and x' are two points of $[a, b]$, then for all x_1

$$\begin{aligned} f_n(x) &\geqq f(x_1) - n\,|x - x_1| \geqq f(x_1) - n(|x - x'| + |x' - x_1|) \\ &= f(x_1) - n\,|x' - x_1| - n\,|x - x'|. \end{aligned}$$

Then $f_n(x) \geqq f_n(x') - n \mid x - x' \mid$. Since x and x' are interchangeable we have $\mid f_n(x) - f_n(x') \mid \leqq n \mid x - x' \mid$, and $f_n(x)$ is continuous in x for each n. These properties hold for the sequence $f_n(x)$ related to any function $f(x)$ bounded above. In particular, it follows that $f_n(x)$ converges to an upper semicontinuous function $g(x) \geqq f(x)$.

From the definition of $f_n(x)$ it follows that for any $e > 0$, n and x, there exists an x_{ne} such that

$$f_n(x) \leqq f(x_{ne}) - n \mid x_{ne} - x \mid + e.$$

Consequently, $n \mid x_{ne} - x \mid \leqq f(x_{ne}) - f_n(x) + e$, where the right-hand side of the inequality is bounded in n and x, since l.u.b. $_x f_n(x) =$ l.u.b. $_x f(x)$. Then $\lim_n \mid x_{ne} - x \mid = 0$, for all e. The upper semicontinuity of $f(x)$ at x gives $(e > 0,\ d_{ex},\ \mid x' - x \mid < d_{ex})$: $f(x') \leqq f(x) + e$. If for $n > n_e$ we have $\mid x_{ne} - x \mid < d_{ex}$, then

$$f_n(x) \leqq f(x_{ne}) - n \mid x_{ne} - x \mid + e \leqq f(x) + 2e.$$

Since $f(x) \leqq f_n(x)$ for all n, it follows that $\lim_n f_n(x) = f(x)$.

The same demonstration is effective if X is a metric space and $f(x)$ on X to the reals is an upper semicontinuous function bounded above.

The fact that the statement: "for every c the set $E[f(x) \geqq c]$ is closed" characterizes upper semicontinuous functions suggests that classes of functions can be defined by statements of the form: "for every c the set $E[f(x) \geqq c]$ belongs to a given class of sets." The given class of sets might be the class of sets having content, or the class of Borel measurable sets or the class of α-measurable sets.

EXERCISES

1. For any bounded function $f(x)$ there are defined the functions

$$M(f, x) = \text{g.l.b. [l.u.b. } (f(y) \text{ for } y \text{ in } I_x) \text{ for all } I_x \text{ containing } x]$$
$$= \text{the larger of } \overline{\lim_{x' \to x}}\, f(x'), \text{ and } f(x);$$

$$m(f, x) = \text{l.u.b. [g.l.b. } (f(y) \text{ for } y \text{ in } I_x) \text{ for all } I_x \text{ containing } x]$$
$$= \text{the smaller of } \underline{\lim_{x' \to x}}\, f(x') \text{ and } f(x);$$

$\omega(f; x) =$ g.l.b. $[\omega(f; I_x)$ for I_x containing $x]$, where $\omega(f; I)$ is the oscillation of f on the interval I. Show that $M(f, x)$ and $\omega(f, x)$ are upper semicontinuous functions while $m(f, x)$ is lower semicontinuous.

2. Let $f(x)$ be bounded on [0, 1]. For $x = m/2^n$, $m = 0, 1, \ldots, 2^n - 1$ set $f_n(x) =$ the l.u.b. of $f(x)$ on $(m-1)/2^n \leqq x \leqq (m+1)/2^n$, and linear between $m/2^n$ and $(m+1)/2^n$. Show that $f_n(x) \geqq f_{n+1}(x) \geqq f(x)$ for all n and x and if $f(x)$ is upper semicontinuous on [0, 1] then $\lim_n f_n(x) = f(x)$ for all x.

2. Measurable Functions

The closing lines of the preceding paragraph suggest a procedure for defining "measurable" functions in terms of "measurable" sets. Since the basic properties of such functions depend only on those of the class of measurable sets and not the measure function defining such sets, we proceed abstractly, with the observation that the developments apply in the one and two-dimensional cases considered in the preceding chapter.

We assume a basic set X and $\mathfrak{E}$ the class of all subsets E of X. Further we postulate a class $\mathfrak{M}$ of measurable sets M, which is an s-algebra of sets, that is it has the s-additive, s-multiplicative, subtractive and complementary properties.

Real valued functions $f(x)$ will be assumed to be either finite valued, i.e. f is on X to $Y = (-\infty < x < +\infty)$ or in many cases $+\infty$ and $-\infty$ will also be allowed as values (called the *extended real line*).

We define:

2.1. Definition. The function $f(x)$ on X to $Y \equiv (-\infty \leqq y \leqq +\infty)$ is *measurable relative to the class* $\mathfrak{M}$ if for every y of Y, the set $E[f(x) \geqq y]$ is in $\mathfrak{M}$ or measurable.

This definition applies for instance to the case where $X \equiv (-\infty < x < \infty)$, $\alpha(x)$ is monotone nondecreasing on X, and $\mathfrak{M}$ is the class of α-measurable sets. If $\mathfrak{M}$ is the class of Borel measurable subsets of $(-\infty, +\infty)$, we shall call $f(x)$ Borel measurable.

For convenience, we shall in the sequel omit the x in $E[f(x) \geqq y]$ and assume that $E[f \geqq y]$ means the set of x such that $f(x) \geqq y$, with corresponding interpretations of similar symbols.

We note that the following sets could also have been used for the definition of measurable functions:

(1) $E[f < y]$; (2) $E[f \leqq y]$; (3) $E[f > y]$; (4) $E[y' \leqq f \leqq y'']$;

or the three variants of (4) if $\leqq$ is replaced by $<$. We have:

2.2. THEOREM. The conditions: for all y: (0) $E[f \geqq y]$, (1) $E[f < y]$, (2) $E[f \leqq y]$, and (3) $E[f < y]$ belong to $\mathfrak{M}$ are all equivalent so that each could be used for a definition of a measurable function. If $f(x)$ is finite valued the condition (4): $E[y' \leqq f \leqq y'']$ for all $y' \leqq y''$ is also equivalent to (0) for all y.

We show that (0) implies (1) implies (2) implies (3) implies (0), where (0) means: for all y: $E[f \geqq y]$ belongs to $\mathfrak{M}$, and similarly for (1), (2), and (3).

(0) implies (1) since $E[f < y] = C(E[f \geqq y])$, and $\mathfrak{M}$ is closed under complementation.

(1) implies (2) since $E[f \leqq y] = \Pi_n E[f < y + 1/n]$ and $\mathfrak{M}$ has the s-multiplicative property.

(2) implies (3) since $E[f > y] = C(E[f \leqq y])$.

(3) implies (0) since $E[f \geqq y] = \Pi_n E[f > y - 1/n]$.

To relate condition (4) to the others, we note that $E[y' \leqq f \leqq y''] = E[f \geqq y'] \cdot E[f \leqq y'']$, so that if f is measurable then the sets $E[y' \leqq f \leqq y'']$ or their variants are in $\mathfrak{M}$ for all y', y''. Further if f is finite valued, then $E[f \geqq y] = \Sigma_n E[y \leqq f \leqq n]$, so that f is measurable if (4) is in $\mathfrak{M}$ for all y' and y''. If f is not restricted to be finite valued, then $f(x)$ will be measurable if and only if the set $E[y' \leqq f \leqq y'']$ is in $\mathfrak{M}$ for all $-\infty < y' \leqq y'' < \infty$, and either $E[f = +\infty]$ or $E[f = -\infty]$ is in $\mathfrak{M}$. For $E[y \leqq f < +\infty]$ will belong to $\mathfrak{M}$ and $E[f \geqq y] = E[f = +\infty] + E[y \leqq f < \infty]$.

Since $E[f = y] = E[f \geqq y] \cdot E[f \leqq y]$ it follows that:

2.3. If $f(x)$ is measurable relative to $\mathfrak{M}$, then the sets $E[f(x) = y]$ are in $\mathfrak{M}$ or measurable for every y.

For the measurability of a function $f(x)$ it is not necessary to verify that the sets $E[f \geqq y]$ are in $\mathfrak{M}$ for all y. We have:

2.4. If $[y_n]$ is a denumerable dense set on Y (for instance, the rational numbers), then $f(x)$ is measurable if and only if the sets $E[f \geqq y_n]$ are in $\mathfrak{M}$ for all n.

If y is not in the sequence $\{y_n\}$, then $E[f \geqq y] = \Pi_n E[f \geqq y_n]$ for the $y_n > y$. Consequently, $E[f \geqq y]$ is in $\mathfrak{M}$ for all y.

We note in passing that any point function on X to Y determines the sets $E_y = E[f \geqq y]$, a function on $Y = (-\infty \leqq y \leqq +\infty)$ to the subsets of X. This collection of sets has the following properties: (1) if $y' \geqq y''$ then $E_{y'} \leqq E_{y''}$; (2) $E_y = \Pi_{y'}(E_{y'}$ for $y' < y)$; (3) $E_{-\infty} = X$. If $f(x)$ is finite valued then $\Sigma_y(E_y$ for $y > -\infty) = X$ and $E_{+\infty} = \Pi_y(E_y$ for $y < +\infty) = 0$. The set $E[f > y]$ is given by $\bar{E}_y = \Sigma_{y'}(E_{y'}$ for $y' > y)$, and consequently $E[f = y] = E_y - \bar{E}_y$.

2.5. The procedure is reversible. If we have a function E_y on $(-\infty \leqq y \leqq +\infty)$ to subsets of X satisfying the conditions (1), (2) and (3), then E_y gives rise to the point function defined: $f(x) = y$ if x belongs to the set $E_y - \bar{E}_y = E_y - \Sigma_{y'}(E_{y'}$, for $y' > y)$, and $E_y = E[f(x) \geqq y]$.

If we had started with a point function and the sets E_y defined as $E[f > y]$ or $E[f \leqq y]$ or $E[f < y]$, we get variants of the properties (1), (2) and (3) which in turn define point functions.

If the sets E_y satisfying (1), (2), and (3) belong to $\mathfrak{M}$ then the corresponding point function is measurable relative to $\mathfrak{M}$.

3. Properties of Measurable Functions

The following theorems hold when the functions involved are on a set X to reals, and measurability is with respect to an s-algebra of subsets of X.

3.1. If f is measurable so is $-f$.

For $E[-f \geqq y] = E[f \leqq -y]$.

3.2. If f is measurable and c is any constant, then cf is also measurable.

If $c > 0$, then $E[cf \geqq y] = E[f \geqq y/c]$ and if $c < 0$, then $E[cf \geqq y] = E[f \leqq y/c]$.

3.3. If f is measurable, so is $|f|$.

For if $y < 0$, then $E[|f| \geqq y] = X$, and if $y \geqq 0$, then $E[|f| \geqq y] = E[f \geqq y] + E[f \leqq -y]$.

3.4. If f is measurable, so is $|f|^p$ for $p > 0$.

For if $y < 0$, then $E[|f|^p \geqq y] = X$, if $y \geqq 0$, then $E[|f|^p \geqq y] = E[f \geqq y^{1/p}] + E[f \leqq -y^{1/p}]$. If p is an odd integer, then a slightly altered proof yields that f^p is measurable if f is.

3.5. If f is measurable and $f \neq 0$ on X, then $1/f$ is measurable.

If $y > 0$, then $E[1/f \geqq y] = E[0 < f \leqq 1/y]$, and if $y < 0$, then $E[1/f \geqq y] = E[1/f > 0] + E[1/f = 0] + E[0 > 1/f \geqq y] = E[f > 0] + E[f = +\infty] + E[f = -\infty] + E[-\infty < f \leqq 1/y]$; and if $y = 0$, then $E[1/f \geqq 0] = E[+\infty > f > 0] + E[f = +\infty] + E[f = -\infty]$, all of which are measurable sets if f is measurable. The condition $f \neq 0$ can be dropped if we define $1/0 = +\infty$.

3.6. If f_1 and f_2 are measurable, then $f_1 \vee f_2$, the greater of f_1 and f_2, and $f_1 \wedge f_2$, the lesser of f_1 and f_2 are each measurable.

For $E[f_1 \vee f_2 \geqq y] = E[f_1 \geqq y] + E[f_2 \geqq y]$ and $E[f_1 \wedge f_2 \leqq y] = E[f_1 \leqq y] \cdot E[f_2 \leqq y]$. Consequently, the class of measurable functions forms a lattice under the ordering $f_1 (\leqq) f_2 \equiv f_1(x) \leqq f_2(x)$ for all x of X. If we take $f_1 = f$ and $f_2 = 0$, then $f \vee 0 = f^+$ and $f \wedge 0 = -f^-$ are both measurable if f is. Here f^+ is the *positive part* of f and may be defined: $f^+(x) = f(x)$ if $f(x) \geqq 0$ and $f^+(x) = 0$ if $f(x) \leqq 0$; while f^- is the *negative part* of f, namely $f^-(x) = 0$ if $f(x) \geqq 0$, and $f^-(x) = -f(x)$ if $f(x) \leqq 0$. Then $f(x) = f^+(x) - f^-(x)$ and $|f(x)| = f^+(x) + f^-(x)$ for all x.

3.7. If f_1 and f_2 are measurable and finite valued, so is $f_1 + f_2$.

We note that if for a given x: $f_1(x) + f_2(x) > y$, or $f_1(x) > y - f_2(x)$, then for any rational r between $f_1(x)$ and $y - f_2(x)$ we have $f_1(x) > r$ and $r > y - f_2(x)$ or $f_2(x) > y - r$. As a consequence $E[f_1 + f_2 > y] \leqq \Sigma_r E[f_1 > r] \cdot E[f_2 > y - r]$, where r runs over the rationals, that is a denumerable set. On the other hand, if for some r $f_1(x) > r$ and $f_2(x) > y - r$, then $f_1(x) + f_2(x) > y$. Consequently, $E[f_1 + f_2 > y] = \Sigma_r E[f_1 > r] \cdot E[f_2 > r - y]$, and so $E[f_1 + f_2 > y]$ is measurable if f_1 and f_2 are.

3.8. If f_1 and f_2 are finite valued and measurable, then $f_1 \cdot f_2$ is measurable, that is the class of finite valued measurable functions is multiplicative, and forms a ring.

For $f_1 \cdot f_2 = \frac{1}{4} [(f_1 + f_2)^2 - (f_1 - f_2)^2]$, where in view of the preceding theorems, the right hand side is a measurable function if f_1 and f_2 are. An alternative proof can be made by applying the method of the preceding theorem to the case when $f_1(x) \geqq 0$ and $f_2(x) \geqq 0$ for all x, leading to the general case by expressing f_1 and f_2 in terms of their positive and negative parts.

3.9. If $f_n(x)$ is a sequence of measurable functions, then $\text{l.u.b.}_n f_n(x) = g(x)$ and $\text{g.l.b.}_n f_n(x) = h(x)$ are each measurable.

For $E[g(x) > y] = E[\text{l.u.b.}_n f_n(x) > y] = \Sigma_n E[f_n(x) > y]$ and $E[h(x) < y] = E[\text{g.l.b.}_n f_n(x) < y] = \Pi_n E[f_n(x) < y]$, and the s-additivity and s-multiplicativity of $\mathfrak{M}$ gives the desired result.

3.10. If each of the functions $f_n(x)$ is measurable, then $\overline{\lim}_n f_n(x)$ and $\underline{\lim}_n f_n(x)$ are each measurable. If $\lim_n f_n(x) = f(x)$ exists for each x, then $f(x)$ is measurable.

For $\overline{\lim}_n f_n(x) = \text{g.l.b.}_m(\text{l.u.b.}_{n \geqq m} f_n(x))$ and $\underline{\lim}_n f_n(x) = \text{l.u.b.}_m (\text{g.l.b.}_{n \geqq m} f_n(x))$, and the preceding theorem applies. If we limit ourselves to finite valued functions, then the sequence $f_n(x)$ must be bounded for each x.

The proofs of the last theorems involve the fact that we are dealing with sequences of functions. It is then to be expected that corresponding results are not always valid for sets of functions $f_q(x)$ where q is on a directed set Q. For instance if X is the interval [0, 1], the class $\mathfrak{M}$ is the class of Lebesgue measurable subsets of X, Q is the class of elements q consisting of finite subsets of a nonmeasurable set E of X, ordered by inclusion, and $f_q(x) = \chi(q, x)$, the characteristic function of q (0 for x not in q and 1 for x in q), then $\lim_q f_q(x) = 1$ on E and 0 on CE, and is not measurable although all $f_q(x)$ are.

We summarize the principal results of the preceding theorems in the statement:

3.11. THEOREM. The class of finite valued measurable functions is a linear lattice, multiplicative and closed under pointwise sequential convergence.

4. Examples of Measurable Functions

Suppose that X is the linear closed interval $[a, b]$, and f is on X to Y: $-\infty < y < +\infty$. Let $\mathfrak{M}$ be the class of measurable subsets of X determined by the monotone nondecreasing function α on X to Y. Then

4.1. Every continuous function on X to Y is α-measurable.

If $f(x)$ is continuous then for all y, the set $E[f \geqq y]$ is closed and consequently belongs to the class $\mathfrak{M}$ determined by any monotone nondecreasing α.

4.2. Any function on X to Y having at most a denumerable number of discontinuities is α-measurable.

For suppose $E[f \geqq y]$ is not closed for a particular y. Then there will exist a limiting point x_0 of E such that $f(x_0) < y$. Then $\lim_{x \to x_0} f(x) \neq f(x_0)$, since for a sequence x_n such that $\lim_n x_n = x_0$ and $f(x_n) \geqq y$, any value approached by $f(x_n)$ would be greater than or equal to y.

So that x_0 is a point of discontinuity of f. It follows that the set $E[f \geqq y]$ differs from its closure $E + E'$ by a denumerable set of points. Now a denumerable set is α-measurable for every α. Then $E[f \geqq y]$ as the difference of a closed set and a denumerable set of points, that is of two α-measurable sets, is α-measurable. As a corollary we have:

4.3. Any function of bounded variation on X is α-measurable relative to any monotonic nondecreasing function $\alpha(x)$.

4.4. Any upper semicontinuous function on X to Y is α-measurable, and the same thing is true for lower semicontinuous functions.

For if f is upper semicontinuous, then the set $E[f \geqq y]$ is closed for all y, and so measurable. We could also use the fact that any upper semi-continuous function is the limit of a monotone nondecreasing sequence of continuous functions, that is of a sequence of α-measurable functions.

As a matter of fact, any function which is the limit of a sequence of continuous functions on X will be α-measurable. Such functions studied by Baire, are called Baire functions of the first class. Since the Baire functions of higher classes are limits of sequences of Baire funcions of the lower classes, it follows that all Baire functions are measurable, actually Borel measurable, since the continuous functions which initiate the series are Borel measurable.

4.5. Definition. A function $f(x)$ on a set X will be called a *step function* on X if $\{E_n\}$ is a sequence of disjoint subsets of X such that $\Sigma_n E_n = X$, and $f(x)$ is constant on E_n, that is $f(x) = y_n$ for x on E_n. If the sequence E_n consists of a finite number of sets, $f(x)$ will said to be a *finite-step function*.

4.6. If $\mathfrak{M}$ is an s-algebra of subsets of X, and M_n is a sequence of disjoint subsets belonging to $\mathfrak{M}$ such that $\Sigma_n M_n = X$, then any step function constant on each M_n is measurable relative to $\mathfrak{M}$.

For the set $E[f \geqq y]$ will consist of the sets M_n for which the corresponding values of f, that is the y_n, are $\geqq y$, and so will be in $\mathfrak{M}$.

The strength of this theorem is in the fact that:

4.7. Any finite valued measurable function is the uniform limit of a sequence of measurable step functions.

For suppose that the function $f(x)$ is measurable. Then the sets $E_{mn} = E[(m-1)/n < f(x) \leqq m/n]$ for m ranging over the positive and negative integers are all measurable for any n, and $\Sigma_m E_{mn} = X$ for all n. If we set $f(x) = m/n$ for x on E_{mn}, then $\lim_n f_n(x) = f(x)$ uniformly on X. This observation is of importance for the Lebesgue approach to integration. It can also serve as an approach to measurable functions, by defining a measurable function as the point wise limit (or uniform limit) of elementary measurable functions such as step functions.

5. Properties of Measurable Functions Depending on the Measure Functions

In the preceding paragraphs, we have derived properties of measurable functions which depended only on the fact that the class $\mathfrak{M}$ of measurable sets is an s-algebra: s-additive, s-multiplicative, subtractive, and complementary. In this section we assume that $\mathfrak{M}$ is defined in terms of an upper measure α^* a function on all subsets E of the set X which has the properties: $0 \leqq \alpha^*(E) \leqq +\infty$ for all E, and if $E \leqq \Sigma_n E_n$, then $\alpha^*(E) \leqq \Sigma_n \alpha^*(E_n)$. These imply also monotoneity: if $E_1 \leqq E_2$ then $\alpha^*(E_1) \leqq \alpha^*(E_2)$. The class $\mathfrak{M}$ consists of the sets M which satisfy the measurability condition $\alpha^*(E) = \alpha^*(EM) + \alpha^*(ECM)$ for all E. This induces a subclass $\mathfrak{N}$ of $\mathfrak{M}$ of sets such that for all E of $\mathfrak{N}$: $\alpha^*(E) = 0$. As indicated in the exercise of V.16, the class $\mathfrak{N}$ is s-additive and subtractive, that is an s-ring, and has the socalled *hereditary* property: if E is in $\mathfrak{N}$ and $E_1 \leqq E_2$ then E_1 is also in $\mathfrak{N}$. Moreover if M is in $\mathfrak{M}$ and E differs from M by a set in $\mathfrak{N}$ that is $\alpha^*(M \Delta E) = \alpha^*(MCE + ECM) = 0$, then E is also in $\mathfrak{M}$, and $\alpha(M) = \alpha(E)$. We shall call the sets of $\mathfrak{N}$, sets of zero α-measure or α-null sets.

We say that two functions $f_1(x)$ and $f_2(x)$ *differ at most by an α-null set* or *are equal almost everywhere* (a.e.) if $\alpha^*(E[|f_1 - f_2| > 0]) = 0$, or $E[|f_1 - f_2| > 0]$ belongs to $\mathfrak{N}$. We can then assert:

5.1. If $f_1(x)$ is α-measurable and $f_2(x)$ differs from $f_1(x)$ at most by an α-null set, then $f_2(x)$ is α-measurable also.

This is almost obvious since $E[f_1 \geqq y]$ and $E[f_2 \geqq y]$ differ by a subset of $E[|f_1 - f_2| > 0]$, that is at most an α-null set and so are simultaneously measurable.

A consequence is:

5.2. If $f_n(x)$ are α-measurable, and $\lim_n f_n(x) = f(x)$ for all x except an α-null set, then $f(x)$ is α-measurable.

For $f(x)$ will differ from the α-measurable function $\overline{\lim}_n f_n(x)$ at most at the points where $\lim_n f_n(x)$ does not exist, that is on an α-null set. Note that in a sense the values of $f(x)$ are undetermined at the points of the α-null set where $\lim_n f_n(x)$ does not exist.

In case $\alpha(X) < \infty$, it is possible to intensify the nature of the convergence of a sequence of α-measurable functions convergent except for an α-null set.

5.3. If $\alpha(X) < \infty$, and $f_n(x)$ on X are α-measurable, and such that $\lim_n f_n(x) = f(x)$ except for an α-null set, then for every $e > 0$, there exists a set M_e of $\mathfrak{M}$, such that $\alpha(M_e) < e$, and $\lim_n f_n(x) = f(x)$ uniformly on $X - M_e$.

Let M_0 be the set on which $f_n(x)$ does not converge to $f(x)$, so that $\alpha(M_0) = 0$. By the preceding theorem $f(x)$ is measurable. Then for fixed n and e the set $E[|f_n - f| > e]$ is measurable, and so $M_{ne} = \Sigma_{m=n}^{\infty} E[|f_n - f| > e]$ is measurable for each e and n. Now M_{ne} is the set of all x such that for some m greater than n: $|f_m(x) - f(x)| > e$. For any x not in M_0, $\lim_n f_n(x) = f(x)$, or $(e, n_e, n \geqq n_e): |f_n(x) - f(x)| \leqq e$, that is x is not in M_{ne} for $n \geqq n_e$. Consequently, $\Pi_n M_{ne} = M_0$ for all e. Then by V.6.10 $\lim_n \alpha(M_{ne}) = \alpha(M_0) = 0$, for all e. This is equivalent to $(d, n_{de}, n \geqq n_{de}): \alpha(M_{ne}) \leqq d$. Let $e_m = d_m = 1/2^m$, and set $n_m = n_{de}$ for $d = e = d_m$. Also set $M_k = \Sigma_{m=k}^{\infty} M_{n_m e_m}$. Then

$$\alpha(M_k) = \alpha\left(\sum_{m=k}^{\infty} M_{n_m e_m n}\right) \leqq \sum_{m=k}^{\infty} 1/2^m = 1/2^{k-1},$$

so that $\lim_k \alpha(M_k) = 0$.

We show that $\lim_n f_n(x) = f(x)$ uniformly on $X - M_k$ for all k. For suppose that x belongs to $X - M_k$ for fixed k. Then x is not in $M_{n_m e_m}$ for $m \geqq k$. Then for $m \geqq k$, and $n \geqq n_m$, and all x in $X - M_k$ we have $|f_n(x) - f(x)| \leqq e_m = 1/2^m$. This means uniform convergence of $f_n(x)$ to $f(x)$ on $X - M_k$, since the n_m does not depend on x. Since $\lim_k \alpha(M_k) = 0$, we have completed the proof of the theorem.

Observe that this theorem does not assert that if the sequence of α-measurable functions $f_n(x)$ converges to $f(x)$ except for an α-null set, then the convergence is also uniform except for an α-null set, that is on $X - M_0'$ for some M_0' such that $\alpha(M_0') = 0$.

In the preceding theorem, we showed that if $M_{ne} = \Sigma_m^{\infty} E[|f_n - f| > e]$, then $\lim_n \alpha(M_{ne}) = 0$ for all e. As a consequence $\lim_n \alpha(E[|f_n - f| > e]) = 0$ also, if the sequence f_n converges to f except at an α-null set. This condition suggests a weaker type of convergence in which the functions need not even be assumed to be measurable relative to α.

5.4. Definition. The sequence of functions $f_n(x)$ *on* X *converge to* $f(x)$ *in the* α^* *sense, or relative to* α^*, if $\lim_n \alpha^*(E[|f_n - f| > e] = 0$ for all $e > 0$. We denote such convergence by $f_n \to f(\alpha^*)$.

In a way this type of convergence shifts the burden of convergence from the functions to the measure of the sets E_{ne}, where $E_{ne} = E[|f_n - f| > e]$, that is where f_n differs from f by too much. The following theorem gives an indication of the amount of convergence induced on the sequence f_n by the convergence relative to α^*.

5.5. If $f_n \to f(\alpha^*)$, then there exists a subsequence f_{n_m} such that $\lim_m f_{n_m}(x) = f(x)$ for all x of X except an α-null set.

Let e_m and d_m be sequences of positive numbers such that $\Sigma_m e_m$ and $\Sigma_m d_m$ are convergent, for instance $e_m = d_m = 1/2^m$. Choose n_m so that $\alpha^*(E_{n_m e_m}) < d_m$, and set $E_k = \Sigma_k^\infty E_{n_m e_m}$, with $E_{n_m e_m} = E[|f_{n_m} - f| > e_m]$. Then since

$$\alpha^*(E_k) \leqq \sum_k^\infty \alpha^*(E_{n_m e_m}) \leqq \sum_k^\infty d_m ,$$

it follows that $\lim_k \alpha^*(E_k) = 0$. Consequently, if $E_0 = \Pi_k E_k$, we have $\alpha^*(E_0) \leqq \alpha^*(E_k)$ for all k, so that $\alpha^*(E_0) = 0$. Suppose x is in $X - E_0 = CE_0$. Then since $E_{k+1} \leqq E_k$, there exists a k_x such that for $k \geqq k_x$, x is not in E_k. Consequently, for $m \geqq k_x$, we have $|f_{n_m}(x) - f(x)| \leqq e_{n_m}$, which means that $f_{n_m}(x)$ converges to $f(x)$. Then $\lim_m f_{n_m}(x) = f(x)$ for all x in $X - E_0$, that is excepting for an α-null set.

α^*-convergence of a sequence of functions $f_n(x)$ gives rise to a Cauchy condition of convergence, stated:

5.6. A sequence of functions $f_n(x)$ *converges relative to* α^* or *satisfies a Cauchy condition relative to* α^*, if and only if $|f_n - f_m| \to 0(\alpha^*)$, or if $E_{nme} = E[|f_n - f_m| > e]$, then $\lim_{mn} \alpha^*(E_{mne}) = 0$ for all $e > 0$.

The following Cauchy theorem of convergence is then valid:

5.7. If the sequence of functions $f_n(x)$ satisfies the Cauchy condition relative to α^*, then there exists a function $f(x)$ such that $f_n \to f(\alpha^*)$.

Select again d_m and e_m sequences of positive numbers such that $\Sigma_m d_m$ and $\Sigma_m e_m$ converge. In virtue of the Cauchy condition on f_n, it is possible to select an increasing sequence of integers n_m such that if

$$E_{n_m n_{m+1} e_m} = E[|f_{n_m}(x) - f_{n_{m+1}}(x)| > e_m],$$

then

$$\alpha^*(E_{n_m n_{m+1} e_m}) < d_m.$$

Set

$$E_k = \sum_k^\infty E_{n_m n_{m+1} e_m}.$$

Then

$$\alpha^*(E_k) \leqq \sum_k^\infty \alpha^*(E_{n_m n_{m+1} e_m}) \leqq \sum_k^\infty d_m,$$

so that $\lim_k \alpha^*(E_k) = 0$. Consequently, if $E_0 = \Pi_k E_k$, then $\alpha^*(E_0) \leqq \alpha^*(E_k)$ for all k, and $\alpha^*(E_0) = 0$. Consider a point x in $X - E_0 = CE_0$. Since $E_{k+1} \leqq E_k$, there exists a k_x such that if $k \geqq k_x$, then x x is not in E_k and so not in $E_{n_m n_{m+1} e_m}$ for $m \geqq k_x$, or $|f_{n_m}(x) - f_{n_{m+1}}(x)| \leqq e_m$. Then for $m'' > m' \geqq k_x$:

$$|f_{n_{m'}}(x) - f_{n_{m''}}(x)| \leqq \sum_{m'}^{m''-1} |f_{n_m}(x) - f_{n_{m+1}}(x)| \leqq \sum_{m'}^{m''-1} e_m.$$

Then the sequence $f_{n_m}(x)$ is a Cauchy sequence of numbers and $\lim_m f_{n_m}(x)$ exists equal to say $f(x)$ for all x not in E_0, which is an α-null set.

We show next that $f_{n_m} \to f(\alpha^*)$, that is that $\lim_m \alpha^*(E[|f_{n_m} - f| > e]) = 0$. Suppose x is in $X - E_k$, where E_k is the set defined above. Then as we have shown, for $m' \geqq m \geqq k$:

$$|f_{n_{m'}}(x) - f_{n_m}(x)| \leqq \sum_m^{m'} e_p \leqq \sum_m^\infty e_p.$$

Since $X - E_k$ is contained in $X - E_0$, $f_{n_{m'}}(x)$ converges to $f(x)$ so that by taking limits as to m' we find for $m \geqq k$ that $|f_{n_m}(x) - f(x)| \leqq \Sigma_m^\infty e_p$. If now for $m \geqq m_e : \Sigma_m^\infty e_p < e$, then for x in $X - E_k$, $m \geqq m_e$, $m \geqq k$, we have $|f_{n_m}(x) - f(x)| \leqq e$. Consequently, no points of the set $E_{me} = E[|f_{n_m} - f| > e]$ belongs to $X - E_k$, or E_{me} is contained in E_k for $m \geqq m_e$ and $m \geqq k$. But $\lim_k \alpha^*(E_k) = 0$. Consequently $\lim_m \alpha^*(E_{me}) = 0$ for all e or $f_{n_m} \to f(\alpha^*)$.

Finally to show that $f_n \to f(\alpha^*)$, we observe that

$$E[|f_n - f| > e] \leqq E[|f_n - f_{n_m}| > e/2] + E[|f_{n_m} - f| > e/2],$$

since if $|f_n - f_{n_m}| \leqq e/2$ and $|f_{n_m} - f| \leqq e/2$ then $|f_n - f| \leqq e$. But

$\lim_{nm}\alpha^*(E[|f_n - f_{n_m}| > e/2]) = 0$ and $\lim_n \alpha^*(E[|f_n - f| > e/2]) = 0$, so that $\lim_n \alpha^*(E[|f_n - f| > e]) = 0$, or $f_n \to f(\alpha^*)$.

These results apply to any sequence of functions on a set X, if an upper measure is defined on subsets of X. Incidentally it should be noted that a sequence can converge relative to an α^* without converging at a single point of X. For instance, suppose X is the open unit interval $0 < x < 1$, with $\alpha^*(E)$ Lebesgue upper measure. Let the functions $f_{nm}(x)$ with $0 \leqq m < n$, be the characteristic functions of the open intervals $(m/n, (m+1)/n)$: 1 for $m/n < x < (m+1)/n$ and 0 elsewhere. These functions can be arranged as a single sequence if $(m', n') < (m'', n'')$ when $n' < n''$ and for $n' = n''$, when $m' < m''$. Then the resulting sequence converges to the zero function relative to Lebesgue upper measure, but does not converge for any point x with $0 < x < 1$. However, the subsequence $f_{n,0}(x)$ converges to zero for all x of $0 < x < 1$.

If we consider functions measurable with respect to the class $\mathfrak{M}$ of measurable sets M determined by the measurability condition applied to α^*, then we have:

5.8. If $f_n(x)$ are α-measurable, and $f_n \to f(\alpha)$, then f is measurable.

For if $f_n \to f(\alpha)$, then there exists a subsequence f_{n_m} of α-measurable functions converging to f excepting for an α-null set, so that f is α-measurable.

On the other hand:

5.9. If $f_n(x)$ are α-measurable, and f_n converges to f, except at an α-null set, then $f_n \to f(\alpha)$.

We have already seen that in this case, if $E_n = \Sigma_{m>n} E[|f_m - f| > e]$, then $\lim_n \alpha(E_n) = 0$, so that $\lim_n \alpha(E[|f_n - f| > e]) = 0$.

The measurability condition here is necessary since there exist sequences of nonmeasurable functions converging to zero everywhere, but for which it is not true that $\lim_n \alpha^*(E[|f_n| > e]) = 0$. For let $X = [0, 1]$, $\alpha(x) = x$, α^* be upper Lebesgue measure, E_n the disjoint nonmeasurable sets such that $\alpha^*(E_m) = \alpha^*(E_n)$ for all m and n, and $\Sigma_n E_n = X$, defined in V. 12. Let $f_m(x)$ be the characteristic functions of the sets $\Sigma_m^\infty E_n$. Then $\lim_m f_m(x) = 0$ for all x, but for $e < 1$ and all m: $\alpha^*(E[f_m > e]) > \alpha^*(E_m) = c$, a fixed positive constant.

In the case of sequences of numbers a_n, we have the theorem that if for every subsequence a_{n_m}, there exists a subsequence $a_{n_{m_k}}$ converging to a, then $\lim_n a_n = a$. This theorem does not carry over to convergence of measurable functions, if the sequence converges except for an α-null set. We can, however, say:

5.10. If f_n is a sequence of α-measurable functions on X, and the function f is such that for every subsequence f_{n_m} of f_n, there exists a subsequence $f_{n_{m_k}}$ such that $\lim_k f_{n_{m_k}}(x) = f(x)$ except for an α-null set then $f_n \to f(\alpha)$.

For it would then follow that $f_{n_{m_k}} \to f(\alpha)$ so that $\lim_k \alpha(E[|f_{n_{m_k}} - f| > e]) = 0$ for all e. Then for any e, the real number sequence $a_n = \alpha([E|f_n - f| > e])$ has the property that for any subsequence a_{n_m} there exists a subsequence $a_{n_{m_k}}$ such that $\lim_k a_{n_{m_k}} = 0$. Then $\lim_n a_n = 0$ or $f_n \to f(\alpha)$.

EXERCISES

1. Show that the α^*-convergence of a sequence of functions $f_n(x)$ on X has the linearity properties: (a) if $f_n \to f(\alpha^*)$, and a c is a constant then $cf_n \to cf(\alpha^*)$; (b) if $f_{1n} \to f_1(\alpha^*)$ and $f_{2n} \to f_2(\alpha^*)$, then $f_{1n} + f_{2n} \to f_1 + f_2(\alpha^*)$.

2. Shown that if $f_n \to f(\alpha^*)$, then f_n satisfies the corresponding Cauchy condition of convergence $f_n - f_m \to 0(\alpha^*)$, or $\lim_{nm} \alpha^*(E[|f_n - f_m| > e]) = 0$ for all $e > 0$.

3. If $f_q(x)$ is a set of functions on X with q on the directed set Q, α^* an upper measure function on all subsets of X, and if $f(x)$ is such that $f_q \to f(\alpha^*)$, or $\lim_q \alpha(E[|f_q - f| > e]) = 0$ for all $e > 0$, then there exists a monotone sequence of elements q_n and an α-null set E_0 such that $\lim_n f_{q_n}(x) = f(x)$ for all x on $X - E_0$. If $f_q(x)$ are α-measurable, then $f(x)$ is α-measurable. Note that the sequence q_n need not be cofinal with Q.

4. If $f_q(x)$ is a set of functions on X with q on a directed set Q, satisfying a Cauchy condition of convergence: $\lim_{q_1 q_2} \alpha^*(E[|f_{q_1} - f_{q_2}| > e]) = 0$ for all $e > 0$, then there exists a monotone sequence of elements q_n, a function $f(x)$ and an α-null set E_0 such that $\lim_n f_{q_n}(x) = f(x)$ on $X - E_0$. Further $f_q \to f(\alpha^*)$.

5. Show that there exists a directed set Q of elements q, a set $f_q(x)$ of Lebesgue measurable functions on [0, 1] and a measurable function $f(x)$ such that $\lim_q f_q(x) = f(x)$ for all x, but $\lim_q \alpha(E[|f_q - f| > e]) = 1$, for all $e < 1$, α being Lebesgue measure.

6. If Q is a directed set with sequential character (there exists a sequence q_n of Q cofinal with Q), $f_q(x)$ a set of α-measurable functions on X, $f(x)$ such that $\lim_q f_q(x) = f(x)$ except on an α-null set, then $f(x)$ is measurable and $f_q \to f(\alpha)$.

6. Approximations to Measurable Functions. Lusin's Theorem

We have already seen in VI.4.6 that if $f(x)$ is any finite valued function on a set X, then there exists a sequence of step functions $f_n(x)$ such that $\lim_n f_n(x) = f(x)$ uniformly on X. These step functions can be obtained by dividing the Y-axis by the points $x = m/n$, m ranging over the positive and negative integers, and setting $f_n(x) = m/n$ on $E[m/n \leqq f < (m+1)/n]$. If $f(x)$ is any function on X and we define $f_n(x) = m/n$ for x on $E[m/n \leqq f < (m+1)/n]$ for $-n^2 \leqq m < n^2$, and $f_n(x) = n$ on $E[f \geqq n]$ and $f_n(x) = -n$ on $E[f \leqq -n]$, then $f_n(x)$ will be a finite-step function (assuming a finite number of distinct values), such that $\lim_n f_n(x) - f(x)$ for all x of X, with uniform convergence on the sets $E[a \leqq f \leqq b]$ for all a and b. In case $\mathfrak{M}$ is a class of measurable subsets of X and $f(x)$ is measurable, then the functions $f_n(x)$ in each case are measurable.

If we limit ourselves to the case when $X = (-\infty < x < +\infty)$, and $\alpha(x)$ is a bounded monotonic nondecreasing function on X which gives rise to an α-measure and a class $\mathfrak{M}$ of α-measurable sets M, as expounded in Chapter V, we can go further.

Let $f(x)$ be an α-measurable function on X. Set $M_{mn} = E[m/n \leqq f < (m+1)/n]$, for $-n^2 \leqq m < n^2$, and $M_n = \Sigma_m M_{mn}$, so that $X - M_n = CM_n = E[f \geqq n] + E[f < -n]$. Then the sets M_{mn} and CM_n are mutually disjoint for fixed n, and α-measurable. Since $f(x)$ is finite valued and $\alpha(X) < \infty$, we have $\lim_n \alpha(CM_n) = 0$. By V.10.2 we can then find closed sets F_{mn} contained in the corresponding M_{mn} such that $\alpha(M_{mn} - F_{mn}) < 1/2n^3$. Then because of the additive property of α, it follows that $\alpha(\Sigma_m M_{mn} - \Sigma_m F_{mn}) < 1/n$, where m ranges over the integers $-n^2 \leqq m < n^2$. Set $F_n = \Sigma_m F_{mn}$, since for fixed n, there are a finite number of closed sets F_{mn}, F_n will be closed and $\alpha(M_n - F_n) < 1/n$. We define the function $f_n(x) = m/n$ if x belongs to F_{mn}, and linearly on the open intervals complementary to F_n. If F_n has a maximum point x_0 on the X-axis, which belongs to F_{mn} then $f_n(x) = m/n$ for $x \geqq x_0$, and similarly if F_n has a minimal point. Then the functions $f_n(x)$ are continuous on

$X = (-\infty < x < +\infty)$. If x_0 is in the complement of F_n, then $f_n(x_0)$ is on a straight line part of $f_n(x)$ so that $f_n(x)$ is continuous at x_0. If x_0 is an isolated point of F_n, then two straight line portions of $f_n(x)$ meet at x_0 so that $f_n(x)$ is continuous at x_0. If x_0 is a limiting point of F_n, then since the F_{mn} are disjoint for fixed n, it is a limiting point of only one F_{mn}. Consequently there exists a neighborhood $V(x_0)$ of x_0 such that $V(x_0) \cdot F_n = V(x_0) \cdot F_{mn}$. Then $f_n(x)$ is constant on $V(x_0)$ if x_0 is a two sided limiting point of F_{mn}, or constant on one side of x_0 and linear on the other side of x_0, if x_0 is a one sided limiting point. In either case $f_n(x)$ is continuous at x_0. *

We show that for the continuous functions $f_n(x)$ we have $f_n \to f(\alpha)$. For the set $E[|f - f_n| > 1/n$ will belong to $X - F_n$. Now $\alpha(X - F_n) \leqq \alpha(X - M_n) + \alpha(M_n - F_n)$. Since $\lim_n \alpha(X - M_n) = 0$ and $\lim_n \alpha(M_n - F_n) = 0$, it follows that $\lim_n \alpha(X - F_n) = 0$, and so $\lim_n \alpha(E[|f_n - f| > 1/n]) = 0$. If $e > 1/n$, then $E[|f_n - f| > e] \leq E[|f_n - f| > 1/n]$. Then $\lim_n \alpha(E[|f_n - f| > e]) = 0$ for all e, and $f_n \to f(\alpha)$.

If $f_n \to f(\alpha)$, then there exists a subsequence f_{n_m} such that $\lim_m f_{n_m}(x) = f(x)$ except for an α-null set. We have then demonstrated:

6.1. THEOREM. If X is $-\infty < x < +\infty$, $\alpha(x)$ monotonic nondecreasing and bounded on X, $f(x)$ finite valued on X and measurable, then there exists a sequence of continuous functions $f_m(x)$ such that $\lim_m f_m(x) = f(x)$ except for an α-null set.

Now from the convergence properties of measurable functions it follows that for any $e > 0$, there exists a measurable set M_e such that $\alpha(M_e) < e$, and $\lim_n f_n(x) = f(x)$ uniformly on $X - M_e$. Since the $f_n(x)$ are continuous it follows that $f(x)$ is continuous in x if x is restricted to $X - M_e$. Now $X - M_e$ contains a closed set F_e such that $\alpha(X - M_e - F_e) < e$, so that $\alpha(X - F_e) < 2e$. Then $f(x)$ will be continuous on F_e. Consequently:

6.2 (Lusin's Theorem). If X is $-\infty < x < +\infty$, $\alpha(x)$ is monotonic nondecreasing and bounded on X, $f(x)$ is finite valued and measur-

* Essentially $f_n(x)$ is continuous on the closed set F_n, if only the values of $f_n(x)$ F_n are considered. By adding to $f_n(x)$, values on the complement of F_n, we extend the function $f_n(x)$ to all X so as to be continuous in x on X. An alternative way of obtaining such a function is to define $g_n(x) = \text{l.u.b.}\ [f_n(x') - n\,|x - x'|$, for x' on $F_n]$, which is similar to the functions used in VI.1.6. The functions $f_n(x)$ will be continuous for all x, and agree with $f_n(x)$ on F_n [see E. J. McShane: Extension of range of functions, *Bull. Am. Math. Soc.* 40 (1934) 837].

able relative to α, then for $e > 0$, there exists a closed set F_e such that $\alpha(X - F_e) < e$ and $f(x)$ is continuous if restricted to F_e.

This theorem asserts in a way that a measurable function is almost continuous. It has been used as a basis for the definition of measurable functions. Like many important results in mathematics, there are several different ways of proving Lusin's theorem. Consequently we think it worth while to give another proof which links up with the definition of measurability of a function. [See L. W. Cohen: A new proof of Lusin's theorem, *Fundamenta Math.* 9 (1927) 122-3.]

A finite valued function $f(x)$ is measurable if for a sequence y_n dense on the Y-axis, the sets $E[f \geqq y_n]$ or the sets $E[f \leqq y_n]$ are measurable for every n. Similarly if X is the closed interval [0, 1], then the function $f(x)$ on X is continuous if for a denumerable dense set y_n on the Y-axis, both $E[f \geqq y_n]$ and $E[f \leqq y_n]$ are closed for all n. If F is a closed subset of X, and $F \cdot E[f \geqq y_n]$ and $F \cdot E[f \leqq y_n]$ are closed for all n, then f is continuous on F, using only the values of $f(x)$ on F.

Let $M_n = E[f \geqq y_n]$ and $M_n' = E[f \leqq y_n]$. Then there exist closed sets F_n in M_n and F_n' in M_n' such that if $M_n - F_n = R_n$ and $M_n' - F_n' = R_n'$, then $\alpha(R_n) < e/2^n$ and $\alpha(R_n') < e/2^n$. Then $\alpha(\Sigma_n R_n) \leqq \Sigma_n \alpha(R_n) < e$ and $\alpha(\Sigma_n R_n') \leqq \Sigma_n \alpha(R_n') < e$. Set $R = \Sigma_n(R_n + R_n')$, so that $\alpha(R) < 2e$. If $M = X - R$, then $\alpha(X - M) = \alpha(R) < 2e$. Now there exists in M a closed set F such that $\alpha(M - F) \leqq e$, so that $\alpha(X - F) = \alpha(X - M) + \alpha(M - F) < 3e$. Now $f(x)$ limited to the set F is continous on F. For

$$F \cdot E[f \geqq y_n] = F \cdot M_n = F(F_n + R_n) = F \cdot F_n$$

and

$$F \cdot E[f \leqq y_n] = F \cdot M_n' = F(F_n' + R_n') = F \cdot F_n',$$

since R_n and R_n' are in R. Then these sets are closed for all n and so $f(x)$ is continuous if restricted to F.

Since by the Weierstrass polynomial approximation theorem a continuous function on a closed interval can be uniformly approximated by polynomials, it follows that for the continuous functions $f_n(x)$ defined relative to the α-measurable function $f(x)$ above, there exists a polynomial $P_n(x)$ such that $|f_n(x) - P_n(x)| < 1/n$ for all x of $-n \leqq x \leqq n$. Consequently, we can state:

6.3. If X is $-\infty < x < +\infty$, $\alpha(x)$ is monotonic nondecreasing and bounded on X, $f(x)$ is finite valued and α-measurable, then there exists a sequence of polynomials $P_n(x)$ such that $\lim_n P_n(x) = f(x)$ except for an α-null set.

Another type of approximation to a continuous function on a closed interval is by means of staircase or interval step functions, that is functions which are constant on each of a finite number of intervals. For the continuous functions $f_n(x)$ above, there exists then a staircase function $s_n(x)$ vanishing for $x > n$, and such that $|f_n(x) - s_n(x)| < 1/n$ for all x with $|x| \leqq n$. Then we have:

6.4. If $f(x)$ is finite valued and α-measurable on $X = -\infty < x < +\infty$, with $\alpha(X) < \infty$, then there exists a sequence $s_n(x)$ of staircase functions, which are constant on a finite number of intervals and vanish outside of a bounded interval, such that $\lim_n s_n(x) = f(x)$ except for an α-null set.

It is possible to prove a theorem of the Lusin type for the case when the finite valued function $f(x)$ is on a topological space X, if the s-additive measure function $\alpha(M)$ on the s-algebra $\mathfrak{M}$ of α-measurable subsets of X has the property that closed sets F belong to $\mathfrak{M}$ and for any M of $\mathfrak{M}$, and $e > 0$, there exists a closed set F_e belonging to M such that $\alpha(M - F_e) < e$.

CHAPTER VII

LEBESGUE-STIELTJES INTEGRATION

1. The Lebesgue Postulates on Integration

Before taking up in detail the theory of Lebesgue or Lebesgue-Stieltjes integration, we feel that it is interesting and instructive to list the properties of an integral which Lebesgue considered fundamental and which in a natural way lead to his definition of integral. In his "Leçons sur l'Integration" (second edition, Gauthier-Villars, Paris, 1928, p. 105 ff), he considers the problem of determining for any bounded function on $-\infty < x < +\infty$ and for any finite interval $a \leqq x \leqq b$, a finite real number or a real valued functional, which we shall denote by $\int_a^b f(x)dx$ or $\int_a^b f$, which satisfies the following postulates:

(1) For any a, b, and h: $\int_a^b f(x)dx = \int_{a+h}^{b+h} f(x-h)dx$;

(2) For all a, b, and c: $\int_a^b f + \int_b^c f + \int_c^a f = 0$.

(3) For f_1 and f_2 any two bounded functions and all a, b:

$$\int_a^b (f_1 + f_2) = \int_a^b f_1 + \int_a^b f_2.$$

(4) If $f(x) \geqq 0$ for all x and $a \leqq b$, then $\int_a^b f \geqq 0$.

(5) $\int_0^1 1 \cdot dx = 1$.

(6) If f_n is a monotonic nondecreasing sequence of functions converging to the (bounded) function f for all x, then $\lim_n \int_a^b f_n = \int_a^b f$.

It is tacitly assumed that the value of $\int_a^b f(x)dx$ depends only on the values of $f(x)$ for $a \leqq x \leqq b$.

We consider briefly the import and consequences of these postulates.

Postulate (1): for all a, b, h: $\int_a^b f(x) = \int_{a+h}^{b+h} f(x-h)dx$, says that integration is invariant under translation in x. This is connected with the invariance of length of an interval and ultimately measure under translation.

Postulate (2): for all a, b, c: $\int_a^b f + \int_b^c f + \int_c^a f = 0$. If we set $a = b = c$, then $3 \int_a^a f = 0$ so that for all a: $\int_a^a f = 0$. If now $a = c$, then $\int_a^b f + \int_b^a f = 0$, or $\int_a^b f = -\int_b^a f$, and so $\int_a^b f + \int_b^c f = \int_a^c f$. This last asserts that the integral $\int_a^b f$ is an additive function of intervals for fixed f, and consequently is completely determined by the point function $F(x) = \int_a^x f$, with $F(b) - F(a) = \int_a^b f$.

Postulate (3): $\int_a^b (f_1 + f_2) = \int_a^b f_1 + \int_a^b f_2$, says that the integral is an additive functional on the class of bounded functions for fixed a and b. If we take $f_2 = 0$, then $\int_a^b f_1 = \int_a^b f_1 + \int_a^b 0$, so that $\int_a^b 0 = 0$. If $f = f_1 = -f_2$, then $0 = \int_a^b 0 = \int_a^b f + \int_a^b (-f)$, so that $\int_a^b (-f) = -\int_a^b f$. If we take $f_1 = f_2 = \dots = f_n = f$, then $\int_a^b nf = n \int_a^b f$ for all integers n, from which we deduce that $\int_a^b rf = r \int_a^b f$ for all rational numbers r. We can then conclude that under postulate (3) the integral $\int_a^b f$ is rationally linear in f for fixed a and b.

Postulate (4): If $f(x) \geqq 0$ for all x and $b \geqq a$, then $\int_a^b f \geqq 0$ is the statement that $\int_a^b f$ is a positive functional for fixed $a \leqq b$. If we use the linearity condition (3), then this postulate is equivalent to the following order condition:

(4 *a*): If $f_1(x) \leqq f_2(x)$ for all x, and $b \geq a$, then $\int_a^b f_1 \leq \int_a^b f_2$.

We can also demonstrate the theorem:

1.1. If $\int_a^b f$ satisfies the postulates (3) and (4) and if $\lim_n f_n = f$ uniformly on $[a, b]$ then $\lim_n \int_a^b f_n = \int_a^b f$.

For then ($e > 0$, n_e, $n \geqq n_e$, $a \leqq x \leqq b$): $f(x) - e \leqq f_n(x) \leqq f(x) + e$. If we assume e to be rational, then by the rational linearity of $\int_a^b f$ and the order relation (4 *a*), we have:

$$\int_a^b f - e \int_a^b 1 \leqq \int_a^b f_n \leqq \int_a^b f + e \int_a^b 1.$$

Since $\int_a^b 1$ is a finite number, it follows that $\lim_n \int_a^b f_n = \int_a^b f$.

If now c is any real number and r_n any sequence of rational numbers such that $\lim_n r_n = c$, then for any bounded function $\lim_n r_n f = cf$ uniformly. Then $\int_a^b cf = c \int_a^b f$ for all real c. We can then state:

1.2. If $\int_a^b f$ is an additive positive functional on the class of bounded functions on $[a, b]$ [satisfying (3) and (4)], then it is linear and continuous in the sense of uniform convergence of functions.

Postulate (5): $\int_0^1 1 = 1$. We show that in the presence of (1), (2), and (4) this condition implies that $\int_a^b 1 = b - a$ for all a and b.

From the additive property (2) we have

$$\sum_{1}^{n} \int_{(m-1)/n}^{m/n} 1 = \int_{0}^{1} 1.$$

From the invariance condition (1) it follows that

$$\int_{(m-1)/n}^{m/n} 1 = \int_{0}^{1/n} 1,$$

for all m, so that $\int_0^{1/n} 1 = 1/n$. From a repeated use of (2) it now follows that

$$\int_{r_1}^{r_2} 1 = r_2 - r_1$$

for all rational numbers r_1 and r_2.

If we define the function $f_1(x) = 0$ for $x \leqq a$ and $x \geqq b$, and $f_1(x) = 1$ for $a < a' \leqq x \leqq b' < b$, and linear between a and a', and b and b', and if $f_2(x) = 1$ for all x, then $f_2(x) \geqq f_1(x)$, so that

$$\int_a^b f_2(x) \geqq \int_a^b f_1(x) = \int_a^{a'} f_1(x) + \int_{a'}^{b'} f_1(x) + \int_{b'}^{b} f_1(x) \geqq \int_{a'}^{b'} f(x).$$

Then $\int_a^b 1 \geqq \int_{a'}^{b'} 1$. If now a and b are any, and $r_1 < a < r_1' < r_2' < b < r_2$, then

$$\int_{r_1}^{r_2} 1 \geq \int_a^b 1 \geqq \int_{r_1'}^{r_2'} 1 \quad \text{or} \quad r_2 - r_1 \geqq \int_a^b 1 \geqq r_2' - r_1'.$$

Then $\int_a^b 1 = b - a$.

This postulate then ties the integral to the lengths of intervals. From the point of view of Stieltjes integrals, this postulate would be omitted.

Postulate (6): If f_n is a monotone nondecreasing sequence on $[a, b]$ converging to the bounded function f, so that $f_n(x) \leqq f_{n+1}(x) \leqq f(x)$ for all x, then $\lim_n \int_a^b f_n = \int_a^b f$. Since by postulate (2): $\int_a^b (-f) = -\int_a^b f$, an equivalent statement of this postulate replaces "monotone nondecreasing" by "monotone nonincreasing." Further since under postulate (3) $\int_a^b (f_n - f) - \int_a^b f_n = \int_a^b f$, each of these statements is equivalent to:

(6 *a*): If f_n are positive or zero for all x, and monotonic nonincreasing in n for each x, with $\lim_n f_n(x) = 0$ for all x, then $\lim_n \int_a^b f_n = 0$ for all a and b.

The conditions (6) are of the nature of continuity conditions on the functional $\int_a^b f$. In the case when f_n is a sequence of Riemann integrable functions converging monotonely to a Riemann integrable function, the sequence f_n is uniformly bounded and Osgood's theorem II.5.6 can be used to give (6) if our class of functions is limited to functions Riemann integrable on $[a, b]$. As a matter of fact postulate (6) is equivalent to a property of the Osgood type, that is, we can state:

1.3. If for every monotone nondecreasing sequence of bounded functions f_n on $[a, b]$, converging to the bounded function f, we have $\lim_n \int_a^b f_n = \int_a^b f$, then for any sequence $g_n(x)$ of functions uniformly bounded on $[a, b]$, such that $\lim_n g_n(x) = g(x)$ for all x of $[a, b]$, we have $\lim_n \int_a^b g_n = \int_a^b g$; and conversely.

The converse is obvious. For the direct theorem we note that if g_n is a uniformly bounded sequence of functions, then in view of postulate (3):

$$\int_a^b (\text{g.l.b.}_n g_n) \leqq \text{g.l.b.}_n \int_a^b g_n \leqq \text{l.u.b.}_n \int_a^b g_n \leqq \int_a^b (\text{l.u.b.}_n g_n).$$

If we set

$$\Phi_n(x) = \underset{m \geqq n}{\text{l.u.b.}}\, g_m(x) \quad \text{and} \quad \Psi_n(x) = \underset{m \geqq n}{\text{g.l.b.}}\, g_m(x),$$

then for all n:

$$\int_a^b \Psi_n \leqq \underset{m \geqq n}{\text{g.l.b.}} \int_a^b g_n \leqq \underset{m \geqq n}{\text{l.u.b.}} \int_a^b g_n \leqq \int_a^b \Phi_n.$$

Now Ψ_n are monotone nondecreasing in n, and Φ_n are monotone nonincreasing in n, so that $\lim_n \Psi_n = \text{l.u.b.}_n \Psi_n = \underline{\lim}_n g_n$ and $\lim_n \Phi_n = \text{g.l.b.}_n \Phi_n = \overline{\lim}_n g_n$. In view of postulate (6), we then have:

$$\int_a^b \underline{\lim}_n g_n = \int_a^b \lim_n \Psi_n = \lim_n \int_a^b \Psi_n \leqq \lim_n (\underset{m \geqq n}{\text{g.l.b.}} \int_a^b g_n)$$
$$\leqq \lim_n (\underset{m \geqq n}{\text{l.u.b.}} \int_a^b g_n) \leqq \lim_n \int_a^b \Phi_n = \int_a^b \lim_n \Phi_n = \int_a^b \overline{\lim}_n g_n.$$

From these inequalities we deduce at once that for any uniformly bounded sequence of functions g_n on $[a, b]$ we have:

$$\int_a^b \underline{\lim}_n g_n \leqq \underline{\lim}_n \int_a^b g_n \leqq \overline{\lim}_n \int_a^b g_n \leqq \int_a^b \overline{\lim}_n g_n.$$

If we assume that $\lim_n g_n$ exists for all x then

$$\int_a^b \lim_n g_n = \lim_n \int_a^b g_n.$$

As has previously been indicated (see VI.4.7) any function can be uniformly approximated by a sequence of step functions. In particular any bounded function is the uniform limit of a sequence of finite-step functions, which assume only a finite number of values.

In particular, if $c < f(x) < d$ for all x, and we divide the interval $[c, d]$ into n equal parts by the points $c = y_{0n} < y_{1n} < y_{2n} < \dots < y_{nn} = d$, and set $f_n(x) = y_{mn}$ for x on $E_{mn} = E[y_{mn} \leqq f < y_{(m+1)n}]$, then $\lim_n f_n = f$ uniformly on X. If $\chi(E; x)$ is the characteristic function of the set E (unity for x on E and vanishing for x not on E), then $f_n(x) = \Sigma_m y_{mn} \chi(E_{mn}; x)$. If we assume that $\int_a^b f$ satisfies postulates (1)-(5), so that it is a linear functional continuous under uniform convergence, then $\int_a^b f = \lim_n \Sigma_m y_{mn} \int_a^b \chi(E_{mn})$ for all a and b. In other words if $\int_a^b f$ satisfies postulates (1)-(5), then its value is completely determined if the values of $\int_a^b \chi(E; x)dx = \alpha(E; a, b)$ are known for all intervals $[a, b]$ and subsets E of X. The question is what conditions are imposed on the set function $\alpha(E; a, b)$ by conditions (1)-(5). We find:

1.4. The postulates (1)-(5) on $\int_a^b f$ induce the following properties on $\alpha(E; a, b) = \int_a^b \chi(E; x)dx$ for subsets E of $[a, b]$:

(1 α) $\alpha(E + h; a, b) = \alpha(E; a - h, b - h)$ or α is invariant under translation.

(2 α) $\alpha(E; a, b) + \alpha(E; b, c) + \alpha(E; c, a) = 0.$

(3 α) $\alpha(E_1 + E_2; a, b) + \alpha(E_1E_2; a, b) - \alpha(E_1; a, b) + \alpha(E_2; a, b)$ This is based on the identity $\chi(E_1 + E_2; x) + \chi(E_1E_2; x) = \chi(E_1; x) + \chi(E_2; x)$. It follows that $\alpha(E; a, b)$ is a finitely additive set function for fixed $[a, b]$.

(4 α) $\alpha(E; a, b) \geqq 0$ for all E and $a \leqq b$.

(5 α) If $E = 0 \leqq x \leqq 1$, then $\alpha(E; 0, 1) = 1$.

If we consider only subsets of [0, 1], then these conditions require an additive measure on all subsets of [0, 1] invariant under translation, with the measure of the unit interval being 1. As we have noted in V.12 such a measure for all subsets of [0, 1] has been constructed by S. Banach. Linear content satisfies the conditions (1 α)-(5 α) only if we limit ourselves to subsets which have content for every finite interval $[a, b]$.

Postulate (6) adds a further requirement on $\alpha(E; a, b)$. We note that if E_n is a sequence of disjoint sets, then the sequence of functions $f_n(x) = \Sigma_{m=1}^n \chi(E_m; x)$ is monotonic nondecreasing and converges to $\chi(E; x) = \Sigma_n \chi(E_n; x)$, where $E = \Sigma_n E_n$. Using linearity as well as postulate (6), we find that for any interval $[a, b]$ we have:

(6 α) $\alpha(\Sigma_n E_n; a, b) = \Sigma_n \alpha(E_n; a, b)$.

This means that $\alpha(E; a, b)$ is s-additive for all $[a, b]$.

We have already seen in V.12 that for the interval [0, 1] no measure function invariant under translation exists for all subsets of [0, 1]. It is possible that Lebesgue suspected this, because he abandoned the project of finding an integral for all bounded functions satisfying (1)-(6), and developed the notion of measurable sets as well as a measure function as discussed in Chapter V. This measure function [based on $\alpha(x) = x$] satisfies postulates (1 α)-(6 α), on measurable sets. By limiting himself to measurable functions defined in terms of (Lebesgue) measurability of the sets $E(c < f \leqq d)$ for all c, d, and using subdivisions of the range Y of $f(x)$, he set up an integration process yielding an integral which for bounded measurable functions satisfies postulates (1)-(6).

In addition, then, to introducing the notion of measurable sets, and an s-additive set function on this s-algebra of sets, Lebesgue also changed the method of defining an integration process by taking subdivisions of the Y-axis into intervals, instead of subdivisions of the X-axis, convergence of the approximating sums being as the maximum length of the subintervals of the subdivision approaches zero. On the other hand, the availability of measurable subsets and a measure function suggests the possibility of replacing subdivisions of $X = [a, b]$ into a finite number of intervals as is done in the Riemann type of integrals, by subdivisions into a finite or denumerable number of disjoint measurable sets, convergence being by successive subdivisions. We shall present the integration process along both of these lines, and show that they lead to the same class of integrable functions and the same value for the integral.

2. The Lebesgue Method of Defining an Integral

We take up first the definition of integration due to Lebesgue, which depends on subdivisions of the range of the function.

We assume X to be a one-dimensional interval, either $a \leqq x \leqq b$ or $-\infty < x < +\infty$. The function $f(x)$ is assumed to be finite valued, that is on X to Y: $-\infty < y < +\infty$. We assume a monotonic non-decreasing function $\alpha(x)$ on X, which for the present will be assumed *bounded*, which gives rise to a class $\mathfrak{M}$ of α-measurable subsets of X, which is an s-algebra, and an s-additive measure function on α-measurable sets, as derived in Chapter V.

We take up first the case when the function $f(x)$ is bounded and α-measurable. Let $m < f(x) < M$ for all x. Following ideas suggested in the paragraph 1 above, we divide the interval $[m, M]$ by a subdivision σ_y or σ, consisting of the points $m = y_0 < y_1 < ... < y_n = M$, and suppose $y_{k-1} < y_k' \leqq y_k$. Let $E_k = E[y_{k-1} < f \leqq y_k]$ for $k = 1 ... n$. These sets are α-measurable. Then we have:

2.1. THEOREM. If $f(x)$ is bounded and α-measurable, then $\lim_{|\sigma| \to 0} \Sigma_k y_k' \alpha(E_k)$ exists. This is defined as the Lebesgue integral: $L \int_X f d\alpha$.

The existence of $\lim_{|\sigma| \to 0} \Sigma_k y_k' \alpha(E_k)$, is a consequence of the following observation. If we define $\mu(y) = \alpha(E[f \leqq y])$, then $\mu(y)$ is a monotonic nondecreasing function of y, such that $\mu(y_k) - \mu(y_{k-1}) = \alpha(E[y_{k-1} < f \leqq y_k]) = \alpha(E_k)$. Obviously the function y is integrable with respect to μ, so that $\lim_{|\sigma| \to 0} \Sigma_k y_k' \alpha(E_k)$ exists and is equal to $\int_m^M y d\mu(y)$. Consequently:

2.2. For any bounded α-measurable function $f(x)$ the Lebesgue integral $L \int_X f d\alpha$ exists and is expressible as the Stieltjes integral $\int_m^M y d\mu(y)$, where $\mu(y) = \alpha(E[f \leqq y])$.

Because of the fact that $\mu(y)$ is zero for $y <$ g.l.b. $[f(x), x$ on $X]$ and constant for $y \geqq$ l.u.b.$[f(x), x$ on $X]$, it follows that $\int_m^M y d\mu(y)$ has the same value for all $M \geqq$ l.u.b. $[f(x), x$ on $X)$ and all $m \leqq$ g.l.b. $[f(x), x$ on $X]$. Further, we can apply integration by parts and obtain $L \int_X f d\alpha = M\alpha(X) - \int_m^M \mu(y) dy$, so that the Lebesgue integral for a bounded function is expressible in terms of the Riemann integral of the monotone function $\mu(y)$, on the range of $f(x)$.

In case the function $f(x)$ is α-measurable, but not bounded, two procedures are available. Following Lebesgue, we divide the infinite interval $-\infty < y < +\infty$ by a subdivision σ_y or σ, determined by the points $... y_{-k} < y_{-k+1} < ... < y_{k-1} < y_k < ...$ such that $y_{-k} \to -\infty$, $y_k \to +\infty$, and $|\sigma_y| = \text{l.u.b.}_k |y_k - y_{k-1}| < \infty$, and set up $\Sigma_{k=-\infty}^{+\infty} y_k' \alpha(E_k)$, with $E_k = E[y_{k-1} < f \leqq y_k]$ and $y_{k-1} \leqq y_k' \leqq y_k$. We define $L \int_X f d\alpha = \lim_{|\sigma| \to 0} \Sigma_k y_k' \alpha(E_k)$, when this limit exists as a finite number. The alternative procedure is to set $\mu(y) = \alpha(E[f \leqq y])$ and define

$$L \int_X f d\alpha = \lim_{(y', y'') \to (-\infty, +\infty)} \int_{y'}^{y''} y d\mu(y),$$

when this limit exists.

The important result is:

2.3. If $f(x)$ is α-measurable on X, and $\alpha(X) < \infty$, then a necessary and sufficient condition that $\int_X f d\alpha$ exist according to either procedure, is that there exist a subdivision σ of the Y-axis of finite norm, and a sequence $y_k{}'$ such that $y_{k-1} \leqq y_k{}' \leqq y_k$ for which $\Sigma_k y_k{}'\alpha(E_k)$ is absolutely convergent. Then $\lim_{|\sigma|\to 0} \Sigma_\sigma y_k{}'\alpha(E_k)$, with $y_{k-1} \leqq y_k{}' \leqq y_k$, as well as

$$\lim_{(y', y'')\to(-\infty, +\infty)} \int_{y'}^{y''} y d\mu(y)$$

both exist and are equal.

For the necessity, if $\lim_{|\sigma|\to 0} \Sigma_\sigma y_k{}'\alpha(E_k)$ exists, there exists a σ with $|\sigma| < \infty$, such that $\Sigma_\sigma y_k{}'\alpha(E_k)$ converges for all choices of $y_{k-1} \leqq y_k{}' \leqq y_k$. This means that

$$\lim_{(k', k'')\to(-\infty, +\infty)} \sum_{k'}^{k''} y_k{}'\alpha(E_k)$$

exists. Since $k' \to -\infty$ and $k'' \to +\infty$ independently, the series converges absolutely.

If $\alpha(X) < \infty$, and $\Sigma_k y_k{}'\alpha(E_k)$ converges absolutely for a particular choice of the $y_k{}'$ such that $y_{k-1} \leqq y_k{}' \leqq y_k$, then the series converges absolutely for all such $y_k{}'$. This follows at once from the fact that for any finite set of k, and $y_{k-1} \leqq y_k{}', y_k{}'' \leqq y_k$, we have

$$\left| \sum_k |y_k{}'| \alpha(E_k) - \sum_k |y_k{}''| \alpha(E_k) \right| \leqq \sum_k |y_k{}' - y_k{}''| \alpha(E_k)$$
$$\leqq |\sigma| \sum_k \alpha(E_k) \leqq |\sigma| \alpha(X).$$

If

$$\lim_{(y', y'')\to(-\infty, +\infty)} \int_{y'}^{y''} y d\mu(y)$$

exists, then since y' and y'' are independent, $\int_0^\infty y d\mu(y)$ and $\int_{-\infty}^0 y d\mu(y)$ both exist. For any subdivision σ:

$$\sum_{y_{k-1}>0} y'_{k-1}\alpha(E_k) < \int_\infty^0 y d\mu(y) \quad \text{and} \quad \sum_{y_k<0} |y_k{}'| \alpha(E_k) < \left| \int_{-\infty}^0 y d\mu \right|,$$

so that by the preceding paragraph $\Sigma_k |y_k{}'| \alpha(E_k) < \infty$, for all $y_{k-1} \leqq y_k{}' \leqq y_k$.

To prove the sufficiency of the condition, we prove first the following lemma:

2.4. If for $\alpha(X) < \infty$ and the α-measurable function $f(x)$, there exists a subdivision σ_0 of the Y-axis into intervals such that $|\sigma_0| < \infty$, and $\Sigma_{\sigma_0} |y_k{}'| \alpha(E_{0k}) < \infty$, for some $y_k{}'$: $y_{k-1} \leqq y_k{}' \leqq y_k$, then for any subdivision of the Y-axis such that $|\sigma| < \infty$, and any choice of y_k' on $[y_{k-1}, y_k]$, we have $\Sigma_\sigma |y_k'| \alpha(E_k) < \infty$. If, moreover, σ_1 and σ_2 are any two subdivisions of the Y-axis of finite norm then

$$\left|\sum_{\sigma_1} - \sum_{\sigma_2}\right| \leqq (|\sigma_1| + |\sigma_2|)\alpha(X),$$

where Σ_σ stands for an expression of the form $\Sigma_k y_k' \alpha(E_k)$.

Suppose that $[y', y'']$ is any interval of the Y-axis and $y' = y_0 < y_1 < \dots < y_n = y''$ any subdivision of $[y', y'']$. Then

$$\left|\sum_k |\eta_k| \alpha(E_k) - |\eta| \alpha(E)\right| \leqq |y'' - y'| \alpha(E),$$

where $E = E[y' < f \leqq y'']$, $y' \leqq \eta \leqq y''$, and similarly for E_k and η_k. This follows from $\alpha(E) = \Sigma_k \alpha(E_k)$.

If we apply this remark to any subdivision σ finer than σ_0 $(\sigma \geqq \sigma_0)$, then

$$\begin{aligned}\sum_\sigma |y_k'| \alpha(E_k) &\leqq \sum_{\sigma_0} |y'_{0k}| \alpha(E_{0k}) + |\sigma_0| \sum_{\sigma_0} \alpha(E_{0k}) \\ &\leqq \sum_{\sigma_0} |y'_{0k}| \alpha(E_{0k}) + |\sigma_0| \alpha(X),\end{aligned}$$

where the sums as to σ and σ_0 are initially taken for a finite subset of each, and ultimately valid for the entire subdivisions. It follows that $\Sigma_\sigma |y_k'| \alpha(E_k) < \infty$ for all $\sigma \geqq \sigma_0$.

Consider now any subdivision σ of finite norm. Then for the σ_0 in the hypothesis of the lemma, the product $\sigma \cdot \sigma_0$ will be finer than σ_0. Using the inequality demonstrated above for any interval $[y', y'']$, we can show that

$$\sum_\sigma |y_k'| \alpha(E_k) \leqq \sum_{\sigma \cdot \sigma_0} |\eta_k| \alpha(\bar{E}_k) + |\sigma| \alpha(X),$$

where initially the sums are taken for finite subsets of the σ. It follows that $\Sigma_\sigma |y_k'| \alpha(E_k) < \infty$, for all σ such that $|\sigma| < \infty$, and all choices of y_k' on $[y_{k-1}, y_k]$.

Finally, if σ_1 and σ_2 are two subdivisions of finite norm, then

$$\left|\sum_{\sigma_1} - \sum_{\sigma_2}\right| \leqq \left|\sum_{\sigma_1} - \sum_{\sigma_1\sigma_2}\right| + \left|\sum_{\sigma_1\sigma_2} - \sum_{\sigma_2}\right| \leqq (|\sigma_1| + |\sigma_2|)\alpha(X),$$

where $\sigma_1\sigma_2$ is the product of the subdivisions, containing all points of both σ_1 and σ_2, and Σ_σ stands for the sum of the type $\Sigma_\sigma y_k' \alpha(E_k)$.

The existence of $\lim_{|\sigma| \to 0} \Sigma_\sigma y_k' \alpha(E_k)$ is an immediate consequence of the last inequality of the lemma, leading as it does to the validity of the Cauchy condition of convergence for the approximating sums.

We note in passing that if $L \int_X f d\alpha$ exists, then for any σ of finite norm

$$\left| \int_X f d\alpha - \sum_\sigma y_k' \alpha(E_k) \right| \leqq |\sigma| \alpha(X).$$

We show next that if for some σ with $|\sigma| < +\infty$, and some y_k' with $y_{k-1} \leqq y_k' \leqq y_k$ (and so for all such y_k') $\Sigma_\sigma |y_k'| \alpha(E_k) < \infty$, then $\int_{-\infty}^{+\infty} y d\mu(y)$ exists. For if $0 < y_{m-1} < y' < y'' < y_n$, then

$$\int_{y'}^{y''} y d\mu(y) < \sum_m^n y_k(\mu(y_k) - \mu(y_{k-1})) = \sum_m^n y_k \alpha(E_k).$$

From the convergence of $\Sigma |y_k'| \alpha(E_k)$ it follows that

$$\lim_{(y', y'') \to (\infty, \infty)} \int_{y'}^{y''} y d\mu(y) = 0,$$

so that $\int_0^\infty y d\mu(y)$ exists. Similarly $\int_{-\infty}^0 y d\mu(y)$ exists.

To show that

$$\int_{-\infty}^{+\infty} y d\mu(y) = \lim_{|\sigma| \to 0} \sum_\sigma y_k' \alpha(E_k) = L \int_X f d\alpha,$$

we note that if $[y', y'']$ is any interval of the Y-axis, and σ is any subdivision of $[y', y'']$, then

$$\left| \int_{y'}^{y''} y d\mu(y) - \sum_\sigma y_k' \alpha(E_k) \right| \leqq |\sigma| \sum_k \alpha(E_k) \leqq |\sigma| \alpha(X).$$

Then $(e, d_e, |\sigma| \leqq d_e)$: $\left| \int_{y'}^{y''} y d\mu(y) - \Sigma_\sigma y_k'(E_k) \right| < e$, where the d_e is independent of $[y', y'']$ and σ is a subdivision of this interval. Since $\int_{-\infty}^{+\infty} y d\mu(y)$ exists, we have $(e > 0, M_e > 0, y'' > M_e, -y' > M_e)$: $\int_{y''}^{\infty} y d\mu(y) + \left| \int_{-\infty}^{y'} y d\mu(y) \right| < e$. Chose any subdivision σ of $(-\infty, +\infty)$ such that $|\sigma| \leqq d_e$, and select n so that $y_n < M_e$ and $y_{-n} < -M_e$, while

$$\sum_{n+1}^{\infty} y_k' \alpha(E_k) + \left| \sum_{-\infty}^{-n-1} y_k' \alpha(E_k) \right| < e.$$

This is possible since $\Sigma_k y_k' \alpha(E_k)$ is absolutely convergent. Then for $|\sigma| \leqq d_e$:

$$\left| \int_{-\infty}^{+\infty} y d\mu(y) - \sum_\sigma y_k' \alpha(E_k) \right| \leqq \int_{y_n}^{+\infty} y d\mu(y) + \left| \int_{-\infty}^{y_{-n}} y d\mu(y) \right|$$

$$\left| \int_{y_{-n}}^{y_n} y d(y) - \sum_{-n}^{n} y_k' \alpha(E_k) \right| + \sum_{n+1}^{\infty} y_k' \alpha(E_k) + \left| \sum_{-\infty}^{-n-1} y_k' \alpha(E_k) \right| < 3e.$$

Then $\lim_{|\sigma| \to 0} \Sigma_\sigma y_k' \alpha(E_k) = \int_{-\infty}^{+\infty} y d\mu(y)$.

We note that the definition of an L-integral for an unbounded function involves essentially an iterated limit, one of the nature of convergence of an infinite series, the other as the norm of the subdivision approaches zero. The statement just proved is in an extended way, the equality of iterated limits in two orders.

Since the conditions: (1) $f(x)$ is α-measurable, and (2) there exists a σ_y such that $|\sigma_y| < \infty$, for which $\Sigma_k y_k' \alpha(E[y_{k-1} < f \leqq y_k])$ is absolutely convergent is sufficient to guarantee the existence of $L \int_X f d\alpha$, Lebesgue calls such functions "sommable." However, the transliterated word summable has other connotations, so we shall call a function satisfying these two conditions *L-integrable relative to* α, or *Lebesgue-Stieltjes* (L-S) *integrable relative to* α.

2.4.1. In addition to the bounded α-measurable functions, the class of L-integrable functions includes also the α-measurable functions which are *almost bounded* in the sense that there exists a constant M such that the set $E[|f| > M]$ is an α-null set, since for such functions the sets $E[y_{k-1} < f \leqq y_k]$ are α-null sets when $y_{k-1} > M$ and $y_k < -M$.

If $\alpha(X) < \infty$, and f is α-measurable then $\Sigma_k \alpha(E_k) = \Sigma_k \alpha(E[y_{k-1} < f \leqq y_k])$ converges for any subdivision σ_y with $|\sigma_y| < \infty$. Because of the s-additivity of the measure function α, it follows that if $E_M = E[|f| \geqq M]$, then $\lim_{M\to\infty} \alpha(E_M) = 0$.

2.5. If the function f is L-integrable with respect to α, then we have the stronger condition $\lim_{M\to\infty} M\alpha(E_M) = 0$.

For by condition (2) on L-integrability, for any σ_y with $|\sigma_y| < \infty$, we have $\Sigma_k |y_k'| \alpha(E_k) < \infty$, with $y_{k-1} \leqq y_k' \leqq y_k$. Take $y_k' = y_k$ if $y_{k-1} > 0$, and $y_k' = y_{k-1}$ if $y_{k-1} < 0$. If $0 < y_{n-1} < M \leqq y_n$, then

$$\sum_{k=n}^{\infty} y_k \alpha(E_k) > M \sum_{n}^{\infty} \alpha(E_k) > M\, \alpha(\sum_{n}^{\infty} E_k) > M\alpha(E[f \geqq M]).$$

If $y_{-n-1} < -M \leqq y_{-n} < 0$, then

$$\sum_{k=-n}^{-\infty} |y_{k-1}| \alpha(E_k) > M \sum_{-n}^{-\infty} \alpha(E_k) > M(E[f \leqq -M]).$$

It follows that

$$\lim_{M\to\infty} M\alpha(E_M) = \lim_{M\to\infty} M(\alpha(E[f \geqq M]) + \alpha(E[f \leqq -M])) = 0.$$

We have shown incidentally that if f is L-integrable with respect to

α, then $\lim_{M\to\infty} M\alpha(E[f \geqq M]) = 0$, and $\lim_{M\to\infty} M\alpha(E[f \leqq -M]) = 0$. In each case, the equality sign can be omitted in the definition of the sets E.

There is an additional approach to the definition of the L-integral of an unbounded function due to Ch. de La Vallee Poussin [see, for instance, "Cours d'Analyse Infinitesimale," I, third edition, Gauthier-Villars, Paris, 1914, p. 260]. If $f(x)$ is α-measurable and we define $f(m, M; x) = m$ if $f(x) \leqq m$, $f(m, M; x) = f(x)$ if $m \leqq f(x) \leqq M$, and $f(m, M; x) = M$ if $f(x) \geqq M$, that is, level off $f(x)$ at the top and bottom, then $f(m, M; x)$ is L-integrable for all m, M. We can then state:

2.6. A necessary and sufficient condition that $f(x)$ be L-integrable with respect to α, is that

$$\lim_{(m, M)\to(-\infty, +\infty)} \int_X f(m, M; x)d\alpha(x)$$

exist, $L\int_X f d\alpha$ being the value of this limit.

We have $E[f(m, M; x) \leqq y] = O$ if $y < m$; $E[f(m, M; x) \leqq y] = E[f \leqq y]$ if $m \leqq y < M$, and $E[f(m, M; x) \leqq y] = X$ if $y \geqq M$. Consequently, if $m' < m \leq M < M'$ and $\mu(y) = \alpha(E[f \leq y])$,

$$\int_X f(m, M; x)d\alpha(x) = \int_{m'}^{M'} y d\alpha(E[f(m, M; x) \leqq y])$$
$$= m\alpha(E[f \leqq m]) + \int_m^M y d\mu(y) + M(\alpha(X) - \alpha(E[f \leqq M]))$$
$$= m\alpha(E[f \leqq m]) + \int_m^M y d\mu(y) + M\alpha(E[f > M]).$$

We use here the fact that the function $\alpha(E[f(m, M; x) \leqq y])$ has a discontinuity of magnitude $\alpha(E[f \leqq m])$ at $y = m$. Since $L\int_X f d\alpha$ exists, the first term on the right converges to zero as $m \to -\infty$, the last term converges to zero as $M \to +\infty$, and the middle term to $L\int_X f d\alpha$ as $(m, M) \to (-\infty, +\infty)$. Consequently

$$\lim_{(m, M)\to(-\infty, +\infty)} \int_X f(m, M; x)d\alpha(x) = L\int_X f d\alpha.$$

Suppose, on the other hand, that

$$\lim_{(m, M)\to(-\infty, +\infty)} \int_X f(m, M; x)d\alpha(x)$$

exists. Consider any subdivision σ_y with $|\sigma_y| < \infty$, and let $0 \leqq y_0 < y_1 < \ldots < y_n \leqq M$.

Then

$$\sum_{k=1}^{n} y_{k-1}\alpha(E_k) \leqq \int_X f(0, M; x)d\alpha(x) < \infty$$

for all M, so that $\Sigma_{y_k>0}\, y_{k-1}\alpha(E_k) < \infty$. In a similar way we prove that $-\Sigma_{y_k<0}\, y_k\alpha(E_k) < \infty$. Then $\Sigma_{\sigma_k} | y_k' | \alpha(E_k) < \infty$, and f is L-integrable with respect to α.

Since $|f|$ is α-measurable when f is, an examination of the proof above shows that:

2.7. A necessary and sufficient condition that an α-measurable function f be L-integrable is that $\int_X |f(-M, M; x)| d\alpha(x)$ be bounded in M.

3. A Riemann-Young Type of Integral Definition. The Y-Integral

In defining a Riemann type of integral of a function $f(x)$ on a finite interval $[a, b]$, the basic interval is divided into a finite number of nonoverlapping intervals and approximating sums of the form $\Sigma f\Delta x$ determine the value of the integral when it exists. One reason for using subintervals in this procedure is that the length of an interval is available as a basis for linear measure. Because of the extension of the notion of measure to measurable sets determined by a (bounded) monotonic function α, we can extend the subdivision idea in two ways: (a) by allowing subdivisions of the fundamental interval into disjoint measurable sets, and (b) by allowing subdivisions into a denumerable as well as a finite number of disjoint measurable sets. Consequently, for this section σ_x or σ *shall stand for a subdivision of the set X into a finite or denumerable number of disjoint α-measurable sets*, a collection of sets E_n such that $E_nE_m = O$ for $n \neq m$, and $\Sigma_n E_n = X$.

Since a norm cannot be associated with such subdivisions in any obvious way, we fall back on the idea of successive subdivisions or refinements. We introduce order into the class of all subdivisions σ of X into α-measurable sets, so as to make this class a directed set. We define $\sigma_1 \geqq \sigma_2$ if every set in σ_1 is a subset of some set in σ_2, or equivalently if σ_1 is obtainable from σ_2 by subdividing the sets of σ_2. This class is directed since, the subdivision $\sigma_1 \cdot \sigma_2$ consisting of the products of any set in σ_1 with any set in σ_2, is finer than σ_1 and σ_2, or $\sigma_1 \cdot \sigma_2 \geqq \sigma_1$ and $\sigma_1 \cdot \sigma_2 \geqq \sigma_2$.

Following the procedure for the definition of Riemann-Stieltjes integrals, we can then set up the following definition for $\int_X f d\alpha$ of the finite valued function $f(x)$ with respect to the bounded monotonic function α:

3.1. $\int_X f d\alpha$ is the σ-limit of the approximating sums $\Sigma_\sigma f(x_n)\alpha(E_n)$ with x_n in E_n, provided this limit exists as a finite number.

There is a difficulty in this definition, which centers in the expression $\Sigma_\sigma f(x_n)\alpha(E_n)$. If σ consists of a finite number of sets, there is no trouble. Also, if f is bounded on X, then $\Sigma_\sigma f(x_n)\alpha(E_n)$ is an absolutely convergent series if σ is denumerable, since if $|f(x)| \leqq M$, for all x, then $\Sigma_n |f(x_n)| \alpha(E_n) \leqq M \Sigma_n \alpha(E_n) = M\alpha(X)$. If $f(x)$ is unbounded on X, then the question of convergence is pertinent, especially in view of the fact that although we denote a subdivision σ by $E_1, \ldots, E_n, \ldots$, the order indicated by n means denumerability rather than an ordering of the sets. However, for P any set of elements p and a_p a set of real numbers, we have defined (see I.6)

$$\sum_p a_p = \lim \sum_{i=1}^n a_{p_i},$$

where $p_1 \ldots p_n$ is a finite subset of P and limit is as to the set Q of finite subsets of P directed by inclusion. Such a sum exists if and only if a_p vanishes except for a denumerable set of p and if $\Sigma_n |a_{p_n}| < \infty$, p_n ranging over the p for which $a_p \neq 0$. In view of this, we shall attach a number to $\Sigma_\sigma f(x_n)\alpha(E_n)$ if and only if $\Sigma_n |f(x_n)| \alpha(E_n) < \infty$. We then modify our definition of integral:

3.1.1. Definition. If there exists a subdivision σ_0 of X into α-measurable sets such that for $\sigma \geqq \sigma_0$ we have $\Sigma_\sigma f(x_n)\alpha(E_n)$ absolutely convergent for all choices of x_n in E_n, and if $\lim_\sigma \Sigma_\sigma f(x_n)\alpha(E_n)$ exists as a finite number (where we need only consider $\sigma \geqq \sigma_0$), then $\int_X f d\alpha$ exists and we definite $\int_X f d\alpha = \lim_\sigma \Sigma_\sigma f(x_n)\alpha(E_n)$.

The existence of $\int_X f d\alpha$ implies that

$$(e > 0, \sigma_e, \sigma \geqq \sigma_e): \int_X f d\alpha - e \leqq \sum\nolimits_\sigma f(x_n)\alpha(E_n) \leqq \int_X f d\alpha + e.$$

For any particular $\sigma \geqq \sigma_e$ the expression $\Sigma_\sigma f(x_n)\alpha(E_n)$ is then bounded for all choices of x_n in E_n.

Suppose then that for a given subdivision σ, $\Sigma_\sigma f(x_n)\alpha(E_n)$ is bounded as the x_n range over E_n. Then the product $f(x_n)\alpha(E_n)$ is bounded, that is $f(x)$ is bounded on all E_n for which $\alpha(E_n) \neq 0$. Let $M(f; E) =$ l.u.b. $[f(x), x$ on $E]$ and $m(f; E) =$ g.l.b. $[f(x), x$ on $E]$. We then show:

3.2. If for a given σ, $\Sigma_\sigma f(x_n)\alpha(E_n)$ is bounded as x_n ranges over the E_n, then $\Sigma_n M(|f|; E_n)\alpha(E_n) < \infty$, provided we define $M(|f|; E)\alpha(E)$

$= 0$ if $\alpha(E) = 0$. Moreover, for all $\sigma' \geqq \sigma$ with $\sigma' = \{E_n'\}$, the sums $\Sigma_n f(x_n')\alpha(E_n')$ are absolutely convergent for all x_n' in E_n' and bounded as x_n' ranges over E_n'.

The convention that $M(|f|; E)\alpha(E) = 0$ if $\alpha(E) = 0$ might be justified by the fact that $M(|f|; E)\alpha(E) =$ l.u.b. $[|f(x)|\alpha(E)$ for x on $E]$, when $\alpha(E) \neq 0$, and l.u.b. $[|f(x)|\alpha(E), x$ on $E] = 0$ if $\alpha(E) = 0$.

For $e > 0$, let x_n on E_n with $\alpha(E_n) \neq 0$ be such that $M(|f|; E_n) \leqq |f(x_n)| + e$. Then for all m:

$$\sum_1^m M(|f|; E_n)\alpha(E_n) \leqq \sum_1^m |f(x_n)|\alpha(E_n) + e\sum_1^m \alpha(E_n)$$
$$\leqq \sum_\sigma |f(x_n)|\alpha(E_n) + e\alpha(X).$$

Since $\Sigma_n f(x_n)\alpha(E_n)$ is absolutely convergent it follows that $\Sigma_n M(|f|; E_n)\alpha(E_n)$ is convergent.

Let $\sigma' \geqq \sigma$. If E_{nk} are the sets in σ' subsets of E_n in σ, then

$$\sum_{nk} M(|f|; E_{nk})\alpha(E_{nk}) \leqq \sum_n (\sum_k M(|f|; E_{nk})\alpha(E_{nk}))$$
$$\leqq \sum_n M(|f|; E_n)\alpha(E_n),$$

since $M(|f|; E_{nk}) \leqq M(|f|; E_n)$ for all k and n, and $\Sigma_k \alpha(E_{nk}) = \alpha(E_n)$. Then $\Sigma_{\sigma'} f(x_{nk})\alpha(E_{nk})$ converges absolutely for all x_{nk} in E_{nk} and is bounded.

We remark that if for a fixed σ, $\Sigma_\sigma f(x_n)\alpha(E_n)$ is convergent for all x_n in E_n, then the condition that $\Sigma_\sigma f(x_n)\alpha(E_n)$ be bounded in the x_n is equivalent to the condition that $f(x)$ be bounded on each E_n for which $\alpha(E_n) \neq 0$. Moreover, we have l.u.b. $[\Sigma_\sigma f(x_n)\alpha(E_n)$ for x_n on $E_n] = \Sigma_\sigma M(f; E_n)\alpha(E_n)$ and g.l.b. $[\Sigma_\sigma f(x_n)\alpha(E_n)$ for x_n on $E_n] = \Sigma_\sigma m(f; E_n)\alpha(E_n)$, where $\Sigma_n M(f; E_n)\alpha(E_n)$ and $\Sigma_n m(f; E_n)\cdot\alpha(E_n)$ are both absolutely convergent since they are dominated by $\Sigma_n M(|f|; E_n)\alpha(E_n)$. We assume as usual that $M(f; E)\alpha(E) = m(f, E)\alpha(E) = 0$ if $\alpha(E) = 0$.

As in the case of Riemann integration we can now define integrals similar to the upper and lower Darboux integrals.

3.3. Definition. If $f(x)$ is finite valued on X, and $\alpha(x)$ is monotone bounded on X, and there exists a subdivision $\sigma_0 = \{E_n]$ of X of α-measurable subsets, such that $f(x)$ is bounded on each E_n, while $\Sigma_{\sigma_0} f(x_n)\alpha(E_n)$ converges absolutely for all choices of x_n on E_n, then we define the upper integral $\overline{\int}_X f d\alpha = \text{g.l.b. } [\Sigma_\sigma M(f, E_n)\alpha(E_n)$ for all $\sigma \geqq \sigma_0]$ and the lower integral $\underline{\int}_X f d\alpha = \text{l.u.b. } [\Sigma_\sigma m(f; E_n) \cdot \alpha(E_n)$ for all $\sigma \geqq \sigma_0]$.

Since the sums $\Sigma_\sigma M(f; E_n)\alpha(E_n)$ and $\Sigma_\sigma m(f; E_n)\alpha(E_n)$ are monotone in σ, these integrals exist also as σ-limits. Moreover, since for each $\sigma \geqq \sigma_0$

$$\sum_\sigma m(f; E_n)\alpha(E_n) = \text{g.l.b. } [\sum_\sigma f(x_n)\alpha(E_n) \text{ for } x_n \text{ on } E_n]$$
$$\leqq \text{l.u.b. } [\sum_\sigma f(x_n)\alpha(E_n) \text{ for } x_n \text{ on } E_n] = \sum_\sigma M(f, E_n)\ (E_n)$$

we conclude:

3.4. If $f(x)$ is finite valued on X, and if $\alpha(x)$ is montone bounded on X, then necessary and sufficient conditions that $\int_X f d\alpha$ exist are (1), there exists a subdivision σ_0 of X into α-measurable sets, such that $f(x)$ is bounded on each set E of σ_0, and $\Sigma_n f(x_n')\alpha(E_n)$ converges absolutely for all x_n in E_n; and (2) $\overline{\int}_X f d\alpha = \underline{\int}_X f d\alpha$.

3.4.1. Condition (2) can be replaced by the equivalent condition:

(2 *a*) $\text{g.l.b. } [\Sigma_\sigma \omega(f; E_n)\alpha(E_n)$ in $\sigma] = \lim_\sigma \Sigma_\sigma \omega(f; E_n)\alpha(E_n) = 0$, where $\omega(f; E) = \text{l.u.b. } [|f(x_1) - f(x_2)|$ for x_1, x_2 on $E]$, that is, the oscillation of f on E.

A third replacement of condition (2) comes from the fact that a Cauchy condition of convergence induces the existence of a σ-limit, so that we have:

3.5. $\int_X f d\alpha$ exists if and only if condition (1) of 3.4 is satisfied and if the Cauchy condition of convergence: $(e > 0, \sigma_e, \sigma \geqq \sigma_e, \sigma' \geqq \sigma_e)$: $|\Sigma_\sigma f(x_n)\alpha(E_n) - \Sigma_{\sigma'} f(x_n')\alpha(E_n')| < e$ holds.

We note that if $\sigma_0 = \{E_n\}$ is such that $f(x)$ is bounded on each E_n for which $\alpha(E_n) \neq 0$, then there exists a $\sigma \geqq \sigma_0$, such that $f(x)$ is bounded on each E of σ. For if E is any subset in σ_0 such that $\alpha(E) = 0$, and $f(x)$ is not bounded on E, we can redivide E into the sequence of sets $E \cdot E_n'$ of x for which $n \leqq f(x) < n + 1$, and x on E, which will also be α-null sets.

The idea of using subdivisions of Lebesgue measurable subsets of a finite interval as a basis for defining upper and lower integrals of bounded functions is due to W. H. Young [A general theory of integration, *Phil. Trans. Roy. Soc. London* 204A (1905) 211-252 (p. 243)]. In order to distinguish the integral just developed from the Lebesgue definition: $L \int_X f d\alpha$ (which assumes that f is α-measurable), we shall label the integral of this section as the Y-integral: $Y \int_X f d\alpha$.

We give some instances of existence of $Y \int_X f d\alpha$.

3.6. If $f(x)$ is an α-measurable step function on X, that is, if $X = \Sigma_n E_n$, where the E_n are α-measurable and disjoint, and $f(x) = c_n$ on E_n, then $Y \int_X f d\alpha$ exists if and only if $\Sigma_n |c_n| \alpha(E_n) < \infty$, and then $Y \int_X f d\alpha = \Sigma_n c_n \alpha(E_n)$.

If we set $\sigma_0 = \{E_n\}$, and if $\Sigma_n |c_n| \alpha(E_n) < \infty$, then because of the s-additivity of α, $\Sigma_\sigma f(x)\alpha(E) = \Sigma_n c_n \alpha(E_n)$ for all $\sigma \geqq \sigma_0$. Conversely, if $Y \int_X f d\alpha$ exists, there is a subdivision σ, such that $\Sigma_\sigma M(|f|; E)\alpha(E) < \infty$. Then for the subdivision $\sigma_0 \cdot \sigma$, we have

$$\sum_{\sigma \cdot \sigma_0} M(|f|; E)\alpha(E) = \sum_n |c_n| \alpha(E_n) \leqq \sum_\sigma M(|f|; E)\alpha(E) < \infty.$$

Note that the sums $\Sigma_\sigma f(x_n)\alpha(E_n)$ which occur in the definitions of $\int_X f d\alpha$ can be expressed in the form $\int_X f_\sigma d\alpha$, where f_σ is the step function $\Sigma_n f(x_n)\chi(E_n; x)$.

3.7. If $f(x)$ is bounded and $\alpha(x)$ is monotonic nondecreasing on $[a, b]$ and if the Riemann-Stieltjes integral $\sigma \int_a^b f d\alpha$ exists, then the $Y \int_a^b f d\alpha$ exists also and the integrals are equal.

We recall that if $\alpha(x)$ is monotone on $[a, b]$ and if $\sigma \equiv (a = x_0 < x_1 < \dots x_n = b)$, then

$$\overline{\int_a^b} f d\alpha = \text{g.l.b.}_\sigma [\textstyle\sum_\sigma M(f; [x_{i-1}, x_i])(\alpha(x_i) - \alpha(x_{i-1})),$$

where $[x_{i-1}, x_i] \equiv x_{i-1} \leqq x \leqq x_i$. Similarly for $\underline{\int_a^b} f d\alpha$. Let σ_1 be the subdivision of $[a, b]$ into α-measurable subsets consisting of the points $a, x_1, \dots, x_{n-1}, b$ and the open intervals (x_{i-1}, x_i), $i = 1 \dots n$. Let $M_i = \text{l.u.b.}\ [f(x)$ for x on $[x_{i-1}, x_i]$ and $M_i' = \text{l.u.b.}\ [f(x)$ on $(x_{i-1}, x_i)]$. Then

$$M_i(\alpha(x_i) - \alpha(x_{i-1})) \geqq f(x_i)(\alpha(x_i) - \alpha(x_i - 0)) + M_i'(\alpha(x_i - 0) - \alpha(x_{i-1} + 0)) + f(x_{i-1})(\alpha(x_{i-1} + 0) - \alpha(x_{i-1})),$$

and so

$$\textstyle\sum_i M_i(\alpha(x_i) - \alpha(x_{i-1})) \geqq \sum_i [f(x_i)(\alpha(x_i + 0) - \alpha(x_i - 0)) + M_i'(\alpha(x_i - 0) - \alpha(x_{i-1} + 0))],$$

where $\alpha(a - 0) = \alpha(a)$ and $\alpha(b + 0) = \alpha(b)$. But the right-hand side of this inequality is the upper sum corresponding to the subdivision σ_1. Taking greatest lower bounds, we find that $\sigma \overline{\int} fd\alpha \geqq Y \overline{\int} fd\alpha$. Similarly, $\sigma \underline{\int} fd\alpha \leqq Y \underline{\int} fd\alpha$. Consequently, if $\sigma \int fd\alpha$ exists so that $\sigma \overline{\int} fd\alpha = \sigma \underline{\int} fd\alpha$, then $Y \int fd\alpha$ exists also and agrees with $\sigma \int fd\alpha$.

Since the existence of the $N \int_a^b fd\alpha$ implies the existence of the $\sigma \int_a^b fd\alpha$, we also have:

3.8. If α is monotonic nondecreasing and the Riemann-Stieltjes $N \int_a^b fd\alpha$ exists, then the $Y \int_a^b fd\alpha$ exists and the integrals are equal.

Since when the $N \int_a^b fd\alpha$ exists, the function f is α-measurable, it follows that the $L \int_a^b fd\alpha$ exists also. For then f will be bounded on a finite set of nonoverlapping intervals and on the complement of this set the function α is constant, that is, f is bounded if one excludes an α-null set of $[a, b]$. In view of the next theorem $Y \int_a^b fd\alpha$ exists also, giving us another proof of the present theorem.

3.9. THEOREM. If $f(x)$ is α-measurable, then the existence of the $L \int_X fd\alpha$ implies the existence of the $Y \int_X fd\alpha$ and conversely, and the integrals are equal.

If the $L \int_X fd\alpha$ exists, and σ_y is a subdivision of the Y-axis with $|\sigma_y| < \infty$, then

$$\left|\sum_{\sigma_y} y_k'\alpha(E_k) - L \int fd\alpha\right| \leqq |\sigma_y|\, \alpha(X),$$

where $E_k = E[y_{k-1} < f \leqq y_k]$ and $y_{k-1} \leqq y_k' \leqq y_k$, the sum term being absolutely convergent. Any σ_y determines a σ_x, consisting of the E_k. Then since $M(|f|;\, E_k) = y_k$ if $y_k < 0$, and $M(|f|;\, E_k) = |y_{k-1}|$ if $y_{k-1} < 0$, it follows that for $\sigma = \sigma_x$: $\Sigma_\sigma M(|f|;\, E_k)\alpha(E_k) < \infty$. Suppose $\sigma_{1x} \geqq \sigma_x$, and let E_{nk} be the sets of σ_{1x} in E_k. Then for fixed k:

$$\begin{aligned} &\left| y_k'\alpha(E_k) - \textstyle\sum_n f(x_{nk})\alpha(E_{nk}) \right| \\ &= \left| y_k' \textstyle\sum_n \alpha(E_{nk}) - \sum_n f(x_{nk})\alpha(E_{nk}) \right| \leqq |\sigma_y|\, \alpha(E_k). \end{aligned}$$

Consequently, if $\sigma_{1x} \geqq \sigma_x$, then

$$\begin{aligned} \left|\sum_{\sigma_{1x}} f(x_{nk})\alpha(E_{nk}) - L \int_X fd\alpha \right| &\leqq \left|\sum_{\sigma_{1x}} f(x_{nk})\alpha(E_{nk}) - \sum_{\sigma_y} y_k'\alpha(E_k)\right| \\ &+ \left|\sum_{\sigma_y} y_k'\alpha(E_k) - L \int_X fd\alpha \right| \leqq 2\, |\sigma_y|\, \alpha(X). \end{aligned}$$

If we let $|\sigma_y| \to 0$, it follows that $Y \int_X fd\alpha = L \int_X fd\alpha$.

Conversely suppose that f is α-measurable and that $Y \int_X fd\alpha$ exists.

Then to prove that $L \int_X f d\alpha$ exists, it is sufficient to show that for some subdivision σ_y of Y with $|\sigma_y| < \infty$ we have

$$\sum_{\sigma_y} |y_k'| \alpha(E[y_{k-1} < f \leqq y_k]) < \infty.$$

We take σ_y so that $y_k = k$, for all positive and negative integers k. Since $Y \int f d\alpha$ exists, there exists a $\sigma_x \equiv \{E_n'\}$, $n = 1 \ldots$, a subdivision of X into α-measurable sets, such that $\Sigma_n M(|f|; E_n')\alpha(E_n') < \infty$. The same type of inequality will then hold for any $\sigma_x' \geqq \sigma_x$. If $E_k = E[k-1 < f \leqq k]$, let $E_{nk} = E_k \cdot E_n'$ and set $\sigma_x' \equiv \{E_{nk}\}$, so that $\sigma_x' \geqq \sigma_x$. If $k > 0$, then $M(|f|; E_{nk}) \geqq k - 1$ and if $k < 0$, then $M(|f|; E_{nk}) > |k|$, so that for fixed $k > 0$:

$$\sum\nolimits_n M(|f|; E_{nk})\alpha(E_{nk}) \geqq (k-1) \sum\nolimits_n \alpha(E_{nk}) = (k-1)\alpha(E_k);$$

while for $k < 0$:

$$\sum\nolimits_n M(|f|; E_{nk})\alpha(E_{nk}) \geqq |k| \sum\nolimits_n \alpha(E_{nk}) = |k|\, \alpha(E_k).$$

If we take $y_k' = k - 1$ for $k > 0$ and $y_k' = k$ for $k < 0$, then

$$\sum_k |y_k'| \alpha(E_k) \leqq \sum_{\sigma_{x'}} M(|f|; E_{nk})\alpha(E_{nk}) < \infty.$$

Then $L \int_X f d\alpha$ exists and by what we have proved above is equal to $Y \int_X f d\alpha$. We shall show later that if $Y \int_X f d\alpha$ exists, then f is α-measurable (see VII. 8.11).

In case both $f(x)$ and $\alpha(x)$ are bounded, it is sufficient to limit subdivisions to those consisting of a finite number of sets of X. Let $|f(x)| \leqq M$ for all x. Let $\sigma_x \equiv \{E_n\}$ be such that

$$\sum_{\sigma_x} M(f; E_n)\alpha(E_n) \leqq \overline{\int}_X f d\alpha + e.$$

Since $\Sigma_n \alpha(E_n) = \alpha(X)$, it follows that $(e > 0, n_e, n \geqq n_e) : \Sigma_n^\infty \alpha(E_m) < e/M$. Let $\overline{E}_n = \Sigma_n^\infty E_m$, and let $\sigma_1 \equiv E_1, \ldots, E_{n-1}, \overline{E}_n$. Then

$$\Big|\sum_{\sigma_1} M(f, E)\alpha(E) - \sum_{\sigma} M(f, E)\alpha(E)\Big|$$
$$\leqq \sum_{m=n}^{\infty} [M(f, \overline{E}_n) - M(f, E_m)]\alpha(E_m) \leqq 2e.$$

Then

$$\sum_{\sigma_1} M(f, E)\alpha(E) \leqq \sum_{\sigma} M(f, E)\alpha(E) + 2e \leqq \overline{\int}_X f d\alpha + 3e.$$

It follows that $\overline{\int}_X f d\alpha = \text{g.l.b.}\,[\Sigma_\sigma M(f; E)\alpha(E)$ for all finite σ of $X]$. Similarly, $\underline{\int}_X f d\alpha = \text{l.u.b.}\,[\Sigma_\sigma m(f, E)\alpha(E)$ for all finite σ of $X]$.

Since both of these bounds are limits in the σ-sense, it follows that if $\int_X f d\alpha$ exists with f and α both bounded on X, then $\int_X f d\alpha = \lim_\sigma \Sigma_\sigma f(x)\alpha(E)$ where the σ are limited to be finite subdivisions of X.

For the existence of $Y \int_X f d\alpha$ it also sufficient to limit subdivisions of X to consist entirely of Borel measurable sets. We have:

3.10. A necessary and sufficient condition that $Y \int_X f d\alpha$ exist is that $\lim_\sigma \Sigma_\sigma f(x)\alpha(E)$ exist for all subdivisions consisting entirely of Borel measurable sets.

If $Y \int_X f d\alpha$ exists, there exists a σ_0 such that $\Sigma_{\sigma_0} M(|f|; E)\alpha(E) < \infty$. Let $\sigma_0 \equiv \{E_n\}$ with E_n α-measurable. Then if $\alpha(E_n) \neq 0$, there exists a Borel measurable set B_n (actually an F_σ, sum of a denumerable number of closed sets) contained in E_n such that $\alpha(E_n - B_n) = 0$. If we set $B_0 = X - \Sigma_n B_n$, then B_0 will be a Borel measurable set with $\alpha(B_0) = 0$, and $B_0, B_1, \ldots$ will be a subdivision of X such that $\Sigma_n M(|f|; B_n)\alpha(B_n) \leqq \Sigma_{\sigma_0} M(|f|; E_n)\alpha(E_n)$, with the usual convention that $M(|f|; E)\alpha(E) = 0$ if $\alpha(E) = 0$. Then there exists the subdivision σ into Borel measurable sets such that $\Sigma_\sigma M(|f|; B_n)\alpha(B_n)$ converges. In the same way we show that if we define $\overline{\int}_X f d\alpha$ and $\underline{\int}_X f d\alpha$ on the basis of Borel measurable sets, we get the same value as for the same integrals defined on α-measurable sets. Consequently, if $Y \int_X f d\alpha$ exists as a σ-limit based on α-measurable sets, it will also exist if based on the smaller group of Borel measurable sets, and determine the same value.

Conversely, if $\lim_\sigma \Sigma_\sigma f(x)\alpha(E)$ exists for σ consisting of Borel measurable sets, then the σ_0 for which $\Sigma_{\sigma_0} M(|f|; B)\alpha(B) < \infty$ will also serve as a subdivision into α-measurable sets. Moreover, we will have g.l.b. $[\Sigma_\sigma \omega(f, B)\alpha(B)$ for σ of Borel measurable sets$] = 0$ and consequently g.l.b. $[\Sigma_\sigma \omega(f, E)\alpha(E)$ for σ of α-measurable sets$] = 0$ also, so that $Y \int_X f d\alpha$ exists.

EXERCISES

1. Suppose $\alpha(x)$ is a monotone bounded pure break function on X, so that all subsets E of X are α-measurable, and $\alpha(E) = \Sigma_{x \text{ in } E}(\alpha(x+0) - \alpha(x-0))$. Show that $\int_X f d\alpha$ exists and is equal to $\Sigma_x f(x)(\alpha(x+0) - \alpha(x-0))$ if and only if $\Sigma_x |f(x)|\,(\alpha(x+0) - \alpha(x-0)) < \infty$.

2. For the α-measurable function $f(x)$ define $f(m, M; x) = f(x)$ if $m < f(x) \leqq M$, and $f(m, M; x) = 0$ if $f(x) \leqq m$, or $f(x) > M$. Show that $L \int_X f(m, M; x) d\alpha(x) = \int_m^M y d\mu(y)$ where $\mu(y) = \alpha(E[f \leqq y])$.

4. Properties of the Integrals

Since for α-measurable functions the two definitions of integration we have given in the previous section agree, it is possible to use either definition for the derivation of properties of integrals of such functions. As a consequence, for most of the theorems in this and the following sections, methods of proof alternative to the one used exist.

For Riemann integrals, if the integral exists for the basic interval $[a, b]$, then it exists also for every subinterval $[c, d]$ of $[a, b]$. Correspondingly, we can consider an integral on a measurable subset of X. This can be obtained by considering the function $f_E(x) = f(x)$ if x is in E and $f_E(x) = 0$ if x is in CE, or $f_E(x) = f(x)\chi(E; x)$ where $\chi(E; x)$ is the characteristic function of E. For the Y-integral, this is equivalent to considering for any subdivision σ of X which is finer than the subdivision (E, CE) determined by E only the terms of $\Sigma_\sigma f(x_n)\alpha(E_n)$, for which E_n are subsets of E. We have:

4.1. If $\int_X f d\alpha$ exists, then $\int_E f d\alpha = \int_X f_E(x) d\alpha(x) \doteq \int_X f(x)\chi(E; x) d\alpha(x)$ exists for every α-measurable subset E of X.

If $\int_E f d\alpha$ exists it will be the σ-limit of sums $\Sigma_\sigma f(x_n)\alpha(EE_n)$ with x_n in EE_n. If $\int_X f d\alpha$ exists, then (a) there exists a σ_0 such that for $\sigma \geqq \sigma_0 : \Sigma_\sigma M(|f|; E_n)\alpha(E_n) < \infty$. Consequently, if $\sigma = \sigma_0 \cdot (E, CE)$, then

$$\sum_{\sigma_0} (M(|f|; EE_n)\alpha(EE_n) + M(|f|; (CE)E_n)\alpha((CE)E_n)) < \infty,$$

and so $\Sigma_{\sigma_0} M(|f|; EE_n)\alpha(EE_n) < \infty$. If $\int_X f d\alpha$ exists, then (b) g.l.b.$_\sigma \Sigma_\sigma \omega(f, E_n)\alpha(E_n) = 0$. But this implies g.l.b.$_\sigma \Sigma_\sigma \omega(f; EE_n) \alpha(EE_n) = 0$. Since the two conditions (a) and (b) are sufficient for the existence of the integral it follows that $\int_E f d\alpha$ exists, for all α-measurable E.

The integral $\int_E f d\alpha$ is then a function of $f(x)$, $\alpha(x)$ and E, which we can bring into focus by writing $I(f, \alpha, E) = \int_E f d\alpha$. We shall treat in succession, $I(f, \alpha, E)$ as a function of E, of f and of α.

5. The Integral as a Function of Measurable Sets

Corresponding to the fact that the Riemann integral is an additive function of intervals, we have:

5.1. If $\int_X f d\alpha$, exists, then $\int_E f d\alpha$ is an s-additive function of α-measurable sets. In particular if $E = \Sigma_n E_n$, with E_n, α-measurable and disjoint then $\int_E f d\alpha = \Sigma_n \int_{E_n} f d\alpha$, where the series on the right is absolutely convergent.

Since $\int_{E_n} f d\alpha$ exists for each α-measurable E_n, we have $(e>0, \sigma_{ne}, \sigma_n \geqq \sigma_{ne}) : \left| \Sigma_{\sigma_n} f(x_{ni}) \alpha(E_{ni}) - \int_{E_n} f d\alpha \right| < e/2^n$, where σ_n are subdivisions of E_n and consist of the sets E_{ni}. We also have $(e>0, \sigma_e, \sigma \geqq \sigma_e) : \left| \Sigma_\sigma f(x^i)\alpha(E^i) - \int_E f d\alpha \right| < e$. If $\sigma_e{}' = \sigma_e(\Sigma_n \sigma_{ne})$ and if $\sigma \geqq \sigma_e{}'$, then $\sigma \geqq \sigma_e$ and $\sigma \cdot E_n \geqq \sigma_{ne}$, and the absolute convergence of the series involved yields

$$\begin{aligned}\sum_n \left| \int_{E_n} f d\alpha \right| &\leqq \sum_n \left| \sum_{\sigma_n} f(x_{ni})\alpha(E_{ni}) \right| + \sum_n e/2^n \\ &\leqq \sum_n \sum_i \left| f(x_{ni}) \right| \alpha(E_{ni}) + 2e \\ &= \sum_\sigma \left| f(x) \right| \alpha(E) + 2e < \infty.\end{aligned}$$

Then the series $\Sigma_n \int_{E_n} f d\alpha$ converges absolutely. Further, for the same σ we have

$$\begin{aligned}\left| \int_E f d\alpha - \sum_n \int_{E_n} f d\alpha \right| &\leqq \left| \int_E f d\alpha - \sum_\sigma f(x)\alpha(E) \right| \\ &\quad + \left| \sum_\sigma f(x)\alpha(E) - \sum_n \int_{E_n} f d\alpha \right| \\ &= \left| \int_E f d\alpha - \sum_\sigma f(x)\alpha(E) \right| \\ &\quad + \left| \sum_n \sum_i f(x_{ni})\alpha(E_{ni}) - \sum_n \int_{E_n} f d\alpha \right| \\ &\leqq \left| \int_E f d\alpha - \sum_\sigma f(x)\alpha(E) \right| \\ &\quad + \sum_n \left| \sum_{\sigma_n} f(x_{ni})\alpha(E_{ni}) - \int_{E_n} f d\alpha \right| \leqq 3e.\end{aligned}$$

This completes the proof of the theorem.

The *s*-additivity of $\int_E f d\alpha$ leads immediately to the finite additivity:

5.2. If $\int_X f d\alpha$ exists and E_1 and E_2 are any two α-measurable subsets of X, then

$$\int_{E_1} f d\alpha + \int_{E_2} f d\alpha = \int_{E_1+E_2} f d\alpha + \int_{E_1 \cdot E_2} f d\alpha.$$

We can also prove the following converse to the *s*-additivity theorem:

5.3. If E_n are disjoint α-measurable sets with $E = \Sigma_n E_n$, if $\int_{E_n} f d\alpha$ exist for each n, and if $\Sigma_n \int_{E_n} |f| \, d\alpha < \infty$, then $\int_E f d\alpha$ exists and is equal to $\Sigma_n \int_{E_n} f d\alpha$.

We shall show later in VII.8.3. that if $\int_X f d\alpha$ exists, then $\int_X |f| d\alpha$ exists also.

To show that if $E = \Sigma_n E_n$, then $\int_E f d\alpha$ exists, we need to show first that there exists a subdivision σ of E such that $\Sigma_\sigma M(|f|; E)\alpha(E) < \infty$. The existence of $\int_{E_n} f d\alpha$ implies the existence of $\int_{E_n} |f| \, d\alpha$, so that for $e > 0$, there exists $\sigma_n = \{E_{ni}\}$ of E_n such that $\Sigma_{\sigma_n} M(|f|; E_{ni})\alpha(E_{ni}) \leqq \int_{E_n} |f| \, d\alpha + e/2^n$. Then

$$\sum_n \sum_{\sigma_n} M(|f|; E_{ni})\alpha(E_{ni}) \leqq \sum_n \int_{E_n} |f| \, d\alpha + e < \infty.$$

This gives the desired convergence for $\sigma = \Sigma_n \sigma_n$. Further,

$$(e > 0, n, \sigma_{ne}, \sigma_n \geqq \sigma_{ne}) : \left| \int_{E_n} f d\alpha - \sum_{\sigma_n} f(x_{ni})\alpha(E_{ni}) \right| < e/2^n.$$

Then for any subdivision $\sigma \geqq \sigma_e = \Sigma_n \sigma_{ne}$, so that $\sigma \cdot E_n = \sigma_n \geqq \sigma_{ne}$:

$$\left| \sum_\sigma f(x)\alpha(E) - \sum_n \int_{E_n} f d\alpha \right| = \left| \sum_n \sum_{\sigma_n} f(x_{ni})\alpha(E_{ni}) - \sum_n \int_{E_n} f d\alpha \right|$$
$$\leqq \sum_n \left| \sum_{\sigma_n} f(x_{ni})\alpha(E_{ni}) - \int_{E_n} f d\alpha \right| < e.$$

Then $\int_E f d\alpha$ exists and has $\Sigma_n \int_{E_n} f d\alpha$ as its value.

We note that in the hypothesis of this theorem, the condition $\Sigma_n \int_{E_n} |f| \, d\alpha < \infty$ cannot be weakened to $\Sigma_n \left| \int_{E_n} f d\alpha \right| < \infty$. For take E_n disjoint α-measurable sets, and $f(x)$ the step function $f(x) = c_n$ on E_n. Select c_n so that $c_{2n}\alpha(E_{2n}) = -c_{2n+1}\alpha(E_{2n+1})$ and $\Sigma_n |c_n| \alpha(E_n) = \infty$. If $E_n' = E_{2n} + E_{2n+1}$, then $\int_{E_n'} f d\alpha = 0$ for all n, but if $E = \Sigma_n E_n' = \Sigma_n E_n$ then $\int_E f d\alpha$ does not exist.

6. L-S Integrals as Functions of Intervals

In the Riemann-Stieltjes type of integrals we did not distinguish between open and closed intervals for the basic interval function nor for the interval function determined by the integral. For additive properties, intervals were permitted to be nonoverlapping, without being entirely disjoint. The Lebesgue-Stieltjes integral determines a function of sets, and when we consider integration over an interval, there may be ambiguity as to whether we are considering the closed interval $[a, b]$, or the open interval (a, b) or the half-open intervals $[a, b)$ and $(a, b]$. For instance, if a and b are points of discontinuity of $\alpha(x)$ and if $I = [a, b]$ and $I_0 = (a, b)$, then

$$\int_I f d\alpha - \int_{I_0} f d\alpha = f(b)(\alpha(b+0) - \alpha(b-0)) + f(a)(\alpha(a+0) - \alpha(a-0)),$$

so that the integrals agree only when the right side vanishes. We note, moreover, that the value of α at the points $x = a$, or $x = b$ plays no role in the values of the integral, and what is more the value of $\int_I f d\alpha$ for the closed interval depends on the behavior of α *outside* of I. Since the additive property of $\int_E f d\alpha$ as a function of E depends on the disjointedness of the sets involved, to secure a corresponding property for intervals we must impose limitations. A simple way out is to restrict the word interval in this connection to intervals closed on the right and open on the left (or open on the right and closed on the left). If I is so restricted then for $a < c < b$, we have $\int_a^c f d\alpha + \int_c^b f d\alpha = \int_a^b f d\alpha$, and even

$$\sum_n \int_{a_{n+1}}^{a_n} f d\alpha = \int_a^{a_1} f d\alpha \quad \text{if} \quad a_1 > a_2 > \ldots > a_n \to a.$$

Observe that there are two ways of obtaining $\int_a^b f d\alpha$ on $(a, b]$ from $\int_X f d\alpha$: (1) $\int_a^b f d\alpha = \int_X f_1 d\alpha$ where $f_1(x) = f(x)\chi(I; x)$, or $f_1(x) = f(x)$ for $a < x \leqq b$, and $f_1(x) = 0$, for $x \leqq a$ or $x > b$; (2) $\int_a^b f d\alpha = \int_X f d\alpha_1$, where $\alpha_1(x) = \alpha(x)$ for $a < x < b$, $\alpha_1(x) = \alpha(a+0)$ for $x \leqq a$, and $\alpha_1(x) = \alpha(b+0)$ for $x \geqq b$.

7. Absolute Continuity

If f is bounded on X and $\int_X f d\alpha$ exists, then for any α-measurable set E $\left| \int_E f d\alpha \right| \leqq M(|f|; E)\alpha(E)$, so that $\int_E f d\alpha \to 0$ as $\alpha(E) \to 0$. This is a continuity property of set functions. We define:

7.1. Definition. A set function β on a class $\mathfrak{E}$ of subsets E of a fundamental set X is absolutely continuous with respect to the positive set function α on $\mathfrak{E}$, if $\lim_{\alpha(E)\to 0} \beta(E) = 0$.

The word "positive" includes positive or zero. We have:

7.2. If $\int_X f d\alpha$ exists then the set function $\int_E f d\alpha$ on α-measurable sets is absolutely continuous with respect to the function $\alpha(E)$.

For if $\int_X f d\alpha$ exists, then there exists a subdivision σ of X such that $\Sigma_\sigma M(|f|; E_k)\alpha(E_k) < \infty$. For $e > 0$ choose n so that $\Sigma_{k=n}^\infty M(|f|; E_k)\cdot \alpha(E_k) < e$. Let $E' = \Sigma_1^{n-1} E_k$ and $E'' = \Sigma_n^\infty E_k$, and let E be any α-measurable set. Then $|\int_{E\cdot E''} f d\alpha \leqq \Sigma_n^\infty M(|f|; E_k)\alpha(E_k) < e$, since $M(|f|; E \cdot E_k) \leqq M(|f|; E_k)$ and $\alpha(E_k \cdot E) \leqq \alpha(E_k)$. On the other hand, $f(x)$ is bounded on E', since it is bounded on each E_k with $k < n$. Consequently $\lim_{\alpha(E)\to 0} \int_{E\cdot E'} f d\alpha = 0$, or $(e > 0, d_e, \alpha(E) \leqq d_e)$: $|\int_{E\cdot E'} f d\alpha| \leqq e$. Consequently, if $\alpha(E) \leqq d_e$, then

$$\left|\int_E f d\alpha\right| \leqq \left|\int_{E\cdot E'} f d\alpha\right| + \left|\int_{E\cdot E''} f d\alpha\right| \leqq 2e.$$

If β is a set function on a class $\mathfrak{E}$ of sets, which is absolutely continuous with respect to a positive set function α on $\mathfrak{E}$, then $\alpha(E) = 0$ implies $\beta(E) = 0$. This last condition: "$\alpha(E) = 0$ implies $\beta(E) = 0$" is sometimes used as the definition of absolute continuity of set functions, though it is difficult to see that such a condition is a continuity condition. However, under special circumstances it does imply the absolute continuity property as we have defined it. We prove:

7.3. If $\mathfrak{E}$ is an s-algebra of subsets of a set X; if $\alpha(E)$ and $\beta(E)$ are s-additive and positive set functions on E; if β is finite valued; and if $\alpha(E)=0$ implies $\beta(E)=0$, then β is absolutely continuous relative to α.

The proof proceeds contrapositively. If β is not absolutely continuous, then there exists $e > 0$, such that for each of a sequence of constants $e_n > 0$ with $\Sigma_n e_n < \infty$, there exists a set E_n with $\alpha(E_n) < e_n$ and $\beta(E_n) > e$. If $E^m = \Sigma_m^\infty E_n$, then $\alpha(E^m) \leqq \Sigma_m^\infty \alpha(E_n)$, so that $\alpha(\Pi_m E^m) = \lim_m \alpha(E^m) = 0$. On the other hand, $\beta(E^m) \geqq \beta(E_m) > e$ for all m. Since β is finite valued and s-additive, it follows that

$$\lim_m \beta(E^m) = \beta(\prod_m E^m) > e.$$

Then for $E_0 = \Pi_m E^m$, we have $\alpha(E_0) = 0$ but $\beta(E_0) > e$.

It can be shown (see IX.4, Exs. 1 and 2) that the condition that β be positive or zero on $\mathfrak{E}$ can be dropped.

We note also the following:

7.4. If $\mathfrak{E}$ is an s-algebra of sets; if α is an s-additive, and finite valued, positive or zero function on $\mathfrak{E}$, and if β is an additive, finite valued set function on $\mathfrak{E}$ which is absolutely continuous relative to α, then β is s-additive.

Let E_n be disjoint sets in $\mathfrak{E}$ with $E = \Sigma_n E_n$. Denote by E_q the set $\Sigma_q E_{n_i}$, where $q = (n_1, ..., n_i, ..., n_m)$, any finite set of integers. Then since α is s-additive and finite valued $\lim_q \alpha(E - E_q) = \lim_q (\alpha(E) - \alpha(E_q)) = 0$. Since β is additive $\beta(E - E_q) = \beta(E) - \Sigma_q \beta(E_n)$. Then the absolute continuity condition gives $\lim_q (\beta(E) - \Sigma_q \beta(E_n)) = 0$, so that by I.6.2. $\Sigma_n |\beta(E_n)| < \infty$, and $\Sigma_n \beta(E_n) = \beta(\Sigma_n E_n) = \beta(E)$.

EXERCISE

Show that the upper and lower integrals when they exist as g.l.b.$_\sigma(\Sigma_\sigma M(f; E_n)\alpha(E_n))$ and l.u.b.$_\sigma(\Sigma_\sigma m(f; E_n)\alpha(E_n))$ are completely additive as functions of α-measurable sets. Are they also absolutely continuous with respect to α?

8. Properties of the Integral $I(f, \alpha, E) = \int_E f d\alpha$ as a Function of f

For a fixed α, and a fixed α-measurable E, the existence of $\int_E f d\alpha$ determines a class of functions f. We shall limit ourselves to the case when $E = X$, since

$$\int_E f d\alpha = \int_X f_E(x) d\alpha(x) = \int_X f(x) \chi(E; x) d\alpha(x).$$

As an immediate consequence of the definition of the Y-integral and the linear properties of limits, we have:

8.1. If $\int_X f d\alpha$ exists and c is any constant, then $\int_X (cf) d\alpha$ exists and $\int_X cf d\alpha = c \int_X f d\alpha$.

8.2. If $\int_X f_1 d\alpha$ exists and $\int_X f_2 d\alpha$ exists, then $\int_X (f_1 + f_2)\, d\alpha$ exists and $\int_X (f_1 + f_2) d\alpha = \int_X f_1 d\alpha + \int_X f_2 d\alpha$.

These two theorems assert that the class of functions integrable with respect to a fixed function α is linear and that the integral is a linear functional on this class.

We have further:

8.3. If $\int_X f d\alpha$ exists then $\int_X |f|\, d\alpha$ exists and $|\int_X f d\alpha| \leqq \int_X |f|\, d\alpha$.

For the condition: there exists a σ_0 such that if $\sigma \geqq \sigma_0$, then $\Sigma_\sigma M(|f|; E)\alpha(E) < \infty$, is really a condition on $|f|$. Further, $\omega(|f|; E) \leqq \omega(f; E)$, and so g.l.b.$_\sigma \Sigma_\sigma \omega(f; E)\alpha(E)) = 0$ implies g.l.b.$_\sigma(\Sigma_\sigma \omega(|f|; E)\alpha(E)) = 0$. Then the conditions for the existence of $\int_X |f|\, d\alpha$ are fulfilled. The inequality $|\Sigma_\sigma f(x)\alpha(E)| \leqq \Sigma_\sigma |f(x)|\, \alpha(E)$ for all σ induces the corresponding inequality on the integrals.

This theorem asserts that the class of Y-integrable (and so L-integrable) functions has the absolute property. If we adjoin the linear property, we find that with f, the functions $f^+ = (|f| + f)/2$ and $f^- = (|f| - f)/2$, that is the positive and negative parts of f are also integrable. This fact is sometimes made the basis for a definition of integral, the integral being first defined for functions $f \geqq 0$ on X, and then extended linearly to functions of arbitrary sign. Further, if f_1 and f_2 are integrable, then $f_1 \vee f_2 = (f_1 + f_2 + |f_1 - f_2|)/2$ and $f_1 \wedge f_2 = (f_1 + f_2 - |f_1 - f_2|)/2$ are also integrable, that is, the integrable functions form a linear or vector lattice, with $f_1 (\leqq) f_2$ equivalent to $f_1(x) \leqq f_2(x)$ for all x (or all x except for an α-null set).

The fact that any L-integrable function is also absolutely integrable shows that the class of L-integrable functions does not include all improperly Riemann integrable functions, since some of these are not absolutely integrable. For instance, $\int_0^1 (1/x) \sin (1/x)\, dx$ exists as an improper integral since $\lim_{e\to 0} \int_e^1 (1/x) \sin (1/x)\, dx$ exists, but $\int_0^1 (1/x)\, |\sin (1/x)|\, dx = \infty$. Then $(1/x) \sin (1/x)$ is not L-integrable on $[0, 1]$.

In the existence of integral after the manner of Lebesgue, we have noted that in addition to α-measurability, a single convergence condition is sufficient to guarantee the existence of the integral. A generalization is the following:

8.4. If $f \geqq 0$ on X, and $\int_X f d\alpha$ exists; if further f_1 is α-measurable and $|f_1| \leqq f$ except for an α-null set, then $\int_X f_1 d\alpha$ exists and $|\int_X f_1 d\alpha| \leqq \int_X f d\alpha$.

For if for $\sigma \geqq \sigma_0 : \Sigma_\sigma M(f; E)\alpha(E) < \infty$, and σ includes the α-null set E_0 for which $|f_1| > f$, then $\Sigma_\sigma M(|f_1|; E)\alpha(E) \leqq \Sigma_\sigma M(f; E)\alpha(E) < \infty$. If we add the α-measurability of f_1 we conclude that $\int_X f_1 d\alpha$ exists. The inequality between the integrals is a direct consequence of the definition of integration in terms of σ-limits.

The class of integrable functions does not have the multiplicative property, that is, if f_1 and f_2 are integrable, then $f_1 \cdot f_2$ is also integrable. This is due to the fact that if f_1 and f_2 are both unbounded, the unboundedness of $f_1 \cdot f_2$ might be of higher order than that permissible for integrability. To obtain a theorem, we restrict one of the functions.

8.5. If f_1 is α-measurable and almost bounded, and if $\int_X f_2 d\alpha$ exists, then $\int_X f_1 \cdot f_2 d\alpha$ exists and $\int_X f_1 \cdot f_2 d\alpha \leqq M \int_X |f_2|\, d\alpha_2$, where $M =$ g.l.b. $[M'$ such that $\alpha(E[|f_1| > M']) = 0]$.

For if $\int_X f_2 d\alpha$ exists, there exists a σ_0 such that if $\sigma \geqq \sigma_0$ then $\Sigma_\sigma M(|f_2|;\ E)\alpha(E) < \infty$. Since f_1 is almost bounded let M_1 and E_0 be such that $\alpha(E_0) = \alpha(E[|f_1| > M_1]) = 0$. Then if σ is finer than σ_0 as well as (E_0, CE_0), we have $\Sigma_\sigma M(|f_1 \cdot f_2|, E)\alpha(E) < M_1 \Sigma_\sigma M(|f_2|;\ E) < \infty$. Further if the α-measurable set E is disjoint from E_0, and if f_2 is bounded on E, then

$$\omega(f_1 \cdot f_2;\ E)\alpha(E) \leqq M_1 \omega(f_2;\ E)\alpha(E) + M(|f_2|;\ E)\alpha(E)\omega(f_1;\ E).$$

If then σ is finer than σ_0 as well as (E_0, CE_0), then:

$$\begin{aligned}\sum_\sigma \omega(f_1 \cdot f_2; E)\alpha(E) &\leqq M_1 \sum_\sigma \omega(f_2; E)\alpha(E) + \sum_\sigma M(|f_2|; E)\alpha(E)\omega(f_1; E) \\ &\leqq M_1 \sum_\sigma \omega(f_2;\ E)\alpha(E) + \text{l.u.b.}(\omega(f_1;\ E), E \text{ on } \sigma) \cdot K\end{aligned}$$

where $K = \Sigma_\sigma M(|f_2|;\ E)\alpha(E)$. Now the Lebesgue procedure of subdivisions of the Y-axis yields subdivisions σ into α-measurable sets such that for $e > 0$: $\omega(f;\ E), < e$ for all E of σ. It follows that $\text{g.l.b.}_\sigma [\Sigma_\sigma \omega(f_1 \cdot f_2;\ E)\alpha(E)] = 0$ and $\int_X f_1 \cdot f_2 d\alpha$ exists.

Since for any subdivision $\sigma \geqq (E_0, CE_0)$, where $\alpha(E_0) = \alpha(E[|f_1| > M_1]) = 0$ we have

$$\left|\sum_\sigma f_1(x) f_2(x)\alpha(E)\right| \leqq M_1 \sum_\sigma |f_2(x)|\, \alpha(E),$$

it follows that $|\int_X f_1 \cdot f_2 d\alpha| \leqq M_1 \int_X |f_2|\, d\alpha$, for all M_1 such that $\alpha(E[|f_1| > M_1]) = 0$. Consequently, the same inequality holds if M is the greatest lower bound of M_1 for which $\alpha(E[|f_1| > M_1]) = 0$.

In case we know that f_2 is also α-measurable, then the theorem follows from the fact that $f_1 \cdot f_2$ is also α-measurable and $|f_1(x) f_2(x)| \leqq M_1 |f_2(x)|$ except for an α-null set, $M_1 |f_2|$ being L-integrable, so that $f_1 \cdot f_2$ is also L-integrable.

For L-integrable functions, we note:

8.6. If $f(x)$ is α-measurable; if $f(x) \geqq 0$ for all x except at most an α-null set, and if $\int_X f d\alpha = 0$, then $f(x) = 0$ for all x, except at most an α-null set.

Assume first that $f(x) \geqq 0$ for all x, and let $E_n = E[f > 1/n]$. If $f_n(x) = \chi(E_n;\ x)/n$, then $0 \leqq f_n(x) \leqq f(x)$ for all x, and is α-measurable. Now $0 \leqq \int_X f_n d\alpha \leqq \int_X f d\alpha = 0$, or $\alpha(E_n)/n = 0$, and so $\alpha(E_n) = 0$ for all n. Since $E[f > 0] = \Sigma_n E_n = \Sigma_n E[f > 1/n]$, it follows that $\alpha(E[f > 0]) = 0$, or f vanishes except for an α-null set. In case $f \geqq 0$, except for an α-null set, we let $\bar{f}(x) = f(x)$ if $\bar{f}(x) \geqq 0$ and

$\bar{f}(x) = 0$ if $f(x) \leqq 0$. Then $\int_X \bar{f} d\alpha = \int_X f d\alpha = 0$, so that $\bar{f}$ vanishes except for an α-null set, and the same thing holds for f.

We take up next the interchange of limit and integration and consider first the case when the sequence of functions $f_n(x)$ is uniformly bounded on X.

8.7. If (a) $f_n(x)$ are α-measurable and uniformly bounded on X, so that there exists an M such that $|f_n(x)| \leqq M$ for all n and x, and if (b) $\lim_n f_n(x) = f(x)$ excepting at most an α-null set, then $\lim_n \int_X f_n d\alpha = \int_X f d\alpha$, as a matter of fact $\lim_n \int_X |f_n - f| \, d\alpha = 0$, and $\lim_n \int_E f_n d\alpha = \int_E f d\alpha$ for all α-measurable sets E.

If f_n are α-measurable and uniformly bounded, then f is α-measurable and almost bounded so that f_n and f are L-integrable on X. Then $| \int_X f_n d\alpha - \int_X f d\alpha | \leqq \int_X |f_n - f| \, d\alpha$. If we set $E_{ne} = E[|f_n - f| > e]$, then $\lim_n \alpha(E_{ne}) = 0$ since $\lim_n f_n(x) = f(x)$ except for an α-null set and f_n are α-measurable.

Now

$$\int_X |f_n - f| \, d\alpha = \int_{X-E_{ne}} |f_n - f| \, d\alpha + \int_{E_{ne}} |f_n - f| \, d\alpha$$

$$\leqq e\alpha(X - E_{ne}) + \int_{E_{ne}} |f_n| \, d\alpha + \int_{E_{ne}} |f| \, d\alpha \leqq e\alpha(X) + 2M\alpha(E_{ne}).$$

For a given $e_0 > 0$, we select e so that $e\alpha(X) < e_0/2$, and then n_{e_0} so that for $n \geqq n_{e_0}$ we have $2M\alpha(E_{ne}) < e_0/2$. Then

$$\left| \int_X f_n d\alpha - \int_X f d\alpha \right| \leqq \int_X |f_n - f| \, d\alpha \leqq e_0.$$

This theorem includes the Osgood theorem for monotonic α as a special case (see II.15.6).

If we examine the proof of this theorem, we note in the first place that we have used the convergence of f_n to f only to assure us that $\lim_n \alpha(E_{ne}) = 0$ for all $e > 0$. It then would have been sufficient to assume that $f_n \to f(\alpha)$, or f_n converges to f relative to α. Further the uniform boundedness of the sequence f_n actually leads to the *uniform absolute continuity* condition: $\lim_{\alpha(E) \to 0} \int_E f_n d\alpha = 0$ uniformly in n. This leads to the stronger theorem:

8.8. If (a) $f_n(x)$ and $f(x)$ are α-measurable; if (b) $\int_X f_n d\alpha$ exists for all n; if (b′) $\int_X f d\alpha$ exists; if (c) $f_n \to f(\alpha)$; if (d) $\int_E f_n d\alpha$ are uniformly absolutely continuous relative to α; then $\lim_n \int_X |f_n - f| \, d\alpha = 0$, and so $\lim_n \int_E f_n d\alpha = \int_E f d\alpha$ for all α-measurable sets E.

The proof of 8.7 applies verbatim, if we show that if $\int_E f_n d\alpha$ are uniformly absolutely continuous, the same is true of $\int_E |f_n| d\alpha$. For if $(e > 0, d_e, \alpha(E) < d_e, n) : |\int_E f_n d\alpha| < e$, then if $E = E_n^+ + E_n^-$, where E_n^+ are the points of E for which $f_n \geq 0$, and E_n^- the points of E for which $f_n < 0$, then $\alpha(E_n^+) < d_e$ and $\alpha(E_n^-) < d_e$ and

$$\int_E |f_n| d\alpha = \int_{E_n^+} f_n d\alpha + \left| \int_{E_n^-} f_n d\alpha \right| \leq 2e.$$

The hypothesis of 8.8. can be weakened further by dropping (b′) the assumption that $\int_X f d\alpha$ exist, because we can show:

8.8.1. The conditions (a), (b), (c), and (d) of 8.8. imply the condition (b′) that $\int_X f d\alpha$ exists.

Of the various convergence conditions which together with α-measurability give integrability, we can use VII.2.4. to prove that if $E_M = E[|f| \leq M]$ and if $\int_{E_M} |f| d\alpha$ is bounded in M, then $\int_X f d\alpha$ exists.

We have:

$$\begin{aligned}\int_{E_M} |f| d\alpha &\leq \int_{E_M} |f_n - f| d\alpha + \int_{E_M} |f_n| d\alpha \\ &\leqq \int_{E_M} |f_n - f| d\alpha + \int_X |f_n| d\alpha.\end{aligned}$$

Of the two expressions on the right-hand side of the inequality, the first, by VII.8.8 converges to zero as $n \to \infty$, for each M, since $\int_{E_M} |f| d\alpha$ exists. Consequently, our theorem is proved if we can show that the sequence $\int_X |f_n| d\alpha$ is bounded. Now

$$\int_X |f_n| d\alpha = \int_{E_M} |f_n| d\alpha + \int_{CE_M} |f_n| d\alpha,$$

where E_M is again the set $E[|f| \leqq M]$. Then $\lim_{M \to \infty} \alpha(CE_M) = 0$, since $f(x)$ is assumed to be finite valued. By the uniform absolute continuity of $\int_E f_n d\alpha$ and consequently that of $\int_E |f_n| d\alpha$, for any $k > 0$, we can find $M = M_k$ so that $\int_{CE_M} |f_n| d\alpha \leq k$ for all n. On the other hand, for this M

$$\int_{E_M} |f_n| d\alpha \leqq \int_{E_M} |f_n - f| d\alpha + \int_{E_M} |f| d\alpha.$$

Since the first term on the right-hand side converges to zero, we can for $e > 0$, find n_e such that for $n \geqq n_e$

$$\int_{E_M} |f_n| d\alpha \leqq e + \int_{E_M} |f| d\alpha \leqq e + M\alpha(E_M).$$

Consequently for $n \geqq n_e$: $\int_X |f_n| d\alpha \leqq e + M\alpha(E_M) + k$, where the right-hand side is a constant independent of n. Since there are only a finite number of $n < n_e$, it follows that $\int_X |f_n| d\alpha$ is a bounded sequence.

For the sake of emphasis and completeness we restate the fundamental convergence theorem:

8.8.2. THEOREM. If (a) $f_n(x)$ and $f(x)$ are α-measurable; (b) $\int_X f_n d\alpha$ exists for all n; (c) $f_n \to f(\alpha)$, that is $\lim_n \alpha(E[|f_n - f| > e]) = 0$ for all $e > 0$; and (d) $\int_E f_n d\alpha$ are uniformly absolutely continuous relative to α, then $\int_X f d\alpha$ exists, and $\lim_n \int_X |f_n - f| d\alpha = 0$, so that also $\lim_n \int_E f_n d\alpha = \int_E f d\alpha$ for all α-measurable E.

As a corollary, we have the convergence theorem due to Lebesgue:

8.8.3. If (a) $f_n(x)$ and $f(x)$ are α-measurable; (b) $\lim_n f_n(x) = f(x)$ except at most an α-null set; (c) there exists an L-integrable function $g(x) \geqq 0$ such that $|f_n(x)| \leqq g(x)$ for all n and x, then $\lim_n \int_X f_n d\alpha = \int_X f d\alpha$.

For if $|f_n(x)| \leqq g(x)$ for all n and x, then $\int_X f_n d\alpha$ exists and $\int_E |f_n| d\alpha \leqq \int_E g d\alpha$ for all α-measurable E, so that $\int_E f_n\, d\alpha$ are uniformly absolutely continuous.

For the case when the sequence $f_n(x)$ is monotone in n, we have the following simpler convergence theorem:

8.9. If (a) $f_n(x)$ are α-measurable with $f_n(x) \leqq f_{n+1}(x)$ for all n and x; if (b) $\lim_n f_n(x) = f(x)$ so that f is also α-measurable; and if (c) the sequence $\int_X f_n d\alpha$ is bounded, then $\int_X f d\alpha$ exists and $\lim_n \int_X f_n d\alpha = \int_X f d\alpha$.

It is sufficient to demonstrate this theorem for the case when $f_n(x) \geqq 0$ for all n and x, the general case results by applying the special case to the functions $f_n(x) - f_1(x)$. We show that $\int_{E_M} f d\alpha$ is bounded in M, where $E_M = E[0 \leqq f \leqq M]$. Now $\lim_n \int_{E_M} f_n d\alpha = \int_{E_M} f d\alpha$ since the f_n are uniformly bounded on E_M. Also

$$\int_{E_M} f_n d\alpha \leqq \int_X f_n d\alpha \leqq K,$$

where $K = \text{l.u.b.}_n(\int_X f_n d\alpha)$. Then $\int_{E_M} f d\alpha \leqq K$ for all M, and $\int_X f d\alpha$ exists. Since $f(x) \geqq f_n(x)$ for all n and x, Lebesgue's theorem VII.8.8.3 applies and $\lim_n \int_X f_n d\alpha = \int_X f d\alpha$.

The condition (a) of the hypothesis of this theorem can be replaced by $f_n(x) \leqq f_{n+1}(x)$ for all n, and all x except for an α-null set.

Moreover the monotonic nondecreasing sequence f_n can be replaced by a monotone nonincreasing sequence, whose integrals are bounded below.

As a corollary to this theorem, we have:

8.10. Fatou's Lemma. If $f_n(x)$ are L-integrable on X with respect to α, and such that $\overline{\lim}_n \int_X f_n(x)\,d\alpha > -\infty$, and if there exists an L-integrable function $g(x)$ such that $f_n(x) \leqq g(x)$ for all n and x, then $\overline{\lim}_n \int_X f_n(x) d\alpha(x) \leqq \int_X \overline{\lim}_n f_n(x) d\alpha(x)$.

Let $g_m(x) = \text{l.u.b.}\ [f_n(x)$ for $n \geq m]$. Then the functions $g_m(x)$ are α-measurable and $f_m(x) \leqq g_m(x) \leqq g(x)$ or $0 \leqq g(x) - g_m(x) \leqq g(x) - f_m(x)$ for all m and x. Since $g(x) - f_m(x)$ is L-integrable, $g(x) - g_m(x)$ will also be L-integrable, and so will $g_m(x) = g(x) - (g(x) - g_m(x))$ for all m. Further, $\int_X g_m d\alpha \geqq \int_X f_n d\alpha$ for $n \geqq m$, and consequently

$$\int_X g_m d\alpha \geqq \underset{n \geqq m}{\text{l.u.b.}} \int_X f_n d\alpha \geqq \overline{\lim_n} \int_X f_n d\alpha > -\infty.$$

Since the $g_m(x)$ are monotonic nonincreasing in m, converge to $\overline{\lim}_n f_n(x)$, and the integrals $\int_X g_m(x) d\alpha(x)$ are bounded, it follows from the preceding theorem that $\int_X \lim_m g_m(x) d\alpha(x) = \int_X \overline{\lim}_n f_n(x) d\alpha(x)$ exists and is equal to $\lim_m \int_X g_m(x) d\alpha(x)$. Then

$$\int_X \overline{\lim_n} f_n(x) d\alpha(x) = \int_X \lim_m g_m(x) d\alpha(x)$$
$$= \lim_m \int_X g_m(x) d\alpha(x) \geqq \overline{\lim_n} \int_X f_n(x) d\alpha(x).$$

The lemma has an obvious counterpart involving the least of the limits.

We are now in position to prove that:

8.11. THEOREM. The Y-integral definition and the L-integral definition lead to the same class of integrable functions.

In view of VII.3.9 it is sufficient to prove that if $Y \int_X f d\alpha$ exists, then the function $f(x)$ is α-measurable.

Since the $Y \int_X f d\alpha$ exists the upper and lower integrals $\overline{\int}_X f d\alpha$ and $\underline{\int}_X f d\alpha$ exist, are finite and equal to each other and to $Y \int_X f d\alpha$. We can then determine serially, a sequence of subdivisions σ_k such that $\sigma_{k+1} \geqq \sigma_k$, and

$$\lim_k \sum_{\sigma_k} M(f; E)\alpha(E) = \lim_k \sum_{\sigma_k} m(f; E)\alpha(E) = \int_X f d\alpha.$$

Let E_{kn} be the sets in σ_k with $\alpha(E_{kn}) \neq 0$. Let $g_k(x) = \Sigma_n M(f; E_{kn}) \chi(E_{kn}; x)$ and $h_k(x) = \Sigma_n m(f; E_{kn})\chi(E_{kn}; x)$, each function being zero on $X - \Sigma_n E_{kn}$, an α-null set. Then $g_k(x)$ and $h_k(x)$ are α-measurable, and $g_{k+1}(x) \geqq g_k(x) \geqq f(x) \geqq h_k(x) \geqq h_{k+1}(x)$ for all k and all x except an α-null set. Since the $g_k(x)$ and $h_k(x)$ are step functions which are α-measurable and satisfy the integrability condition for such functions it follows that

$$\sum_n M(f; E_{kn})\alpha(E_{kn}) = \int_X g_k(x)d\alpha(x) \geqq \int_X f(x)d\alpha(x)$$
$$\geqq \int_X h_k(x)d\alpha(x) = \sum_n m(f; E_{kn})\alpha(E_{kn}).$$

Let $\lim_k g_k(x) = g(x)$, and $\lim_k h_k(x) = h(x)$, each except for an α-null set. Then $g(x) \geqq f(x) \geqq h(x)$ except for an α-null set. Moreover, by VII.8.9,

$$\int_X g d\alpha = \lim_k \int_X g_k d\alpha = \int_X f d\alpha = \lim_k \int_X h_k d\alpha = \int_X h d\alpha.$$

Then $\int_X (h(x) - g(x))d\alpha(x) = 0$, with $h(x) - g(x) \geqq 0$, except for an α-null set. Since $h(x)$ and $g(x)$ are α-measurable as the limits of α-measurable functions, it follows from VII.8.6 that $h(x) - g(x) = 0$ except for an α-null set. Now $h(x) \leqq f(x) \leqq g(x)$ except for an α-null set, so that $f(x)$ differs from the α-measurable functions $g(x)$ and $h(x)$ by at most an α-null set, and is therefore also α-measurable. Consequently, $L \int_X f d\alpha = Y \int_X f d\alpha$, the two definitions of integration lead to the same class of integrable functions and are equivalent.

Returning to the basic convergence theorem VII.8.8.2, it is natural to inquire whether the uniform absolute continuity of the integrals $\int_E f_n d\alpha$ is necessary. We have the following theorem of converse type:

8.12. THEOREM. If for the functions $f_n(x)$ and $f(x)$ on X, the integrals $\int_X f_n d\alpha$ and $\int_X f d\alpha$ exist in such a way that for every α-measurable set E we have $\lim_n \int_E f_n d\alpha = \int_E f d\alpha$, then the integrals $\int_E f_n d\alpha$ are uniformly absolutely continuous relative to α.

In the proof of this theorem we use the following lemma which plays a role in the space l^1 of sequences $\{a_n\}$ whose sums are absolutely convergent: $\Sigma_n |a_n| < \infty$.

8.13. Lemma. Suppose a_{mn} and a_n are real numbers such that (a) $\Sigma_n |a_{mn}| < \infty$ for all m, and $\Sigma_n |a_n| < \infty$; and (b) $\lim_m \Sigma_\sigma a_{mn} =$

$\Sigma_\sigma a_n$ for every set σ (finite or infinite) of the integers: $\sigma = n_1, \ldots, n_k, \ldots$; then $\Sigma_n |a_{mn}|$ converges uniformly in m.

Because of the condition (b), it follows that $\lim_m a_{mn} = a_n$ for each n. Also because of the inequality $\Sigma_n |a_{mn}| \leqq \Sigma_n |a_{mn} - a_n| + \Sigma_n |a_n|$ it is sufficient to prove the lemma for the case when $a_n = 0$ for all n.

We proceed by the contrapositive method. We assume that $\lim_m a_{mn} = 0$ for each n, and that $\Sigma_m |a_{mn}|$ are not uniformly convergent in n, and show that there exists a set of integers σ such that $\lim_m \Sigma_\sigma a_{mn} \neq 0$. Then there exists an $e > 0$ such that for every integer k, there exists $n_k > k$, and $m_k > k$ such that $\Sigma_{n=n_k}^\infty ||a_{m_k n}|| > e$. We proceed to establish the existence of a sequence of disjoint finite sets of integers $\sigma_1, \sigma_2, \ldots, \sigma_k, \ldots$ and an increasing sequence of integers m_k such that

$$\Big| \sum_{\sigma_1 + \sigma_2 + \ldots + \sigma_{k-1}} a_{m_k n} \Big| < e/8 \qquad (1)$$

$$\Big| \sum_{\sigma_k} a_{m_k n} \Big| > e/2 \qquad (2)$$

$$\Big| \sum_{n > \sigma_k} |a_{m_k n}| < e/8. \qquad (3)$$

Suppose the finite sets $\sigma_1 \ldots \sigma_{k-1}$ have been determined. Since $\lim_m a_m{}_m = 0$ for each n, inequality (1) will hold for all $m >$ some m_k'. By the nonuniformity condition on $\Sigma_m |a_{mn}|$, we can select $m_k > m_{k-1}$ and m_k' and $n_k >$ all the integers in σ_{k-1} so that $\Sigma_{n=n_k}^\infty |a_{m_k n}| > e$. Then there exists an integer n_k' so that

$$\sum_{n=n_k}^{n_k'} |a_{m_k n}| > e, \quad \text{and} \quad \sum_{n=n_k'}^{\infty} |a_{m_k n}| < e/8.$$

We select σ_k as that subset of the integers between n_k and n_k' for which $a_{m_k n}$ are all of the same sign and such that $|\Sigma_{\sigma_k} a_{m_k n}| > e/2$. It follows that if $\sigma = \Sigma_i \sigma_i$, then

$$\Big| \sum_\sigma a_{m_k n} \Big| = \Big| \sum_i \sum_{\sigma_i} a_{m_k n} \Big| \geqq \Big| \sum_{\sigma_k} a_{m_k n} \Big| - \Big| \sum_{i \neq k} \sum_{\sigma_i} a_{m_k n} \Big| > e/4.$$

Then $\lim_k \Sigma_\sigma a_{m_k n} \neq \Sigma_\sigma a_n = 0$, and so the same holds for $\lim_m \Sigma_\sigma a_{mn}$.

By using the iterated limits theorem I.7.4, we can conclude further that under the hypothesis of the lemma, $\lim_m \Sigma_n |a_{mn} - a_n| = 0$, which in the language of linear spaces says that in l^1, the space of absolutely convergent series, weak convergence implies strong convergence. (See S. Banach, "Theorie des Operations Lineaires," Warsaw, 1932, pp. 137-139). Further, the lemma can be strengthened to read:

8.14. If (a) $\Sigma_n |a_{mn}| < \infty$ for all m, and if (b) $\lim_m \Sigma_\sigma a_{mn}$ exists for every set σ (finite or infinite) of the integers, then $\Sigma_n |a_{mn}|$ converges uniformly in m, $\lim_m a_{mn} = a_n$ is in l^1 $(\Sigma_n |a_n| < \infty)$ and

$$\lim_m \sum_n |a_{mn} - a_n| = 0.$$

For the existence of $\lim_m \Sigma_\sigma a_{mn}$ is equivalent to

$$\lim_{(m_1, m_2) \to (\infty, \infty)} \sum_\sigma (a_{m_1 n} - a_{m_2 n}) = 0.$$

Since the double sequence (m_1, m_2) has sequential character, the proof for the single sequence case can be adapted to show that $\Sigma_n |a_{m_1 n} - a_{m_2 n}|$ converges uniformly in m_1 and m_2, that is $(e > 0, k_e\ k \geq k_e, m_1, m_2): \Sigma_{n=k}^\infty |a_{m_1 n} - a_{m_2 n}| < e$, and consequently

$$\sum_{n=k}^\infty |a_{m_1 n}| \leqq \sum_{n=k}^\infty (|a_{m_2 n}| + |a_{m_1 n} - a_{m_2 n}|) \leqq \sum_{n=k}^\infty |a_{m_2 n}| + e.$$

If we also take $k \geqq k'_e$ so that $\Sigma_{n=k}^\infty |a_{m_2 n}| < e$, then for $k \geqq$ the larger of k_e and k_e' and every m_1: $\Sigma_{n=k}^\infty |a_{m_1 n}| < 2e$, which implies the uniform convergence of $\Sigma_n |a_{mn}|$ in m. The convergence of $\Sigma_n |a_n|$ follows then from the iterated limits theorem I.7.4.

Returning to the proof of our theorem, the assumptions that $\lim_n \int_E f_n d\alpha = \int_E f d\alpha$ for all α-measurable E and the fact that $\int_E f_n d\alpha$ are s-additive functions of E imply that for any sequence $\{E_m\}$ of disjoint α-measurable sets

$$\lim_n \sum_m \int_{E_m} f_n d\alpha = \lim_n \int_{\Sigma_m E_m} f_n d\alpha = \int_{\Sigma_m E_m} f d\alpha = \sum_m \int_{E_m} f d\alpha.$$

Then for any fixed sequence E_m it follows that for any subset σ of the integers m, we have

$$\lim_n \sum_\sigma \int_{E_m} f_n d\alpha = \sum_\sigma \int_{E_m} f d\alpha.$$

Applying the lemma, we conclude that:

8.15. If $\lim_n \int_E f_n d\alpha = \int_E f d\alpha$ for all α-measurable sets E, then for any sequence E_m of disjoint α-measurable sets, the series $\Sigma_m |\int_{E_m} f_n d\alpha|$ converge uniformly as to n.

We complete the proof of our theorem by showing that if $\int_E f_n d\alpha$ are not uniformly absolutely continous with respect to α, then for some sequence of disjoint sets E_m, the series $\Sigma_m \mid \int_{E_m} f_n d\alpha \mid$ do not converge uniformly as to n.

If $\int_E f_n d\alpha$ are not uniformly absolutely continuous, and if for $e > 0$, d_{ne} = l.u.b. of d such that $\alpha(E) < d$ implies $\mid \int_E f_n d\alpha \mid < e$, then for some $e > 0$, g.l.b.$_n d_{ne} = 0$. Consequently, there exists $e > 0$, such that N, d imply the existence of $n_{Nd} > N$, and E_{Nd} with $\alpha(E_{Nd}) < d$ and $\mid \int_{E_{Nd}} f_{n_{Nd}} d\alpha \mid > e$. Take $N = d = 1$, and find n_1 and E_1 so that $\alpha(E_{n_1}) < 1$ and $\mid \int_{E_1} f_{n_1} d\alpha \mid > e$. Let d_1 be such that $\alpha(E) < d_1$ implies $\mid \int_E f_{n_1} d\alpha \mid < e/2$, which is possible since $\int_E f_{n_1} d\alpha$ is absolutely continuous. Select $n_2 > n_1$ and E_2 with $\alpha(E_2) < d_1/2$ so that $\mid \int_{E_2} f_{n_2} d\alpha \mid > e$. Determine $d_2 < d_1/2$ so that $\alpha(E) < d_2$ implies $\mid \int_E f_{n_2} d\alpha \mid < e/2$. At the kth stage we have determined $n_1 < n_2 < \ldots < n_{k-1}$ and $d_1 \ldots d_{k-1}$ with $0 < d_i < d_{i-1}/2$. We then find E_k and n_k such that $\alpha(E_k) < d_{k-1}/2$, $n_k > n_{k-1}$, and $\mid \int_{E_k} f_{n_k} d\alpha \mid > e$. Now the sets E_k are not necessarily disjoint. We therefore set

$$E_k' = E_k - E_k\,(\sum_{m=k+1}^{\infty} E_m) = E_k - E_k''.$$

Then the E_k' are disjoint and

$$\alpha(E_k'') \leqq \alpha(\sum_{m=k+1}^{\infty} E_m) \leqq \sum_{k+1}^{\infty} \alpha(E_m) \leqq \sum_{m=k+1}^{\infty} d_{m-1}/2 < d_k \sum_{m=k+1}^{\infty} 1/2^m = d_k.$$

It follows that

$$\Big| \int_{E_k'} f_{n_k} d\alpha \Big| = \Big| \int_{E_k} f_{n_k} d\alpha - \int_{E_k''} f_{n_k} d\alpha \Big|$$
$$\geqq \Big| \int_{E_k} f_{n_k} d\alpha \Big| - \Big| \int_{E_k''} f_{n_k} d\alpha \Big| > e - \tfrac{1}{2}\, e = \tfrac{1}{2}\, e.$$

Consequently, the series $\Sigma_m \mid \int_{E_m'} f_{n_k} d\alpha \mid$ are not uniformly convergent in k, since for every k: $\mid \int_{E_k'} f_{n_k} d\alpha \mid > e/2$. Then $\Sigma_m \int_{E_m'} f_n d\alpha$ is not uniformly convergent in m either, giving us the contradiction we sought.

Supplementary remarks: We note that the proofs of the lemma and of the theorem depend on the fact that we are dealing with sequences of elements of the space of absolutely convergent series, and sequences of integrable functions, that is they are of sequential character.

Further observe that the statement: there exists $e > 0$ such that N, d imply the existence of $n_N > N$, and E_{Nd} such that $\alpha(E_{Nd}) < d$ and $|\int_{E_{Nd}} f_{n_N} d\alpha| > e$, is the negative of the statement: $(e > 0, n_e, d_e, n \geq n_e, \alpha(E) < d_e): |\int_E f_n d\alpha| \leq e$, or $\lim \int_E f_n d\alpha = 0$, where the limit is the double limit $n \to \infty$, $\alpha(E) \to 0$. We have consequently shown:

8.16. If for all disjoint sequences $\{E_m\}$ of α-measurable sets $\Sigma_m |\int_{E_m} f_n d\alpha|$ are uniformly convergent in n, then

$$\lim_{n,\alpha(E)\to(\infty,0)} \int_E f_n d\alpha = 0.$$

This might have been expected since it follows from considerations in connection with the iterated limits theorem, that if for a directed set Q and a sequence of functions $\{f_n(q)\}$ such that $\lim_n f_n(q)$ exists for all q and $\lim_q f_n(q)$ exists for all n, then the existence of the double limit: $\lim_{n,q} f_n(q)$ implies and is implied by the uniformity of $\lim_q f_n(q)$ in n.

An examination of the proofs shows further that only the properties of $\int_E f d\alpha$ as a function of measurable sets, and not the fact that they are integrals are used. If we use the supplementary statement to the lemma (VII.8.14), it can be verified that the following theorems hold:

8.17. If $\mathfrak{E}$ is an s-ring of sets E of a fundamental set X, if $\beta_n(E)$ are finite valued and s-additive on $\mathfrak{E}$, and such that $\lim_n \beta_n(E)$ exists for all E of $\mathfrak{E}$, then $\Sigma_m |\beta_n(E_m)|$ is uniformly convergent in n for each sequence of disjoint sets E_m in $\mathfrak{E}$. Further $\Sigma_m \beta_n(E_m)$ are also uniformly convergent in n, so that $\beta(E)$ is also s-additive on $\mathfrak{E}$.

8.18. If $\beta_n(E)$ are finite valued and s-additive on the s-ring $\mathfrak{E}$ of sets E of X; if $\lim_n \beta_n(E)$ exists for all E of $\mathfrak{E}$; if $\alpha(E)$ is s-additive and positive or zero on $\mathfrak{E}$; and if $\beta_n(E)$ are absolutely continuous relative to $\alpha(E)$ for each n; then $\beta_n(E)$ are uniformly absolutely continuous relative to α.

For more sophisticated proofs of theorems of this type see S. Saks: On some functionals, *Trans. Am. Math. Soc.* 35 (1933) 549.

9. Directed Limits and L-S Integration

We discuss briefly, the extension of the convergence theorems of the last section, when the sequence of functions $f_n(x)$ on X is replaced by a set of functions $f_q(x)$, q on the directed set Q. An examination of the proof of the basic convergence theorem VII.8.8.2 shows that it can be adapted to prove the following:

9.1. Assume that Q is a directed set of elements q. If (a) the functions $f_q(x)$ and $f(x)$ are α-measurable; if (b) $\int_X f_q d\alpha$ exists for each q; if (c) $f_q \to f(\alpha)$, that is, $\lim_q \alpha(E[|f_q - f| > e]) = 0$ for each $e > 0$; and if (d) the integrals $\int_E f_q d\alpha$ are ultimately uniformly absolutely continuous in the sense that there exists a q_0 such that $\int_E f_q d\alpha$ are uniformly absolutely continuous on the set of q for which qRq_0, then $\int_X f d\alpha$ exists, $\lim_q \int_X |f_q - f| d\alpha = 0$, and so $\lim_q \int_E f_q d\alpha = \int_E f d\alpha$ for all α-measurable subsets E of X.

Note that the ultimate uniform absolute continuity of the integrals $\int_E f_q d\alpha$ implies the same property for $\int_E |f_q| d\alpha$, since

$$\int_E |f_q| d\alpha = \int_{EE_q^+} f_q d\alpha + \left| \int_{EE_q^-} f_q d\alpha \right|,$$

where $E_q^+ = E[f_q \geqq 0]$ and $E_q^- = E[f_q \leqq 0]$. Further, that in the demonstration of the existence of $\int_X f d\alpha$, we can prove and need only the boundedness of $\left| \int_X f_q d\alpha \right|$ in the sense that there exists an M and a q_0 such that if qRq_0, then $\left| \int_X f_q d\alpha \right| \leqq M$.

In addition, a careful examination of the proof of the convergence theorem shows that condition (d) that $\int_E f_q d\alpha$ be ultimately uniformly absolutely continuous can be replaced by (d′): $\lim_{q,\alpha(E)\to 0} \int_E f_q d\alpha = 0$, which in case Q is not the sequence of integers n in their natural order may be weaker than (d).

We also call attention to the fact that in the proof of this theorem, the α-measure convergence of f_q to f, rather than pointwise convergence plays a role. In order to obtain a theorem in which we start with the pointwise convergence of $f_q(x)$ to $f(x)$, we need to add additional conditions so as to secure also the α-measure convergence. We recall that in the case where Q is the sequence of positive integers pointwise convergence implies α-measure convergence. This suggests:

9.2. If Q is a directed set of sequential character (where there exist sequences q_n cofinal with Q); if (a) $f_q(x)$ are α-measurable; if (b) $\lim_q f_q(x) = f(x)$ except for an α-null set; if (c) $\int_X f_q d\alpha$ exists for each q, and if (d) $\int_E f_q d\alpha$ are ultimately uniformly absolutely continuous (or alternatively if $\lim_{q,\alpha(E)\to 0} \int_E f_q d\alpha = 0$); then $\int_X f d\alpha$ exists, $\lim_q \int_X |f_q - f| d\alpha = 0$ and $\lim_q \int_E f_q d\alpha = \int_E f d\alpha$ for all α-measurable E.

For if Q is a directed set of sequential character, and if a_q is on Q to real numbers, then $\lim_q a_q = a$ if and only if for every monotone sequence $(q_n R q_{n-1}$ for all $n)$ cofinal with Q we have $\lim_n a_{q_n} = a$ (see I.5.1). Suppose then that $\{q_n\}$ is a monotone sequence cofinal with Q. Then $\lim_n f_{q_n}(x) = f(x)$ except for an α-null set, so that f is α-measurable. Further the hypotheses for the sequential convergence theorem will hold for $f_{q_n}(x)$ so that $\int_X f d\alpha$ exists, and $\lim_n \int_X |f_{q_n} - f| \, d\alpha = 0$. Since this is true for every monotone sequence q_n cofinal with Q, it follows that $\lim_q \int |f_q - f| \, d\alpha = 0$, and so $\lim_q \int_E f_q d\alpha = \int_E f d\alpha$ for all α-measurable E.

The converse type of theorem in this setting reads:

9.3. If Q is of sequential character and if $\int_X f_q d\alpha$ and $\int_X f d\alpha$ exist in such a way that $\lim_q \int_E f_q d\alpha = \int_E f d\alpha$ for every α-measurable set E, then $\lim_{q,\alpha(E)\to 0} \int_E f_q d\alpha = 0$.

For if q_n is any monotonic sequence cofinal with Q, then by the sequential case where Q is the sequence of positive integers, $\lim_{n,\alpha(E)\to 0} \int_E f_{q_n} \, d\alpha = 0$. Consequently, if $\lim_m \alpha(E_m) = 0$, then $\lim_{m,n} \int_{E_m} f_{q_n} d\alpha = 0$. Now the product set (Q, E) is a directed set of sequential character if we define order by the condition that: $(q_1, E_1)R(q_2, E_2)$ is equivalent to $q_1 R q_2$ and $\alpha(E_1) \leq \alpha(E_2)$. Then $\lim_{q,\alpha(E)\to 0} \int_E f_q d\alpha = 0$. We note that it is not always possible to replace the conclusion by the condition that the integrals $\int_E f_q d\alpha$ be ultimately uniformly absolutely continuous. This indicates that the double limit condition $\lim_{q,\alpha(E)\to 0} \int_E f_q d\alpha = 0$ is the natural one for these convergence theorems.

In the set function setting, the last theorem becomes:

9.4. If Q is a directed set of sequential character; if $\mathfrak{E}$ is an s-ring of subsets of a fundamental set X, if $\beta_q(E)$ are finite valued and s-additive on $\mathfrak{E}$ and such that $\lim_q \beta_q(E) = \beta(E)$ for all E of $\mathfrak{E}$, then $\lim_{q,m} \Sigma_{n=m}^{\infty} \, |\beta_q(E_n)| = 0$ for all sequences E_m of disjoint sets in $\mathfrak{E}$, and $\beta(E)$ is also s-additive on $\mathfrak{E}$. If moreover $\alpha(E)$ is s-additive and positive or zero on $\mathfrak{E}$, and if the $\beta_q(E)$ are absolutely continuous relative to α, then $\lim_{q,\alpha(E)\to 0} \beta_q(E) = 0$.

The conclusion that $\lim_{q,m} \Sigma_{n=m}^{\infty} \, |\beta_q(E_n)| = 0$ follows as above from the case when Q is the integers in their natural order. By applying the iterated limits theorem in its alternative form [if $\lim_q f(p, q)$ exists for all p of P, and if $\lim f(p, q) = g(q)$ for all q of Q in such a way that $\lim_{p,q}(f(p, q) - g(q)) = 0$, then $\lim_p \lim_q f(p, q) = \lim_p \lim_q f(p, q)$] to the expressions $f(m, q) = \Sigma_{n=1}^{m} | \beta_q(E_n) |$ and to $f(m, q) = \Sigma_{n=1}^{m} \beta_q(E_n)$, then we obtain at once that $\Sigma_n | \beta(E_n) |$ converges, and that $\Sigma_1^\infty \beta(E_n) = \beta(\Sigma_1^\infty E_n)$ for each sequence E_n of disjoint set in $\mathfrak{E}$. The last part of the conclusion of the theorem is again a direct consequence of the sequential case.

10. Properties of the Integral $I(f, \alpha, E) = \int_E f d\alpha$ as a Function of α

In this section we shall consider properties of the integral $\int_E f d\alpha$ as α varies on the class of monotonic nondecreasing bounded functions on $X \equiv -\infty < x < +\infty$. We note that the class of α-measurable sets varies with α, which may prove disturbing. However, all α-measurable sets have in common the Borel measurable sets, and these play an important role in the definition of integration. For the present we shall assume that $E = X$, since the results for other permissible sets can be obtained by considering the functions $f_E(x) = f(x)\chi(E; x)$

10.1. If $\alpha(x)$ is monotonic nondecreasing on X, and $c > 0$, and if $\int_X f d\alpha$ exists, then $\int_X f d(c\alpha)$ exists also and is equal to $c \int_X f d\alpha$.

The condition $c > 0$ is introduced so that $c\alpha$ is also monotonic nondecreasing. If we wish to include the case $c < 0$, we may observe that a simple change of sign allows one to go from monotonic nondecreasing to monotonic nonincreasing, and the same kind of theory of integration can be set up for the latter.

10.2. If α_1 and α_2 are monotonic nondecreasing, and such that if $I = [a, b]$ then $\alpha_1(I) = \alpha_1(b) - \alpha_1(a) \geqq \alpha_2(b) - \alpha_2(a) = \alpha_2(I)$ for all I, and if $\int_X f d\alpha_1$ exists, then $\int_X f d\alpha_2$ exists also. If $f \geqq 0$ for all x, then $\int_X f d\alpha_1 \geqq \int_X f d\alpha_2$.

For under the hypothesis of the theorem $\alpha_1{}^*(E) \geqq \alpha_2{}^*(E)$ for all E, so that by V.14.1 if E is measurable relative to α_1 it is also measurable relative to α_2. Consequently, if f is α_1-measurable, it is also α_2-measurable. Moreover, if for a given subdivision σ, we have $\Sigma_\sigma M(|f|; E)\alpha_1(E) < \infty$, then $\Sigma_\sigma M(|f|; E)\alpha_2(E) < \infty$ also. Then if $\int_X f d\alpha_1$ exists so will $\int_X f d\alpha_2$. The inequality between the integrals follows at once by applying limits to the inequalities between the approximating sums.

10.3. If $\alpha_1(x)$ and $\alpha_2(x)$ are monotonic nondecreasing on X and $f(x)$ is such that $\int_X f d\alpha_1$ and $\int_X f d\alpha_2$ exist, then $\int_X f d(\alpha_1 + \alpha_2)$ exists also and is equal to $\int_X f d\alpha_1 + \int_X f d\alpha_2$.

We recall that for the existence of the integral by the Y-integral definition it is necessary and sufficient that the limits involved exist when based on subdivisions into Borel measurable sets in X, such sets being measurable relative to all monotonic α (see VII.3.10). The theorem then follows from the additive property of limits.

There is a sort of converse involving the last two theorems.

10.4. If $\alpha_1(x)$ and $\alpha_2(x)$ are monotonic nondecreasing and $\alpha(x) = \alpha_1(x) + \alpha_2(x)$ and if $\int_X f d\alpha$ exists, then $\int_X f d\alpha_1$ and $\int_X f d\alpha_2$ exist and $\int_X f d\alpha = \int_X f d\alpha_1 + \int_X f d\alpha_2$.

10.4.1. In particular, if $\alpha(x) = \alpha_b(x) + \alpha_c(x)$, where $\alpha_c(x)$ is the continuous part of α, and $\alpha_b(x)$ the function of the breaks, then

$$\int_X f d\alpha = \int_X f d\alpha_b + \int_X f d\alpha_c = \sum_x f(x)(\alpha(x+0) - \alpha(x-0)) + \int_X f d\alpha_c,$$

since $\int_X f d\alpha_b = \Sigma_x f(x)\,(\alpha(x+0) - \alpha(x-0))$ for any function $f(x)$ for which the right-hand side is absolutely convergent.

In connection with the interchange of limit and integration we have:

10.5. If (a) f is bounded on X; (b) $\alpha_n(x)$ and $\alpha(x)$ are monotonic nondecreasing bounded on X, with $\alpha_n(0) = \alpha(0) = 0$ for all n; (c) $\lim_n \alpha_n(B) = \alpha(B)$ for every Borel measurable subset B of X; and if (d) $\int_X f d\alpha_n$ exists for each n, then $\int_X f d\alpha$ exists and $\lim_n \int_X f d\alpha_n = \int_X f d\alpha$.

For by V.14.7 if $\lim_n \alpha_n(B) = \alpha(B)$ for every Borel measurable set B, and if E is measurable relative to all α_n, then E is also measurable relative to α and $\lim_n \alpha_n(E) = \alpha(E)$. If $\int_X f d\alpha_n$ exists then f is measurable relative to each α_n, every set $E[f \leqq y]$ is measurable relative to all α_n, and consequently relative to α, so that f is α-measurable. Since f is bounded on X, it follows that $\int_X f d\alpha$ exists.

Let $\mu_n(y) = \alpha_n(E[f \leqq y])$ and $\mu(y) = \alpha(E[f \leqq y])$. Then $\lim_n \mu_n(y) = \mu(y)$ for all y. Moreover, if $m < f(x) < M$ for x on X, then $\int_X f d\alpha_n = \int_m^M y d\mu_n(y)$ and $\int_X f d\alpha = \int_m^M y d\mu(y)$. From the convergence theorem for Riemann-Stieltjes integrals (II.15.3) it now follows that $\lim_n \int_X f d\alpha_n = \int_X f d\alpha$.

For the case when the sequence $\alpha_n(x)$ is replaced by the set of functions $\alpha_q(x)$ with q on directed Q, we have:

10.6. If (a) $f(x)$ is bounded on X; (b) $\alpha_q(x)$ and $\alpha(x)$ are monotonic nondecreasing bounded on X with $\alpha_q(0) = \alpha(0) = 0$; (c) $\lim_q \alpha_q{}^*(E)$

$= \alpha^*(E)$ for all subsets E of X; and if (d) $\int_X f d\alpha_q$ exists for all q, then $\int_x f d\alpha$ exists and $\lim_q \int_X f d\alpha_q = \int_X f d\alpha$.

For under condition (c) if E is measurable relative to all α_q it will be measurable relative to α. The rest follows as in the case of sequences.

If we assume that the directed set Q has sequential character, then condition (c) can be replaced by $\lim_q \alpha_q(B) = \alpha(B)$ for all Borel measurable sets, and the convergence of $\int_X f d\alpha_q$ follows from the sequential case.

In these theorems the integral over X can be replaced by the integral over any set E which is measurable relative to all α_q.

If the function $f(x)$ is unbounded on X, then the question of the convergence of $\int_X f d\alpha_n$ to $\int_X f d\alpha$ involves an additional iterated limits operation. For if $E_{m,M} = E[m \leqq f \leqq M]$ then

$$\int_X f d\alpha = \lim_{(m,\, M)\to(-\infty,\, +\infty)} \int_{E_{m,\, M}} f d\alpha = \lim_{(m,\, M)} \lim_n \int_{E_{m,\, M}} f d\alpha_n .$$

We let $E_M = E[|f| \leqq M]$. The iterated limits theorem I.7.4 then suggests the following:

10.7. If (a): $\alpha_n(x)$ and $\alpha(x)$ are monotonic nondecreasing bounded with $\alpha_n(0) = \alpha(0) = 0$ and $\lim_n \alpha_n(B) = \alpha(B)$ for every Borel measurable subset B of X; and if (b): $f(x)$ on X is such that the integrals $\int_X f d\alpha_n$ exist uniformly in the sense that $\lim_M \int_{CE_M} |f|\, d\alpha_n = 0$ uniformly in n, then $\int_X f d\alpha$ exists and $\lim_n \int_X f d\alpha_n = \int_X f d\alpha$. Condition (b) can be replaced either by (b′): $\lim_n \int_{E_M} |f|\, d\alpha_n = \int_{E_M} |f|\, d\alpha$ uniformly in M, or (b″): $\lim_{M,n} \int_{CE_M} |f|\, d\alpha_n = 0$.

By the iterated limits theorem, the hypotheses of the theorem are sufficient to guarantee the existence of $\int_X |f|\, d\alpha$ as $\lim_M \int_{E_M} |f|\, d\alpha$. Further the same theorem gives us

$$\int_X f d\alpha = \lim_M \lim_n \int_{E_M} f d\alpha_n = \lim_n \lim_M \int_{E_M} f d\alpha_n = \lim_n \int_X f d\alpha_n .$$

Condition (b) can be deduced from the condition: there exists a subdivision $\sigma_0 \equiv \{E_m\}$ of X such that $\Sigma_{\sigma_0} M(|f|;\, E_m)\alpha_n(E_m)$ converges uniformly in n. The sets E_m are assumed to be measurable relative to all α_n. For then $(e > 0,\, m_e,\, k \geqq m_e,\, n) : \Sigma_{m=k}^{\infty} M(|f|;\, E_m)\alpha_n(E_m) < e$. Let M_0 be the least upper bound of $|f|$ on $\Sigma_{m=1}^{k-1} E_m$, and set $E^k = \Sigma_{m=k}^{\infty} E_m$. Then if $M > M_0$ we have $(CE_M)E^k = CE_M$.

Consequently for $M > M_0$ and for all n:

$$\int_{CE_M} |f|\, d\alpha_n = \int_{(CE_M)E^k} |f|\, d\alpha_n \leqq \sum_{m=k}^{\infty} \int_{E_m} |f|\, d\alpha_n$$
$$\leqq \sum_{m=k}^{\infty} M(|f|; E_m)\alpha_n(E_m) < e.$$

For the case when the sequence $\alpha_n(x)$ is replaced by the set $\alpha_q(x)$ with q on directed Q, the theorem reads:

10.8. If (a) $\alpha_q(x)$ and $\alpha(x)$ are bounded monotonic nonincreasing on X; if (b) there exists a q_0 such that $\lim_q \alpha_q(E) = \alpha(E)$ for all sets E measurable relative to α and all α_q for qRq_0; if (c) $\int_X fd\alpha_q$ exists uniformly in q for qRq_0, in the sense that $\lim_{M\to\infty} \int_{CE_M} |f|\, d\alpha_q = 0$, with $E_M = E[|f| \leqq M]$, then $\int_X fd\alpha$ exists and $\lim_q \int_X fd\alpha_q = \int_X fd\alpha$. The condition (d) can be replaced by either of the following: (d′) $\lim_q \int_{E_M} |f|\, d\alpha_q = \int_{E_M} fd\alpha$ uniformly in M or (d″) $\lim_{(M,q)} \int_{CE_M} fd\alpha_q = 0$.

Condition (d) is a consequence of the assumption: (d‴) there exists a q_0 and a subdivision σ_0 such that for qRq_0, the series $\Sigma_{\sigma_0} M(|f|; E_m)\alpha_q(E_m)$ converges uniformly in q. This latter assumption implies that the integrals $\int_E |f|\, d\alpha_q$ are uniformly absolutely continuous on sets measurable relative to all α_q for qRq_0 in the sense $(e > 0,\ d_e,\ \alpha_q(E) \leqq d_e,\ qRq_0)$: $\int_E |f|\, d\alpha_q < e$. The proof follows the lines we used in VII.7.2 in proving $\int_E fd\alpha$ absolutely continuous relative to α. This type of uniform absolutely continuity does not seem to be sufficient to replace condition (d), since the rate at which $\lim_M \alpha_q(E_M)$ approaches zero would depend on q.

11. Integration with Respect to Functions of Bounded Variation

The additivity of $\int_X fd\alpha$ as a function of α suggests that if for α_1 and α_2 monotonic nondecreasing bounded, on X, the integrals $\int_X fd\alpha_1$ and $\int_X fd\alpha_2$ exist, we define $\int_X fd(\alpha_1 - \alpha_2) = \int_X fd\alpha_1 - \int_X fd\alpha_2$. Since $\alpha_1(x) - \alpha_2(x)$ is at most of bounded variation on X, we are faced with the extension of the integral $\int_X fd\alpha$ to the case when $\alpha(x)$ is of bounded variation on X. $\alpha(x)$ is of bounded variation on X if $\int_{-N}^{+N} \int |d\alpha|$ is bounded in N, or $\Sigma_\sigma |\alpha(x_i) - \alpha(x_{i-1})|$ is bounded in σ for all subdivisions σ of X into a finite or denumerable set of nonoverlapping intervals by the points x_i. If $\alpha(x)$ is of bounded variation on X, then there exist monotonic nondecreasing functions $p(\alpha, x)$ and $n(\alpha, x)$ as well as the total variation function $v(\alpha, x)$ with $p(\alpha, 0) = n(\alpha, 0) = v(\alpha, 0) = 0$, $\alpha(x) = p(\alpha; x) - n(\alpha; x) + \alpha(0)$, $v(\alpha; x) = p(\alpha; x) + n(\alpha; x)$, and $v(\alpha; +\infty) - v(\alpha; -\infty) = \int_{-\infty}^{+\infty} |d\alpha| = v(\alpha; X)$. In the case of Riemann-Stieltjes integrals, with α of bounded variation on $[a, b]$, we found that $\int_a^b f d\alpha$ exists if and only if $\int_a^b f dv(\alpha)$ exists, or if and only if $\int_a^b f dp(\alpha)$ and $\int_a^b f dn(\alpha)$ both exist. (See II.13.4.) This suggests that we define:

11.1. Definition. If $\alpha(x)$ is of bounded variation on X, then $\int_X f d\alpha$ exists if and only if $\int_X f dv(a)$ exists, and then we set

$$\int_X f d\alpha = \int_X f dp(\alpha) - \int_X f dn(\alpha).$$

For if $\int_X f dv(\alpha)$ exists, then f is measurable relative to $v(\alpha)$. Since for any interval $I = [a, b]$, $v(\alpha; I) = v(\alpha; b) - v(\alpha; a) \geqq p(\alpha; b) - p(\alpha, a) = p(\alpha, I)$, and also $v(\alpha; I) \geqq n(\alpha; I)$, it follows that $\int_X f dp(\alpha)$ and $\int_X f dn(\alpha)$ exist also. Since $\alpha(x) = p(\alpha; x) - n(\alpha; x)$, the relation $\int_X f d\alpha = \int_X f dp(\alpha) - \int_X f dn(\alpha)$ is logical.

Suppose for two monotone nondecreasing bounded functions α_1 and α_2 the integrals $\int_X f d\alpha_1$ and $\int_X f d\alpha_2$ exist. Will $\int_X f d(\alpha_1 - \alpha_2)$ exist also and be equal to $\int_X f d\alpha_1 - \int_X f d\alpha_2$? In the first place $\int_X f d\alpha_1 + \int_X f d\alpha_2 = \int_X f d(\alpha_1 + \alpha_2)$ will exist. Moreover, for any $I = [a, b]$: $(\alpha_1 + \alpha_2)(I) = v(\alpha_1 + \alpha_2; I) \geqq v(\alpha_1 - \alpha_2; I)$. Consequently, $\int_X f dv(\alpha_1 - \alpha_2)$ exists. If for the difference of the two monotonic functions $\alpha_1 - \alpha_2$, α_1 and α_2 are not equal to the positive and negative variations $p(\alpha_1 - \alpha_2; x)$ and $n(\alpha_1 - \alpha_2; x)$, respectively, then because of the minimal character of $p(\alpha, x)$ for any function α of bounded variation, there exists a monotone nondecreasing function $\beta(x)$ such that $\alpha_1(x) = p(\alpha_1 - \alpha_2; x) + \beta(x)$ and $\alpha_2(x) = n(\alpha_1 - \alpha_2; x) + \beta(x)$. Since $\int_X f d\alpha_1$ exists, it follows that $\int_X f d\beta$ exists and $\int_X f d\alpha_1 = \int_X f dp(\alpha_1 - \alpha_2) + \int_X f d\beta$, $\int_X f d\alpha_2 = \int_X f dn(\alpha_1 - \alpha_2) + \int_X f d\beta$. Consequently $\int_X f d(\alpha_1 - \alpha_2) = \int_X f dp(\alpha_1 - \alpha_2) - \int_X f dn(\alpha_1 - \alpha_2) = \int_X f d\alpha_1 - \int_X f d\alpha_2$. We can then assert:

11.2. If α_1 and α_2 are bounded, monotonic nondecreasing on X, and f on X is such that $\int_X f d\alpha_1$ and $\int_X f d\alpha_2$ exist, then $\int_X f d(\alpha_1 - \alpha_2)$ exists and is equal to $\int_X f d\alpha_1 - \int_X f d\alpha_2$.

If E is any $v(\alpha)$-measurable set, and $\int_X f d\alpha$ exists, then $\int_E f d\alpha = \int_E f dp(\alpha) - \int_E f dn(\alpha)$. Since $\int_E f dp(\alpha)$ and $\int_E f dn(\alpha)$ are s-additive on $v(\alpha)$-measurable sets, it follows that $\int_E f d\alpha$ is also s-additive on $v(\alpha)$-measurable sets. In particular if $f(x) \equiv 1$, we can define $\alpha(E) = \int_E d\alpha = \int_E dp(\alpha) - \int_E dn(\alpha) = p(\alpha;\ E) - n(\alpha;\ E)$, and $\alpha(E)$ will be s-additive on the class of $v(\alpha)$-measurable sets.

If E consists of the point x, then

$$\alpha(E) = p(\alpha; E) - n(\alpha; E) = p(x+0) - p(x-0) - (n(x+0) - n(x-0)) = p(x+0) - n(x+0)) - (p(x-0) - n(x-0)) = \alpha(x+0) - \alpha(x-0).$$

It follows that if E consists of the set of discontinuities of α, and $\int_X fd\alpha$ exists then $\int_E fd\alpha = \Sigma_x f(x)\ (\alpha(x+0) - \alpha(x-0))$, where the series converges absolutely. If we decompose $\alpha(x) = \alpha_b(x) + \alpha_c(x)$, where $\alpha_c(x)$ is the continuous part of α and $\alpha_b(x)$ is the function of the breaks, then by decomposing $\alpha_b(x)$ and $\alpha_c(x)$ into their positive and negative variations, it turns out that

$$\int_X fd\alpha = \sum_x f(x)\ (\alpha(x+0) - \alpha(x-0)) + \int_X fd\alpha_c(x).$$

Now the term $\Sigma_x f(x)\ (\alpha(x+0) - \alpha(x-0))$ is entirely independent of the value of $\alpha(x)$ at the points of discontinuity of α, and the same holds true of $\alpha(E)$. However the monotonic point functions $v(\alpha;\ x)$, $p(\alpha;\ x)$ and $n(\alpha;\ x)$ may change with $\alpha(x)$, and the existence of the integrals depends to some extent on the absolute convergence of $\Sigma_x f(x)\ (v(\alpha;\ x+0) - v(\alpha;\ x-0))$. If $\alpha(x)$ lies between $\alpha(x+0)$ and $\alpha(x-0)$, then $v(\alpha;\ x+0) - v(\alpha;\ x-0) = |\alpha(x+0) - \alpha(x-0)|$, but if $\alpha(x)$ is exterior to $(\alpha(x-0),\ \alpha(x+0))$, then $v(\alpha;\ x+0) - v(\alpha;\ x-0) = |\alpha(x+0) - \alpha(x)| + |\alpha(x) - \alpha(x-0)| > |\alpha(x+0) - \alpha(x-0)|$. Consequently,

$$\sum_x f(x)\ (\alpha(x+0) - \alpha(x-0)) + \int_X fd\alpha_c$$

may be finite but $\int_X fd\alpha$ as we have defined it may not exist.

In view of these considerations, it seems sensible either to limit the functions of bounded variation $\alpha(x)$ considered to those which satisfy the regularity condition that $\alpha(x)$ lies between $\alpha(x+0)$ and $\alpha(x-0)$ or $(\alpha(x+0) - \alpha(x))\ (\alpha(x) - \alpha(x-0)) \geq 0$ for all x, or to determine integrability conditions by a variation function associated with a regularizing equivalent of $\alpha(x)$, for instance by the function $\alpha_1(x) = \alpha(x+0)$ for all x, which is right continuous in x and agrees with $\alpha(x)$, where $\alpha(x)$ is continuous. We select the former of these alternatives and define:

11.3. Definition. The function $\alpha(x)$ of bounded variation on X is *regular* if for all x of X, $\alpha(x)$ lies between $\alpha(x+0)$ and $\alpha(x-0)$, or $(\alpha(x+0)-\alpha(x))\,(\alpha(x)-\alpha(x-0))\geq 0$.

We then have the following:

11.4. THEOREM. If $\alpha(x)$ is a regular function of bounded variation on X, then $v(\alpha;\ X) = \text{l.u.b.}\ [\Sigma_\sigma \,|\, \alpha(E_m)\,|$ for all subdivisions $\sigma = \{E_m\}$ of X into $v(\alpha)$-measurable sets].

For

$$\sum_m |\,\alpha(E_m)\,| = \sum_m |\,p(\alpha;\ E_m) - n(\alpha;\ E_m)\,|$$
$$\leq \sum_m (p(\alpha;\ E_m) + n(\alpha;\ E_m)) = v(\alpha;\ X).$$

On the other hand, suppose for $e > 0$, σ is a subdivision of X into nonoverlapping intervals by the points x_i, i ranging over the negative and positive integers, such that $v(\alpha;\ X) \leq \Sigma_i\,|\,\alpha(x_i) - \alpha(x_{i-1})\,| + e$. Then

$$\sum_i |\,\alpha(x_i) - \alpha(x_{i-1})\,| \leq \sum_i (|\,\alpha(x_i) - \alpha(x_i - 0)\,|$$
$$+ |\,\alpha(x_i - 0) - \alpha(x_{i-1} + 0)\,| + |\,\alpha(x_{i-1}+0) - \alpha(x_{i-1})\,|)$$
$$= \sum_i (|\,\alpha(x_i+0) - \alpha(x_i - 0)\,| + |\,\alpha(x_i - 0) - \alpha(x_{i-1}+0)\,|),$$

since $\alpha(x)$ is regular. Now the subdivision of X consisting of the points x_i and the open intervals (x_{i-1}, x_i) is a subdivision of X into $v(\alpha)$-measurable sets and for an open interval we have $\alpha(a, b) = \alpha(b-0) - \alpha(a+0)$. Then for $e > 0$, there exists a σ of X into $v(\alpha)$-measurable sets such that $v(\alpha;\ X) \leq \Sigma_i\,|\,\alpha(E_i)\,| + e$. As a consequence $v(\alpha;\ X) = \text{l.u.b.}_\sigma\, \Sigma_\sigma\,|\,\alpha(E)\,|$.

Because of the s-additive property of $\alpha(E)$, the sums $\Sigma_\sigma\,|\,\alpha(E)\,|$ are monotonic nondecreasing in σ, so that we have $v(\alpha;\ X) = \text{l.u.b.}_\sigma \Sigma_\sigma\,|\,\alpha(E)\,| = \lim_\sigma \Sigma_\sigma\,|\,\alpha(E)\,|$. In other words, the total variation $v(\alpha;\ X)$ is of the nature of an integral of the set function $|\,\alpha(E)\,|$ and could be written $\int_X |\,d\alpha(E)\,|$.

If E_0 is any $v(\alpha)$-measurable set, then

$$v(\alpha,\ E_0) + v(\alpha;\ CE_0) = v(\alpha;\ X) = \lim_\sigma \sum_\sigma |\,\alpha(E)\,|$$

$$= \lim_\sigma \Big(\sum_{\sigma\cdot E_0} |\,\alpha(E)\,| + \sum_{\sigma\cdot CE_0} |\,\alpha(E)\,|\Big) = \lim_\sigma \sum_{\sigma\cdot E_0} |\,\alpha(E)\,| + \lim_\sigma \sum_{\sigma\cdot CE_0} |\,\alpha(E)\,|$$

since the two terms on the right are monotone and bounded in σ, so that the limits exist. Now $v(\alpha,\ E') \geqq \Sigma_{\sigma\cdot E'}|\,\alpha(E)\,|$ for all $v(\alpha)$-measurable E' and all σ. Consequently:

11.5. If E_0 is a $v(\alpha)$-measurable set and $\alpha(x)$ is regular, then:

$$v(\alpha; E_0) = \lim_{\sigma} \sum_{\sigma \cdot E_0} |\alpha(E)| = \text{l.u.b.}_{\sigma} [\sum_{\sigma} |\alpha(E)|$$

for all subdivisions σ of E_0 into $v(\alpha)$-measurable sets].

In analogy to the Jordan procedure for defining the total variation of a function on an interval, it is possible to define for $\alpha(x)$ regular, $p(\alpha; X)$ and $n(\alpha; X)$ by least upper bounds and as limits as to subdivisions. This leads incidentally to additional information on the functions $p(\alpha; E)$ and $n(\alpha; E)$. For convenience we shall omit the α in $v(\alpha:E)$, $p(\alpha; E)$, and $n(\alpha; E)$, and assume that $v(E)$, $p(E)$, and $n(E)$ have been determined by a regular function of bounded variation $\alpha(x)$.

Let σ be any subdivision of X into $v(\alpha)$-measurable sets, and let $E_n{}'$ be the sets in σ, for which $\alpha(E_n{}') \geqq 0$ and $E_n{}''$ those for which $\alpha(E_n{}'') < 0$. Define $p_\sigma(X) = \Sigma_\sigma \alpha(E_n{}') = \alpha(\Sigma_\sigma E_n{}')$, and $n_\sigma(X) = -\Sigma_\sigma \alpha(E_n{}'') = -\alpha(\Sigma_\sigma E_n{}'')$. Then for all σ, we have $v(X) \geqq p_\sigma(X) + n_\sigma(X)$ and $\alpha(X) = p_\sigma(X) - n_\sigma(X)$. Let $E_\sigma^+ = \Sigma_\sigma E_n{}'$, and $E_\sigma^- - \Sigma_\sigma E_n{}'' = X - E_\sigma^+$. We show that if $\sigma_1 \geqq \sigma$, then

$$\alpha(E_\sigma^+) \leqq \alpha(E_\sigma^+ E_{\sigma_1}^+) \leqq \alpha(E_{\sigma_1}^+).$$

For if E is any α-measurable set, such that $\alpha(E) \geqq 0$, and we apply a subdivision $\sigma = \{E_m\}$ to E yielding $\{EE_m{}'\}$ and $\{EE_m{}''\}$, with $\alpha(EE_m{}') \geqq 0$, and $\alpha(EE_m{}'') < 0$, then $\alpha(E) = \alpha(\Sigma_m EE_m{}') + \alpha(\Sigma_m EE_m{}'')$. But $\alpha(\Sigma_m EE_m{}'') < 0$, so that $\alpha(E) \leqq \alpha(E\Sigma_m E_m{}')$. Applying this to every subset $E_n{}'$ in E_σ^+ yields: if $\sigma_1 \geqq \sigma$, then $\alpha(E_\sigma^+) \leqq \alpha(E_\sigma^+ \cdot E_{\sigma_1}^+)$. Now $E_{\sigma_1}^+$ will also contain sets which are subsets of E_σ^-. Consequently, $\alpha(E_\sigma^+ E_{\sigma_1}^+) \leqq \alpha(E_{\sigma_1}^+)$.

We conclude then than $p_\sigma(X)$ and $n_\sigma(X)$ are monotonic nondecreasing in σ, and since they are bounded by $v(\alpha; X)$, that $\lim_\sigma p_\sigma(X)$ and $\lim_\sigma n_\sigma(X)$ exist. Since for all σ: $\alpha(X) = p_\sigma(X) - n_\sigma(X)$, it follows that $\alpha(X) = \lim_\sigma p_\sigma(X) - \lim_\sigma n_\sigma(X)$ and $v(X) = \lim_\sigma p_\sigma(X) + \lim_\sigma n_\sigma(X)$. Consequently, $\lim_\sigma p_\sigma(X) = p(X)$ and $\lim_\sigma n_\sigma(X) = n(X)$.

We can conclude more. Because of the monotonic character of $p_\sigma(X) = \alpha(E_\sigma^+)$, there exists an increasing sequence of subdivisions σ_m with $o_m \geqq \sigma_{m-1}$ such that $p(X) = \lim_m p_{\sigma_m}(X) = \lim_m \alpha(E_{\sigma_m}^+)$. We show:

If $X^+ = \underline{\lim}_m E_{\sigma_m}^+$, then

$$p(X) = \alpha(X^+), \quad \text{and} \quad n(X) = -\alpha(X - X^+) = -\alpha(X^-).$$

For the inequality $\alpha(E_\sigma^+) \leqq (E_\sigma^+ E_{\sigma_1}^+) \leqq \alpha(E_{\sigma_1}^+)$ can be at once extended to any finite number of subdivisions $\sigma_1 \leqq \sigma_2 \leqq \dots \leqq \sigma_k$, to read

$$\alpha(E_{\sigma_1}^+) \leqq \alpha(\prod_{i=1}^{k} E_{\sigma_1}^+) \leqq \alpha(E_{\sigma_k}^+).$$

For instance:

$$\alpha(E_{\sigma_1}^+) \leqq \alpha(E_{\sigma_1}^+ \cdot E_{\sigma_2}^+) \leqq \alpha(E_{\sigma_1}^+ \cdot E_{\sigma_2}^+ \cdot E_{\sigma_3}^+) \leqq \alpha(E_{\sigma_2}^+ \cdot E_{\sigma_3}^+) \leqq \alpha(E_{\sigma_3}^+).$$

Now

$$\underline{\lim}_m E_{\sigma_m}^+ = \sum_{k=1}^{\infty} \prod_{m=k}^{\infty} E_{\sigma_m}^+ = \lim_k (\lim_i \prod_{m=k}^{i} E_{\sigma_m}^+).$$

Since α is the difference between two bounded s-additive set functions on $v(\alpha)$-measurable sets, it follows that

$$\lim_i \alpha(\prod_{m=k}^{i} E_{\sigma_m}^+) = \alpha(\prod_{m=k}^{\infty} E_{\sigma_m}^+).$$

Since

$$\alpha(E_{\sigma_k}^+) \leqq \alpha(\prod_{m=k}^{i} E_{\sigma_m}^+) \leqq \alpha(E_{\sigma_i}) \leqq p(X),$$

we have for all k:

$$\alpha(E_{\sigma_k}^+) \leqq \alpha(\prod_{m=k}^{\infty} E_{\sigma_m}^+) \leqq p(X).$$

But $\lim_k \alpha(E_{\sigma_k}^+) = p(X)$, and since α is s-additive

$$\lim_k \alpha(\prod_{m=k}^{\infty} E_{\sigma_m}^+) = \alpha(\lim_k \prod_{m=k}^{\infty} E_{\sigma_m}^+) = \alpha(\underline{\lim}_m E_{\sigma_m}^+).$$

Consequently $\alpha(X^+) = \alpha(\underline{\lim}_m E_{\sigma_m}^+) = p(X)$. Since $\alpha(X) = \alpha(X^+) + \alpha(X - X^+) = p(X) - n(X)$, and $p(X) = \alpha(X^+)$ it follows that $n(X) = n(X - X^+) = -\alpha(X^-)$. Further, since $p(X) = \alpha(X^+) = p(X^+) - n(X^+), p(X) \geqq p(X^+)$, and $n(X^+) \geqq 0$, it follows that $n(X^+) = 0$, and consequently $n(E) = 0$ for all $v(\alpha)$-measurable sets $E \leqq X^+$. Similarly $p(X^-) = 0$, and $p(E) = 0$ for all $v(\alpha)$-measurable sets $E \leqq X^-$.

If now E is any $v(\alpha)$-measurable set, then

$$p(E) - n(E) = \alpha(E) = \alpha(EX^+) + \alpha(EX^-) = p(EX^+) - n(EX^-),$$

since $n(EX^+) = p(EX^-) = 0$. Then

$$p(E) = p(EX^+) = \alpha(EX^+) = v(EX^+)$$

and

$$n(E) = n(EX^-) = -\alpha(EX^-) = -v(EX^-)$$

for all $v(\alpha)$-measurable sets E. Summing up we have shown:

11.6. THEOREM. If $\alpha(x)$ is of bounded variation on X and regular in the sense that $(\alpha(x+0)-\alpha(x))\,(\alpha(x)-\alpha(x-0)) \geqq 0$ for all x, then there exist disjoint $v(\alpha)$-measurable sets X^+ and X^-, such that $X = X^+ + X^-$,

$$p(X) = p(X^+) = \alpha(X^+) = v(X^+);\ p(X^-) = 0;$$

and

$$n(X) = n(X^-) = -\alpha(X^-) = -v(X^-);\ n(X^+) = 0.$$

For all $v(\alpha)$-measurable sets E, the sets $E^+ = EX^+$ and $E^- = EX^-$, effect the same decomposition for E.

An immediate consequence of this theorem is:

11.7. If $\alpha(x)$ is of bounded variation on X and regular, then for all $v(\alpha)$-measurable sets E, we have $p(E) =$ l.u.b. $[\alpha(E_1)$ for all $v(\alpha)$-measurable $E_1 \leqq E]$, and $n(E) = -$ g.l.b. $[\alpha(E_1)$ for all $v(\alpha)$-measurable sets $E_1 \leqq E]$.

For if $E_1 \leqq E$, and $v(\alpha)$-measurable, then $\alpha(E_1) = p(E_1X^+) - n(E_1X^-) = p(E_1X^+) \leqq p(E)$. The least upper bound is attained for $E_1 = EX^+$. Similarly for $n(E)$.

We are now in position to prove:

11.8. If $\alpha(x)$ is of bounded variation on X and regular in the sense that $(\alpha(x+0)-\alpha(x))\,(\alpha(x)-\alpha(x-0)) \geqq 0$ for all x, then $\int_X f d\alpha$ exists if and only if: (a) there exists a subdivision σ_0 of X into $v(\alpha)$-measurable sets, such that for $\sigma \geqq \sigma_0$, $\Sigma_\sigma f(x)\alpha(E)$ is absolutely convergent for all choices of x in the sets E of σ, and (b) $\lim_\sigma \Sigma_\sigma f(x)\cdot \alpha(E)$ exists, $\int_X f d\alpha$ being this limit.

The necessity part of the theorem follows at once from the definition of $\int_X f d\alpha = \int_X f dp(\alpha) - \int_X f dn(\alpha)$, and the Y-definition of integral for the case when α is monotone bounded.

To show that the conditions are also sufficient, suppose that $\Sigma_\sigma f(x)\alpha(E)$ converges absolutely for $\sigma \geqq \sigma_0$. Let $\sigma_0 = \{E_m\}$ and set $\sigma_1 = \sigma_0 \cdot [X^+, X^-]$, where X^+, X^-, is the decomposition of X induced by α, in accordance with VII.11.6 above. Then $\alpha(E_mX^+) = v(\alpha;\ E_mX^+)$ and $\alpha(E_mX^-) = -v(\alpha;\ E_mX^-)$ and

$$\sum_{\sigma_1} f(x)\alpha(E) = \sum_m (f(x')v(\alpha;\ E_mX^+) - f(x_m'')v(\alpha;\ E_mX^-)).$$

This latter series is absolutely convergent, so that $\Sigma\,|f(x)|\,v(\alpha; E) < \infty$ for all $\sigma \geqq \sigma_1$. If next we assume that $\lim_\sigma \Sigma_\sigma f(x)\alpha(E)$ exists, then there exists a subdivision σ_0' such that for $\sigma \geqq \sigma_0'$: $\Sigma_\sigma f(x_m)\alpha(E_m)$ is absolutely convergent and bounded for all choices of x_m on E_m. By taking $\sigma_1' = \sigma_0' \cdot (X^+, X^-)$, we find that $f(x)$ is bounded on any set E of σ_1' for which $v(\alpha; E) \neq 0$, and $\Sigma_\sigma M(|f|; E)\ v(\alpha; E) < \infty$ for any $\sigma \geqq \sigma_1'$. Moreover, for the same σ:

$$\sum_\sigma \omega(f; E_m) \mid \alpha(E_m) \mid \leqq \text{l.u.b.} \left| \sum_\sigma f(x_m')\alpha(E_m) - \sum_\sigma f(x_m'')\alpha(E_m) \right|$$

where x_m' and x_m'' are any two points of E_m. Then the Cauchy condition of convergence gives us that $\lim_\sigma \Sigma_\sigma \omega(f, E) \mid \alpha(E) \mid = 0$. But any set of a $\sigma \geqq \sigma_1'$, is either a subset of X^+ for which $\alpha(E) = v(\alpha; E)$ or of X^- for which $\alpha(E) = -\ v(\alpha; E)$, and so $\mid \alpha(E_m) \mid = v(\alpha; E_m)$ for all m, and $\lim_\sigma \Sigma_\sigma \omega(f; E_m) v(\alpha; E_m) = 0$. But by VII.3.4.1 this is sufficient to gives us the existence of $\int_X f dv(\alpha)$ and consequently that of $\int_X f d\alpha$. As pointed out in the proof of the necessity part of the theorem, we then have $\lim_\sigma \Sigma_\sigma f(x)\alpha(E) = \int_X f d\alpha$.

The properties of $\int_X f d\alpha$ when α is of bounded variation and regular are similar to those for the case when $\alpha(x)$ is monotonic nondecreasing bounded on X, and can frequently be deduced from this special case. We consider briefly a few of these properties.

11.9. If $\int_X f d\alpha$ exists and E is $v(\alpha)$-measurable, then $\int_E f d\alpha$ exists as the difference of $\int_E f dp(\alpha)$ and $\int_E f dn(\alpha)$. If we set $\beta(E) = \int_E f d\alpha$ then $\beta(E)$ is absolutely continuous with respect to $v(\alpha)$, $\beta(E)$ is s-additive on the class of $v(\alpha)$-measurable sets, and is of bounded variation in the sense that $\Sigma_\sigma \mid \beta(E) \mid$ is bounded in σ, the class of subdivisions of X into $v(\alpha)$-measurable sets. Moreover, $v(\beta; X) = \int_X |f|\, dv(\alpha)$.

The first part of this theorem is obvious. For the last part, suppose that E is any $v(\alpha)$-measurable set. Then

$$\begin{aligned} \mid \beta(E)) \mid &\leqq \left| \int_E f dp(\alpha) \right| + \left| \int_E f dn(\alpha) \right| \\ &\leqq \int_E |f|\, dp(\alpha) + \int_E |f|\, dn(\alpha) = \int_E |f|\, dv(\alpha), \end{aligned}$$

and consequently $v(\beta; X) \leqq \int_X |f|\, dv(\alpha)$. On the other hand, let $E' = E[f > 0]$, $E'' = E[f \leqq 0]$, X^+ and X^- be the decomposition of X into sets such that $p(\alpha; X) = \alpha(X^+) = v(\alpha; X^+)$ and $n(\alpha; X) = -\alpha(X^-) = -\ v(\alpha; X^-)$. Then

$$\begin{aligned} \int_X |f|\, dv(\alpha) &= \int_{E'X^+} f dv(\alpha) + \int_{E'X^-} f dv(\alpha) - \int_{E''X^+} f dv(\alpha) \\ - \int_{E''X^-} f dv(\alpha) &= \int_{E'X^+} f d\alpha - \int_{E'X^-} f d\alpha - \int_{E''X^+} f d\alpha + \int_{E''X^-} f d\alpha. \end{aligned}$$

If we set $\sigma = (E'X^+, E'E^-, E''X^+, E''X^-)$, then $\Sigma_\sigma |\beta(E)| = \int_X |f| \cdot dv(\alpha)$. Consequently $v(\beta; X) = \int_X |f| \, dv(\alpha)$.

We have incidentally obtained for $\beta(E)$ a decomposition of X similar to that for $\alpha(E)$, namely: $X^+(\beta) = E[f > 0] \cdot X^+(\alpha) + E[f \leqq 0] \cdot X^-(\alpha)$, and $X^-(\beta) = E[f > 0] \cdot X^-(\alpha) + E[f \leqq 0] \cdot X^-(\alpha)$. Further

$$p(\beta, X) = \int_{E'X^+} fd\alpha + \int_{E''X^-} fd\alpha$$

and

$$n(\beta; X) = -\int_{E'X^-} fd\alpha - \int_{E''X^+} fd\alpha,$$

from which the values of $p(\beta; E)$ and $n(\beta; E)$ for any $v(\alpha)$-measurable set can be written down at once.

If we observe that for any $v(\alpha)$ measurable set E_0 it is true that

$$|\beta(E_0) - f(x)\alpha(E_0)| = \left| \int_{E_0} fd\alpha - f(x)\alpha(E_0) \right| \leqq \omega(f; E_0)v(\alpha; E_0)$$

provided x is on E_0 and f is bounded on E_0, then the s-additivity of $\beta(E)$ gives us at once the

11.10. Approximation Theorem. If $\alpha(x)$ is a regular function of bounded variation on X and $\int_X fd\alpha$ exists, then for every subdivision σ into $v(\alpha)$-measurable sets on each of which f is bounded, we have

$$\left| \int_X fd\alpha - \sum_\sigma f(x)\alpha(E) \right| \leqq \sum_\sigma \omega(f; E)v(\alpha; E).$$

The following linearity properties are deducible from the definitions:

11.11. If $\alpha(x)$ is of bounded variation on X and $\int_X f_1 d\alpha$ and $\int_X f_2 d\alpha$ exist, then for c_1 and c_2 any two constants, we have the existence of $\int_X (c_1 f_1 + c_2 f_2) d\alpha = c_1 \int_X f_1 d\alpha + c_2 \int_X f d\alpha_2$.

11.12. If $\alpha_1(x)$ and $\alpha_2(x)$ are of bounded variation on X, and if for $f(x)$ on X, the integrals $\int_X fd\alpha_1$ and $\int_X fd\alpha_2$ exist, then for any two constants c_1 and c_2, we have the existence of $\int_X fd(c_1\alpha_1 + c_2\alpha_2)$ equal to $c_1 \int_X fd\alpha_1 + c_2 \int_X fd\alpha_2$.

To apply VII.11.8, some regularity condition on α_1 and α_2 would be needed. However, from the definition in VII.11.1, it follows that if $\int_X fd\alpha$ exists, and c is any constant, then $\int_X fd(c\alpha)$ exists with value $c \int_X fd\alpha$. Further if $\int_X fd\alpha_1$ and $\int_X fd\alpha_2$ exist, then since $v(\alpha_1 + \alpha_2; X)$

$\leq v(\alpha_1; X) + v(\alpha_2; X)$ it follows that $\int_X f dv(\alpha_1 + \alpha_2)$ exists and so $\int_X f d(\alpha_1 + \alpha_2)$ exists also. If we decompose $\alpha_1(x) = p_1(x) - n_1(x)$ and $\alpha_2(x) = p_2(x) - n_2(x)$ into their positive and negative parts, and apply VII.11.2 to $\alpha_1(x) + \alpha_2(x) = (p_1(x) + p_2(x)) - (n_1(x) + n_2(x))$, then we find that $\int_X f d(\alpha_1 + \alpha_2)$ exists with value $\int_X f d\alpha_1 + \int_X f d\alpha_2$. The conclusion of the theorem is then immediate.

We observe that $\int_X f d\alpha$ exists for any bounded Borel measurable function f on X relative to any function α of bounded variation on X, since such a function is $v(\alpha)$-measurable for any such α. If (BB) is the class of bounded Borel measurable functions, and (BV) that of functions of bounded variation on X, then by the last two theorems, the integral $\int_X f d\alpha$ is a bilinear functional on the product class $(BB) \times (BV)$.

11.13. If α is of bounded variation on X and f is such that $\int_X f d\alpha$ exists then f is absolutely integrable in the sense that $\int_X |f| dv(\alpha)$ exists. If f is $v(\alpha)$-measurable on X, and such that there exists a function $g(x) \geq 0$ such that for all x of X except at most a $v(\alpha)$-null set: $|f(x)| \leq g(x)$, and $\int_X g dv(\alpha)$ exists, then $\int_X f d\alpha$ exists and $|\int_X f d\alpha| \leq \int_X g dv(\alpha)$.

In the matter of interchange of integration and limits, we have:

11.14. If (a) $\alpha(x)$ is a regular function of bounded variation on X; (b) f_n and f are $v(\alpha)$-measurable on X and such that $f_n \to f(v(\alpha))$; and (c) $\int_E f_n d\alpha$ are uniformly absolutely continuous relative to $v(\alpha)$; then $\int_X f d\alpha$ exists and $\lim_n \int_X |f_n - f| dv(\alpha) = 0$, so that $\lim_n \int_E f_n d\alpha = \int_E f d\alpha$ for all $v(\alpha)$-measurable sets E.

We use the decomposition of X into the sets X^+ and X^- such that $p(X) = \alpha(X^+)$ and $n(X) = -\alpha(X^-)$. Since on subsets of X^+, we have $v(\alpha; E) = \alpha(E)$ and on subsets of X^-, we have $v(\alpha; E) = -\alpha(E)$, then for any $v(\alpha)$-measurable set E

$$\int_E f_n dv(\alpha) = \int_{EX^+} f_n dv(\alpha) + \int_{EX^-} f_n dv(\alpha) = \int_{EX^+} f_n d\alpha - \int_{EX^-} f_n d\alpha.$$

As a consequence the integrals $\int_E f_n dv(\alpha)$ are absolutely continuous relative to $v(\alpha)$ uniformly in n. The theorem then follows from the corresponding theorem for monotonic bounded α. (See VII.8.8.2.)

For a set of functions $f_q(x)$ on a directed set Q, a corresponding theorem holds. For instance:

11.15. If α is a regular function of bounded variation on X; if $f_q(x)$ and $f(x)$ are $v(\alpha)$-measurable on X; if $f_q \to f(v(\alpha))$; and if

$$\lim_{q, v(\alpha;\, E)\to 0} \int_E f_q d\alpha = 0,$$

then $\int_X fd\alpha$ exists, and $\lim_q \int_X |f_q - f| \, dv(\alpha) = 0$, so that $\lim_q \int_E f_q d\alpha = \int_E fd\alpha$ for all $v(\alpha)$ measurable E.

11.16. If α is a function of bounded variation on X; if $f_q(x)$ and $f(x)$ are $v(\alpha)$-measurable; if $\int_X f_q d\alpha$ exists for all q of Q; and if there exists a function $g(x)$ such that $\int_X |g| \, dv(\alpha)$ exists and $\lim_q f_q(x) = f(x)$ *uniformly relative* to g in the sense that $(e, q_e\, qRq_e, x \text{ on } X) : |f_q(x) - f(x)| \leqq e\, |g(x)|$, then $\int_X fd\alpha$ exists, and $\lim_q \int_X |f_q - f| \, dv(\alpha) = 0$, so that $\lim_q \int_E f_q d\alpha = \int_E fd\alpha$ for all $v(\alpha)$-measurable sets E.

For by the hypothesis, if for given $e > 0$, q is any such that qRq_e then $|f(x)| \leqq |f_q(x)| + e\,|g(x)|$. Since $f_q(x)$ and $g(x)$ are integrable with respect to $v(\alpha)$ it follows from VII.11.13 that $\int_X fd\alpha$ exists. From the same theorem we conclude that for qRq_e:

$$\left| \int_X f_q d\alpha - \int_X fd\alpha \right| \leqq \int_X |f_q - f| \, dv(\alpha) \leqq e \int_X |g| \, dv(\alpha).$$

Then $\lim_q \int_E f_q d\alpha = \int_E fd\alpha$ for all $v(\alpha)$-measurable E.

For sequences of functions of bounded variation α_m, the use of the definition $\int_X fd\alpha = \int_X fdp(\alpha) - \int_X fdn(\alpha)$ leads to:

11.17. If $\alpha_n(x)$ and $\alpha(x)$ are of bounded variation and such that $\lim \alpha_n(B) = \alpha(B)$ and $\lim_n v(\alpha_n;\, B) = v(\alpha;\, B)$ for every Borel measurable subset B of X; if $\int_X fd\alpha_n$ exist uniformly in n in the sense that $\lim_M \int_{CE_M} |f| \, dv(\alpha_n) = 0$ uniformly in n, where $E_M = E[|f| \leqq M]$, then $\int_X fd\alpha$ exists, and $\lim_n \int_E fd\alpha_n = \int_E fd\alpha$ for all subsets E of X which are $v(\alpha_n)$-measurable for all n.

Other variants of this convergence theorem can be derived from the corresponding theorems, for the case when α_n are monotonic nondecreasing (see VII.10.7).

Parallel to the substitution theorem of II.11.6 for Riemann-Stieltjes integrals, we have a substitution theorem for L-integrals.

11.18. Substitution Theorem. If (a) $\alpha(x)$ is a regular function of bounded variation on X with $(\alpha(x+0) - \alpha(x))\,(\alpha(x) - \alpha(x-0)) \geqq 0$ for all x; if (b) $f(x)$ and $g(x)$ are $v(\alpha)$-measurable; if (c) $\int_X fd\alpha$

exists and we set $\beta(E) = \int_E f d\alpha$; and if either $\int_X fg d\alpha$ or $\int_X f d\beta$ exists, then both integrals exist, and are equal.

The integral $\int_X f d\beta$ with respect to the function $\beta(E)$ on $v(\alpha)$-measurable sets, we define as the $\lim_\sigma \Sigma_\sigma f(x)\beta(E)$, where the subdivisions σ of X consist of $v(\alpha)$-measurable sets. As in the case of the integral based on the function $\alpha(x)$ of bounded variation on X, it is understood that if $\int_X f d\beta$ exists, then there exists a subdivision σ_0 of X such that for $\sigma \geqq \sigma_0$, the sums $\Sigma_\sigma f(x)\beta(E)$ converge absolutely for all x in the corresponding E, and that one can prove that there exists a subdivision σ_0' such that for all $\sigma \geqq \sigma_0'$, $f(x)$ is bounded on all subsets of σ for which $v(\beta; E) \neq 0$, and $\Sigma_\sigma M(|f|; E)\, v(\beta; E) < \infty$.

Suppose that $f(x)$ is bounded on X, and let σ be a subdivision of X such that $g(x)$ is bounded on all subsets E of σ for which $v(\alpha; E) \neq 0$. Then if $\sigma = \{E_n\}$ we have:

$$| \textstyle\sum_\sigma f(x_n)g(x_n)\alpha(E_n) - \sum_\sigma f(x_n)\beta(E_n) |$$

$$\leqq |\textstyle\sum_\sigma f(x_n)\, (g(x_n)\alpha(E_n) - \int_{E_n} g d\alpha)\, | \leqq M \sum_\sigma \omega(g; E_n)\; v(\alpha; E_n),$$

where $f(x) \leqq M$ on X. Since $\int_X g d\alpha$ exists, $\lim_\sigma \Sigma_\sigma \omega(g; E_n) v(\alpha; E_n) = 0$. Then $\lim_\sigma |\Sigma_\sigma f(x_n)g(x_n)\alpha(E_n) - \Sigma_\sigma f(x_n)\beta(E_n)\,| - 0$, which leads at once to the conclusion of the theorem.

If $f(x)$ is not bounded on X, a different type of proof seems to be needed. Suppose first that $\int_X f d\beta$ exists, and let σ_0 be such that if $\sigma \geqq \sigma_0$, then $\Sigma_\sigma M(|f|; E_n) v(\beta; E_n) < \infty$. If for such a $\sigma = \{E_n\}$ we set $F_\sigma(x) = \Sigma_n f(x_n)\chi(E_n; x)g(x)$, with x_n on E_n, then $F_\sigma(x) = f(x_n)g(x)$ on E_n. $F_\sigma(x)$ being a convergent sequence of $v(\alpha)$ measurable functions, is then also $v(\alpha)$-measurable. Moreover since $\int_{E_n} |F_\sigma|\, dv(\alpha) = |f(x_n)|\, v(\beta; E_n)$ it follows that $\Sigma_n \int_{E_n} |F_\sigma|\, dv(\alpha) < \infty$, so that by VII.2.3 $\int_X F_\sigma d\alpha$ exists, and has as value $\Sigma_n \int_{E_n} F_\sigma d\alpha = \Sigma_n f(x_n)\beta(E_n)$. Let σ_e be any subdivision of X induced via $f(x)$ by a subdivision σ_y of the Y-axis into intervals such that $|\sigma_y| < e$. Then $\omega(f; E) < e$, for any E of $\sigma \geqq \sigma_e$. The possibility of determining such a σ_e depends on the $v(\alpha)$-measurability of f. Consequently, for $\sigma \geqq \sigma_e \cdot \sigma_0$, we have $|F_\sigma(x) - f(x)g(x)\,| \leqq e\, |g(x)|$ for all x, in other words $\lim_\sigma F_\sigma(x) = f(x)g(x)$ relatively uniformly as to $g(x)$. Since $g(x)$ and $F_\sigma(x)$ are integrable with respect to $v(\alpha)$, it follows from VII.11.16 that $\int_X fg d\alpha$ exists and that

$$\int_X fg d\alpha = \lim_\sigma \int_X F_\sigma d\alpha = \lim_\sigma \textstyle\sum_\sigma f(x)\beta(E) = \int_X f d\beta.$$

On the other hand, suppose that $\int_X fgd\alpha$ exists. Then by using the same functions $F_\sigma(x)$, which are $v(\alpha)$-measurable and converge to $f(x)g(x)$ uniformly relative to $g(x)$, we find for $\sigma \geqq \sigma_e$ that $|F_\sigma(x)| \leqq |f(x)g(x)| + e\,|g(x)|$, so that by VII.11.13 $\int_X F_\sigma(x)d\alpha$ exists. Obviously $\int_X F_\sigma(x)d\alpha = \Sigma_\sigma \int_{E_n} f(x_n)g(x)d\alpha = \Sigma_\sigma f(x_n)\beta(E_n)$, which will be absolutely convergent. Using again the convergence of $F_\sigma(x)$ to $f(x)g(x)$ uniform relative to $g(x)$ we obtain:

$$\int_X fgd\alpha = \lim_\sigma \int_X F_\sigma\, d\alpha = \lim_\sigma \sum_\sigma f(x_n)\beta(E_n) = \int_X fd\beta.$$

EXERCISES

1. Suppose $\alpha(x)$ is monotonic bounded on X. Set up a definition for $\int_X fd\alpha$ as follows: Let σ stand for a finite set of disjoint α-measurable sets: $E_1 \ldots E_n$ such that $\Sigma_n E_n \leqq X$, and order the σ by the condition that if $\sigma_1 = E_{11} \ldots E_{1m}$, and $\sigma_2 = E_{21} \ldots E_{2n}$ then $\sigma_1 \geqq \sigma_2$ means that $\Sigma_1^m E_{1i} \geqq \Sigma_1^n E_{2j}$, and each E_{1i} is contained entirely in some E_{2j}. Then define $\int_X fd\alpha = \lim_\sigma \Sigma_\sigma f(x_i)\alpha(E_i)$, if this limit exists. What relation, if any, does this integral bear to the Y-integral, and what properties does such an integral have?

2. Suppose $\alpha(X)$ is bounded monotonic on X giving rise to the upper measure $\alpha^*(E)$ on subsets E of X. Let $f(x)$ be bounded on X. Let σ_y be subdivisions of the range of f: $(m < f(x) < M)$ into intervals by the points $y_0 = m < y_1 < \ldots < y_n = M$, with $y_{k-1} \leqq y_k' \leqq y_k$, and $E_k = E[y_{k-1} < f \leqq y_k]$. Suppose $\lim_{|\sigma_y| \to 0} \Sigma_k y_k' \alpha^*(E_k)$ exists. What properties of integrals, if any, does the resulting type of integral have? As an alternative, define $\mu(y) = \alpha^*(E[f \leqq y])$. Discuss $\int_m^M yd\mu(y)$ as a possible integral of bounded functions on X.

3. For $\alpha(x)$ monotonic bounded on X, and for the α-measurable function $f(x)$ define $f(m, M; x) = f(x)$ if $m < f(x) \leqq M$, and $f(m, M; x) = 0$ if $f(x) \leqq m$ or $f(x) > M$. Show that $\int_X f(m, M; x)d\alpha = \int_m^M yd\mu(y)$ if $\mu(y) = \alpha(E[f \leqq y])$.

4. The function $f(x)\alpha(E)$, x on E, is a multiple valued set function on α-measurable subsets of X, which form an s-algebra. This suggests: Let $\mathfrak{E}$ be an s-algebra of subsets of X. Let $\beta(E)$ be a set function defined on $\mathfrak{E}$. Let σ be subdivisions of X into subsets of $\mathfrak{E}$ directed by the usual order $\sigma_1 \geqq \sigma_2$ if every set of σ_1 lies in some set of σ_2. Define $\int_X \beta(dE) = \lim_\sigma \Sigma_\sigma \beta(E)$

provided this limit exists. What properties parallel to those for integrals of interval functions does the integral $\int_X \beta(dE)$ possess.

5. Let $\alpha(x)$ be a bounded monotone function on X. Let $\mathfrak{F}$ be the class of finite valued functions f on X, which are α-measurable. Show that if for the functions f_1 and f_2 of $\mathfrak{F}$, we set

$$\delta(f_1, f_2) = \int_X |f_1 - f_2| \, d\alpha \, / \, (1 + |f_1 - f_2|),$$

then $\delta(f_1, f_2)$ satisfies the metric properties $0 \leqq \delta(f_1, f_2) = \delta(f_2, f_1)$ and $\delta(f_1, f_3) \leqq \delta(f_1, f_2) + \delta(f_2, f_3)$, but that $\delta(f_1, f_2) = 0$ is equivalent to: f_1 differs from f_2 on an α-null set. Show that $\lim_n \delta(f_n, f) = 0$ is equivalent to the α-convergence of f_n to f, that is $f_n \rightarrow f(\alpha)$. Is it possible to metrize the totality of finite valued functions on X in a similar way so as to secure the equivalence of $\lim_n \delta(f_n, f) = 0$ to $f_n \rightarrow f(\alpha^*)$?

Show that $\int_X \chi(E_1 \Delta E_2) \, d\alpha$, where $E_1 \Delta E_2 = (E_1 - E_2) + (E_2 - E_1)$, sets up a similar metric for α-measurable sets, while $\delta(E_1, E_2) = \alpha^*(E_1 - E_2) + \alpha^*(E_2 - E_1)$ will metrize the totality of subsets of X.

6. Construct an example of a directed set $f_q(x)$ of uniformly bounded Lebesgue measurable functions on $0 \leqq x \leqq 1$, such that $\lim_q f_q(x) = f(x)$ for all x, but $\lim_q \int_0^1 f_q(x)dx \neq \int_0^1 f(x)dx$.

7. What class of functions $f(x)$ on X is determined by the condition that $\int_X f d\alpha$ exists as an L-S integral for all functions $\alpha(X)$ of bounded variation on X?

8. Show that if $\alpha(x)$ is of bounded variation on X, and $\int_E f d\alpha = 0$ for all $v(\alpha)$-measurable sets, then $f(x)$ vanishes except for an $v(\alpha)$-null set.

9. Show that if $\alpha_q(x)$ is a directed set of functions of bounded variation on X, such that there exists a function $\alpha(x)$ of bounded variation with $\lim_q v(\alpha_q - \alpha; X) = \lim_q \int_X |d(\alpha_q - \alpha)| = 0$, and if $f(x)$ is bounded on X such that $\int_X f d\alpha_q$ exists for all q, then $\int_X f d\alpha$ exists and $\lim_q \int_X f d\alpha_q = \int_X f d\alpha$. Can the boundedness condition on $f(x)$ be dropped?

12. Integration with Respect to Unbounded Measure Functions

The obvious case of an unbounded measure function is that in which $X = -\infty < x < +\infty$ and $\alpha(x) = x$. For the case of Riemann-Stieltjes integration we required for the existence of $\int_{-\infty}^{+\infty} f(x)d\alpha(x)$ that (a) $\int_a^b f(x)d\alpha(x)$ exist for all $-\infty < a < b < +\infty$, and that

$$\lim_{(a,b)\to(-\infty,+\infty)} \int_a^b fd\alpha$$

exist. For the Lebesgue setting with $X = -\infty < x < +\infty$, and $\alpha(x)$ of bounded variation on every finite subinterval $a \leqq x \leqq b$ of X, we define:

12.1. Definition. The function $f(x)$ on X is L-integrable with respect to $\alpha(x)$, if and only if (a) $f(x)$ is L-integrable on every finite half-open interval $I_{ab} \equiv a < x \leqq b$ and (b)

$$\lim_{(a,b)\to(-\infty,+\infty)} \int_{a+0}^{b+0} |f|\, dv(\alpha)$$

exists. Then $\int_X fd\alpha = \lim_{a,b} \int_{a+0}^{b+0} fd\alpha$.

It follows that $\int_X fd\alpha$ exists only if $\int_X |f|\, dv(\alpha)$ exists, so that f is integrable if and only if f is $v(\alpha)$-measurable and absolutely integrable with respect to $v(\alpha)$. We might consequently limit ourselves to the case when $\alpha(x)$ is monotone nondecreasing, but not necessarily bounded on X. The condition of absolute integrability is desirable if we expect to obtain properties of the integrals comparable to those for the case when $\alpha(x)$ is of bounded variation.

The results obtained apply with obvious alterations to the case where X is the open interval $a < x < b$, where a is finite or $-\infty$ and b is finite or $+\infty$. It is then assumed that $\alpha(x)$ is of bounded variation on every finite closed interval $[c, d]$ with $a < c \leqq x \leqq d < b$. For convenience we shall call such a function $\alpha(x)$ of *extended bounded variation* on X.

An immediate consequence of the definition of L-integrability is:

12.2. If $\alpha(x)$ is of extended bounded variation on X, $f(x)$ and $g(x) \geqq 0$ are $v(\alpha)$-measurable on X with $|f(x)| \leqq g(x)$ except at most on a $v(\alpha)$-null set then $\int_X fd\alpha$ exists and $|\int_X fd\alpha| \leqq \int_X gdv(\alpha)$ provided $\int_X gdv(\alpha)$ exists.

Assuming that $\alpha(x)$ and $f(x)$ satisfy condition (a) of the definition of integrability 12.1 above, we observe that condition (b) is equivalent to the following, where throughout $\int_a^b$ means L-integration over the half-open interval $a < x \leqq b$:

12.1 (b′). $\lim_{(a,b)\to(+\infty,+\infty)} \int_a^b |f|\, dv(\alpha) = 0$, and
$\lim_{(a,b)\to(-\infty,-\infty)} \int_a^b |f|\, dv(\alpha) = 0$.

12.1 (b″). For every sequence $\{a_n\}$, n ranging over the positive and negative integers, such that $a_n < a_{n+1}$, with $\lim_{n\to-\infty} a_n = -\infty$ and $\lim_{n\to+\infty} a_n = +\infty$, the series $\Sigma_n \int_{a_n}^{a_{n+1}} |f|\, dv(\alpha)$ converges. Moreover, $\int_X f d\alpha = \Sigma_n \int_{a_n}^{a_{n+1}} f d\alpha$.

12.1 (b‴). There exists a subdivision σ of X such that $\Sigma_\sigma M(|f|; E)$ $v(\alpha; E) < \infty$, where as usual $M(|f|; E) =$ l.u.b. $[|f(x)| \mid x$ on $E]$, and $M(|f|; E)v(\alpha; E) = 0$ if $v(\alpha; E) = 0$.

There is no difficulty about showing that (b′) or (b″) can replace (b). If condition (b‴) is fulfilled and we set $g(x) = M(|f|; E_m)$ on the sets E_m of σ when $M(|f|; E_m) < \infty$, and zero elsewhere, then $g(x)$ is $v(\alpha)$-measurable, $\int_X g dv(\alpha)$ exists, since for any finite subinterval $(a, b]$: $\int_a^b g dv(\alpha) \leq \Sigma_\sigma M(|f|; E_m)v(\alpha; E_m)$. Consequently, since $|f(x)| \leq g(x)$ except at most for a $v(\alpha)$-null set, it follows from VII. 12.2 that $\int_X f d\alpha$ exists and $|\int_X f d\alpha| \leq \Sigma_\sigma M(|f|; E_m)v(\alpha; E_m)$. That the condition (b‴) is also necessary will be shown below.

An alternate definition of integrability is contained in the theorem:

12.3. If $\alpha(x)$ is of extended bounded variation on X, and regular with $(\alpha(x+0) - \alpha(x))\,(\alpha(x) - \alpha(x-0)) \geq 0$ for all x, then a necessary and sufficient condition that $f(x)$ be L-integrable is that $\lim_\sigma \Sigma_\sigma f(x)\alpha(E)$ exist, where subdivisions are into denumerable sets of $v(\alpha)$-measurable subsets for each of which $v(\alpha; E) < \infty$.

The set function $\alpha(E)$ is defined in terms of the functions $p(E)$ and $n(E)$ based on the monotone point functions $p(x) = (\int_0^x |d\alpha| + \alpha(x) - \alpha(0))/2$ and $n(x) = (\int_0^x |d\alpha| - (\alpha(x) - \alpha(0)))/2$, repectively, by the relation $\alpha(E) = p(E) - n(E)$. This assigns a definite value to $\alpha(E)$ if $v(\alpha; E) < \infty$. The condition that σ consist only of sets E for which $v(\alpha; E) < \infty$ imposes no essential restrictions, since the product of any subdivision and the subdivision determined by the intervals $(n, n+1]$, n ranging over the positive and negative integers will satisfy this condition. Moreover, in asserting that $\lim_\sigma \Sigma_\sigma f(x)$ $\alpha(E)$ exists, it is understood that $\Sigma_\sigma f(x)\alpha(E)$ ultimately has meaning, in particular there exists a σ_0 such that for $\sigma \geqq \sigma_0$, the sum $\Sigma_\sigma f(x)\alpha(E)$ exists as a general sum (see I.6). This means that $\Sigma_n f(x_n)\alpha(E_n)$ converges absolutely where $\sigma = \{E_n\}$ and x_n is on E_n. Consequently, the existence of $\lim_\sigma \Sigma_\sigma f(x)\alpha(E)$ carries with it, not only that there exists a σ_0 such that for $\sigma \geqq \sigma_0$ the expression $\Sigma_\sigma f(x)\alpha(E)$ is absolutely convergent for all x on the corresponding E, but also the boundedness of the same sums for $\sigma \geqq \sigma_0$.

Suppose $\int_X f d\alpha$ exists. Then $\Sigma_{n=-\infty}^{+\infty} \int_n^{n+1} |f| \, dv(\alpha) < \infty$ and $\int_X f d\alpha = \Sigma_{n=-\infty}^{+\infty} \int_n^{n+1} f d\alpha$. For $e > 0$ let σ_{ne} and σ_n be subdivisions of $(n, n+1]$ such that for $\sigma_n \geq \sigma_{ne}$:

$$\left| \int_n^{n+1} f d\alpha - \sum_{\sigma_n} f(x)\alpha(E) \right| \leqq e/2^n$$

and

$$\left| \int_n^{n+1} |f| \, dv(\alpha) - \sum_{\sigma_n} |f(x)| \, v(\alpha;\ E) \right| \leqq e/2^n.$$

Then

$$\sum_n \sum_{\sigma_n} |f(x)| \, v(\alpha;\ E) \leqq \sum_n \int_n^{n+1} |f| \, dv(\alpha) + 2e,$$

where in Σ_n, n ranges over any finite set of integers. If $\sigma_e = \Sigma_n \sigma_{ne}$, and $\sigma \geqq \sigma_e$, then

$$\sum\nolimits_\sigma |f(x)| \, |\alpha(E)| \leqq \sum\nolimits_\sigma |f(x)| \, v(\alpha, E) < \int_X |f| \, dv(\alpha) + 2e < \infty.$$

We then have also for $\sigma \geqq \sigma_e$

$$\left| \sum_n \int_n^{n+1} f d\alpha - \sum_\sigma f(x)\alpha(E) \right| \leqq \sum_n \left| \int_n^{n+1} f d\alpha - \sum_{\sigma_n} f(x)\alpha(E) \right| \leqq 2e,$$

so that $\lim_\sigma \Sigma_\sigma f(x)\alpha(E)$ exists and is $\int_X f d\alpha$.

On the other hand, suppose that $\lim_\sigma \Sigma_\sigma f(x)\alpha(E)$ exists. Then by the Cauchy theorem of convergence, we have $(e > 0,\ \sigma_e,\ \sigma_1 \geqq \sigma_e,\ \sigma_2 \geqq \sigma_e) : |\Sigma_{\sigma_1} f(x)\alpha(E) - \Sigma_{\sigma_2} f(x)\alpha(E)| \leqq e$, the sums being absolutely convergent. Let $I_{ab} = (a, b]$, and suppose that σ_1 and σ_2 are finer than the subdivision determined by I_{ab}, $X - I_{ab}$. If we keep σ_1 and σ_2 fixed and equal to each other outside of the interval I_{ab}, so that they differ only inside of this interval, the condition for the existence of $\int_a^b f d\alpha$ are satisfied. This will be true for all a and b with $-\infty < a < b < +\infty$. It follows that $f(x)$ is $v(\alpha)$-measurable on X.

Since $\lim_\sigma \Sigma_\sigma f(x)\alpha(E)$ exists, there exists a σ_0 such that the sums $\Sigma_\sigma f(x)\alpha(E)$ are bounded in σ for $\sigma \geqq \sigma_0$, and in x for x on the corresponding sets E of σ. As in the proof of VII.11.9 we can divide each interval $(n, n+1]$ into sets E_n^+ and E_n^-, so that $f(x) \geqq 0$ on E_n^+ and $f(x) < 0$ on E_n^-. Further E_n^+ can be divided into E_n^{++} and E_n^{+-} such that $v(\alpha, E) = \alpha(E)$ for any subset of E_n^{++} and $v(\alpha; E) = -\alpha(E)$ for any subset of E_n^{+-}, and similarly for E_n^{-+} and E_n^{--}, all sets being $v(\alpha)$-measurable. It follows that $0 \leqq f(x)\alpha(E) = f(x)v(\alpha;$

$E)$ for any $v(\alpha)$-measurable subset of E_n^{++} or E_n^{--}, and $0 \geqq f(x)\alpha(E) = -f(x)v(\alpha; E)$ for any $v(\alpha)$-measurable subset of E_n^{+-} or E_n^{-+}. Let $\sigma_n^+ = (E_n^{++}, E_n^{--})$ and $\sigma_n^- = (E_n^{-+}, E_n^{+-})$. For $\sigma \geqq \sigma_0$, let σ^+ stand for the collection of sets σ_n^+ and σ^- for the collection σ_n^-. Then

$$\sum_\sigma f(x)\alpha(E) = \sum_{\sigma+} f(x)\alpha(E) + \sum_{\sigma-} f(x)\alpha(E) = \sum_{\sigma+} f(x)v(\alpha; E) - \sum_{\sigma-} f(x)v(\alpha; E).$$

Since $\Sigma_\sigma f(x)\alpha(E)$ is bounded in σ for $\sigma \geqq \sigma_0$, by varying subdivisions of σ^+ and σ^- independently if follows that $\Sigma_{\sigma+} f(x)v(\alpha; E)$ and $\Sigma_{\sigma-} f(x)v(\alpha; E)$ are bounded for all redivisions of σ^+ and σ^-. Consequently, $\Sigma_\sigma f(x)v(\alpha; E) = \Sigma_{\sigma-} f(x)v(\alpha; E) + \Sigma_{\sigma-} f(x)v(\alpha; E)$ is bounded in σ for $\sigma \geqq \sigma_0$.

It follows that if $\sigma \geqq \sigma_0$, and $\sigma \equiv \{E_m\}$, then $f(x)$ is bounded on each set E_m for which $v(\alpha; E_m) > 0$. If $M(|f|; E_m) = \text{l.u.b.}\ [|f(x)|,\ x$ on E_m such that $v(\alpha; E_m) > 0]$ then for $e > 0$ there exists an x_m in E_m such that $M(|f|; E_m) \leqq |f(x_m)| + e/(2^m v(\alpha; E_m))$. It follows that

$$\sum_m M(|f|; E_m)v(\alpha; E_m) \leqq \sum_m |f(x_m)|\, v(\alpha; E_m) + e < \infty,$$

where $M(|f|; E)v(\alpha; E) = 0$ if $v(\alpha; E) = 0$. Then by VII.12.1 (b''') $\int_X f d\alpha$ exists, and as proved above has for its value $\lim_\sigma \Sigma_\sigma f(x)\alpha(E)$.

The proof of this theorem shows incidentally that if $\int_X f d\alpha$ exists, then there exists a subdivision σ_0 such that for $\sigma \geqq \sigma_0$, we have $\Sigma_\sigma M(|f|; E)v(\alpha; E) < \infty$.

The linearity of $\int_X f d\alpha$ in f for fixed α, and in α for a fixed f, follow in the usual way from the definition VII.12.1. We also have:

12.4. If $\alpha(x)$ is of extended bounded variation on X, $\int_X f_1 d\alpha$ exists, $f_2(x)$ is $v(\alpha)$-measurable and bounded except for a $v(\alpha)$-null set, then $\int_X f_1 f_2 d\alpha$ exists and $|\int_X f_1 f_2 d\alpha| \leqq M \int_X |f_1|\, dv(\alpha)$, where $|f_2(x)| \leqq M$ except for a $v(\alpha)$-null set.

For the product $f_1(x) f_2(x)$ will be dominated by $M|f_1(x)|$ except for a $v(\alpha)$-null set. If we set $f_2(x) = \chi(E; x)$, where E is a $v(\alpha)$-measurable set then we find:

12.5. If E is a $v(\alpha)$-measurable set, and $\int_X f d\alpha$ exists, then $\int_E f d\alpha = \int_X f(x)\chi(E; x) d\alpha(x)$ exists. Further if $\beta(E) = \int_E f d\alpha$, then $\beta(E)$ is finitely additive in the sense that if E_1 and E_2 are $v(\alpha)$-measurable then $\beta(E_1) + \beta(E_2) = \beta(E_1E_2) + \beta(E_1 + E_2)$, and s-additive in the sense that if $\{E_n\}$ is a sequence of disjoint $v(\alpha)$-measurable sets, then $\beta(\Sigma E_n) = \Sigma_n \beta(E_n)$.

The additivity follows as usual from the identity: $\chi(E_1; x) + \chi(E_2; x) = \chi(E_1 + E_2; x) + \chi(E_1 E_2; x)$, and the linear properties of the integral. The s-additivity can be deduced from the fact that if $I = (a, b]$ then

$$\lim_{(a,b)\to(-\infty,+\infty)} \left| \int_E f d\alpha - \int_{E\cdot I} f d\alpha \right| = 0$$

uniformly in E.

As a converse we have:

12.6. If E_n is a sequence of disjoint $v(\alpha)$-measurable sets such that $\int_{E_n} f d\alpha$ exist and $\Sigma_n \int_{E_n} |f| \, dv(\alpha) < \infty$, then if $E = \Sigma_n E_n$, $\int_E f d\alpha$ exists as $\Sigma_n \int_{E_n} f d\alpha$.

12.6.1. In particular if the function $f(x)$ is a step function on X, and $f(x) = c_n$ for x on E_n, and such that $\Sigma_n |c_n| \, v(\alpha, E_n) < \infty$, E_n being disjoint $v(\alpha)$-measurable sets, then $\int_X f d\alpha$ exists with $\Sigma_n c_n \alpha(E_n)$ as its value.

12.7. The integral $\int_E f d\alpha = \beta(E)$ is absolutely continuous relative to $v(\alpha; E)$. Also if $I_{ab} = (a, b]$ and $CI_{ab} = X - I_{ab}$, then

$$\lim_{(a,b)\to(-\infty,+\infty)} \int_{E\cdot CI_{ab}} f d\alpha = 0$$

for all $v(\alpha)$-measurable E.

The last part follows from the inequality

$$\left| \int_{E\cdot CI_{ab}} f d\alpha \right| \leqq \int_{CI_{ab}} |f| \, dv(\alpha).$$

The first part from the decomposition of $E = E \cdot I_{ab} + E \cdot CI_{ab}$, and the absolute continuity on every I_{ab}.

No new proof is needed for the following:

12.8. If $\alpha(x)$ is monotonic nondecreasing on X, $f(x) \geqq 0$ on X, and $\int_X f d\alpha = 0$, then $f = 0$ except for an α-null set.

When it comes to a consideration of the integrals $\int f_n d\alpha$ for a sequence of integrable functions $f_n(x)$, we note that any theorem on the interchange of limit and integral involves an additional interchange of iterated limits. Additional conditions making possible interchange of order in limits are then needed. Since we already have sufficient conditions so that $\lim_n \int_X f_n d\alpha = \int_X f d\alpha$, when α is of bounded variation on X, which can be applied to the case when $X = I_{ab} = (a, b]$, we need only an additional condition permitting the interchange of limit as to n, and limit as to (a, b). The result is the following:

12.9. If (a) $\alpha(x)$ is of extended bounded variation on X, (b) $f_n(x)$ and $f(x)$ on X are such that $\lim_n f_n \to f(v(\alpha))$, (c) $\int_X f_n d\alpha$ exists for each n, (d) $\int_E f_n d\alpha$ are uniformly absolutely continuous relative to $v(\alpha)$, and (e)

$$\lim_{(a,b)\to(-\infty,+\infty)} \int_a^b | f_n | \, dv(\alpha)$$

exist uniformly in n (or $\int_X f_n d\alpha$ exist uniformly in n), then $\int_X f d\alpha$ exists and $\lim_n \int_X |f_n - f| \, dv(\alpha) = 0$ so that $\lim_n \int_E f_n d\alpha = \int_E f d\alpha$ for all $v(\alpha)$-measurable sets including X.

Conditions (a), (b), (c), and (d) imply that $\lim_n \int_a^b |f_n - f| \, dv(\alpha) = 0$, for all $-\infty < a < b < +\infty$. Since

$$\left| \int_a^b | f_n | \, dv(\alpha) - \int_a^b | f | \, dv(\alpha) \right| \leqq \int_a^b | f_n - f | \, dv(\alpha),$$

it follows that $\lim_n \int_a^b |f_n| \, dv(\alpha) = \int_a^b |f| \, dv(\alpha)$ for all $-\infty < a < b < \infty$. In view of condition (e), the iterated limits theorem applies to give us the existence of $\int_X |f| \, dv(\alpha) = \lim_n \int_X |f_n| \, dv(\alpha)$. Since

$$\left| \int_X | f_n - f | \, dv(\alpha) - \int_a^b | f_n - f | \, dv(\alpha) \right|$$
$$\leqq \left| \int_X | f_n | \, dv(\alpha) - \int_a^b | f_n | \, dv(\alpha) \right| + \left| \int_X | f | \, dv(\alpha) - \int_a^b | f | \, dv(\alpha) \right|,$$

it follows that

$$\lim_{(a,b)\to(-\infty,+\infty)} \int_a^b |f_n - f| \, dv(\alpha) = \int_X | f_n - f | \, dv(\alpha)$$

uniformly in n. Since on the other hand, $\lim_n \int_a^b |f_n - f| \, dv(\alpha) = 0$ for all a and b, we can apply the iterated limits theorem to give:

$$\lim_n \int_X |f_n - f| \, dv(\alpha) = \lim_n \lim_{a,b} \int_a^b | f_n - f | \, dv(\alpha)$$
$$= \lim_{a,b} \lim_n \int_a^b | f_n - f | \, dv(\alpha) = 0.$$

We have the following theorem of converse type:

12.10. If $\alpha(x)$ is of extended bounded variation on X, if $f_n(x)$ and $f(x)$ on X are such that $\int_X f_n d\alpha$ and $\int_X f d\alpha$ exist, and if $\lim_n \int_E f_n d\alpha = \int_E f d\alpha$ for every $v(\alpha)$-measurable set E, then $\Sigma_m \mid \int_{E_m} f_n d\alpha \mid$ converge uniformly in n for each sequence E_m of disjoint $v(\alpha)$-measurable sets, and $\int_E f_n d\alpha$ are uniformly absolutely continuous relative to $v(\alpha)$.

For if we set $\beta_n(E) = \int_E f_n d\alpha$, then the $\beta_n(E)$ are s-additive on the class of $v(\alpha)$-measurable sets, $\lim_n \beta_n(E) = \beta(E) = \int_E f d\alpha$, and $\beta_n(E)$ are absolutely continuous relative to $v(\alpha)$. Then VII.8.17 and VII.8.18 apply, and yield at once the conclusion of the theorem.

In case the function $\alpha(x)$ is monotonic nondecreasing, we can state:

12.11. If (a) $\alpha(x)$ is monotonic nondecreasing on X; if (b) f_n and f are such that $\lim_n f_n \rightarrow f(\alpha)$, if (c) $\int_X f_n d\alpha$ exists for each n, and if (d): $\Sigma_m \int_{E_m} f_n d\alpha$ is uniformly convergent in n for each sequence $\{E_m\}$ of disjoint α-measurable sets, then $\int_X f d\alpha$ exists, and $\lim_n \int_E f_n d\alpha = \int_E f d\alpha$ for all α-measurable E.

In order to prove this we derive first the following

12.12. Lemma. Under the conditions (a), (c), and (d) of the theorem the series $\Sigma_m \int_{E_m} |f_n| \, d\alpha$ converges uniformly in n for every sequence E_m of disjoint measurable sets.

The proof of this lemma is by the contrapositive method, and follows the procedure of the proof of VII.8.12. Suppose if possible $\Sigma_m \int_{E_m} |f_n| d\alpha$ do not converge uniformly in n, for some sequence E_m of disjoint α-measurable sets. Then there exists $e > 0$, such that for every N, there exists $n_N > N$ and $m_N > N$ such that $\Sigma_{m_N}^{\infty} \int_{E_m} |f_{n_N}| \, d\alpha > e$. Take $N = 1$ and m_1 and n_1 so that $\Sigma_{m_1}^{\infty} \int_{E_m} |f_{n_1}| \, d\alpha > e$. Then there exists an integer $m_1' > m_1$ such that

$$\sum_{m=m_1'+1}^{\infty} \int_{E_m} |f_{n_1}| \, d\alpha < e/4 \quad \text{and} \quad \sum_{m=m_1}^{m_1'} \int_{E_m} |f_{n_1}| \, d\alpha > e.$$

Let E_1' be that subset of $\Sigma_{m_1}^{m_1'} E_m$ on which f_{n_1} is invariant in sign (that is entirely positive or zero, or negative or zero) and $| \int_{E_1'} f_{n_1'} \, d\alpha \; | > e/2$. Take n_2, m_2 so that $n_2 > m_1'$ and $m_2 > m_1'$ and $\Sigma_{m=m_2}^{\infty} \int_{E_m} |f_{n_2}| \, d\alpha > e$. Then we can find m_2' such that $\Sigma_{m=m_2}^{m_2'} \int_{E_m} |f_{n_2}| \, d\alpha > e$, while $\Sigma_{m_2'+1}^{\infty} \int_{E_m} |f_{n_2}| \, d\alpha < e/4$. E_2' is then the subset of $\Sigma_{m_2}^{m_2'} E_m$ on which

f_{n_2} is invariant in sign and such that $|\int_{E_2'} f_{n_2} d\alpha| > e/2$. By continuing the process, we get then a sequence of disjoint sets E_i', an increasing sequence of integers n_i. such that f_{n_i} is of fixed sign on E_i', $|\int_{E_i'} f_{n_i} d\alpha| > e/2$, while

$$\sum_{k=i+1}^{\infty} \int_{E_k'} |f_{n_i}| \, d\alpha < e/4.$$

The last inequality holds because $\Sigma_{k=i+1}^{\infty} E_i'$ is contained in the set

$$\sum_{m=m_i'+1}^{\infty} E_m .$$

It follows that for each i:

$$\left| \sum_{k=i}^{\infty} \int_{E_k'} f_{n_i} \, d\alpha \right| > \left| \int_{E_i'} f_{n_i} d\alpha \right| - \sum_{k=i+1}^{\infty} \int_{E_k'} |f_{n_i}| \, d\alpha > e/4.$$

Consequently the series $\Sigma_{k=1}^{\infty} \int_{E_k'} f_{n_i} \, d\alpha$ does not converge uniformly in i, which contradicts the assumption (d).

To return to the proof of our theorem, we show that the condition that for each sequence of disjoint measurable sets E_m, the series $\Sigma_m \int_{E_m} |f_n| \, d\alpha$ converges uniformly in n, gives the uniform absolute continuity of $\int_E f_n d\alpha$ relative to α, and the uniform existence of $\int_X f_n d\alpha$. The first of these can be inferred from the proof of VII.8.12 if one observes that the finiteness of $\alpha(X)$ does not enter into the proof. For the second statement, we note that if we set $E_m = (m, m+1]$, for all positive and negative integers m, then $\Sigma_m \int_{E_m} |f_n| \, d\alpha$ converges uniformly in n, which implies that $\lim \int_a^b |f_n| \, d\alpha$ exists uniformly in n as $a \to -\infty$ and $b \to +\infty$. It follows that the hypotheses of VII.12.9 are fulfilled and we can conclude that $\lim_n \int_E f_n d\alpha = \int_E f d\alpha$ for all $v(\alpha)$-measurable E.

For the case of a set of functions $f_q(x)$ for q on a directed set Q, the following theorem analogous to VII.9.2 can be proved:

12.13. If (a) $\alpha(x)$ is of extended bounded variation on X; if (b) $f_q(x)$ are such that $\int_X f_q d\alpha$ exists for all q; if (c) $f_q \to f(v(\alpha))$; if (d)

$$\lim_{q,\, v(\alpha;E)\to 0} \int_E f_q d\alpha = 0,$$

and if $\int_X |f_q| \, dv(\alpha)$ exist uniformly for qRq_0, then $\int_X f d\alpha$ exists,

$\lim_q \int_X |f_q - f| \, dv(\alpha) = 0$, and $\lim_q \int_E f_q d\alpha = \int_E f d\alpha$ for every $v(\alpha)$-measurable set E.

The following convergence theorem may at times be easier to apply:

12.14. If (a) $\alpha(x)$ is of extended bounded variation on X, if (b) $f_q(x)$ on X and on the directed set Q are such that $\int_X f_q d\alpha$ exists for every q; if (c) f_q converge to f relatively uniformly as to the integrable function $g(x) \geqq 0$ in the sense that there exists a $v(\alpha)$-null set E_0 such that $(e, q_e, qRq_e, x \text{ on } X - E_0) : |f_q(x) - f(x)| \leqq e \cdot g(x)$, then $\int_X f d\alpha$ exists and $\lim_q \int_X |f_q - f| \, dv(\alpha) = 0$.

By setting $e = 1/n$, we can select a monotone sequence of q: q_n such that $\lim_n f_{q_n}(x) = f(x)$ except for x on E_0 a $v(\alpha)$-null set. Since $\int_X f_q d\alpha$ exists, $f_q(x)$ is $v(\alpha)$-measurable, and so $f(x)$ is also $v(\alpha)$-measurable, as the limit of a sequence of $v(\alpha)$-measurable functions excepting for an α-null set. Further, for an $e > 0$, and a fixed q_0Rq_e we will havc $|f(x)| \leqq e \cdot g(x) + |f_{q_0}(x)|$, except for x on E_0, a $v(\alpha)$-null set.. Consequently by VII.12.2 $\int_X |f| \, dv(\alpha)$ exists. The linearity of the integral then gives for qRq_e:

$$\int_X |f_q - f| \, dv(\alpha) \leqq e \int_X g dv(\alpha),$$

and so $\lim_q \int_X |f_q - f| \, dv(\alpha) = 0$.

EXERCISES

1. Show that if $\alpha(x)$ is of extended bounded variation and regular on X, then there exist disjoint $v(\alpha)$-measurable sets X^+ and X^- such that $X = X^+ + X^-$, and for any E with $v(\alpha; E) < \infty$, we have $v(\alpha; EX^+) = \alpha(EX^+)$ and $v(\alpha; EX^-) = -\alpha(EX^-)$.

2. Show that if for a given $v(\alpha)$-measurable set E: $\int_E |f| \, dv(\alpha) > e$ then there exists a subset E_1 of E such that $f(x)$ is entirely positive or zero, or entirely negative or zero on E_1 and $|\int_{E_1} f d\alpha| > e/4$.

3. Is it possible to replace condition (a) in theorem VII.12.11 that $\alpha(x)$ be monotonic nondecreasing by the condition (a′) that $\alpha(x)$ be of extended bounded variation on X, the sets E occurring in the theorem being then assumed to be $v(\alpha)$-measurable?

4. Suppose $\alpha_n(x)$ and $\alpha(x)$ are of extended bounded variation on X. Find conditions sufficient to guarantee that if $\int_X f d\alpha_n$ exists for all n, then $\int_X f d\alpha$ exists as the $\lim_n \int_X f d\alpha_n$.

5. Suppose $\alpha(x)$ is of extended bounded variation on X, and $f(x)$ is such that $\int_X f d\alpha$ exists. If $\int_a^x f d\alpha$ is the integral on the half-open interval $(a, x]$ in X, is this (indefinite) integral a continuous function of x at all points where $\alpha(x)$ is continuous?

CHAPTER VIII

CLASSES OF MEASURABLE AND INTEGRABLE FUNCTIONS

Any fixed monotonic nondecreasing function α on $X \equiv -\infty < x < +\infty$ defines a class of functions possessing certain measurability and integral properties relative to α. We treat briefly some classes which have proved important and useful especially in connection with the study of linear spaces. Since most of the properties mentioned for a function $\alpha(x)$ of extended bounded variation, that is of bounded variation on every finite subinterval of X, depend on the total variation function which is monotonic, we limit ourselves in this section to the case where $\alpha(x)$ is monotone nondecreasing, and bounded on any finite subinterval of X.

1. The Class of α-Measurable Functions

We have already seen in VI.3 that the class of all α-measurable functions f on X is linear and has the absolute property, that it contains $|f|$ if it contains f. Further that a natural mode of convergence in this class is α-convergence or α-measure convergence: $f_n \to f(\alpha)$, equivalent to $\lim_n \alpha(E[|f_n - f| > e]) = 0$ for all $e > 0$. With the aid of integration, it is possible to set up a metric in this space such that $\delta(f_n, f) \to 0$ is equivalent to $f_n \to f(\alpha)$, for α bounded.

For this purpose we note that the function $y = x/(1 + x)$ for $0 \leqq x < +\infty$, is a monotone increasing continuous function which maps the positive real axis on the interval [0, 1], and has the property that if $x_1 > 0$, and $x_2 > 0$, then

$$\frac{x_1 + x_2}{1 + x_1 + x_2} \leqq \frac{x_1}{1 + x_1 + x_2} + \frac{x_2}{1 + x_1 + x_2} \leqq \frac{x_1}{1 + x_1} + \frac{x_2}{1 + x_2}.$$

As a consequence for x_1 and x_2 real we have:

$$\frac{|x_1 + x_2|}{1 + |x_1 + x_2|} \leqq \frac{|x_1| + |x_2|}{1 + |x_1| + |x_2|} \leqq \frac{|x_1|}{1 + |x_1|} + \frac{|x_2|}{1 + |x_2|}.$$

If now $\delta(x_1, x_2)$ is a metric on a space X, then the expression $\delta_1(x_1, x_2) = \delta(x_1, x_2)/(1 + \delta(x_1, x_2))$ defines a bounded metric on X, such that $\lim_n \delta(x_n, x) = 0$ is equivalent to $\lim_n \delta_1(x_n, x) = 0$.

We apply this to the space of functions $f(x)$ on $X = -\infty < x < \infty$ which are measurable relative to the monotone bounded function $\alpha(x)$ on X.

1.1. If f_1 and f_2 are α-measurable, then the function $|f_1(x) - f_2(x)|/(1 + |f_1(x) - f_2(x)|)$ is α-measurable and bounded so that

$$\delta(f_1, f_2) = \int_X \frac{|f_1 - f_2|}{1 + |f_1 - f_2|} \, d\alpha$$

exists and satisfies the metric conditions $0 \leqq \delta(f_1, f_2) = \delta(f_2, f_1)$ and $\delta(f_1, f_2) \leqq \delta(f_1, f_3) + \delta(f_3, f_2)$ for all f_1, f_2, and f_3. The conditions $\delta(f_1, f_2) = 0$ is equivalent to the statement that $|f_1(x) - f_2(x)|/(1 + |f_1(x) - f_2(x)|)$ vanishes excepting for an α-null set, so that f_1 and f_2 differ at most on an α-null set. The value of $\delta(f_1, f_2)$ is unchanged if we replace each function f_1 and f_2 by a corresponding function differing from it by an α-null set. $\delta(f_1, f_2)$ gives us a metric on the α-measurable functions if we consider two functions differing on an α-null set as equal.

1.2. A necessary and sufficient condition that $\lim_n \delta(f_n, f) = 0$ is that $f_n \to f(\alpha)$.

For suppose $f_n \to f(\alpha)$, then $|f_n - f|/(1 + |f_n - f|) \to 0(\alpha)$. For if $x/(1 + x) > e$, and $e < 1$, then $x > (1 - e)/e$, so that the set $E[|f_n - f|/(1 + |f_n - f|) > e]$ is contained in the set $E[|f_n - f| > (1 - e)/e]$ for $e < 1$, and in α-measure convergence we need worry only about the case when e is small. By the integral convergence theorem for a uniformly bounded sequence of α-measurable functions with α bounded (VII.8.7), it then follows that

$$\lim_n \delta(f_n, f) = \lim_n \int_X \frac{|f_n - f|}{1 + |f_n - f|} \, d\alpha = 0.$$

On the other hand, we note that for any sequence g_n of functions integrable with respect to α, the condition $\lim_n \int_X |g_n| \, d\alpha = 0$ together with $E_{ne} = E[|g_n| > e]$ implies $\lim_n e \cdot \alpha(E_{ne}) = 0$, so that $g_n \to 0(\alpha)$. Now $E[|f_n - f| / (1 + |f_n - f|) > e]$ contains the set $E[|f_n - f| > e]$, so that $\lim_n \delta(f_n, f) = 0$ implies $f_n \to f(\alpha)$.

In case the function $\alpha(x)$ is not bounded, we alter the procedure slightly. Let I_m be the sequence of disjoint half open intervals $(m, m+1]$, m ranging over the positive and negative integers so that $\Sigma_m I_m = X$. Let c_m be a sequence of positive numbers such that $\Sigma_m c_m \cdot \alpha(I_m) < \infty$. Then the step function $g(x) = c_m$ for x on I_m will be α-integrable. It follows that for any two α-measurable functions f_1 and f_2, the function

$$h(x) = \frac{|f_1(x) - f_2(x)| \cdot g(x)}{1 + |f_1(x) - f_2(x)|}$$

is integrable with respect to α so that we can set $\delta(f_1, f_2) = \int_X h d\alpha$. This will define a metric as in the case when α is bounded as it possesses metric properties for each I_m. Since

$$\delta(f_1, f_2) = \sum_m c_m \int_{I_m} \frac{|f_1 - f_2|}{1 + |f_1 - f_2|} d\alpha ,$$

it follows that the condition $\lim_n \delta(f_n, f) = 0$ implies the condition

$$\lim_n \int_{I_m} \frac{|f_n - f|}{1 + |f_n - f|} d\alpha = 0$$

for every I_m, so that $f_n \to f(\alpha;\ x \text{ on } I_m)$. From this we conclude that $f_n \to f(\alpha;\ x \text{ on } E)$, where E is any bounded subset of X. On the other hand, suppose $f_n \to f(\alpha;\ x \text{ on } I_m)$ for all I_m. Then

$$\lim_n \sum_{m=1}^{k} c_m \int_{I_m} \frac{|f_n - f|}{1 + |f_n - f|} d\alpha = 0$$

for each k. Moreover,

$$\sum_{m=k}^{\infty} c_m \int_{I_m} \frac{|f_n - f|}{1 + |f_n - f|} d\alpha \leq \sum_{m=k}^{\infty} c_m \alpha(I_m),$$

giving uniform convergence in n for the series on the right. The iterated limits theorem then gives us $\lim_n \delta(f_n, f) = 0$. It follows then that for our definition of $\delta(f_1, f_2)$, the condition $\lim_n \delta(f_n, f) = 0$ is equivalent to the condition: $f_n \to f(\alpha,\ x \text{ on } I_m)$ for all I_m, or $f_n \to f(\alpha,\ x \text{ on } E)$ for all bounded α-measurable E.

1.3. For unbounded functions $\alpha(x)$, the condition $f_n \to f(\alpha; x \text{ on } E)$ for all bounded α-measurable E, is weaker than $f_n \to f(\alpha, x \text{ on } X)$.

1.4. Since the space of α-measurable functions is complete under α-measure convergence, it follows that it is also complete under the metric convergence, that is, $\lim_{n,m} \delta(f_n, f_m) = 0$ implies the existence of a function f such that $\lim_n \delta(f_n, f) = 0$. The space is also complete in the more general sense, if $f_q(x)$ is a set of α-measurable functions with q on the directed set Q, and $\lim_{q_1 q_2} \delta(f_{q_1}, f_{q_2}) = 0$, then there exists an α-measurable function f such that $\lim_q \delta(f_q, f) = 0$.

The last sentence is a result of the following general property of metric spaces:

1.5. Let Y be a sequentially complete metric space of elements y in the sense that $\lim_{m,n} \delta(y_m, y_n) = 0$ implies the existence of an element y of Y such that $\lim_n \delta(y_n, y) = 0$. Now if y_q is a set of elements on directed Q with $\lim_{q_1 q_2} \delta(y_{q_1}, y_{q_2}) = 0$, then there exists an element y of Y such that $\lim_q \delta(y_q, y) = 0$.

The proof follows the procedure for the case when the metric space is that of real numbers (see I.2.11).

2. The Class of Almost Bounded α-Measurable Functions

For a monotonic nondecreasing function $\alpha(x)$ on $X = -\infty < x < +\infty$, the class of almost bounded functions has already been defined (see VII.2.4.1) as the class of α-measurable functions for which there exists an $N > 0$ such that $\alpha(E[|f| > N]) = 0$. This class of functions is usually denoted by M or L^∞. It is linear and has the absolute property.

2.1. If we define:

$$||f|| = \text{g.l.b. } (N \text{ such that } \alpha(E[f > N]) = 0),$$

then $||f||$ is a norm on M, with the following properties:

(a) $||f|| \geqq 0$; $||f|| = 0$ if and only if $f = 0$ except for an α-null set.

(b) $||af|| = |a|\ ||f||$ and $||\,|f|\,|| = ||f||$.

(c) $||f_1 + f_2|| \leqq ||\,|f_1| + |f_2|\,|| \leqq ||f_1|| + ||f_2||$.

(d) If f belongs to M and g is such that g is α-measurable and

$|g(x)| \leqq |f(x)|$ except for an α-null set, then g belongs to M and $\|g\| \leqq \|f\|$.

Properties (a), (b), and (d) and the first inequality of (c) are obvious. For the rest of (c), with $e > 0$, let N_1 and N_2 be such that $N_1 > \|f_1\| > N_1 - e$ and $N_2 > \|f_2\| > N_2 - e$. Then $\alpha(E_1) = \alpha(E[|f_1| > N_1]) = 0$ and $\alpha(E_2) = \alpha(E[|f_2| > N_2]) = 0$. If $E_0 = E_1 + E_2$, then $\alpha(E_0) = 0$. On CE_0, the complement of E_0 $|f_1 + f_2| \leq |f_1| + |f_2| \leqq N_1 + N_2$, so that $E[|f_1 + f_2| > N_1 + N_2]$ is a subset of E_0 and so an α-null set. Then $\|f_1 + f_2\| \leqq N_1 + N_2 < \|f_1\| + \|f_2\| - 2e$ for all $e > 0$ and so for $e = 0$. If we consider functions of M as equivalent when they differ by an α-null set, then the conditions for a norm are satisfied by $\|f\|$.

We have:

2.2. A necessary and sufficient condition that $\lim_n \|f_n - f\| = 0$ in the class M, is that f_n converges to f uniformly excepting for an α-null set, that is, that there exists a set E_0 for which $\alpha(E_0) = 0$ such that $\lim_n f_n(x) = f(x)$ uniformly for x on CE_0.

The sufficiency is obvious. For the necessity suppose $\lim_n \|f_n - f\| = 0$, so that $(1/m, n_m, n \geqq n_m) : \|f_n - f\| \leqq 1/m$. Let $E_{nm} = E[|f_n - f| > 1/m]$. Then $\alpha(E_{nm}) = 0$ if $n \geqq n_m$. Let $E_0 = \Sigma_m \Sigma_{n_m}^{\infty} E_{nm}$. Then $\alpha(E_0) = 0$. If x belongs to CE_0, then x is in no E_{nm} for $n \geqq n_m$, that is for $n \geqq n_m$ and all x in CE_0 we have $|f_n(x) - f(x)| \leqq 1/m$. This means uniform convergence of f_n to f on CE_0.

2.3. The space M is complete in this norm, that is, $\lim_{nm} \|f_n - f_m\| = 0$ implies that there exists an f in M such that $\lim_n \|f_n - f\| = 0$.

Since $\lim_{nm} \|f_n - f_m\| = 0$. We have $(1/k, n_k, n \geqq n_k, m \geqq n_k)$: $\|f_n - f_m\| \leqq 1/k$. Set $E_{nmk} = E[|f_n - f_m| > 1/k]$. Then $\alpha(E_{nmk}) = 0$ if $n \geqq n_k$, and $m \geqq n_k$. Let $E_0 = \Sigma_k \Sigma_{n_k}^{\infty} \Sigma_{m_k}^{\infty} E_{nmk}$. Then $\alpha(E_0) = 0$, and on CE_0: $\lim_{n,m} |f_n(x) - f_m(x)| = 0$ uniformly. Then there exists an α-measurable function f defined on CE_0, and arbitrary on E_0 such that $\lim_n f_n(x) = f(x)$ uniformly for x on CE_0. Consequently, $|f(x)| \leqq |f_n(x)| + e$ for some $n > n_e$ and x on CE_0. Since f_n is almost bounded it follows that f has the same property. Moreover, since $\lim_n f_n(x) = f(x)$ uniformly on CE_0, it follows that

$$\lim_n \|f_n - f\| = 0.$$

Since in the space M, convergence depends on a metric, M is also complete relative to the convergence of a set $f_q(x)$, q on a directed Q.

2.4. We recall that if α is monotone bounded and f is in M, then $\int_X f d\alpha$ exists. Also if f_n and f are in M and $\lim_n \|f_n - f\| = 0$, then $\lim_n \int_X |f_n - f| \, d\alpha = 0$. These statements need not hold if α is unbounded.

3. The Space L^1

For a given monotone α on X, L^1 is the class or space of L-integrable functions f on X, that is such that $\int_X f d\alpha$ and so $\int_X |f| \, d\alpha$ exists. We have already noted in VII.8.1 and VII.8.2 that L^1 is linear and possesses the absolute property. We have also shown (VII.12.9) that if (a) f_n belongs to L^1, (b) $f_n \to f(\alpha)$, (c) $\int_E f_n d\alpha$ are uniformly absolutely continuous in n relative to α, and (d)

$$\lim_{(a,b)\to(-\infty,\infty)} \int_a^b |f_n| \, d\alpha$$

exist uniformly in n, then f is in L^1 and $\lim_n \int_X |f_n - f| \, d\alpha = 0$.

3.1. If we introduce in L^1 the notation $\|f\| = \int_X |f| \, d\alpha$, then for f in L^1:

(a) $\|f\| \geqq 0$; $\|f\| = 0$ if and only if $f = 0$ except for an α-null set.

(b) $\|cf\| = |c| \, \|f\|$; $\| \, |f| \, \| = \|f\|$.

(c) $\|f_1 + f_2\| \leqq \|f_1\| + \|f_2\|$.

(d) if g is α-measurable, and f is in L^1, and $|g(x)| \leqq |f(x)|$ except for an α-null set then g is in L^1 and $\|g\| \leqq \|f\|$.

Properties (a), (b), and (d) are obvious; (c) follows from

$$\int_X |f_1 + f_2| \, d\alpha \leq \int_X (|f_1| + |f_2|) \, d\alpha = \int_X |f_1| \, d\alpha + \int_X |f_2| \, d\alpha.$$

Since $\int_X |f| \, d\alpha$ has properties (a), (b), and (c) it is a norm on L^1, provided functions which differ on an α-null set are considered equivalent.

3.2. The space L^1 is complete under $\|f\| = \int_X |f| \, d\alpha$, that is if f_n is a sequence of functions in L^1 such that $\lim_{mn} \|f_m - f_n\| = 0$, then there exists an f in L^1 such that

$$\lim_n \|f_n - f\| = \lim_n \int_X |f_n - f| \, d\alpha = 0.$$

For if $\lim_{mn} \int_X |f_m - f_n| \, d\alpha = 0$, then for fixed e

$$\lim_{mn} e\alpha(E[|f_m - f_n| > e]) \leqq \lim_{mn} \int_X |f_m - f_n| \, d\alpha = 0,$$

so that the sequence of functions f_n satisfies the Cauchy condition for α-measure convergence. Consequently by VI.5.7 there exists a sequence of functions f_{n_k} and a function f such that $\lim_k f_{n_k}(x) = f(x)$ except for an α-null set and $f_n \to f(\alpha)$. From the inequalities

$$\int_E |f_n| \, d\alpha \leqq \int_E |f_n - f_m| \, d\alpha + \int_E |f_m| \, d\alpha$$

and

$$\int_E |f_m - f_n| \, d\alpha \leqq \int_X |f_m - f_n| \, d\alpha$$

for any α-measurable set E, it follows that $(e, n_e, m \geqq n_e, n \geqq n_e)$: $\int_E |f_n| \, d\alpha \leqq e + \int_E |f_m| \, d\alpha$. Now $\int_E |f_m| \, d\alpha$ is absolutely continuous relative to α, so that for $\alpha(E) \leqq d_e$, we have $\int_E |f_m| \, d\alpha \leqq e$. Then also for $\alpha(E) \leqq d_e$ and $n \geqq n_e$: $\int_E |f_n| \, d\alpha \leqq 2e$. Since there are only a finite number of $n < n_e$, for each of which $\int_E |f_n| \, d\alpha$ is absolutely continuous, it follows that there exists a $d_e' \leqq d_e$ such that for $\alpha(E) \leqq d_e'$ and for all n: $\int_E |f_n| \, d\alpha \leq e$, or absolute continuity uniform in n. In a parallel way we show that the

$$\lim_{(a,b)\to(-\infty,\infty)} \int_a^b |f_n| \, d\alpha$$

exist uniformly in n. We can then conclude that f is in L^1 and

$$\lim_n \int_X |f_n - f| \, d\alpha = \lim_n \|f_n - f\| = 0.$$

4. The Space L^p with $0 < p < \infty$

4.1. Definition. The space L^p, with $0 < p < \infty$ relative to a monotone α is defined as the space of all functions f on X such that $\int_X |f|^p \, d\alpha$ exists.

If α is bounded, and $p_1 \geqq p_2$, then the space L^{p_1} is contained in the space L^{p_2}. For if α is bounded, admission to L^p depends particularly on the large values of $f(x)$. If $|f(x)| > 1$, and $p_1 \geqq p_2$, then $|f(x)|^{p_1} \geqq |f(x)|^{p_2}$, so that if $\int_X |f|^{p_1} \, d\alpha < \infty$, then $\int_X |f|^{p_2} \, d\alpha < \infty$ also. For α unbounded, no such simple relation exists between the spaces L^p. For α bounded, the class M of almost bounded functions is contained in L^p for all $p > 0$, and so is sometimes labeled L^∞.

4.2. The space L^p obviously has the absolute property of containing $|f|$ with f. It is also linear.

For if f is in L^p, so is cf for any constant c. To obtain the additive property we need the following:

4.2.1. If $a \geqq 0$ and $b \geqq 0$, then

$$2^{p-1}(a^p + b^p) \leqq (a + b)^p \leqq a^p + b^p \quad \text{if} \quad 0 < p \leqq 1,$$

and

$$a^p + b^p \leqq (a + b)^p \leqq 2^{p-1}(a^p + b^p) \quad \text{if} \quad 1 \leqq p < \infty.$$

For the function $(1 + x)^p/(1 + x^p)$ on $0 \leqq x < \infty$ assumes the value 1 at $x = 0$, approaches 1 as $x \to \infty$, and has a maximum or minimum at $x = 1$. If $p > 1$, the value 2^{p-1} is maximal, if $p < 1$, the value 2^{p-1} is minimal. If we replace x by b/a, the inequalities mentioned result. It follows that:

4.2.2. If a and b are any two real (or complex) numbers, then

$$|a + b|^p \leqq (|a| + |b|)^p \leqq |a|^p + |b|^p \quad \text{if} \quad p \leqq 1$$

and

$$|a + b|^p \leqq 2^{p-1}(|a|^p + |b|^p) \quad \text{if} \quad p \geqq 1.$$

These two inequalities can be combined into a single statement

$$|a + b|^p \leqq g(p)\, (|a|^p + |b|^p)$$

if we define $g(p) = 1$ for $0 < p \leqq 1$, and $g(p) = 2^{p-1}$ if $1 \leqq p < \infty$

In view of VII.12.2 this inequality yields:

4.2.3. If $p > 0$, and f_1 and f_2 are in L^p, then $f_1 + f_2$ is in L^p and

$$\int_X |f_1 + f_2|^p \, d\alpha \leqq g(p) \left(\int_X |f_1|^p \, d\alpha + \int_X |f_2|^p \, d\alpha\right).$$

For $0 < p < 1$, $\int_X |f_1 - f_2|^p \, d\alpha$ plays the role of a metric on L^p. But $\int_X |f|^p \, d\alpha$ is not a norm, since $\int_X |cf|^p \, d\alpha = |c|^p \int_X |f|^p \, d\alpha$. The spaces L^p with $0 < p < 1$ are not normable, but we do not demonstrate this here.

4.3. For $p > 1$, $\int_X |f|^p \, d\alpha$ is not a metric, but $(\int_X |f|^p \, d\alpha)^{1/p}$ is not only a metric but a norm on L^p for $1 \leqq p < \infty$.

The expression obviously satisfies the conditions (a), (b), and (d) listed for $\|f\|$ in Section VIII.2. In order to show that the triangle inequality (c) also holds, we develope some inequalities which have (c) as consequence and are interesting in themselves.

We start from the statement that for $x \geqq 0$, and $p > 1$:

$$x^p \geqq px + 1 - p \quad \text{or} \quad px \leqq x^p + p - 1.$$

This follows from the fact that x^p for $p > 1$ is concave upward and so the curve $y = x^p$ lies entirely above its tangent at $x = 1$. If we set $x = a/c$, then for $a \geqq 0$ and $c \geqq 0$:

$$ac^{p-1} \leqq (1/p)a^p + (1 - 1/p)c^p.$$

If $b = c^{p-1}$, then for $a \geqq 0$ and $b \geqq 0$

$$ab \leqq (1/p)a^p + (1 - 1/p)b^{p/(p-1)}$$

If we let $p' = p/(p-1)$, so that $(1/p) + (1/p') = 1$, then

$$ab \leqq (1/p)\, a^p + (1/p')b^{p'},$$

so that if a and b are any real numbers,

$$|ab| \leqq (1/p)\, |a|^p + (1/p')\, |b|^{p'}.$$

For $p = 2$, we get the well known inequality

$$2\,|ab| \leqq a^2 + b^2 .$$

It now follows that if f_1 is in L^p and f_2 is in $L^{p'}$, then $f_1 \cdot f_2$ is in L^1 and

$$\int_X |f_1 \cdot f_2|\, d\alpha \leqq (1/p) \int_X |f_1|^p\, d\alpha + (1/p') \int_X |f_2|^{p'} d\alpha.$$

If in particular $\int_X |f_1|^p\, d\alpha = 1$ and $\int_X |f_2|^{p'}\, d\alpha = 1$ (that is f_1 and f_2 have norm 1), then

$$\int_X |f_1 \cdot f_2|\, d\alpha \leqq 1.$$

If for g_1 in L^p and g_2 in $L^{p'}$ we set $f_1 = g_1/(\int_X |g_1|^p\, d\alpha)^{1/p}$ and $f_2 = g_2/(\int_X |g_2|^{p'}\, d\alpha)^{1/p'}$, so that f_1 and f_2 each have norm 1 in their space, then we can conclude:

4.4. If g_1 is in L^p and g_2 is in $L^{p'}$ with $(1/p) + (1/p') = 1$, then $g_1 \cdot g_2$ is in L^1 and

$$\int_X |g_1 \cdot g_2|\, d\alpha \leqq \left(\int_X |g_1|^p\, d\alpha\right)^{1/p} \left(\int_X |g_2|^{p'}\, d\alpha\right)^{1/p'}.$$

This is known as *Hoelder's inequality*. For $p = 2$, it reduces to the *Schwarz inequality*:

4.4.1. If g_1 and g_2 are in L^2, then $g_1 \cdot g_2$ is in L^1 and

$$\left(\int_X |g_1 \cdot g_2 \,| d\alpha\right)^2 \leqq \int_X |g_1|^2 d\alpha \cdot \int_X |g_2|^2 d\alpha .$$

The Schwarz inequality can also be deduced from the fact that L^2 is linear and that

$$\int_X (g_1 + cg_2)^2 d\alpha = \int_X g_1^2 d\alpha + 2c \int_X g_1 \cdot g_2 d\alpha + c^2 \int_X g_2^2 d\alpha$$

is a positive quadratic form in c.

To obtain the triangle inequality for $\|f\| = (\int_X |f|^p d\alpha)^{1/p}$ we assume that f_1 and f_2 are in L^p and set $g_1 = |f_1|$ or $|f_2|$ and $g_2 = (|f_1| + |f_2|)^{p-1}$ in Hoelder's inequality. For then g_1 is in L^p and g_2 is in $L^{p'}$, since $p'(p-1) = p$. Using the additive property of integrals we obtain:

$$\begin{aligned}\int_X (|f_1| + |f_2|)^p d\alpha &= \int_X (|f_1| + |f_2|)\,(|f_1| + |f_2|)^{p-1} d\alpha \\ &\leqq \left(\int_X |f_1|^p d\alpha\right)^{1/p} \left(\int_X (|f_1| + |f_2|^p d\alpha\right)^{1/p'} \\ &\quad + \left(\int_X |f_2|^p d\alpha\right)^{1/p} \left(\int_X (|f_1| + |f_2|)^p d\alpha\right)^{1/p'}\end{aligned}$$

Dividing through by $(\int_X (|f_1| + |f_2|)^p d\alpha)^{1/p'}$ and remembering that $1 - (1/p') = 1/p$, gives us

$$\left(\int_X (|f_1| + |f_2|)^p d\alpha\right)^{1/p} \leqq \left(\int_X |f_1|^p d\alpha\right)^{1/p} + \left(\int_X |f_2|^p d\alpha\right)^{1/p}.$$

In terms of $\|f\| = (\int_X |f|^p d\alpha)^{1/p}$ this says

$$\|f_1 + f_2\| \leqq \|f_1\| + \|f_2\|.$$

We proceed to show that:

4.5. If $\|f\| = (\int_X |f|^p \, d\alpha)^{1/p}$, then the spaces L^p with $p > 1$ are complete in terms of this norm.

Assume that $\lim_{m,n} \|f_m - f_n\| = 0$, or equivalently $\lim_{m,n} \int_X |f_m - f_n|^p \, d\alpha = 0$. Then for $e > 0$, $\lim_{m,n} e \cdot \alpha(E[|f_m - f_n|^p > e]) = 0$ so that the sequence f_n satisfies the Cauchy condition for α-measure convergence. Consequently, there exists a subsequence f_{n_k} and a function f such that $\lim_k f_{n_k}(x) = f(x)$ except for an α-null set. Then $\lim_k |f_{n_k}(x)|^p = |f(x)|^p$ except for an α-null set. Since the $f_{n_k}(x)$ are α-measurable it follows that $|f_{n_k}(x)|^p \to |f(x)|^p(\alpha)$.

We now show that for any sequence of disjoint α-measurable sets E_m, the series $\Sigma_m \int_{E_m} |f_n|^p d\alpha$ converges uniformly in n. For if $p > 1$, then

$$\sum_m \int_{E_m} |f_n|^p \, d\alpha \leqq 2^{p-1} \left(\sum_m \int_{E_m} |f_n - f_{n'}|^p d\alpha + \sum_m \int_{E_m} |f_{n'}|^p d\alpha\right)$$
$$\leqq 2^{p-1} \left(\int_X |f_n - f_{n'}|^p d\alpha + \sum_m \int_{E_m} |f_{n'}|^p d\alpha\right).$$

Since $\lim_{n,n'} \int_X |f_n - f_{n'}|^p d\alpha = 0$, it follows that $(e > 0, n_e, n \geqq n_e, n' \geqq n_e) : \Sigma_m \int_{E_m} |f_n|^p d\alpha \leqq 2^{p-1} (e + \Sigma_m \int_{E_m} |f_{n'}|^p d\alpha)$. If $n' = n_e$, we can select m_e in such a way that for $m' \geqq m_e : \Sigma_{m'}^{\infty} \int_{E_m} |f_{n'}|^p d\alpha \leqq e$. Then for $n \geqq n_e$ and $m' \geqq m_e$ we have $\Sigma_{m'}^{\infty} \int_{E_m} |f_n|^p d\alpha \leqq 2^p e$, from which the uniform convergence of the series $\Sigma_m \int_{E_m} |f_n|^p d\alpha$ in n can be deduced in the usual way. Applied to the subsequence f_{n_k}, it now follows by VII.12.11 that $\int_X |f|^p d\alpha$ exists and that $\lim_k \int_X |f_{n_k}|^p d\alpha = \int_X |f|^p d\alpha$. The same procedure gives us that if $g(x)$ is any function in L^p, then $\lim_k \int_X |f_{n_k} - g|^p d\alpha = \int_X |f - g|^p d\alpha$. If we set $g(x) = f_n(x)$, we have $\lim_k \int_X |f_{n_k} - f_n|^p d\alpha = \int_X |f - f_n|^p d\alpha$ for all n. Consequently,

$$\lim_n \int_X |f - f_n|^p d\alpha = \lim_n \lim_k \int_X |f_{n_k} - f_n| \, d\alpha = 0,$$

which concludes the proof of the completeness of L^p in the norm.

As a result of Hoelder's inequality we can state:

4.6. If f_n and f are functions in L^p with $1 < p < \infty$, and such that $\lim_n \|f_n - f\| = 0$, then for every function g in $L^{p'}$: $\lim_n \int_X f_n g d\alpha = \int_X fg d\alpha$. For

$$\left| \int_X f_n g d\alpha - \int_X fg d\alpha \right| \leqq \int_X |f_n - f| \cdot |g| \, d\alpha \leqq \|f_n - f\| \cdot \|g\|.$$

Since for g in $L^{p'}$, the integral $\int_X fg d\alpha$ is linear on L^p, it follows that $\int_X fg d\alpha$ is a linear continuous functional on the linear class L^p. It can be shown that every linear continuous functional on L^p has this form.

5. Separability

5.1. Definition. A topological space X in which the notion of limiting point is defined, is *separable* if there exists a sequence or denumerable set of elements $\{x_n\}$ of the space which is dense in the space. In particular if X is a metric space, than X is separable if there exists a sequence of elements $\{x_n\}$ such that for any x of X and $e > 0$, there exists an n_e such that $\delta(x, x_{n_e}) < e$.

5.2. If X is a separable metric space, and X_0 is a subset of X such that the mutual distances of any two distinct elements x' and x'' of X_0 is greater than some fixed positive constant e, then X_0 will consist of a denumerable number of elements.

For if the sequence x_n is dense in X, and x' is any element of X_0, there will exist an element x_{n_1}, such that $\delta(x', x_{n_1}) < e/2$ and $\delta(x'', x_{n_1}) > e/2$ for all elements $x'' \neq x'$ of X_0, since $\delta(x', x'') > e$. This sets up a one to one correspondence between a subset of $\{x_n\}$ and the set X_0, so that X_0 is denumerable.

5.3. If $\alpha(x)$ is monotonic nondecreasing on $X \equiv -\infty < x < \infty$, and such that there exists a sequence of disjoint α-measurable sets E_n such that $\alpha(E_n) > 0$ for all n, and if M is the space of almost bounded functions $f(x)$ on X relative to α, normed by the almost least upper bound, then M is not separable.

For let q stand for any subset of the integers: $q = n_1, \ldots n_k, \ldots$ and define $f_q(x) = \chi(\Sigma_q E_n; x)$, the characteristic function of $\Sigma_q E_n$. If $q_1 \neq q_2$ then $\|f_{q_1} - f_{q_2}\| = 1$, since the two functions will differ on some subset E_n, which is of positive measure. But the set of q, being the set of all subsets of the integers is nondenumerable, being of the same order as that of the real numbers.

5.3.1. If $\alpha(x) = x$ on $[a, b]$, that is α-measurable sets are Lebesgue measurable, then the space of Lebesgue measurable almost bounded functions M is not separable.

5.4. If $\alpha(x)$ is monotonic nondecreasing on $X = -\infty < x < \infty$, then the spaces L^p for $p > 0$ relative to α are separable.

We prove this for $p = 1$, the other cases are entirely analogous. There are various sequences of functions which belong to L^1 and are dense in L^1. One such sequence consists of all the functions $g_n(x)$ which are finite, rational, interval, step functions on X.

5.4.1. $g(x)$ is a finite, rational, interval, step function on X, if there exists a finite number of disjoint, finite half-open (on the left) intervals $I_1 \ldots I_k$ having rational end points, such that $g(x)$ has a rational value on each I_i, and vanishes on the complement of $\Sigma_i I_i$.

Since there are at most a denumerable number of such interval sets, and the number of distinct rational valued step functions on any set of intervals is denumerable, the set of step functions $g(x)$ so defined is denumerable. Any such $g(x)$ is bounded and α-measurable and so in L^1.

Suppose now that $f(x)$ is in L^1. Then f is α-measurable and

$$\lim_{(a,b)\to(-\infty,\infty)} \int_a^b |f| \, d\alpha$$

exists. For a given $e > 0$, there exists an integer N such that $\left| \int_X |f| \, d\alpha - \int_{-N}^{+N} |f| \, d\alpha \right| < e$. If we set $f_N(x) = f(x)$ for $-N < x \leqq +N$, and $f_N(x) = 0$ for $x > N$, and $x \leqq -N$, then $\int_X |f - f_N| \, d\alpha < e$. For M an integer, set $f_{NM}(x) = f_N(x)$ for x such that $|f_N(x)| \leqq M$, and $f_{NM}(x) = M$ if $f_N(x) \geqq M$, and $f_{NM}(x) = -M$ if $f_N(x) \leqq -M$. Then $f_{NM}(x)$ differs from $f_N(x)$ only on $E_{NM} = E[|f_{NM}| > M]$. Moreover since $\int_{-N}^{+N} |f_N| \, d\alpha$ exists, $\lim_M \alpha(E_{NM}) = 0$. Then $\lim_M \int_{-N}^{+N} |f_N - f_{NM}| \, d\alpha = 0$, and for $e > 0$ there exists M_0 such that $\int_{-N}^{+N} |f_N - f_{NM_0}| \, d\alpha < e$. The function $f_{NM_0}(x)$ is bounded α-measurable and by VI.6.4, there exists a sequence of interval step functions $h_n(x)$ on $-N < x \leqq +N$ such that $\lim_n h_n(x) = f_{NM_0}(x)$, except for an α-null set. These step functions can be taken of the type of the rational step functions defined above and bounded by M, that is, there exists a sequence of finite rational interval step functions $g_n(x)$ such that $-M \leqq g_n(x) \leqq +M$ for $-N < x \leqq +N$, and $g_n(x) = 0$ for $x < N$, or $x \leqq -N$, such that $\lim_n g_n(x) = f_{NM_0}(x)$ except for an α-null set. By the integral convergence theorem we then have $\lim_n \int_{-N}^{+N} |g_n - f_{NM_0}| \, d\alpha = 0$, or for $e > 0$, there exists an n such that $\int_{-N}^{+N} |g_n - f_{NM_0}| \, d\alpha < e$. Consequently,

$$\begin{aligned} \int_X |g_n - f| \, d\alpha &\leqq \int_X |g_n - f_{NM_0}| \, d\alpha + \int_X |f_{NM_0} - f_N| \, d\alpha \\ &\quad + \int_X |f_N - f| \, d\alpha = \int_{-N}^{+N} |g_n - f_{NM_0}| \, d\alpha \\ &\quad + \int_{-N}^{+N} |f_{NM_0} - f_N| \, d\alpha + \int_X |f_N - f| \, d\alpha \leqq 3e. \end{aligned}$$

This means that for $3e > 0$ there exists one of the rational valued interval step functions $g(x)$ such that $\int_X |g - f| d\alpha < 3e$, so that the denumerable set of rational interval step functions is dense in L^1.

Obviously the same procedure is usable for the case L^p, with $\delta(f_1, f_2) = \int_X |f_1 - f_2|^p d\alpha$ if $0 < p < 1$, and $\delta(f_1, f_2) = (\int_X |f_1 - f_2|^p d\alpha)^{1/p}$ if $1 \leqq p < \infty$. We can also prove in the same way that the space of α-measurable functions on $X = -\infty < x < +\infty$ is separable when metrized as in VIII.1.2 above by the condition

$$\delta(f_1, f_2) = \int_X \frac{|f_1 - f_2|}{1 + |f_1 - f_2|} h(x) d\alpha$$

where $h(x)$ is an appropriate nonvanishing positive valued α-measurable step function which is integrable with respect to α on X.

5.5. The class C_0 of continuous functions each of which vanishes on the complement of some bounded interval of X, is dense in L^1.

We might observe that in the proof of the separability of the space L^1, we have incidentally demonstrated that the class of finite valued interval step functions, that is, functions which are constant on each of a finite number of disjoint intervals $I_1 \ldots I_k$ and vanish on the complement of $\Sigma_i I_i$, is dense in the space L^1. If we invoke the theorem that for any α-measurable function $f(x)$, with $\alpha(x)$ bounded, there exists a sequence of continuous functions $f_n(x)$ such that $\lim_n f_n(x) = f(x)$ except for an α-null set, we can show that the class C_0 of functions continuous on X and vanishing on the complement of some bounded interval is also dense in L^1. We need only apply the theorem to the functions f_{NM_0} on the interval $-N - 1 \leqq x \leqq N + 1$, defined in the proof of VIII.5.4. For if the sequence of continuous functions $g_n(x)$ is such that $\lim_n g_n(x) = f_{NM_0}(x)$ except for an α-null set on $[-N - 1, N + 1]$, we can assume that $g_n(x) = 0$ for $|x| \geqq N + 1$, and $|g_n(x)| \leqq M_0$ for all n and x. Consequently,

$$\lim_n \int_X |g_n - f_{NM_0}| d\alpha = \lim_n \int_{-N-1}^{N+1} |g_n - f_{NM_0}| d\alpha = 0.$$

Since

$$\int_X |g_n - f| d\alpha \leqq \int_X |g_n - f_{NM_0}| d\alpha + \int_X |f_{NM_0} - f_N| d\alpha + \int_X |f_N - f| d\alpha = \int_{-N-1}^{N+1} |g_n - f_{NM_0}| d\alpha + \int_{-N}^{+N} |f_{NM_0} - f_N| d\alpha + \int_X |f_N - f| d\alpha,$$

the density of the class C_0, of functions continuous on X and vanishing outside of a bounded closed interval, in the space L^1 is immediate.

If X is the finite closed interval $[a, b]$, we can use the fact that any continuous function on $[a, b]$ can be uniformly approximated by polynomials, and any polynomial can be uniformly approximated by polynomials with rational coefficients — a denumerable set — to give us an alternate proof of the separability of L^1 on a finite interval.

Similar statements hold for L^p with $p > 0$.

6. The Space L^2. Orthogonal Functions. Riesz-Fischer Theorem

Among the spaces L^p, the space L^2 for $p = 2$ has received particular attention because on the one hand it is a generalisation to the continuous variable of Euclidean space in n dimensions with Euclidean distance $\delta(x, y) = (\Sigma_{i=1}^n (x_i - y_i)^2)^{1/2}$ replaced by $(\int_X (f - g)^2 d\alpha)^{1/2}$. In addition, if f and g are in L^2 then $f \cdot g$ is in L^1, or is integrable. As in Euclidean space this fact allows us to set up an inner product for pairs of functions f and g of L^2, by the condition $(f, g) = \int_X f \cdot g d\alpha$. This inner product is bilinear, symmetric on L^2, and has the property that $(f, f) = \|f\|^2 = \int_X f^2 d\alpha \geqq 0$ for all f of L^2, vanishing only for the functions which are zero except for an α-null set. The Schwarz inequality in this setting can be written

$$(f, g) \cdot (g, f) \leqq (f, f) \cdot (g, g).$$

We have been considering throughout only real valued functions. If $f(x)$ is complex valued on X, and $f(x) = g(x) + ih(x)$, with $i = \sqrt{-1}$, then $f(x)$ is in L^1 if and only if g and h are in L^1 and $\int_X f d\alpha = \int_X g d\alpha + i \int_X h d\alpha$. f is in L^2 if and only if $|f|^2$ is in L^1 or $\int_X |f|^2 d\alpha$ exists. For complex valued functions, it is usual to define the inner product (f, g) of two complex valued functions in L^2 as $\int_X f \cdot \bar{g} d\alpha$. Then (f, g) is Hermitian: $(f, g) = \overline{(g, f)}$, linear in f, conjugate linear in g and $(f, f) = \int_X |f|^2 d\alpha \geqq 0$ for all f, vanishing only if f is zero except for an α-null set. $\|f\|$ is then defined by $\|f\|^2 = \int_X |f|^2 d\alpha$, and possesses the usual properties.

The space L^2 is an instance of an *abstract Hilbert space* H in which there is defined an inner product (f, g) for pairs of elements f, g of H. The space is a real Hilbert space, if H is real linear, (f, g) is real-valued symmetric, and real bilinear on H with $(f, f) \geqq 0$ for all f of H, and $(f, f) = 0$ if and only f is the zero of H. The space is a complex Hilbert space if H is complex linear, (f, g) is Hermitian: $(f, g) = \overline{(g, f)}$, linear in f and conjugate linear in g, with $(f, f) \geqq 0$ for all f, $(f, f) = 0$ if and only if $f = 0$ of H.

Most of the developments of this section, could be carried out in the abstract setting. We shall, however, stick to integrals of real valued functions on the real axis, for convenience abbreviate $\int_X f d\alpha$ by $\int f$, omitting the X and α, which are considered fixed throughout this section.

6.1. Definition. A finite set of functions $f_1 \ldots f_n$ in L^2 is said to be *linearly independent* if $\int (c_1 f_1 + \ldots + c_n f_n)^2 = 0$ implies $c_1 = c_2 = \ldots = c_n = 0$, or if $\Sigma_1^n c_i f_i = 0$ except for an α-null set implies $c_1 = c_2 = \ldots = c_n = 0$.

An expansion of the integral $\int (\Sigma_i c_i f_i)^2$ gives $\Sigma_{ij} c_i c_j \int f_i f_j$, which if $f_1 \ldots f_n$ are linearly independent is a positive definite quadratic form in $c_1 \ldots c_n$. Since the form $\Sigma_{ij} a_{ij} x_i x_j$ with $a_{ij} = a_{ji}$ is positive definite only if the determinant of a_{ij} (or det a_{ij}) is positive (and not zero), it follows from the definition of linear independence that:

6.2. The functions $f_1 \ldots f_n$ of L^2 are linearly independent if and only if det $(\int f_i f_j) > 0$.

6.2.1. Definition. The det $(\int f_i f_j)$ for the functions $f_1 \ldots f_n$ is called the *Gramian* of these functions and will be denoted by $G(f_1 \ldots f_n)$.

6.3. In view of the fact that for f and g in L^2, the integral $\int f \cdot g d\alpha$ plays the role of an inner product, we say that f and g are *orthogonal* if and only if $\int f \cdot g = 0$. The only self-orthogonal function is equal to zero except for an α-null set, or equivalent to a zero function.

6.4. If f and g are orthogonal to each other, then they satisfy the Pythagorean equality:

$$\int (f + g)^2 = \int f^2 + \int g^2.$$

6.5. A function f in L^2 is *normalized* if it is of unit norm, that is $\int f^2 = 1$. If f is any function in L^2 then the function $f/\|f\| = f/(\int f^2)^{1/2}$ is normalized.

6.6. An *orthonormal system* of functions $f_q(x)$ consists of functions which are mutually orthogonal and each normalized, that is $\int f_{q'} f_{q''} = \delta_{q'q''}$, where $\delta_{q'q''}$ is the Kronecker δ, which vanishes if $q' \neq q''$ and has value unity when $q' = q''$.

If $f_{q'}$ and $f_{q''}$ are two functions of an orthonormal system, then

$$\|f_{q'} - f_{q''}\|^2 = \int (f_{q'} - f_{q''})^2 = \int f_{q'}^2 + \int f_{q''}^2 = 2,$$

that is, the mutual distance between any two distinct functions of an orthonormal system is $\sqrt{2}$. Since the space L^2 relative to a monotonic nondecreasing function α on $X \equiv -\infty < x < +\infty$ is a separable metric space, it follows that:

6.7. Any orthonormal system of functions of the space L^2 determined by a monotonic nondecreasing function α on X is denumerable.

For if $\{g_n\}$ is a sequence of functions dense in L^2 and $[f_q]$ is an orthonormal system, then for each q, there exists an n_q such that $\|f_q - g_{n_q}\| < 1/4$. If $q' \neq q''$ then $n_{q'} \neq n_{q''}$, otherwise $\|f_{q'} - f_{q''}\| < 1/2$. Hence the system $[f_q]$ is denumerable.

We note that any orthonormal system consists of linearly independent functions, since if $\Sigma_i c_i f_i = 0$, then for $1 \leq j \leq n$: $\Sigma_i c_i \int f_i f_j = c_j = 0$.

The question of setting up a system of orthogonal functions is covered by:

6.8. THEOREM. If $f_1, ..., f_n, ...$ is any sequence of functions in L^2 which are linearly independent, in the sense that any finite subset of the sequence consists of linearly independent functions, then there exists an orthonormal system of functions $\varphi_1 ... \varphi_n ...$ in L^2 linearly equivalent to $f_1 ... f_n ...$ in the sense that $\varphi_n = \Sigma_{m=1}^n a_{nm} f_m$ for all n with $a_{nn} \neq 0$, and $f_n = \Sigma_{m=1}^n c_{nm} \varphi_m$ with $c_{nn} = 1/a_{nn}$.

This means that φ_n is a linear combination of $f_1 ... f_n$ for all n, and f_n is a linear combination of $\varphi_1 ... \varphi_n$ or the linear extension $(f_1 ... f_n)_L$ which consists of all functions of the form $\Sigma_{i=1}^n c_i f_i$ is the same as $(\varphi_1 ... \varphi_n)_L$, for each n. It follows that φ_n must be orthogonal to $f_1 ... f_{n-1}$.

The following procedure for setting up an orthonormal system $\varphi_1 ... \varphi_n ...$ equivalent to a sequence of linearly independent functions $f_1 ... f_n ...$ is due to E. Schmidt.

We set $\varphi_1 = c_{11} f_1$, and determine c_{11} by the normalizing condition on φ_1, so that $c_{11} = 1/(\int f_1^2)^{1/2}$.

Set $\varphi_2 = c_{12}\varphi_1 + c_{22} f_2$. Then the condition $\int \varphi_2 \varphi_1 = 0$ gives $c_{12} = -c_{22} \int f_2 \varphi_1$, so that $\varphi_2 = c_{22}[f_2 - (\int f_2 \varphi_1)\varphi_1]$. Since f_2 and f_1, and so f_2 and φ_1 are linearly independent it follows that $f_2 - (\int f_2 \varphi_1)\varphi_1 \neq 0$, and we can set $c_{22}^2 = 1/\int (f_2 - (\int f_2 \varphi_1)\varphi_1)^2$. Assuming that $\varphi_1 ...$

φ_{n-1} have been determined, we set $\varphi_n = c_{n1}f_1 + c_{n2}f_2 + \ldots + c_{nn-1}f_{n-1} + c_{nn}f_n$. Then the conditions $\int \varphi_n \varphi_i = 0$ for $i = 1 \ldots n-1$ give $c_{ni} = - c_{nn} \int f_n \varphi_i$, so that $\varphi_n = c_{nn}(f_n - \Sigma_{i=1}^{n-1} (f_n \varphi_i)\varphi_i)$. Because of the linear independence of $f_1 \ldots f_n$ it follows that $f_n - \Sigma_{i=1}^{n-1} (\int f_n \varphi_i)\varphi_i \neq 0$, and we can take $c_{nn}{}^2 = 1/\int (f_n - \Sigma_{i=1}^{n-1} (\int f_n \varphi_i)\varphi_i)^2$

It is possible to determine φ_n in terms of $f_1 \ldots f_n$ by substituting the values for φ_i, $i = 1, \ldots n-1$ in terms of $f_1 \ldots f_{n-1}$ in $\varphi_n = c_{nn}(f_n - \Sigma_{i=1}^{n-1} (\int f_n \varphi_i)\varphi_i)$. This can, however, be done directly if we remember that φ_n must be orthogonal to $f_1, \ldots f_{n-1}$. If we set $\varphi_n = \Sigma_1^n b_{ni} f_i$, and invoke the conditions $\int \varphi_n \cdot f_j = 0$, $j = 1 \ldots n-1$, then

$$0 = \sum_{i=1}^{n} b_{ni} \int f_i f_j, \quad j = 1 \ldots n-1$$

Now the determinant of $\int f_i f_j$ with $i, j = 1 \ldots n-1$ is the Gramian: $G(f_1, \ldots, f_{n-1})$, which does not vanish, since the functions $f_1 \ldots f_{n-1}$ are linearly independent. Then the relation $\varphi_n = \Sigma_{i=1}^{n} b_{ni} f_i$, and elimination of b_{ni}, $i = 1 \ldots n-1$ yields

$$\begin{vmatrix} f_1 & f_2 & \ldots & f_{n-1} & \varphi_n - b_{nn} f_n \\ \int f_1 f_1 & \int f_2 f_1 & \ldots & \int f_{n-1} f_1 & b_{nn} \int f_n f_1 \\ & & \ldots & & \\ \int f_1 f_{n-1} & \int f_2 f_{n-1} & \ldots & \int f_{n-1} f_{n-1} & b_{nn} \int f_n f_{n-1} \end{vmatrix} = 0$$

so that

$$\varphi_n = (-1)^n b_{nn} \begin{vmatrix} f_1 & f_2 & \ldots & f_{n-1} & f_n \\ \int f_1 f_1 & \int f_2 f_1 & \ldots & \int f_{n-1} f_1 & \int f_n f_1 \\ & & \ldots & & \\ \int f_1 f_{n-1} & \int f_2 f_{n-1} & \ldots & \int f_{n-1} f_{n-1} & \int f_n f_{n-1} \end{vmatrix} \div G(f_1 \ldots f_{n-1})$$

The determinant on the right is a linear combination of $f_1 \ldots f_n$, with unity as the coefficient of f_n and so does not vanish. To determine b_{nn} by the condition $\int \varphi_n^2 = 1$, we note that $\int \varphi_n f_i = 0$, for $i = 1 \ldots n-1$ so that

$$\int \varphi_n^2 = \int \varphi_n \cdot \varphi_n = b_{nn} \int \varphi_n f_n = b_{nn}^2 G(f_1 \ldots f_n)/G(f_1 \ldots f_{n-1}).$$

Then $b_{nn}^2 = G(f_1 \ldots f_{n-1})/G(f_1 \ldots f_n)$ and

$$\varphi_n = \begin{vmatrix} f_1 & f_2 & \ldots & f_n \\ \int f_1 f_1 & \int f_2 f_1 & \ldots & \int f_n f_1 \\ & & \ldots & \\ \int f_1 f_{n-1} & \int f_2 f_{n-1} & \ldots & \int f_n f_{n-1} \end{vmatrix} \div (G(f_1 \ldots f_n))^{1/2} \cdot (G(f_1 \ldots f_{n-1}))^{1/2}$$

Let $\{\varphi_n\}$ be an orthonormal system in L^2, and f be any function in L^2. Then for the square of the distance of f from any function in the linear space determined by $\varphi_1 \dots \varphi_n$, or $(\varphi_1 \dots \varphi_n)_L$ we have

$$\int (f - \sum_1^n c_m \varphi_m)^2 = \int f^2 - 2 \sum_m c_m \int f\varphi_m + \sum_m c_m^2$$
$$= \int f^2 - \sum_m (\int f\varphi_m)^2 + \sum_m (c_m - \int f\varphi_m)^2.$$

It follows that the minimum distance of f from $(\varphi_1 \dots \varphi_m)_L$ is attained for $c_m = \int f\varphi_m$, and has the value $[f^2 - \Sigma_m (\int f\varphi_m)^2]^{1/2}$. If $g = \Sigma_m (f\varphi_m)\varphi_m$, then $\int g\varphi_m = \int f\varphi_m$ for $m = 1 \dots n$, so that $\int (f-g)\varphi_m = 0$ and $f - g$ is orthogonal to each φ_m, consequently to all of the functions in $(\varphi_1 \dots \varphi_n)_L$ and in particular to $g = \Sigma_m (\int f\varphi_m)\varphi_m$. We then have the Pythagorean equality

$$\int f^2 = \int (f-g)^2 + \int g^2 .$$

We observe also that the minimizing distance from f to $(\varphi_1 \dots \varphi_n)_L$ is along the vector $f - g$ which is orthogonal to the linear space $(\varphi_1 \dots \varphi_n)_L$. It follows that if $f_1 \dots f_n$ is any finite set of linearly independent functions of L^2, then the minimum distance from f to the set $(f_1, \dots, f_n)_L$ is attained by a function of the form $f - \Sigma_m c_m f_m$ which is orthogonal to $(f_1, \dots, f_n)_L$ and consequently to each f_m. This can also be verified by applying the differential calculus to the problem of minimizing $F(c_1 \dots c_n) = \int (f - \Sigma_m c_m f_m)^2$ as a function of $c_1 \dots c_n$.

Since

$$0 \leqq \int (f - \sum_1^n (\int f\varphi_m)\varphi_m)^2 = \int f^2 - \sum_1^n (\int \varphi_m)^2,$$

it follows that $\Sigma_1^n (\int f\varphi_m)^2 \leqq \int f^2$ for all n, and we consequently have:

6.9. Bessel's Inequality. If $\{\varphi_n\}$ is any orthonormal system in L^2 and f is any function in L^2, then $\Sigma_n (\int f\varphi_n)^2$ converges and $\Sigma_n (\int f\varphi_n)^2 \leqq \int f^2$.

For the case when $X \equiv 0 \leqq x \leqq 2\pi$, $\alpha(x) = x$, and the orthonormal system consists of the functions: $1/\sqrt{2\pi}$, $(1/\sqrt{\pi}) \cos nx$, $(1/\sqrt{\pi}) \sin nx$, the expressions $\int f\varphi_m$ become

$$a_0 = 1/\sqrt{2\pi} \int_0^{2\pi} f(x)dx; \quad a_n = (1/\sqrt{\pi}) \int_0^{2\pi} f(x) \cos nxdx;$$

and

$$b_n = (1/\sqrt{\pi}) \int_0^{2\pi} f(x) \sin nxdx,$$

and are called the Fourier coefficients of f. By analogy, the term Fourier coefficient is sometimes applied to the $\int f\varphi_n$ relative to any orthonormal system $\{\varphi_n\}$. As a result of Bessel's inequality, we could then say that for any f of L^2 and any orthonormal system $\{\varphi_n\}$ of L^2, the sum of the squares of the Fourier coefficients of f relative $\{\varphi_n\}$ is convergent.

For any orthonormal system in L^2, the expression $a_n = \int f\varphi_n$ effects, then a transformation or map of L^2 on the space l^2 of sequences of convergent square. The following important theorem is a sort of converse:

6.10. Riesz-Fischer Theorem. If $\{a_n\}$ is any sequence of numbers in l^2, that is $\Sigma_n a_n^2 < \infty$, and if $\{\varphi_n\}$ is any orthonormal system in L^2, there exists a function f in L^2 such that $\int f\varphi_n = a_n$ for all n.

The conclusion of the theorem can also be interpreted as saying that under the conditions of the hypothesis, the functional or integral equation $\int f\varphi_n = a_n$ have a solution f in L^2.

The theorem is an immediate consequence of the completeness of the space L^2. For if we set $f_n = \Sigma_1^n a_k\varphi_k$, then for $n > m$

$$\int (f_n - f_m)^2 = \sum_{m+1}^{n} a_k^2 ,$$

so that $\lim_{n,m} \int (f_n - f_m)^2 = 0$. Consequently there exists an f in L^2 such that $\lim_n \int (f_n - f)^2 = 0$. Then since for every g in L^2:

$$(\int f_n g - \int fg)^2 = (\int (f_n - f)g)^2 \leqq (\int (f_n - f)^2 \int g^2),$$

it follows that $\lim_n \int f_n g = \int fg$. Now $\int f_n\varphi_m = a_m$ if $n > m$. Consequently $\int f\varphi_m = a_m$ for all m. Further since

$$\int (f_n - f)^2 = \int f_n^2 - 2\int f_n f + \int f^2 = f^2 - \sum_1^n a_k^2$$

it follows that

$$\int f^2 = \sum_1^{\infty} a_k^2 = \sum_1^{\infty} (\int f\varphi_k)^2.$$

An obvious additional question is: Under what conditions is the function f in this theorem uniquely determined (up to an α-null set), and the obvious answer is that f is uniquely determined if and only if any f of L^2 such that $\int f\varphi_n = 0$ for all n is the zero function. This property of any orthonormal system is called *completeness*. As a matter of fact there are three equivalent ways of defining completeness of an orthonormal system in L^2.

6.11. Definition. An orthonormal system $\{\varphi_n\}$ in L^2 is complete if and only if:

(1) $\int f\varphi_n = 0$ for all n implies $f = 0$ except for an α-null set;

or:

(2) $\Sigma_n (\int f\varphi_n)^2 = \int f^2$ for all f in L^2;

or:

(3) $\lim_n \int (f - \Sigma_1^n (\int f\varphi_m)\varphi_m)^2 = 0$ for all f in L^2.

We show that (1) implies (2) implies (3) implies (1).

(1) implies (2). Let f be any element of L^2. Since $\Sigma_n (\int f\varphi_n)^2 < \infty$ it follows from the Riesz-Fischer theorem that there will exist a function g in L^2 such that $\lim_n \int (g - \Sigma_1^n (\int f\varphi_m)\varphi_m)^2 = 0$, $\int g\varphi_m = \int f\varphi_m$ for all m and $\int g^2 = \Sigma_n (\int f\varphi_n)^2$. But $\int g\varphi_m = \int f\varphi_m$ or $\int (f - g)\varphi_m = 0$ for all m implies $g = f$ except for an α-null set. Then $g^2 = f^2$ except for an α-null set so that $\int f^2 = \int g^2 = \Sigma_n (\int f\varphi_n)^2$.

(2) implies (3). This is an immediate consequence of the fact that: $\int (f - \Sigma_1^n (\int f\varphi_m)\varphi_m)^2 = \int f^2 - \Sigma_1^n (\int f\varphi_m)^2$.

(3) implies (1). For if $\int f\varphi_n = 0$ for all n, then by (3) $\int f^2 = 0$ so that $f = 0$ except for an α-null set.

6.12. In L^2 space there exist complete orthonormal systems, which by VIII.6.7 are at most denumerable.

Since L^2 is a separable space, there exists a sequence of functions f_n in L^2 dense in the space. If we drop from the sequence $\{f_n\}$ any function which is linearly dependent on the functions f_n for $m < n$, then the resulting subsequence $\{f_{n_m}\}$ will consist of linearly independent functions linearly equivalent to $\{f_n\}$. Let $\{\varphi_m\}$ be the orthonormal system linearly equivalent to $\{f_{n_m}\}$. Then any function f_n of the original sequence will be a linear combination of a finite number of functions φ_m. If $\int f\varphi_m = 0$ for all m, then $\int ff_n = 0$ for all n. Consequently

$$\int f^2 = \int ff - \int ff_n = \int f(f - f_n) \leq \|f\| \, \|f - f_n\|$$

for all n. Since the f_n are dense in L^2 it follows that $\int f^2 = 0$, so that the sequence $\{\varphi_m\}$ is a complete orthonormal system in L^2.

As a consequence of the properties of a complete orthonormal system, the Riesz-Fischer theorem has as corollary:

6.13. Any complete orthonormal system $\{\varphi_n\}$ in L^2 sets up a one to one correspondence between functions of L^2 and sequences in l^2, by the condition $\int f\varphi_n = a_n$. This correspondence is isometric in that

$$\sum_n (a_n - b_n)^2 = \sum_n (\int f\varphi_n - \int g\varphi_n)^2 = (f - g)^2.$$

The preceding results throw some light on the relationship between a function f in L^2 and its (Fourier) development in terms of an orthonormal system $\{\varphi_n\}$: $\Sigma_1^\infty (\int f_n \varphi)\varphi_n$. The sequence $\Sigma_1^n (\int f\varphi_n)\varphi_n$ is α-measure convergent to some function g in L^2. Only if the orthonormal system $\{\varphi_n\}$ is complete are we certain that $\Sigma_1^n (\int f\varphi_m)\varphi_m \to f(\alpha)$. As a consequence, there exists a sequence of integers n_k such that $\lim_k \Sigma_1^{n_k} (\int f\varphi_m)\varphi_m = f$, except for an α-null set. The series $\Sigma_1^n (\int \varphi_m)\varphi_m$ need not converge to f at any point of X.

The Riesz-Fischer theorem enables us to prove:

6.14. If $L(f)$ is a linear continuous functional on L^2, then there exists a function g in L^2 such that $L(f) = \int f \cdot g$ for all f in L^2.

We recall that $L(f)$ is continuous on L^2, if for every sequence f_n such that $\lim_n \|f_n - f\| = 0$, we have $\lim_n L(f_n) = L(f)$. The expression $\int f \cdot g$ for g in L^2 is obviously a linear continuous functional on L^2 since

$$|\int f \cdot g - \int f_n g| = |\int (f_n - f)g| \leq \|f_n - f\| \cdot \|g\|.$$

On the other hand, suppose $\{\varphi_n\}$ is a complete orthonormal system in L^2. Then for any f in L^2 we have $\lim_n \|f - \Sigma_1^n (\int f\varphi_m)\varphi_m\| = 0$. If $L(f)$ is linear and continuous then

$$L(f) = \lim_n L(\sum_1^n (\int f\varphi_m)\varphi_m) = \lim_n \sum_1^n (\int f\varphi_m)\,(L(\varphi_m)).$$

Then $\Sigma_1^\infty (\int f\varphi_m)\,(L(\varphi_m))$ converges for every f. But since the system $\{\varphi_m\}$ via $\int f\varphi_m$ sets up a one to one correspondence between functions in L^2 and sequences a_n in l^2, where $\Sigma |a_n|^2 < \infty$, it follows that $\Sigma_1^\infty a_m L(\varphi_m)$ converges for every seqeunce $\{a_n\}$ in l^2. We now use the following:

6.15. Lemma. A necessary and sufficient condition that $\Sigma_1^\infty a_n b_n$ converges for all sequences $\{a_n\}$ in l^2, is that the sequence $\{b_n\}$ be in l^2, that is $\Sigma_n |b_n|^2 < \infty$.

The sufficiency part of this lemma is an immediate consequence of the (Schwarz) inequality: $(\Sigma_n a_n b_n)^2 \leq \Sigma_n |a_n|^2 \Sigma_n |b_n|^2$. To prove the necessity, we proceed contrapositively, and assume that $\Sigma_n |b_n|^2$ is divergent. Now the Abel Dini theorem (see K. Knopp, "Infinite Series," Blackie, London, 1928, Section 39) asserts that if $d_n > 0$, and $\Sigma_n d_n$ is divergent then $\Sigma_n (d_n/(\Sigma_1^n d_m)^p$ is divergent if $p \leq 1$, and convergent if $p > 1$. Consequently $\Sigma_n(|b_n|^2/(\Sigma_1^n |b_m|^2)$ is divergent but $\Sigma_n(|b_n|^2/(\Sigma_1^n |b_m|^2)^2$ is convergent. If then we set $a_n = |b_n| \operatorname{sgn} b_n/(\Sigma_1^n |b_m|^2)$, then $\Sigma_n a_n b_n$ is divergent, but $\Sigma_n |a_n|^2$ is convergent. This contradicts the hypothesis of the lemma and completes its proof.

Returning to the proof of Theorem 6.14, since $\Sigma_n a_n L(\varphi_n)$ converges for all $\{a_n\}$ in L^2, it follows that $\Sigma_n (L(\varphi_n))^2$ converges. Consequently by the Riesz-Fischer theorem, there exists a function g in L^2 such that

$$\lim_n \left\| \sum_1^n L(\varphi_m)\varphi_m - g \right\| = 0.$$

Then

$$\lim_n \left| \int f \cdot \left(\sum_1^n L(\varphi_m)\varphi_m\right) - \int fg \right| = 0,$$

or

$$L(f) = \lim_n L \sum_1^n \left(\int f\varphi_m\right)\varphi_m = \lim_n \int f \cdot \left(\sum_1^n L(\varphi_m)\varphi_m\right) = \int f \cdot g.$$

This gives us the desired representation.

EXERCISES

1. Show that if $\alpha(x) = x$, that is α-measurability is Lebesgue measurability then on $X \equiv -\infty < x < \infty$

$$\delta(f_1, f_2) = \int_{-\infty}^{\infty} \exp(-x^2) \, |f_1(x) - f_2(x)| \, dx/(1 + |f_1(x) - f_2(x)|)$$

can serve as a metric for L-measurable functions, where $\lim_n \delta(f_n, f) = 0$ is equivalent to $f_n \to f$ (in measure) on every bounded measurable set E.

2. Give a proof of the statement 1.3 above that if α is monotonic unbounded on $X \equiv (-\infty, +\infty)$, then $f_n \to f(\alpha; x \text{ on } E)$ for all bounded α-measurable sets E is weaker than $f_n \to f(\alpha, x \text{ on } X)$.

3. Show that if $\{\varphi_n\}$ is a complete orthonormal system in L^2, then (a) for any two functions f and g in L^2, we have $\Sigma_n \int f\varphi_n \int g\varphi_n = \int f \cdot g$; (b) for any two measurable sets E_1 and E_2: $\Sigma_n \int_{E_1} \varphi_n \int_{E_2} \varphi_n = \alpha(E_1E_2)$.

4. Suppose that $\{f_n\}$ is a sequence of functions in L^2 such that if $n < m$, then $f_n - f_m$ is orthogonal to f_m. Show that if the sequence $\int f_n^2$ is bounded then f_n converges to a function f in the sense $\lim_n \int (f_n - f)^2 = 0$.

5. Suppose that $\{f_n\}$ is a sequence of linearly independent functions in L^2. Show that a necessary and sufficient condition that there exist a function f in L^2 which satisfies the infinite system of integral equations $\int f \cdot f_n = a_n$, is that the sequence

$$M_n = - \begin{vmatrix} 0 & a_1 & \cdots & a_n \\ a_1 & \int f_1 f_1 & \cdots & \int f_1 f_n \\ & & \cdots & \\ a_n & \int f_n f_1 & \cdots & \int f_n f_n \end{vmatrix} \div G(f_1, f_2, \ldots, f_n)$$

be bounded in n. Hint: Find a solution of the equations $\int f \cdot f_i = a_i$, $i = 1 \ldots n$ such that $f = \Sigma_1^n c_i f_i$, and show that the result is a solution of minimal norm for this finite system.

6. Suppose $X \equiv 0 \leq x \leq 1$, and consider the class $\mathfrak{F}$ of functions $f(x)$ on X such that $\Sigma_x (f(x))^2$ converges. Show that if f and g are two functions of the class $\mathfrak{F}$, then $\Sigma_x f(x)g(x)$ converges and defines an inner product $(f, g) = \Sigma_x f(x)g(x)$ on $\mathfrak{F}$. Show that there exist orthonormal systems in $\mathfrak{F}$ relative to this inner product which are not denumerable.

7. Show that if g is α-measurable and $\int f \cdot g$ exists for all functions f in L^2, then g is in L^2.

8. Show that if $\Sigma_n a_n b_n$ converges for all sequences $\{a_n\}$ in l^p, that is such that $\Sigma_n | a_n |^p < \infty$, with $p > 1$, then b_n is in $l^{p'}$, or $\Sigma_n | b_n |^{p'} < \infty$, where $p' = p/(p-1)$.

9. In an abstract Hilbert space H based on a Hermitian form (f, g) orthogonality is defined by the condition $(f, g) = 0$. Show that in such a space H, it is possible to determine orthonormal systems of elements $[\varphi_p]$, whose linear closed extension is the space H. If $[\varphi_p]$ is a complete orthonormal system and f is in H, then (f, φ_p) vanishes except for a denumerable set of φ_p and $f = \Sigma_p (f, \varphi_p)\varphi_p$. Also if $L(f)$ is a linear continuous functional on H, then there exists a g in H such that $L(f) = (g, f)$.

CHAPTER IX

OTHER METHODS OF DEFINING THE CLASS OF LEBESGUE INTEGRABLE FUNCTIONS. ABSTRACT INTEGRALS

In the preceding sections, we have defined and developed properties of Lebesgue-Stieltjes integrals of functions $f(x)$ on the linear interval X relative to functions $\alpha(x)$, either of bounded variation on X, or of bounded variation on every bounded subinterval of X. Here X is assumed to be the interval $-\infty < x < +\infty$, but the theory can easily be adapted to the case where X is the bounded closed interval $[a, b]$ or the bounded open interval (a, b), respectively. The integral definitions were of two types, one by an analog of the Rieman-Stieltjes definition using subdivisions into measurable sets instead of intervals and the other, due to Lebesgue using properties of measurable functions depending on the sets $E[f \geqq y]$. In either case, it was necessary to develop first a theory of measure and of measurable functions. Both procedures lead to the same class L^1 of Lebesgue integrable functions with respect to α or Lebesgue-Stieltjes (L-S) integrable functions at least for the case when $\alpha(x)$ is of bounded variation on X, which is either $-\infty < x < +\infty$ or $a \leqq x \leqq b$.

It is natural to pose the question whether the class L^1 and the integrals of functions of L^1 can be obtained by other types of procedure, avoiding perhaps the development of a theory of measurable sets and measurable functions. In this connection, we observe that the class L^1 for X a bounded interval $[a, b]$ and $\alpha(x)$ of bounded variation on $[a, b]$ includes the class of Riemann-Stieltjes integrable functions, with the same values for the integrals, so that L^1 is an extension of the class of R-S integrable functions, and consequently also of the class of continuous functions on $[a, b]$.

In taking our cue from the development of the real number system from the rational numbers, we recall that one extension procedure is to assume that any Cauchy sequence of rational numbers $\{a_n\}$ for which $\lim_{n,m} |a_n - a_m| = 0$, can be considered a new number and yields in effect the real number system. Similarly if X is a metric space which is not complete in the sense that there exist sequences of elements $\{x_n\}$ of X which are Cauchy sequences satisfying the condition $\lim_{n,m} \delta(x_n, x_m) = 0$ but for which no x in X exists such that $\lim_n \delta(x_n, x) = 0$, we can extend the space by adding all Cauchy sequences in X as additional elements. Two Cauchy sequences $\{x_n\}$ and $\{y_n\}$ define the same element in the extended space if $\lim_n \delta(x_n, y_n) = 0$. The sequence $\xi = \{x_n\}$ for which $x_n = x$ for all n corresponds to the element x of X, so that a sequence $\{y_n\}$ corresponds to the element x of X if $\lim_n \delta(y_n, x) = 0$. The extended space becomes a metric space if we define the distance between two elements $\xi = \{x_n\}$ and $\eta = \{y_n\}$ by condition $\delta(\xi, \eta) = \lim_n \delta(x_n, y_n)$, and this distance remains unchanged if we replace the sequences $\{x_n\}$ and $\{y_n\}$ by equivalent sequences. If the space of sequences ξ is metrized in this way, it turns out to be complete relative to Cauchy sequences.

1. The Space L^1 as the Completion of a Metric Space by Cauchy Sequences

If $X = (-\infty < x < +\infty)$, and $\alpha(x)$ is of bounded variation on every bounded interval, we start out with the space C_0 of functions $g(x)$ continuous on X, each vanishing on the complement of some bounded closed interval. The class C_0 is linear. If $g(x) = 0$ for $x \leqq a$ and $x \geqq b$, then $\int_a^b g(x) d\alpha(x)$ exists and can be written $\int_X g d\alpha$. We introduce a metric or norm in C_0, not by the condition that $\| g \| = \max (|g(x)|, x \text{ on } X)$ but by the integral norm: $\| g \| = \int_X |g| dv(\alpha)$, where as usual $v(\alpha, x) = \int_0^x |d\alpha|$. The norm gives rise to the metric $\delta(g_1, g_2) = \int_X |g_1 - g_2| dv(\alpha)$. The class C_0 is not complete under this norm. We show:

1.1. THEOREM. If $\alpha(x)$ is of bounded variation on every bounded subinterval of X and C_0, the class of functions $g(x)$ continuous on X, each vanishing outside a bounded closed interval is normed by setting $\| g \| = \int_X |g| dv(\alpha)$, then the extension of C_0 by Cauchy sequences yields the class L^1 of functions L-S integrable with respect to $v(\alpha)$. If $\{g_n\}$ is a sequence of functions of C_0 "determining" the function f in L^1, then $\int_X f d\alpha = \lim_n \int_X g_n d\alpha$.

(a) Any function in the completed extension of C_0 is in L^1. This is almost obvious. For since L^1 is complete relative to $\|f\| = \int_X |f| \, dv(\alpha)$, and contains the class C_0, any sequence $\{g_n(x)\}$ of C_0 such that $\lim_{n,m} \int_X |g_n - g_m| \, dv(\alpha) = 0$ determines a function in L^1 up to a $v(\alpha)$-null set, where $(g_n x) \to f(x) \ (v(\alpha))$, and there exists a subsequence g_{n_k} such that $\lim_k g_{n_k}(x) = f(x)$ except for a $v(\alpha)$-null set. Two equivalent sequences determine functions in L^1 which differ at most by a $v(\alpha)$-null set and are consequently equivalent in L^1. If f is determined by $\{g_n\}$, then $\int_X f d\alpha = \lim_n \int_X g_n d\alpha$ and $\int_X |f| \, dv(\alpha) = \lim_n \int_X |g_n| \, dv(\alpha) = \|f\|$. The bounded $v(\alpha)$-measurable subsets of X are determined by the condition that the corresponding characteristic functions $\chi(E; x)$ are in the completed extension of C_0, from which the class of $v(\alpha)$-measurable sets is determined in the usual way.

(b) Any function $f(x)$ in L^1 is determined by a Cauchy sequence in C_0. In VIII.5.5 we proved that the class C_0 is dense in L^1 in the sense that for any function f in L^1, there exists a sequence $\{g_n(x)\}$ in C_0 such that $\lim_n \int_X |f - g_n| \, dv(\alpha) = 0$. The sequence $\{g_n\}$ is obviously a Cauchy sequence in C_0 which determines f.

An alternative way of obtaining the space L^1 as the completion of a class of functions is based on the observation made in the proof of VIII.5.5 that the class S of finite valued step functions is dense in L^1 under the norm $\|g\| = \int_X |g| \, dv(\alpha)$. The type of step function $g(x)$ which proves effective here is defined as follows: Let $\mathfrak{J}$ consist of a finite number of disjoint open intervals (x_i', x_i''), $i = 1 \ldots n$ and a finite number of points x_j, $j = 1 \ldots k$ disjoint from the intervals. Then $g(x)$ is in S, if $g(x) = c_i$ for x on (x_i', x_i'') and $g(x_j) = d_j$ and vanishes if x is not in $\mathfrak{J}$. By taking individual points as end points of the intervals, this type includes step functions defined to be constant on sets of closed or half-open intervals. We now define

$$\int_X g(x) d\alpha(x) = \sum_{i=1}^{n} c_i(\alpha(x_i'' - 0) - \alpha(x_i' + 0)) + \sum_{j=1}^{k} g(x_j) \, (\alpha(x_j + 0) - \alpha(x_j - 0))$$

for any such $g(x)$ and $\alpha(x)$ of bounded variation on every bounded interval. This is essentially the L-S integral rather than the R-S integral, since the latter may not exist if g and α have common discontinuities.

If we set

$$\|g\| = \int_X |g(x)| \, dv(\alpha) = \sum_i |c_i| \, (v(\alpha, x_i'' - 0)) - v(\alpha, x_i' + 0))$$
$$+ \sum_j |g(x_j)| \, (|\alpha(x_j + 0) - \alpha(x_j)| + |\alpha(x_j) - \alpha(x_j - 0)|),$$

then the class S of functions $g(x)$ completed under this norm will also yield L^1 and a value for the integrals $\int_X f d\alpha$ for f in L^1.

If we have at our disposal the $v(\alpha)$-measurable subsets of X, then L^1 can also be obtained as the completion by Cauchy sequences of the class of measurable step functions which are constant on each of the sets of a subdivision of X into $v(\alpha)$-measurable subsets, and such that $\int_X |g| \, dv(\alpha) = \Sigma_n |c_n| \, v(\alpha, E_n) < \infty$, where $g(x) = c_n$ on E_n.

The use of Cauchy sequences as a basis for obtaining the space L^1 of L-S integrable functions is due to N. Dunford: *Trans. Am. Math. Soc.* 37 (1935) 441-453. He developed a theory in a more general setting which can be adapted to the space of functions of one variable as indicated in the preceding paragraphs.

2. Construction of the Space L^1 by the Use of Osgood's Theorem

An approach to the L-S integral closely related to the preceding one, at least for the case when X is the finite interval $[a, b]$ is suggested by the Osgood theorem of convergence (II.15.14) which asserts that if $\alpha(x)$ is of bounded variation on $[a, b]$ and $f_n(x)$ is a sequence of functions uniformly bounded on $[a, b]$ for each of which R-S $\int_a^b f_n d\alpha$ exists, and such that $\lim_n f_n(x)$ exists except at most on a $v(\alpha)$-null set, then $\lim_n \int_a^b f_n d\alpha$ exists.

If C is the class of continuous functions $g(x)$ on $[a, b]$ and if $\alpha(x)$ is of bounded variation on $[a, b]$, then we know that $\int_a^b g d\alpha$ is defined for all g in C. We extend the class C by adding the class of functions $f(x)$ for which there exists a uniformly bounded sequence of continuous functions $g_n(x)$ such that $\lim_n g_n(x) = f(x)$ except for a $v(\alpha)$-null set, and define $\int_a^b f d\alpha = \lim_n \int_a^b g_n d\alpha$, since the limit on the right exists. Because of the Osgood theorem this value will be independent of the particular uniformly bounded sequence of continuous functions used to approach $f(x)$ as indicated. It is obvious that the resulting class of functions is contained in the class of almost bounded functions measurable relative to $v(\alpha)$. On the other hand for any almost bounded $v(\alpha)$-measurable function $f(x)$ we can find a sequence $\{g_n(x)\}$ of continuous functions which we can assume to be bounded by the almost bound of $f(x)$ such that $\lim_n g_n(x) = f(x)$ except for a $v(\alpha)$-null set. Moreover,

$$\lim_n \text{R-S} \int_a^b g_n d\alpha = \lim_n \text{L-S} \int_a^b g_n d\alpha = \text{L-S} \int_a^b f d\alpha.$$

Consequently:

2.1. If we extend the class C of continuous functions on $[a, b]$ by adding the class of functions which are limits of uniformly bounded sequences of continuous functions excepting for a $v(\alpha)$-null set, we obtain exactly the class of almost bounded functions in L^1 and the L-S integral of these.

When it comes to the matter of obtaining the unbounded functions on L^1 by this type of extension process, it is obvious that unbounded sequences of functions will be needed. Since there exist sequences of continuous functions $\{g_n(x)\}$ such that $\lim_n g_n(x) = 0$ for all x of $[a, b]$ for which the limit of $\int_a^b g_n(x) d\alpha(x)$ does not exist, it is necessary to impose some restriction on the sequence $\{g_n(x)\}$. One cue to the type of condition which might serve is contained in the basic convergence theorem for L-S integrals on a finite interval $[a, b]$, namely, the uniform absolute continuity of the integrals of the sequence of functions involved (see VII.8.8.2).

If we start from the R-S $\int_a^b g d\alpha$, which determines an interval function (as contrasted with a function on measurable sets), it is necessary to adapt the notion of absolute continuity to interval functions. For this purpose assume a monotonic nondecreasing function $\alpha(x)$, which gives rise to the interval function $\alpha(I) = \alpha(d) - \alpha(c)$, for $I \equiv [c, d]$, and a function of intervals $F(I)$. Each of these defines a function on finite sets of nonoverlapping intervals: $\mathfrak{I} = (I_1 \ldots I_n)$ by the condition $\alpha(\mathfrak{I}) = \Sigma_1^n \alpha(I_k)$ and $F(\mathfrak{I}) = \Sigma_1^n F(I_k)$. Then we define:

2.2. An interval function $F(I)$ is absolutely continuous relative to the monotonic function α, if for $e > 0$, there exists d_e such that if

$$\alpha(\mathfrak{I}) = \sum_1^n \alpha(I_k) < d_e, \quad \text{then} \quad |F(\mathfrak{I})| = \left|\sum_1^n F(I_k)\right| < e.$$

It follows at once that:

2.3. If R-S $\int_a^b f d\alpha$ exists for α of bounded variation, then the interval function $F(I) = \int_c^d f d\alpha$, with $I \equiv [c, d]$, is absolutely continuous relative to $v(\alpha)$.

For if $\int_a^b f d\alpha$ exists, then there exists a finite number of subintervals $I_1 \dots I_k$ and an $M > 0$, such that $\alpha(x)$ is constant on the closure of the intervals complementary to $\Sigma_1^k I_i$ and $|f(x)| \leq M$ on each I_i. Consequently, $|\int_c^d f d\alpha| \leq M(v(\alpha, d) - v(\alpha, c))$ for every interval $[c, d]$

We can then demonstrate an extension of Osgood's theorem in the form:

2.4. Lemma. If $\alpha(x)$ is monotone nondecreasing on $[a, b]$; $g_n(x)$ are such that $g_n(x) \geq 0$ for all n and x; $\lim_n g_n(x) = 0$ except for an α-null set; $\int_a^b g_n d\alpha$ exists for each n and the indefinite integrals $\int_c^d g_n d\alpha$ are uniformly absolutely continuous relative to α, then $\lim_n \int_a^b g_n d\alpha = 0$.

The proof follows that of II.15.7. If $\lim_n \int_a^b g_n d\alpha \neq 0$, there exists an $M > 0$, and a subsequence n_k of the integers such that $\int_a^b g_{n_k} d\alpha > M$ for all k. We can assume that $\{g_{n_k}\}$ is the original sequence. Let $c > 0$ be such that $c(\alpha(b) - \alpha(a)) < M/2$. Then for $0 < e < \int_a^b g_n d\alpha - M$, there exists a subdivision σ_n such that $\Sigma_{\sigma_n} \omega(g_n; I)\alpha(I) < e$. Let I' denote the intervals I in σ_n such that $g_n(x) \geqq c$ for all x in the I', and I'' those intervals of σ_n for which there exists an x in I'' such that $g_n(x) < c$. Then

$$\begin{aligned}\int_a^b g_n d\alpha &= \sum_i \int_{I_i'} g_n d\alpha + \sum_j \int_{I_j''} g_n d\alpha \leqq \sum_i \int_{I_i'} g_n d\alpha \\ &+ \sum_j (g_n(x_j) + \omega(g_n; I_j''))\alpha(I_j'') \leqq \sum_i \int_{I_i'} g_n d\alpha \\ &+ c \sum_j \alpha(I_j'') + e \leqq \sum_i \int_{I_i'} g_n d\alpha + c(\alpha(b) - \alpha(a)) + e,\end{aligned}$$

since

$$\left|\sum_j \int_{I_j''} g_n d\alpha - \sum_j g_n(x_j)\alpha(I_j'')\right| \leqq \sum_j \omega(g_n; I_j'')\alpha(I_j'').$$

It follows that for each n, there exists a finite set of nonoverlapping intervals I_{nk}, such that

$$\sum_k \int_{I_{nk}} g_n d\alpha \geqq \int_a^b g_n d\alpha - c(\alpha(b) - \alpha(a)) - e > M/2.$$

Now the integrals $\int_I g_n d\alpha$ are uniformly absolutely continous, so that there exists a K such that if $\Sigma_i \alpha(I_i) < K$, then $\Sigma_i \int_{I_i} g_n d\alpha < M/2$. It follows that for every n, the intervals I_{nk} determined above satisfy the condition $\Sigma_k \alpha(I_{nk}) \geqq K$, a fixed number independent of n. The use of Arzela's lemma II.15.8 as in II.15.7 gives us that the set $E =$

$\overline{\lim}_n \Sigma_k I_{nk}$ on which $g_n(x)$ does not converge to zero is not an α-null set.

It follows from this lemma, that:

2.5. If $\{g_n(x)\}$ is a sequence of continuous functions such that $\lim_n g_n(x)$ exists except for a $v(\alpha)$-null set and the integrals $\int |g_n| dv(\alpha)$ are uniformly absolutely continuous relative to $v(\alpha)$, then $\lim_n \int_a^b g_n d\alpha$ exists.

For
$$\left| \int_a^b g_n d\alpha - \int_a^b g_m d\alpha \right| \leqq \int_a^b |g_n - g_m| dv(\alpha)$$

and the double sequence $|g_n - g_m|$ satisfies the conditions of our lemma since

$$\int_I |g_n - g_m| dv(\alpha) \leqq \int_I |g_n| dv(\alpha) + \int_I |g_m| dv(\alpha).$$

The extension procedure is now immediate in that we add to the space C of functions continuous on $[a, b]$ the space of all sequences of continuous functions $\{g_n(x)\}$ such that $\lim_n g_n(x)$ exists for all x excepting a $v(\alpha)$-null set and $\int_I |g_n| dv(\alpha)$ are uniformly absolutely continuous relative to $v(\alpha)$.

To show that the functions $f(x)$ so determined are in L^1, we can apply the basic convergence theorem for L-S integrals, provided uniform absolute continuity of $\int_I |g_n| dv(\alpha)$ in the interval sense implies uniform absolute continuity of $\int_E |g_n| dv(\alpha)$ in the measurable set sense, that is

$$e > 0,\ d_e,\ v(\alpha;\ E) < d_e,\ n : \left| \int_E |g_n| dv(\alpha) \right| < e.$$

This is proved seriatim. First in the definition of uniform absolute continuity, the intervals I can be replaced by open intervals I^0, where $v(\alpha; I^0) = v(\alpha; d - 0) - v(\alpha; c + 0)$ if $I^0 = (c, d)$. For if $I_1^0 \ldots I_m^0$ are a finite number of disjoint open intervals such that $\Sigma_i v(\alpha; I_i^0) < d_e$, then there exist intervals I_{ik} in I_i^0 at whose end points α is continuous, and such that $\lim_k v(\alpha; I_{ik}) = v(\alpha; I_i^0)$. Since $\Sigma_i v(\alpha; I_{ik}) < \Sigma_i v(\alpha; I_i^0) < d_e$, we have for all n and k: $\Sigma_i \int_{I_{ik}} |g_n| dv(\alpha) < e$, and so also $\Sigma_i \int_{I_i^0} |g_n| dv(\alpha) < e$, for all n. Similar steps can be taken to replace the sum of a finite number of open intervals by open sets, and then in turn open sets by $v(\alpha)$-measurable sets E to give the uniform absolute continuity defined above.

The basic convergence theorem for L-S integrals VII.8.8 now gives us the fact that functions $f(x)$ determined by the sequences of continuous functions are in L^1.

Conversely, if f is in L^1, then there exists a sequence of continuous functions $\{g_n(x)\}$ such that $\lim_n g_n(x) = f(x)$ except for a $v(\alpha)$-null set, and such that $\lim_n$ L-S $\int_a^b |g_n - f| \, dv(\alpha) = 0$. Consequently,

$$\lim_{n,m} \text{L-S} \int_a^b |g_n - g_m| \, dv(\alpha) = \lim_{n,m} \text{R-S} \int_a^b |g_n - g_m| \, dv(\alpha) = 0.$$

If $I_1 \dots I_k$ is any set of nonoverlapping intervals, then

$$\sum_i \int_{I_i} |g_n| \, dv(\alpha) \leqq \sum_i \int_{I_i} (|g_m| + |g_n - g_m|) \, dv(\alpha)$$
$$\leqq \sum_i \int_{I_i} |g_m| \, dv(\alpha) + \int_a^b |g_n - g_m| \, dv(\alpha).$$

If then

$$e > 0,\ n_e,\ n,\ m \geqq n_e\colon \int_a^b |g_n - g_m| \, dv(\alpha) \leqq e$$

and

$$e > 0,\ d_e,\ \sum_i \alpha(I_i) < d_e,\ m = n_e\colon \sum_i \int_{I_i} |g_m| \, dv(\alpha) < e,$$

then for

$$n \geqq n_e,\ \sum_i \alpha(I_i) < d_e\colon \sum_i \int_{I_i} |g_n| \, dv(\alpha) \leqq 2e.$$

From this one can deduce in the usual way that the integrals $\int_I |g_n| dv(\alpha)$ are uniformly absolutely continuous. Consequently the sequence $\{g_n\}$ determines the function f.

In this extension procedure, the class C of continuous functions on $[a, b]$ can be replaced by the class S of finite valued step functions, constant on intervals. If $g(x) = c_i$ on the open intervals (x_i', x_i''), $i = 1 \dots k$, disjoint, and $g(x_j) = d_j$, $j = 1 \dots m$, for $x = x_j$ not on the (x_i', x_i''), and $g(x)$ zero elsewhere, then as above we define

$$\int_a^b g d\alpha = \sum_i c_i(\alpha(x_i'' - 0) - \alpha(x_i' + 0))$$
$$+ \sum_j g(x_j)(\alpha(x_j + 0) - \alpha(x_j - 0)),$$

or the value of $\int g d\alpha$ as an L-S integral. The space L^1 is then the extension of S by sequences of step functions converging excepting for a $v(\alpha)$-null set, for which the integral $\int_I |g_n| \, dv(\alpha)$ are uniformly absolutely continuous relative to $v(\alpha)$.

It is clear that this method of extension is almost identical with and equivalent to that by Cauchy sequences of continuous functions based on the norm $\int_a^b |g| dv(\alpha)$.

Both of these extensions are illustrations of the fact that new spaces may be obtained as extensions of the space of continuous functions by regarding as new elements the class of sequences of continuous functions which have a certain property in common.

3. L-S Integration Based on Monotonic Sequences of Semicontinuous Functions

We recall that the real number system in addition to being the extension of the rational number system by Cauchy sequences is also the extension of the rational number system by bounded monotonic sequences, with a proper definition of equivalence. We try to adapt this idea to the definition of L-S integrals.

We again assume X to be the finite interval $[a, b]$ but limit $\alpha(x)$ to be a monotonic nondecreasing function on $[a, b]$. C is again the class of continuous functions on X. If $\{g_n(x)\}$ is a monotonic nondecreasing sequence of continuous functions bounded for each x, then $\lim_n g_n(x) = h(x)$ exists finite valued for each x, and by VI.1.5 $h(x)$ is a lower semicontinuous function (l.s.c.) on X. Since $\alpha(x)$ is monotonic nondecreasing, the sequence of integrals $\int_a^b g_n d\alpha$ is monotone in the same way and converges to a finite number or $+\infty$. If $h(x)$ is continuous, then the $g_n(x)$ are uniformly bounded and $\lim_n \int_a^b g_n d\alpha = \int_a^b h d\alpha$. Consequently, it is sensible to define $\int_a^b h d\alpha = \lim_n \int_a^b g_n d\alpha$. This value will be independent of the particular sequence of continuous functions which is monotonic nondecreasing and for which $\lim_n g_n(x) = h(x)$ for x on X. While this can be seen by using Fatou's lemma (VII.8.10), that is the theory of Lebesgue integration, it can be proved directly.

For suppose $f(x)$ is any function in C such that $h(x) \geqq f(x)$ for all x. We show that $\int_a^b h d\alpha \geqq \int_a^b f d\alpha$. Let $f_n(x) = g_n(x) \wedge f(x)$, the lesser of g_n and f. Then $\lim_n f_n(x) = f(x)$ for all x, $\int_a^b g_n d\alpha \geqq \int_a^b f_n d\alpha$ for all n, and so

$$\int_a^b h d\alpha = \lim_n \int_a^b g_n d\alpha \geqq \lim_n \int_a^b f_n d\alpha = \int_a^b f d\alpha.$$

If now $f_n(x)$ is any monotonic nondecreasing sequence in C, such that $\lim_n f_n(x) = h(x)$ for all x on X, then

$$\int_a^b h d\alpha = \lim_n \int_a^b g_n d\alpha \geqq \int_a^b f_n d\alpha$$

for all n so that

$$\lim_n \int_a^b g_n d\alpha \geqq \lim_n \int_a^b f_n d\alpha.$$

Since the sequences $\{f_n\}$ and $\{g_n\}$ are interchangeable, it follows that $\lim_n \int_a^b g_n d\alpha = \lim_n \int_a^b f_n d\alpha$.

In VI.1.6 we have shown that for any finite valued l.s.c. function $h(x)$ there exists a monotone nondecreasing sequence of continuous functions $\{g_n(x)\}$ such that $\lim_n g_n(x) = h(x)$ for all x. As a consequence we can extend $\int_a^b g d\alpha$ on C to $\int_a^b h d\alpha$, h in l.s.c. the class of finite valued lower semicontinuous functions on X, and $\int_a^b h d\alpha$ is finite valued or $+\infty$. In the same way, by using monotone nonincreasing sequences of continuous functions we can obtain an integral for every finite valued upper semicontinuous function (u.s.c.) $k(x)$: $\int_a^b k d\alpha$ as a finite value or $-\infty$.

We now follow the basic idea involved in the Darboux integrals for the case when $\alpha(x) = x$, by defining an upper integral $\overline{\int_a^b} f d\alpha$ and a lower integral $\underline{\int_a^b} f d\alpha$ for any finite valued function f. We define $\overline{\int_a^b} f d\alpha$ as the greatest lower bound of $\int_a^b h d\alpha$ for all lower semicontinuous functions $h(x) \geqq f(x)$ except for an α-null set, and as $+\infty$ if no such l.s.c. function exists. Similarly, $\underline{\int_a^b} f d\alpha$ is the least upper bound of $\int_a^b k d\alpha$ for all upper semicontinuous functions $k(x) \leqq f(x)$ except for an α-null set, and is $-\infty$ if no such u.s.c. function exists. Then:

3.1. Definition. $f(x)$ is integrable if and only if $\overline{\int_a^b} f d\alpha$ and $\underline{\int_a^b} f d\alpha$ are finite and equal.

In order to show that any function integrable by this procedure belongs to the class L^1, we use results demonstrated in the theory of L-S integrals. By Fatou's lemma (VII.8.10) any l.s.c. or u.s.c. function whose integral as defined above is finite, is in L^1 and has the same value for its integral. If $\overline{\int_a^b} f d\alpha$ is finite, then there exists a sequence of l.s.c. functions $\bar{h}_n(x) \geqq f(x)$ except for an α-null set, such that $\int_a^b \bar{h}_n d\alpha - \overline{\int_a^b} f d\alpha < 1/n$. If for $n > 1$, $h_n(x)$ is the lesser of $\bar{h}_n(x)$ and $h_{n-1}(x)$, then the $h_n(x)$ will also be l.s.c., $h_n(x) \geqq h_{n+1}(x)$ and $\lim_n \int_a^b h_n d\alpha$ will be finite and have $\overline{\int_a^b} f d\alpha$ as its value. If $h(x) = \lim_n h_n(x)$, then h will be in L^1, be finite valued except for an α-null set, and $\int_a^b h d\alpha = \overline{\int_a^b} f d\alpha$. Moreover, $h(x) \geqq f(x)$ except for an α-null set. Similarly, if $\underline{\int_a^b} f d\alpha$ is finite, there exists a monotone nondecreasing sequence of u.s.c. functions $\{k_n(x)\}$ with $k_n(x) \leqq f(x)$ except for an α-null set, with $\lim_n \int_a^b k_n d\alpha = \int_a^b k d\alpha = \underline{\int}_a^b f d\alpha$ so that $k(x) = \lim_n k_n(x)$ is in L^1. If $\overline{\int}_a^b f d\alpha = \underline{\int}_a^b f d\alpha$, then $\int_a^b (h - k) d\alpha = 0$, with $h(x) \geqq k(x)$ except for an α-null set. Then $h = k$ except for an α-null set. Since $h(x) \geqq f(x) \geqq k(x)$ except for an α-null set, it follows that $h(x) = f(x)$ except for an α-null set, that is f is in L^1.

On the other hand, suppose f is in L^1. Then there exists a sequence of continuous functions $\{g_n(x)\}$ such that $\lim_n g_n(x) = f(x)$ except for an α-null set and $\lim_n \int_a^b |g_n - f| d\alpha = 0$. By using, if need be, a subsequence, we can select this sequence g_n so that it satisfies the additional condition that for some sequence of positive numbers $\{e_n\}$ such that $\Sigma_n e_n < \infty$, we have $\int_a^b |g_{n+1} - g_n| d\alpha < e_n$. For $m > n$, let $g_{nm}(x) =$ the largest of $g_n(x) \dots g_m(x)$. Then $g_{nm}(x)$ is continuous, for fixed n, the sequence $g_{nm}(x)$ is monotonic nondecreasing in m, so that $\lim_n g_{nm}(x) = h_n(x)$ is a lower semicontinuous function for all n. The sequence $\{h_n(x)\}$ of l.s.c. functions is monotonic nonincreasing in n for each x. Moreover,

$$\lim_n h_n(x) = \lim_n \lim_m g_{nm}(x) = \overline{\lim}_n g_n(x) = \lim_n g_n(x) = f(x);$$

except for an α-null set, with $h_n(x) \geqq f(x)$ except for an α-null set. Similarly, if $g^*_{nm}(x) =$ smallest of $(g_n(x) \dots g_m(x))$ with $m > n$, then $g^*_{nm}(x)$ for fixed n converges monotonically to an upper semicontinuous function $k_n(x)$, the sequence $\{k_n(x)\}$ is monotonic nondecreasing in n, with $k_n(x) \leqq f(x)$ and $\lim_n k_n(x) = f(x)$ except for an α-null set. We proceed to show that $\lim_n \int_a^b h_n d\alpha$ and $\lim_n \int_a^b k_n d\alpha$ are finite and equal to $\int_a^b f d\alpha$. We recall that if $a_1 \dots a_m$ is any finite set of real numbers, then

$$|(\text{greatest of } (a_1 \dots a_m) - a_m| \leqq \sum_{i=1}^{m-1} |a_i - a_{i+1}|.$$

The same is true of $|(\text{least of } a_1 \dots a_m) - a_m|$. Consequently,

$$\left| \int_a^b g_{nm} - g_n \right| d\alpha \leqq \sum_{i=n}^{m-1} |g_{i+1} - g_i| d\alpha \leqq \sum_{i=n}^{m-1} e_i \leqq \sum_{i=n}^{\infty} e_i.$$

Then

$$\left| \int_a^b g_{nm} d\alpha - \int_a^b f d\alpha \right| \leqq \int_a^b |g_{nm} - f| d\alpha \leqq \int_a^b |g_{nm} - g_n| d\alpha$$
$$+ \int_a^b |g_m - f| d\alpha \leqq \sum_{i=n}^{\infty} e_i + \int_a^b |g_m - f| d\alpha \leqq 2e,$$

provided $n \geqq n_e$ and $m \geqq m_e$ for which $\Sigma_n^\infty e_i < e$ and $\int_a^b |g_m - f| d\alpha < e$. This means that $\lim_{mn} \int_a^b g_{nm} d\alpha = \int_a^b f d\alpha$. Then $\int_a^b g_{nm} d\alpha$ are bounded in m for $n \geqq n_e$, so that $\int_a^b h_n d\alpha = \lim_m \int_a^b g_{nm} d\alpha$ exists. We can therefore conclude that $\int_a^b f d\alpha = \lim_{mn} \int_a^b g_{nm} d\alpha = \lim_n \int_a^b h_n d\alpha$. Similarly, we show that $\lim_n \int_a^b k_n d\alpha = \int_a^b f d\alpha$. Since

$$\lim_n \int_a^b h_n d\alpha \geqq \overline{\int_a^b} f d\alpha \geqq \underline{\int_a^b} f d\alpha \geqq \lim_n \int_a^b k_n d\alpha$$

it follows that the upper and lower integrals of f agree, and are finite and f is integrable according to this procedure.

It follows that the space of functions for which the upper and lower integrals are finite and equal is identical with the space L^1, and gives the same value for $\int_a^b f d\alpha$.

For the case of ordinary Lebesgue integration, where $\alpha(x) = x$ on $[a, b]$ the above extension procedure is developed in detail by L. C. Young in his book on "The Theory of Integration" (Cambridge Univ. Press, London, 1927). The steps in this method of arriving at an extended integral have been abstracted to obtain a general integral by P. J. Daniell in the paper "A general form of integral" [*Ann. Math.* (2) 19 (1917) 279-294].

4. Lebesgue-Stieltjes Integrals on an Abstract Set

The theory of Lebesgue-Stieltjes integrals developed in the preceding pages has limited itself to functions of one variable, or functions on the one-dimensional interval. However, many theorems and proofs do not really involve the domain of the function and are valid as well if the linear interval is replaced by a Euclidean space of two or higher dimensions. As a matter of fact, an examination of the theory reveals that it is possible to set up a theory in which the dimension or the character of the domain does not play any particular role. We briefly sketch the salient points in such a theory.

We postulate a basic space X of elements x. Among the subsets of X, we single out a class $\mathfrak{E}$ of sets which we might call "measurable." The class $\mathfrak{E}$ of such sets E of X is assumed to be an s-ring (or sometimes an s-algebra), i.e., closed under s-addition and differences. In case $\mathfrak{E}$ is a ring, we note that the totality of sets of $\mathfrak{E}$ which are subsets of fixed set E of $\mathfrak{E}$, form an s-algebra on E, that is, if we replace X by E as the basic space. Suppose then $\mathfrak{E}$ is an s-ring.

On $\mathfrak{E}$ we assume defined a finite valued function $\alpha(E)$ which is s-additive in the sense that if $\{E_n\}$ is a sequence of disjoint sets of $\mathfrak{E}$ (so that $\Sigma_n E_n$ belongs to $\mathfrak{E}$ also), then $\alpha(\Sigma_n E_n) = \Sigma_n \alpha(E_n)$.

Since a denumerable collection of disjoint sets, does not presuppose any order, it follows that if α is s-additive, and $\{E_n\}$ is any sequence of disjoint sets in $\mathfrak{E}$, then $\Sigma_n \alpha(E_n)$ is convergent in any order (unconditionally convergent) and so $\Sigma_n |\alpha(E_n)| < \infty$. We also have:

4.1. If $\alpha(E)$ is finite valued and s-additive on the s-ring $\mathfrak{E}$, then $\alpha(E)$ is bounded on $\mathfrak{E}$.

If not, then for every $M > 0$, there exists a set E_M such that $|\alpha(E_M)| > M$. We determine a sequence of disjoint sets E_n as follows: Suppose $E_1 \dots E_n$ have been defined as disjoint sets such that $|\alpha(E_i)| > 1$ for $i = 1 \dots n$. Let $\overline{E}_{n+1}$ be such that

$$|\alpha(\overline{E}_{n+1})| > \sum_{k=1}^{n} |\alpha(E_k)| + 1.$$

If $E_{n+1} = \overline{E}_{n+1} - \Sigma_{k=1}^{n} E_k$, then E_{n+1} is disjoint to $E_1 \dots E_n$ and

$$|\alpha(E_{n+1})| \geqq |\alpha(\overline{E}_{n+1})| - |\sum_{k=1}^{n} \alpha(E_k)| > 1.$$

For this sequence $\{E_n\}$ of disjoint sets, $\Sigma_n \alpha(E_n)$ will not converge since $|\alpha(E_n)| > 1$ for all n.

4.2. For any set E_0 of $\mathfrak{E}$ and given function $\alpha(E)$ on $\mathfrak{E}$, the total variation on E_0: $v(\alpha; E_0)$ is defined as follows: Let σ be any subdivision of E_0 consisting of the disjoint sets E_n in $\mathfrak{E}$ such that $\Sigma_n E_n = E_0$. Then

$$v(\alpha; E_0) = \text{l.u.b.}_\sigma \sum_\sigma |\alpha(E_n)|,$$

where the right-hand side may be $+\infty$.

4.3. If $\alpha(E)$ is finite valued and s-additive on $\mathfrak{E}$, then $v(\alpha; E)$ is a positive, finite valued, s-additive function on $\mathfrak{E}$.

In the first place $v(\alpha, E)$ is finite valued. For if $\sigma = \{E_n\}$ is any subdivision of E, and E_n^+ are the sets of the sequence for which $\alpha(E_n) \geqq 0$ while E_n^- are the sets for which $\alpha(E_n) < 0$, then

$$\sum_\sigma |\alpha(E_n)| = \sum_\sigma \alpha(E_n^+) + |\sum_\sigma \alpha(E_n^-)| = \alpha(E_\sigma^+) + |\alpha(E_\sigma^-)|,$$

where $E_\sigma^+ = \Sigma_n E_n^+$ and $E_\sigma^- = \Sigma_n E_n^-$, sets in $\mathfrak{E}$. But for all σ,

$$\alpha(E) = \sum_\sigma \alpha(E_n^+) - \sum_\sigma \alpha(E_n^-) = \alpha(E_\sigma^+) - \alpha(E_\sigma^-).$$

If $\Sigma_\sigma |\alpha(E_n)|$ were unbounded in σ, then both $\alpha(E_\sigma^+)$ and $\alpha(E_\sigma^-)$ would be unbounded in σ which violates the boundedness of α on $\mathfrak{E}$. Then $v(\alpha, E)$ is finite valued on $\mathfrak{E}$.

We observe next that if $\alpha(E)$ is s-additive on $\mathfrak{E}$, then the function $f(\sigma) = \Sigma_\sigma |\alpha(E_n)|$ is monotonic nondecreasing as a function of the subdivisions σ, directed by successive refinements. It follows that

$$v(\alpha, E) = \lim_\sigma \sum_\sigma |\alpha(E_n)| = \int_E |d\alpha|.$$

The s-additive property of $v(\alpha, E)$ as a function of E is now immediate.

Since $v(\alpha, E) \geq |\alpha(E)|$ for all E of $\mathfrak{E}$, we can define the positive and negative variation of α in the usual way:

$$p(\alpha, E) = (v(\alpha, E) + \alpha(E))/2 \text{ and } n(\alpha, E) = (v(\alpha, E) - \alpha(E))/2$$

which will be positive and finite valued for all E of $\mathfrak{E}$, as well as s-additive. As in the case of functions of bounded variation on the line, $p(\alpha, E)$ is also the l.u.b. of $\alpha(E_0)$ for all E_0 of $\mathfrak{E}$ which are subsets of E and $n(\alpha, E)$ is the negative of the g.l.b. of $\alpha(E_0)$ for E_0 of $\mathfrak{E}$ in E. As in VII.11.6 this leads, for every E of $\mathfrak{E}$, to the existence of two sets E^+ and E^- in $\mathfrak{E}$, such that E^+ and E^- are disjoint, $E = E^+ - E^-$ and $p(\alpha, E) = \alpha(E^+)$, $n(\alpha, E) = -\alpha(E^-)$. If E_1 is a subset of the set E in $\mathfrak{E}$, then E_1E^+ and E_1E^- will serve as a similar decomposition for E_1.

Since any s-additive function on $\mathfrak{E}$ is expressible as the difference of two positive s-additive functions on $\mathfrak{E}$, it is sufficient to develope an integral relative to positive s-additive functions on $\mathfrak{E}$. Such s-additive positive functions will be called *measures*. The integral relative to any s-additive function α is then dependent on the existence of the integrals relative to $p(\alpha, E)$ and $n(\alpha, E)$, the positive and negative variations of α, and expressible as their difference.

Assume then that α is a positive s-additive function or a measure on $\mathfrak{E}$, E is a set in $\mathfrak{E}$, and $f(x)$ is a finite valued function on E. Then it is natural to define:

4.4. Definition. The function f on E is integrable with respect to α, if $\lim_\sigma \Sigma_\sigma f(x_n)\alpha(E_n)$ exists, where $\sigma = \{E_n\}$ are subdivisions of E in $\mathfrak{E}$, x_n is any element in E_n, and the limit is taken in the sense of successive subdivisions or refinements.

As in the case when X is a linear interval, we see that:

4.4.1 If $\int_E f d\alpha$ exists, then there exists a subdivision σ_0 of E such that f is bounded on each set of σ_0 for which $\alpha(E) \neq 0$, and $\Sigma_{\sigma_0} M(|f|, E_n)\alpha(E_n) < \infty$, where $M(|f|, E_n)$ is the l.u.b. of $|f|$ on E_n.

4.4.2. If $\int_E f d\alpha$ exists, so does $\int_E |f| d\alpha$ and $|\int_E f d\alpha| \leqq \int_E |f| d\alpha$.

4.4.3. If f_1 and f_2 are functions on E of $\mathfrak{E}$, and such that $\int_E f_1 d\alpha$ and $\int_E f_2 d\alpha$ each exist, and if c_1 and c_2 are any two constants then $\int_E (c_1 f_1 + c_2 f_2) d\alpha$ also exists and has as its value $c_1 \int_E f_1 d\alpha + c_2 \int_E f_2 d\alpha$. In particular, if $\int_E f d\alpha$ exists, then $\int_E f^+ d\alpha$ and $\int_E f^- d\alpha$ exist, and $\int_E f d\alpha = \int_E f^+ d\alpha + \int_E f^- d\alpha$. Here $f^+(x) = f(x)$ for $f(x) \geqq 0$, and zero elsewhere while $f^-(x) = f(x)$ for $f(x) \leqq 0$, and zero elsewhere.

4.4.4. If $\int_E f d\alpha$ exists and E_1 is a subset of E in $\mathfrak{E}$, then $\int_{E_1} f d\alpha$ exists, and the function of sets: $g(E_1) = \int_{E_1} f d\alpha$ is a s-additive function on subsets E_1 of E which belong to $\mathfrak{E}$. If f is defined on all of X and $\int_E f d\alpha$ exists for all E of $\mathfrak{E}$, then $g(E) = \int_E f d\alpha$ is a finite valued s-additive set function on $\mathfrak{E}$ and $v(g; E) = \int_E |f| d\alpha$ for all E of $\mathfrak{E}$. This last holds if X belongs to $\mathfrak{E}$ (that is, $\mathfrak{E}$ in an s-algebra) and $\int_X f d\alpha$ exists.

In some of the theorems on integrals, the notion of measurable functions plays a role. As usual we say that a function $f(x)$ on a set E of $\mathfrak{E}$ is measurable on E, if for all real numbers c, the subsets $E[f > c]$ belong to $\mathfrak{E}$. The condition $E[f > c]$ belongs to $\mathfrak{E}$ for all c, can be replaced by $E[f \geqq c]$, $E[f < c]$, or $E[f \leqq c]$, belongs to $\mathfrak{E}$ for all c where all of these sets are subsets of the original E, relative to which $\mathfrak{E}$ is a s-algebra.

The measurability condition has the consequence that any function measurable on E, is the uniform limit of a sequence of measurable step functions $f_n(x) = \Sigma_{m=-\infty}^{m=+\infty} c_{mn}\chi(E_{mn}; x)$, where for instance

$$E_{mn} = E\left[\frac{m-1}{n} < f(x) \leqq \frac{m}{n}\right] \text{ and } c_{mn} = m/n.$$

For functions measurable on E one can show the equivalence of the Lebesgue procedure for defining an integral, to that used above.

Theorems on measurable functions which do not involve the measure function α, only the s-ring $\mathfrak{E}$, are available in this more general setting. However difficulties arise in connection with statements which contain the phrase: "except for an α-null set." For instance, it is not certain that if f is measurable on $\mathfrak{E}$, and g differs from f by an α-null set, that is, $\alpha(E[|f - g| > 0]) = 0$, then g is measurable. For the sets

$E[f > c]$ and $E[g > c]$ will differ on the set $E[f > c] \Delta E[g > c]$, which is a subset of the set $E[|f - g| > 0]$, but may not belong to $\mathfrak{E}$. This is due to the fact that the subclass $\mathfrak{E}_0$ of α-null sets of $\mathfrak{E}$, may lack the *hereditary* property: if E_0 belongs to $\mathfrak{E}_0$ and E_1 is any subset of X contained in E_0, then E_1 is in $\mathfrak{E}_0$ also, or if $\alpha(E_0) = 0$, and $E_1 \leqq E_0$, then E_1 is in $\mathfrak{E}$ also and $\alpha(E_1) = 0$. For instance the class of Borel measurable subsets of a linear interval $[a, b]$ with $\alpha(E)$ the Lebesgue measure, lacks the hereditary property for its sets of zero measure.

4.5. If $\mathfrak{E}$ is such that the class $\mathfrak{E}_0$ of α-null sets does not have the hereditary property, then one can find an extension of $\mathfrak{E}$ to a class $\overline{\mathfrak{E}}$ which does have the property.

We set up the class $\overline{\mathfrak{E}}_0$ consisting of all sets E of X contained in some E_0 of $\mathfrak{E}_0$, adjoin $\overline{\mathfrak{E}}_0$ to $\mathfrak{E}$, and extend the resulting class to be an s-ring. It can be demonstrated that the resulting class $\overline{\mathfrak{E}}$ consists of all sets of the form $E + E_{01} - E_{02}$, where E belongs to the original $\mathfrak{E}$, E_{01} and E_{02} belong to $\overline{\mathfrak{E}}_0$, E_{01} being disjoint from E and E_{02} being contained in E. The function α on $\mathfrak{E}$ is extended to $\overline{\mathfrak{E}}$ in the obvious way, that is, if $\overline{E}$ is in $\overline{\mathfrak{E}}$, and $\overline{E} = E + E_{01} - E_{02}$, then $\alpha(\overline{E}) = \alpha(E)$.

If the class $\mathfrak{E}$ is such that the class $\mathfrak{E}_0$ of α-null sets has the hereditary property, then theorems concerned with convergence of integrals of sequences of measurable functions are valid as in the one-dimensional case. For instance we have the basic convergence theorem:

If the α-null subclass of $\mathfrak{E}$ has the hereditary property; if f_n and f are measurable functions on E of $\mathfrak{E}$; if $\lim_n \alpha(E[|f_n - f| > e) = 0$ for all $e > 0$; if $\int_E f_n \, d\alpha$ exist and the functions $\int_{E_1} f_n d\alpha$ on subsets E_1 of E in $\mathfrak{E}$, are uniformly absolutely continuous relative to α; then $\int_E f d\alpha$ exists and $\lim_n \int_{E_1} f_n d\alpha = \int_{E_1} f d\alpha$ for all sets E_1, subsets of E in $\mathfrak{E}$. The condition $\lim_n \alpha(E[|f_n - f| > e]) = 0$ for all $e > 0$ can be replaced by the condition $\lim_n f_n(x) = f(x)$ except for an α-null set.

Further if $\int_E f d\alpha$ exists, on E measurable, then we can show that f is necessarily measurable. For we can show that there exist measurable functions $g(x) \geqq f(x) \geqq h(x)$ except for an α-null set of E such that $\int_E g d\alpha = \int_E f d\alpha = \int_E h d\alpha$ so that $g(x) = f(x) = h(x)$ except for an α-null set.

If the measure function $\alpha(E)$ on $\mathfrak{E}$, for which $\alpha(E) \geq 0$ for all E of $\mathfrak{E}$, is allowed to assume the value $+\infty$, then we have a generalization of the measurable sets on the interval $-\infty < x < +\infty$, where

$\alpha(x)$ is monotone but unbounded. If we consider a function f on a set E of $\mathfrak{E}$ integrable only if we can determine $\int_E f d\alpha$ as a finite number, then there exist nontrivial integrable functions on a set E of $\mathfrak{E}$ only if there exists a subdivision σ_0 of E: $\sigma_0 = \{E_n\}$, such that $\alpha(E_n)$ is finite valued for each E_n of σ_0.

4.6. The s-additive function $\alpha(E)$ is said to be σ-finite on a set E of $\mathfrak{E}$, if there exists a subdivision $\sigma_0 = \{E_n\}$ of E into sets of $\mathfrak{E}$ such that $\alpha(E_n)$ is finite valued for all n.

In case α is σ-finite on a set E of $\mathfrak{E}$, we can proceed as usual and say that $\int_E f d\alpha$ exists if and only if $\lim_{\sigma \text{ of } E} \Sigma_\sigma f(x_n)\alpha(E_n)$ exists as a finite number. Integrability then requires among other things that there exist a subdivision σ of E such that f is bounded on every subset E_n of σ for which $0 < \alpha(E_n) < \infty$, and $\Sigma_\sigma M(|f|, E_n)\alpha(E_n) < \infty$.

It is an illuminating exercise to carry through the details indicated above and determine what results valid for Lebesgue-Stieltjes integrals on the linear interval can be extended to abstract sets of elements as outlined above.

Consideration of an abstract integral as sketched in this paragraph was initiated by M. Fréchet: Sur l'integral d'une fonctionelle étendue à une ensemble abstrait, *Bull. soc. math. France*, 43 (1915) 249-267.

EXERCISES

1. Carry through the proof of the statement made after Theorem IX.4.3: If $\alpha(E)$ is finite valued and s-additive on the s-ring $\mathfrak{E}$, then for any E of $\mathfrak{E}$ there exist disjoint sets E^+ and E^- in $\mathfrak{E}$ such that $E = E^+ + E^-$, $p(\alpha, E) = \alpha(E^+)$ and $n(\alpha, E) = -\alpha(E^-)$ so that $v(\alpha; E) = \alpha(E) - \alpha(E^-)$.

2. Show that if $\mathfrak{E}$ is an s-ring, and $\alpha(E)$ and $\beta(E)$ are s-additive functions on $\mathfrak{E}$, with $\alpha(E) \geq 0$ for all E; and if $\alpha(E) = 0$ implies $\beta(E) = 0$, then β is absolutely continuous relative to α (see VII.7.3).

CHAPTER X

PRODUCT MEASURES. ITERATED INTEGRALS. FUBINI THEOREM

1. Product Measures

In V.15 we considered briefly the problem of measurable sets and measure functions determined by point functions $\alpha(x_1\ x_2\ \ldots\ x_n)$ on spaces of two or higher dimension. Thus, for $n = 2$, the point function $\alpha(x, y)$ on $X \times Y$, where X and Y are finite or infinite intervals, gives rise to the interval function

$$\alpha(I)=\alpha([a,b]\times[c,d])=\alpha(b,d)-\alpha(b,c)-\alpha(a,d)+\alpha(a,c)=\Delta_{xy}\alpha(x,y).$$

If $\alpha(I) \geqq 0$ for all $a \leqq b$, $c \leqq d$, then the positive interval function so obtained can be used to determine a class of measurable sets and a measure function α on these measurable sets. If $\alpha(x, y)$ is bounded on $X \times Y$, the class of measurable sets is an s-algebra, and the set function $\alpha(E)$ on this class is s-additive. For any such α, open sets are measurable sets, and are basic in the definition of the upper measure and of measurability. It is to be noted that if I^c is a closed interval: $[a \leqq x \leqq b, c \leqq y \leqq d]$, then as a member of the class of α-measurable sets, we have

$$\alpha(I^c) = \alpha(b+0, d+0) - \alpha(b+0, c-0) - \alpha(a-0, d+0) + \alpha(a-0, c-0),$$

which may be different from

$$\alpha(I) = \Delta_{xy}\alpha(x, y) = \alpha(b, d) - \alpha(b, c) - \alpha(a, d) + \alpha(a, c)$$

on which the measure is based.

Of special interest is the case when $\alpha(x, y) = \beta(x)\gamma(y)$, where $\beta(x)$ and $\gamma(y)$ are monotonic nondecreasing in x and y, respectively. The measure function $\alpha(E)$ determined by such an $\alpha(x, y)$ depends in a sense on the product of the two measure functions $\beta(E(x))$ and $\gamma(E(y))$ and is called a *product measure*. It is then desirable to explore the relations between the measure function $\alpha(E)$ on the measurable subsets of $X \times Y$ and the measure functions and sets defined on X by β and on Y by γ, as well as the relation between the Lebesgue-Stieltjes double integral: $\int_{X \times Y} f(x, y) d\alpha(x, y)$ and the iterated integrals $\int_X d\beta(x) \int_Y f(x, y) d\gamma(y)$ and $\int_Y d\gamma(y) \int_X f(x, y) d\beta(x)$. While we treat only the case when X and Y are each one-dimensional, so that $X \times Y$ is two-dimensional, it is possible to obtain similar results for the case when X is m-dimensional and Y is n-dimensional, so that $X \times Y$ is $(m + n)$-dimensional, and

$$\alpha(x, y) = \alpha(x_1 \dots x_m, y_1 \dots y_n) = \beta(x_1 \dots x_m)\, \gamma(y_1 \dots y_n).$$

Let X be either the open interval $-\infty < x < +\infty$, the closed finite interval $a \leqq x \leqq b$, or the half-open interval $-\infty < x \leqq b$, or $a \leqq x < +\infty$, and similarly for Y. Let E denote subsets of $X \times Y$, $E(x)$ subsets of X and $E(y)$ subsets of Y. Then any subset E of $X \times Y$ determines for each y_0 of Y, the one-dimensional set $E_{y_0}(x)$, the set of x for which (x, y_0) belongs to E; and for each x_0 of X, the one-dimensional set $E_{x_0}(y)$, the set of y for which (x_0, y) belongs to E. If for each y, the set $E_y(x)$ is either the empty set or a fixed set $E(x)$, then for each x, $E_x(y)$ will be either the empty set or a fixed set $E(y)$, and $E = E(x) \times E(y)$. For instance, if $E(x)$ is the fixed closed interval $[a, b]$, and $E(y)$ the fixed closed interval $[c, d]$, then $E = E(x) \times E(y)$ is the closed rectangle $[a, b] \times [c, d]$. By analogy, sets of the form $E = E(x) \times E(y)$ are sometimes called *rectangular sets*.

Let $\beta(x)$ be a monotonic nondecreasing bounded function on X, and $\gamma(y)$ a monotonic nondecreasing bounded function on Y. Then $\alpha(x, y) = \beta(x)\gamma(y)$ will be a bounded monotonic nondecreasing function on $X \times Y$. $\alpha(x, y)$ will give rise to a class of measurable subsets E of $X \times Y$, which will include the open: $(a, b) \times (c, d)$, the closed: $[a, b] \times [c, d]$, and the half (right) open $[a, b) \times [c, d)$ rectangles. If $I^0 = (a, b) \times (c, d)$, $I^c = [a, b] \times [c, d]$ and $I^h = [a, b) \times [c, d)$, then

$$\alpha(I^0) = (\beta(b-0) - \beta(a+0))\,(\gamma(d-0) - \gamma(c+0)),$$
$$\alpha(I^c) = (\beta(b+0) - \beta(a-0))\,(\gamma(d+0) - \gamma(c-0))$$

and

$$\alpha(I^h) = (\beta(b-0) - \beta(a-0))\,(\gamma(d-0) - \gamma(c-0)).$$

We note that for each of these three cases we can write:

$$\alpha(I) = \int_Y \beta(I_y(x))d\gamma(y) = \int_X \gamma(I_x(y))d\beta(x)$$

where the integrals are Lebesgue integrals. Our aim is to extend this result to any set E measurable relative to α, and prove:

1.1. THEOREM. If $\beta(x)$ and $\gamma(y)$ are bounded monotonic non-decreasing functions and E is measurable relative to $\alpha(x, y) = \beta(x)\gamma(y)$, then $E_y(x)$ is measurable relative to β except for a set of y which is a γ-null set, $E_x(y)$ is measurable relative to γ except for a set of x which is a β-null set, and

$$\alpha(E) = \int_X \gamma(E_x(y))d\beta(x) = \int_Y \beta(E_y(x))d\gamma(y)$$

where the integrals are Lebesgue integrals.

We demonstrate this theorem first for the case when E is an open subset of $X \times Y$. On the one-dimensional interval, any open set can be expressed as the sum of a denumerable number of disjoint open intervals, but for the plane this is not always possible. Instead we make the following observation:

1.2. Any open set of $X \times Y$ can be expressed as the sum of a denumerable number of disjoint half (right) open intervals I^h [defined above as the points (x, y) such that $a \leqq x < b$, $c \leqq y < d$, for some $[a, b; c, d]$.

For suppose we divide $X \times Y$ into a network by means of the lines $x = m/2^k$, $y = n/2^k$, $k =$ a positive integer, m and n ranging over all positive and negative integers. We select serially collections of squares S_k. S_1 consists of all half-open squares $m/2 \leqq x < (m+1)/2$, $n/2 \leqq y < (n+1)/2$ which are contained in G. In general, S_k consists of all squares of the form $m/2^k \leqq x < (m+1)/2^k$; $n/2^k \leqq y < (n+1)/2^k$, which have no points in common with any of the half-open squares in $S_1 \dots S_{k-1}$, and which are contained in G. Then each S_k consists of a denumerable number of squares and every point of G belongs to some S_k, so that $G = \Sigma_k S_k$.

Obviously the same type of reasoning is applicable in any finite-dimensional space. In contrast to the case of an open set on a linear interval, where G determines uniquely the open intervals of which it is constituted, any G can be expressed as the sum of a denumerable number of disjoint half (right) open intervals in many different ways.

As noted for any half-open interval $I^h = [a, b) \times [c, d)$, we have

$$\alpha(I^h) = (\gamma(d-0) - \gamma(c-0))\,(\beta(b-0) - \beta(a-0))$$
$$= \int_X \gamma(I_x^h(y))d\beta(x) = \int_Y \beta(I_y^h(x)d\gamma(y)$$

since the step function $\gamma(I_x^h(y)) = \gamma(d-0) - \gamma(c-0)$ for x on $[a, b)$ and zero elsewhere; and similarly for $(I_y^h(x))$. If now G is any open set and $G = \Sigma_n I_n^h$, where the I_n^h are disjoint, then since the intervals I_n^h are α-measurable, and α is s-additive, we have:

$$\alpha(G) = \sum_n \alpha(I_n^h) = \sum_n \int_X \gamma(I_{nx}^h(y))d\beta(x)$$

Now the set $G_x(y) = \Sigma_n I_{nx}^h(y)$. Then $\gamma(G_x(y)) = \Sigma_n \gamma(I_{nx}^h(y))$, which as a function of x is the sum of a convergent sequence of positive step functions all of which are measurable relative to β. Since

$$\sum_{n=1}^{m} \gamma(I_{nx}^h(y)) \leqq \gamma(G_x(y)) \leqq \gamma(Y)$$

for all m and x, we have by the basic convergence theorem for L-S integrals (VII.8.8.3):

$$\alpha(G) = \sum_n \int_X \gamma(I_{nx}^h(y))d\beta(x) = \int_X \sum_n \gamma(I_{nx}^h(y))d\beta(x)$$
$$= \int_X \gamma(G_x(y))d\beta(x).$$

In the same way, one shows that

$$\alpha(G) = \int_Y \beta(G_y(x))d\gamma(y).$$

It is to be noted that the functions $\gamma(G_x(y))$ in x and $\beta(G_y(x))$ in y are measurable relative to β and γ, respectively.

The same type of formula holds for any closed set F. For if $G = X \times Y - F$, then G is open and

$$\alpha(F) = \alpha(X \times Y) - \alpha(G) = \beta(X)\gamma(Y) - \int_X \gamma(G_x(y))d\beta(x)$$
$$= \int_X (\gamma(Y) - \gamma(G_x(y)))d\beta(x) = \int_X \gamma(F_x(y))d\beta(x).$$

For the general case where E is any set of $X \times Y$ which is measurable relative to α, we find open sets $G_n \geqq E$ and closed sets $F_n \leqq E$ such that $\alpha(G_n - F_n) < 1/n$ so that

$$\alpha(G_n - F_n) = \int_X [\gamma(G_{nx}(y)) - \gamma(F_{nx}(y))] d\beta(x) < 1/n.$$

Then

$$\lim_n \int_X \gamma(G_{nx}(y) - F_{nx}(y)) d\beta(x) = 0.$$

But this has as consequence that $\gamma(G_{nx}(y) - F_{nx}(y)) \to 0(\beta)$. Consequently, there exists a subsequence n_m of the integers n, such that

$$\lim_m \gamma(G_{n_m x}(y) - F_{n_m x}(y)) = 0$$

except for a set E_{0x} of x which is a β-null set. But since $G_{nx}(y) \geqq E_x(y) \geqq F_{nx}(y)$ for all n and x, this means that the sets in y, $E_x(y)$, are measurable relative to γ except for x in E_{0x}, and

$$\gamma(E_x(y)) = \lim_m \gamma(G_{n_m x}(y)).$$

If $\gamma(E_x(y))$ is defined arbitrarily for the x for which $E_x(y)$ is not measurable relative to γ, for instance, as the upper measure $\bar{\gamma}(E_x(y))$, then $\gamma(E_x(y))$ as the limit except for x on a β-null set, of a sequence of β-measurable functions, is measurable relative to β. Moreover, since $\gamma(G_{n_m x}(y)) \leqq \gamma(Y)$ for all x, the sequence of functions $\gamma(G_{n_m x})$ is uniformly bounded in m and x. Since $\lim_m \alpha(G_{n_m}) = \alpha(E)$ it follows that

$$\alpha(E) = \lim_m \int_X \gamma(G_{n_m x}(y)) d\beta(x) = \int_X \gamma(E_x(y)) d\beta(x).$$

Similarly the sets in x: $E_y(x)$ are measurable relative to β except for a set of y which is a γ-null set, and $\alpha(E) = \int_Y \beta(E_y(x)) d\gamma(y)$.

As a special case of this theorem, we note that if $G'(x)$ and $G''(y)$ are open sets on X and Y, respectively, and $G = G'(x) \times G''(y)$, the set of all (x, y) for which x belongs to $G'(x)$ and y to $G''(y)$ simultaneously, then $\alpha(G) = \int_Y \beta(G_y(x)) d\gamma(y) = \beta(G'(x))\gamma(G''(y))$, since $G_y(x) = G'(x)$ for y on $G''(y)$ and the null set for y on the complement of $G''(y)$. Similarly, if $F'(x)$ and $F''(y)$ are closed sets on X and Y, respectively, then for $F = F'(x) \times F''(y)$ we have $\alpha(F) = \beta(F'(x))\gamma(F''(y))$. More generally we can show that:

1.3. If $E'(x)$ is measurable relative to β, and $E''(y)$ relative to γ, then $E = E'(x) \times E''(y)$ is measurable relative to

$$\alpha(x, y) = \beta(x)\gamma(y), \quad \text{and} \quad \alpha(E) = \beta(E'(x))\gamma(E''(y)).$$

For there exists for $e > 0$ open $G_e'(x)$ and closed $F_e'(x)$ such that $G_e'(x) \geqq E'(x) \geqq F_e'(x)$ and $\alpha(G_e'(x) - F_e'(x)) < e$; and similarly $G_e''(y) \geqq E''(y) \geqq F_e''(y)$ with $\alpha(G_e''(y) - F_e''(y)) < e$. Then $G_e'(x) \times G_e''(y) \geqq E \geqq F_e'(x) \times F_e''(y)$ and

$$\begin{aligned}
&\alpha(G_e'(x) \times G_e''(y) - F_e'(x) \times F_e''(y)) \\
&= \alpha(G_e'(x) \times G_e''(y)) - \alpha(F_e'(x) \times F_e''(y)) \\
&= \beta(G_e'(x))\gamma(G_e''(y)) - \beta(F_e'(x))\gamma(F_e''(y)) \\
&= \beta(G_e'(x) - F_e'(x))\gamma(G_e''(y)) - \beta(F_e'(x))\gamma(G_e''(y) - F_e''(y)) \\
&\leqq e(\gamma(Y) + \beta(X)).
\end{aligned}$$

Then $E = E'(x) \times E''(y)$ is measurable and

$$\alpha(E) = \beta(E'(x))\gamma(E''(y)).$$

1.4. Suppose now that either of the monotone functions $\beta(x)$ or $\gamma(y)$ is unbounded on $X = -\infty < x < +\infty$ or $Y = -\infty < y < +\infty$, but bounded for every finite subinterval of X or Y. Let E be measurable relative to $\alpha(x, y) = \beta(x)\gamma(y)$, with $\alpha(E) < \infty$. Let I_n be the open rectangle: $(-n, n) \times (-n, n)$ and set $E_n = E \cdot I_n$. Then we can apply Theorem X.1.1 to subsets E_n of I_n and obtain

$$\alpha(E_n) = \int_X \gamma(E_{nx}(y))d\beta(x) = \int_Y \beta(E_{ny}(x))d\gamma(y),$$

since $\gamma(E_{nx}(y)) = 0$ for $|x| > n$, and $\beta(E_{ny}(x)) = 0$ for $|y| > n$. The sets $E_{nx}(y)$ are measurable relative to γ for all x except at most a β-null set, so that $\gamma(E_{nx}(y)$ is defined as a function of x except for a β-null set for each n. If this set is $E_{n0}(x)$, and $E_0(x) = \Sigma_n E_{n0}(x)$, then $E_0(x)$ will be a β-null set. Since $\gamma(E_{nx}(y))$ is monotonic in n except for x in $E_0(x)$, $\lim_n \gamma(E_{nx}(y))$ will exist (finite or $+\infty$) as a function of x defined except for a β-null set. Similarly $\beta(E_{ny}(x))$ is monotonic in n except for at most a γ-null set in y and $\lim_n \beta(E_{ny}(x))$ exists except for a γ-null set. Since $\lim_n \alpha(E_n) = \alpha(E)$ the Fatou convergence theorem VII.8.10 gives us:

$$\begin{aligned}
\alpha(E) &= \lim_n \int_X \gamma(E_{nx}(y))d\beta(x) = \int_X \lim_n \gamma(E_{nx}(y))d\beta(x) \\
&= \lim_n \int_Y \beta(E_{ny}(x))d\gamma(y) = \int_Y \lim_n \beta(E_{ny}(x))d\gamma(y).
\end{aligned}$$

Now $E_{nx}(y)$ for x not in E_{0x} is a sequence of sets of Y measurable relative to γ, with $E_x(y) = \lim_n E_{nx}(y)$. Then $\lim_n \gamma(E_{nx}(y)) = \gamma(E_x(y))$ except for x on $E_0(x)$ or a β-null set, a result of the additive properties of measurable sets and measure. Similarly $\lim_n \beta(E_{ny}(x)) = \beta(E_y(x))$ except for y on $E_0(y)$ a γ-null set. Then

$$\alpha(E) = \int_X \gamma(E_x(y))d\beta(x) = \int_Y \beta(E_y(x))d\gamma(y).$$

Here $\gamma(E_x(y))$ is not defined for x on a β-null set $E_0(x)$, and may be $+\infty$ on a β-null set since $\int_X \gamma(E_x(y))d\beta(x)$ exists. Similarly for $\beta(E_y(x))$.

In case $\alpha(E)$ is not finite, the same type of reasoning applies, $E_x(y)$ is measurable relative to $\gamma(y)$ except for x in a β-null set, and $E_y(x)$ is measurable relative to $\beta(x)$ except for y in a γ-null set, but the equality on the integrals holds only if we allow $+\infty$ as a value for the integral.

2. The Lebesgue-Stieltjes Integrals as the Measure of a Plane Set

The theorem just proved can be made the basis for another method of defining a Lebesgue-Stieltjes integral, at least for positive finite valued functions. Any function $f(x) \geqq 0$ on X determines the plane set $E = \Sigma_x [x, 0 \leqq y \leqq f(x)]$. Let $\beta(x)$ be any monotonic nondecreasing function on X. Then the function $\alpha(x, y) = \beta(x) \cdot y$ defines a planar measure such that for any rectangular set $E = E(x) \times E(y)$, where $E(x)$ is measurable relative to β and $E(y)$ is Lebesgue measurable, we have $\alpha(E) = \beta(E(x))\gamma(E(y))$, where $\gamma(E(y))$ is the Lebesgue measure of $E(y)$. We then have the following theorem:

2.1. THEOREM. If $f(x) \geq 0$ on X, and $\beta(x)$ is monotonic nondecreasing, then a necessary and sufficient condition that $\int_X f(x)d\beta(x)$ exists is that the set $E = \Sigma_x [x, 0 \leqq y \leqq f(x)]$ be of finite measure relative to $\alpha(x, y) = \beta(x) \cdot y$, and then $\alpha(E) = \int_X f(x)d\beta(x)$.

For the necessity, if $\int_X f(x)d\beta(x)$ exists as a finite number, then the upper and lower integrals $\overline{\int}_X fd\alpha$ and $\underline{\int}_X fd\alpha$ are finite and equal. As a consequence there exists a sequence of subdivisions $\sigma_n = \{E_{nm}(x)\}$ of X such that $\sigma_{n+1} \geqq \sigma_n$, f is bounded on each E_{nm} and

$$\lim_n \sum_{\sigma_n} M(f;\ E_{nm}(x))\beta(E_{nm}(x)) = \lim_n \sum_{\sigma_n} m(f;\ E_{nm}(x))\beta(E_{nm}(x)),$$

where as usual $M(f; E) =$ l.u.b. f on E and $m(f; E) =$ g.l.b. f on E.

Define the step functions $\varphi_n(x) = M(f, E_{nm})$ for x on E_{nm} and $\psi_n(x) = m(f, E_{nm})$ for x on $\overline{E}_{nm}$. Let $\overline{E}_n$ be the plane set $\Sigma_x [x, 0 \leqq y \leqq \varphi_n(x)]$ and $\overline{\overline{E}}_n$ the plane set $\Sigma_x [x, 0 \leqq y \leqq \psi_n(x)]$. Then since by X.1.3 the rectangular sets $E_{nm}(x) \times [0 \leqq y \leqq M(f; E_{nm})]$ are plane measurable relative to $\alpha(x, y) = \beta(x) \cdot y$ and $\overline{E}_n$ is the sum as to m of these disjoint sets, it follows that $\overline{E}_n$ are measurable for each n relative to α. Similarly, $\overline{\overline{E}}_n$ are measurable relative to α. Moreover,

$$\alpha(\overline{E}_n) = \sum_{\sigma_n} M(f;\ E_{nm})\beta(E_{nm})$$

and

$$\alpha(\overline{\overline{E}}_n) = \sum_{\sigma_n} m(f;\ E_{nm})\beta(E_{nm}).$$

Now $\overline{E}_n \geqq E \geqq \overline{\overline{E}}_n$ and

$$\lim_n (\alpha(\overline{E}_n) - \alpha(\overline{\overline{E}}_n)) = \lim_n \alpha(\overline{E}_n - \overline{\overline{E}}_n) = 0.$$

Then: $\alpha(\lim_n \overline{E}_n) - \alpha(\lim_n \overline{\overline{E}}_n) = 0$, the set E is measurable relative to α, and $\alpha(E) = \int_X f d\beta$.

For the sufficiency, suppose that E is α-measurable and $\alpha(E) < \infty$. Then

$$\alpha(E) = \int_Y \beta(E_y(x))dy = \int_X \gamma(E_x(y)d\beta(x).$$

Now the set $E_x(y) = [0 \leqq y \leqq f(x)]$ is measurable in y for each x, with measure $f(x)$, so that

$$\alpha(E) = \int_X \gamma(E_x(y))d\beta(x) = \int_X f(x)d\beta(x).$$

We might note that our theorem also tells us that the set $E_y(x)$ is measurable relative to β except for a set of y in a γ-null set, that is, a set of Lebesgue measure zero. Now the set $E_y(x)$ for $E = \Sigma_x[x, 0 \leqq y \leqq f(x)]$ is the set of x: $E[f(x) \geqq y]$. Consequently, the set $E[f(x) \geqq y]$ is β-measurable except for a set of y of Lebesgue measure zero, that is for a set of y which is dense on Y. It follows from VI.2.4 that $E[f(x) \geqq y)$ is measurable for all y, and $f(x)$ is measurable relative to β.

If we apply integration by parts to $\int_Y \beta(E_y(x))dy$, then

$$\begin{aligned}\int_Y \beta(E_y(x))dy &= \lim_{y\to+\infty} \int_0^y \beta(E_y(x))dy \\ &= \lim_{y\to+\infty} [y\beta(E_y(x)) - \int_0^y yd\beta(E_y(x))].\end{aligned}$$

Now if $f(x)$ is L-S integrable with respect to β, then in view of the fact that $E_y(x) = E[f(x) \geqq y]$, we have $\lim_{y\to+\infty} y\beta(E_y(x)) = 0$ by VII.2.5. Consequently,

$$\int_Y \beta(E_y(x)dy = -\int_0^\infty yd_y\beta(E_y(x)) = \int_0^\infty yd\mu(y),$$

if $\mu(y) = \beta(E[f(x) < y])$, which connects with the Lebesgue method of defining the L-S integral (see VII.2.3).

In case $f(x)$ is allowed to take on both positive and negative values, we write $f(x) = f^+(x) - f^-(x)$, where $f^+(x)$ is the greater of $f(x)$ and 0, and $f^-(x)$ the greater of $-f(x)$ and 0. If both sets $E^+ = \Sigma_x[x,\ 0 \leqq y \leqq f^+(x)]$ and $E^- = \Sigma_x[0 \leqq y \leqq f^-(x)]$ are measurable relative to $\alpha(x, y) = \beta(x) \cdot y$, with $\alpha(E^+)$ and $\alpha(E^-)$ both finite, then f is L-S integrable relative to β and $\int_X fd\beta = \alpha(E^+) - \alpha(E^-)$.

3. Fubini Theorem on Double and Iterated Integrals

As we have seen, if $\alpha(x, y) = \beta(x)\gamma(y)$ on $X \times Y$, and E is measurable relative to α, with $\alpha(E) < \infty$, then

$$\alpha(E) = \int_{X\times Y} \chi(E;\ x,\ y)d\alpha(x,\ y) = \int_Y \beta(E_y(x))d\gamma(y)$$
$$= \int_X \gamma(E_x(y))\beta(x).$$

If for a fixed y, the set $E_y(x)$ is measurable relative β, then $\int_X \chi(E;\ x,\ y)d\beta(x) = \beta(E_y(x))$. Since $E_y(x)$ is β-measurable except possibly for a set of y which is a γ-null set, we have

$$\alpha(E) = \int_{X\times Y} \chi(E;\ x,\ y)d\alpha(x,\ y) = \int_Y \beta(E_y(x))d\gamma(y)$$
$$= \int_Y d\gamma(y) \int_X \chi(E; x, y)d\beta(x)$$

where the inner integral exists except for a γ-null set. Similarly,

$$\alpha(E) = \int_{X\times Y} \chi(E; x, y)d\alpha(x, y) = \int_X d\beta(x) \int_Y \chi(E; x, y)\ d\gamma(y).$$

This is a special case of the following theorem relating double integrals to iterated integrals:

3.1. Fubini Theorem. If on $X \times Y$, $\alpha(x, y) = \beta(x)\gamma(y)$, with $\beta(x)$ and $\gamma(y)$ monotonic nondecreasing on X and Y, respectively, and if

$f(x, y)$ on $X \times Y$ is finite valued and such that $\int_{X\times Y} f(x, y)d\alpha(x, y)$ exists, then $\int_X f(x, y)d\beta(x)$ exists except for a γ-null set in y, and $\int_Y f(x, y)d\gamma(y)$ exists except for a β-null set in x, and

$$\int_{X\times Y} f(x, y)d\alpha(x, y) = \int_Y d\gamma(y) \int_X f(x, y)d\beta(x)$$
$$= \int_X d\beta(x) \int_Y f(x, y)d\gamma(y)$$

where the values of $\int_X f(x, y)d\beta(x)$ and $\int_Y f(x, y)d\gamma(y)$ are arbitrary for the y and x in the null sets where these integrals do not exist.

Since the integration process is linear, we see at once that the preliminary observations above, on the theorem, lead to a proof of its validity for any step function $f(x, y)$, which is measurable and assumes only a finite number of values, that is, one expressible in the form $f(x, y) = \Sigma_{m=1}^n c_m \chi(E_m; x, y)$, where E_m are disjoint sets, measurable relative to α, and $\Sigma_m E_m = X \times Y$. In order to extend this to the case where $f(x, y)$ is a general integrable step function, that is, $f(x, y) = \Sigma_m c_m \chi(E_m; x, y)$, with $\Sigma_m |c_m| \alpha(E_m) < \infty$ and $\Sigma_m E_m = X \times Y$, we note that it is sufficient to make the demonstration for the case where $c_m \geq 0$ for all m, as any integrable step function is obviously the difference of two such positive functions. If we set $f_n(x, y) = \Sigma_{m=1}^n c_m \chi(E_m; x, y)$; then $f_n(x, y)$ will converge monotonically in n to $f(x, y)$, the sequence $\int_{X\times Y} f_n(x, y)d\alpha(x, y)$ will be bounded in n and so

$$\lim_n \int_{X\times Y} f_n(x, y)d\alpha(x, y) = \int_{X\times Y} f(x, y)d\alpha(x, y).$$

Now

$$\int_{X\times Y} f_n(x, y)d\alpha(x, y) = \int_X d\beta(x) \int_Y f_n(x, y)d\gamma(y)$$

where the inner integral exists excepting for a β-null set in x. If $E_0(x)$ is the set of x such that $\int_Y f_n(x, y)d\gamma(y)$ does not exist for some n, then $\beta(E_0(x)) = 0$. If x is not in $E_0(x)$ then the sequence $\int_Y f_n(x, y) d\gamma(y)$ will be nondecreasing, and such that $\int_X d\beta(x) \int_Y f_n(x, y)d\gamma(y)$ are bounded in n. Then by the Fatou convergence theorem of VII.8.10, we have

$$\lim_n \int_X d\beta(x) \int_Y f_n(x, y)d\gamma(y) = \int_X d\beta(x) \int \lim_n \int_Y f_n(x, y)d\gamma(y).$$

It follows that $\lim_n \int_Y f_n(x, y)d\gamma(y)$ exists as a finite number, excepting at most a β-null set and because of the monotoneity of $f_n(x,y)$ in n, that

$$\lim_n \int_Y f_n(x, y)d\gamma(y) = \int_Y \lim_n f_n(x, y)d\gamma(y) = \int_Y f(x, y)d\gamma(y).$$

Then we have shown that $\int_Y f(x, y)d\gamma(y)$ exists except for a β-null set, the sum of the sets in x for which $E_{nx}(y)$ are not measurable relative to $\gamma(y)$, and the set on which $\lim_n \int_Y f_n(x, y)d\gamma(y)$ might be infinite. By combining these considerations we have

$$\begin{aligned}\int_{X\times Y} f(x, y)d\alpha(x, y) &= \lim_n \int_{X\times Y} f_n(x, y)d\alpha(x, y)\\ &= \lim_n \int_X d\beta(x) \int_Y f_n(x, y)d\gamma(y)\\ &= \int_X d\beta(x) \lim_n \int_Y f_n(x, y)d\gamma(y)\\ &= \int_X d\beta(x) \int_Y \lim_n f_n(x, y)d\gamma(y)\\ &= \int_X d\beta(x) \int_Y f(x, y)d\gamma(y)\end{aligned}$$

where the inner integral exists except for a β-null set in x, and is arbitrary at the points of this set.

We take up next the case of any finite valued function integrable with respect to $\alpha(x, y)$, and because integrability implies absolute integrability, restrict ourselves to the case when $f(x, y) \geqq 0$ on $X \times Y$. Then there exists a subdivision σ_0 of $X \times Y$, such that $f(x, y)$ is bounded on every subset E of σ_0, and if $\sigma \geqq \sigma_0$, then $\Sigma_\sigma M(f; E_n)\alpha(E_n) < \infty$, and

$$\begin{aligned}\text{g.l.b.}_\sigma \sum_\sigma M(f;\ E)\alpha(E) &= \int_{X\times Y} f(x, y)d\alpha(x, y)\\ &= \text{l.u.b.}_\sigma \sum_\sigma m(f;\ E)\alpha(E).\end{aligned}$$

For any subdivision σ we define the measurable step function $f_\sigma(x, y) = M(f; E)$ if (x, y) is in the set E of σ. Then

$$\begin{aligned}\sum_\sigma M(f; E)\alpha(E) &= \int_{X\times Y} f_\sigma(x, y)d\alpha(x, y)\\ &= \int_X d\beta(x) \int_Y f_\sigma(x, y)d\gamma(y)\end{aligned}$$

where $\int_X f_\sigma(x, y)\, d\gamma(y)$ exists except for a β-null set $E_0(x)$. If x is not in $E_0(x)$, then since $f_\sigma(x, y) \geqq f(x, y)$ for all (x, y), we will have $\int_Y f_\sigma(x, y)d\gamma(y) \geqq \overline{\int}_Y f(x, y)d\gamma(y)$. It follows that

$$\sum_\sigma M(f; E)\alpha(E) = \int_X d\beta(x) \int_Y f_\sigma(x, y)d\gamma(y)$$
$$\geqq \overline{\int}_X d\beta(x) \overline{\int}_Y f(x, y)d\beta(y).$$

This holds for every $\sigma \geqq \sigma_0$. Similarly, we show that

$$\sum_\sigma m(f;\ E)\alpha(E) \leqq \underline{\int}_X d\beta(x) \underline{\int}_Y f(x, y)d\gamma(y)$$

for every $\sigma \geqq \sigma_0$. Taking the greatest lower bound as to σ in the first inequality and the least upper bound as to σ in the second, we obtain

$$\int_{X\times Y} f(x, y)d\alpha(x, y) \geqq \overline{\int}_X d\beta(x) \overline{\int}_Y f(x, y)d\gamma(y)$$
$$\geqq \underline{\int}_X d\beta(x) \underline{\int}_Y f(x, y)d\gamma(y) \geqq \int_{X\times Y} f(x, y)d\alpha(x, y).$$

Then equality holds throughout and because of the properties of integrals we can even assert

$$\overline{\int}_X d\beta(x) \overline{\int}_Y f(x, y)d\gamma(y) = \overline{\int}_X d\beta(x) \underline{\int}_Y f(x, y)d\gamma(y)$$
$$= \underline{\int}_X d\beta(x) \overline{\int}_Y f(x, y)d\gamma(y) = \underline{\int}_X d\beta(x) \underline{\int}_Y f(x, y)d\gamma(y).$$

From these equalities it follows that $\overline{\int}_Y f(x, y)d\gamma(y)$ and $\underline{\int}_Y f(x, y) d\gamma(y)$ are each integrable with respect to β and that

$$\int_X d\beta(x) \overline{\int}_Y f(x, y)d\gamma(y) = \int_X d\beta(x) \underline{\int}_Y f(x, y)d\gamma(y),$$

or

$$\int_X d\beta(x) [\overline{\int}_Y f(x, y)d\gamma(y) - \underline{\int}_Y f(x, y)d\gamma(y)] = 0.$$

Consequently, the positive or zero function $\overline{\int}_Y f(x, y)d\gamma(y) - \underline{\int}_Y f(x, y)d\gamma(y)$ is measurable, and vanishes except on a β-null set. This means that $\int_Y f(x, y)d\gamma(y)$ exists except for a β-null set. Moreover, we can conclude that

$$\int_{X\times Y} f(x, y)d\alpha(x, y) = \int_X d\beta(x) \int_Y f(x, y)d\gamma(y)$$

where the inner integral exists except for a β-null set, where its value can be assigned arbitrarily.

Since X and Y and β and γ are of a parity, we also have

$$\int_{X\times Y} f(x, y)d\alpha(x, y) = \int_Y d\gamma(y) \int_X f(x, y)d\beta(x),$$

where the inner integral exists except on a γ-null set.

As we have indicated, we can deduce the validity of the Fubini theorem for any function $f(x, y)$ integrable with respect to α from the above case where $f(x, y) \geqq 0$, by decomposing $f(x, y) = f^+(x, y) - f^-(x, y)$ into its positive and negative parts.

The existence of $\int_{X\times Y} fd\alpha$ cannot in general be deduced from the existence of the iterated integrals $\int_X d\beta(x) \int_Y f(x, y)d\gamma(y)$ and $\int_Y d\gamma(y) \int_X f(x, y)d\beta(x)$ and their equality. For a counterexample see: W. Sierpinski: Sur une probleme concernant les ensembles mesurables superficiellement, *Fundamenta Math.* 1 (1920) 140-150. However, in case $f(x, y)$ is measurable relative to $\alpha(x, y)$, we have:

3.2. THEOREM. If $\beta(x)$ and $\gamma(y)$ are monotonic nondecreasing on X and Y, respectively; and $\alpha(x, y) = \beta(x)\gamma(y)$; if $f(x, y)$ is measurable relative to $\alpha(x, y)$; if $\int_X d\beta(x) \int_Y |f(x, y)| d\gamma(y)$ exists, ($\int_Y f(x, y)d\gamma(y)$ need exist only for a set which differs from X by a β-null set), then $\int_{X\times Y} f(x, y)d\alpha(x, y)$ and $\int_Y d\gamma(y) \int_X f(x, y)d\beta(x)$ exist and are both equal to $\int_X d\beta(x) \int_Y f(x, y)d\gamma(y)$.

Since the hypotheses of the theorem involve only absolute integrability of $f(x, y)$, it is sufficient to prove this theorem for $f(x, y) \geqq 0$ on $X \times Y$. Let $X_n = [-n, n]$ and $Y_n = [-n, n]$. Further, set $f_M(x, y) = f(x, y)$ if $f(x, y) \leqq M$ and $f_M(x, y) = M$ if $f(x, y) > M$. Then since $f(x, y)$ is measurable relative to α, the functions β and γ are bounded on X_n and Y_n, respectively, and $f_M(x, y)$ is bounded, we know that

$$\int_{X_n\times Y_n} f_M(x, y)d\alpha(x, y), \quad \int_{X_n} d\beta(x) \int_{Y_n} f_M(x, y)d\gamma(y)$$

and

$$\int_{Y_n} d\gamma(y) \int_{X_n} f_M(x, y)d\beta(x)$$

all exist and are equal. Successive applications of the Fatou monotone convergence theorem (VII.8.10) then complete the proof of the theorem.

The Fubini theorem can be extended to the case where for $\alpha(x, y) = \beta(x)\gamma(y)$, $\beta(x)$ and $\gamma(y)$ are each functions of bounded variation on every finite subinterval of $X = -\infty < x < +\infty$ and $Y = -\infty < y < +\infty$, respectively. To this end recall that if a function $\beta(x)$ is of bounded variation on every finite subinterval of X, then there exist monotonic functions $p(\beta; x)$ and $n(\beta; x)$ such that for any finite interval $[a, b]$

$$\begin{aligned}\beta(b) - \beta(a) &= p(\beta; b) - p(\beta; a) - (n(\beta; b) - n(\beta; a)) \\ &= \Delta_a^b p(\beta) - \Delta_a^b n(\beta),\end{aligned}$$

while $v(\beta; [a, b]) = \Delta_a^b p(\beta) + \Delta_a^b n(\beta)$. If $\alpha(x, y) = \beta(x)\gamma(y)$, and R is the rectangle $[a, b] \times [c, d]$, then

$$v(\alpha; R) = v(\beta; [a, b]) \cdot v(\gamma; [c, d])$$

$$= \Delta_a^b p(\beta) \Delta_c^d p(\gamma) + \Delta_a^b p(\beta) \Delta_c^d n(\gamma) + \Delta_a^b n(\beta) \Delta_c^d p(\gamma) + \Delta_a^b n(\beta) \Delta_c^d n(\gamma),$$

while

$$\begin{aligned}\Delta_{xy}(\alpha; R) = \Delta_a^b p(\beta)\, \Delta_c^d p(\gamma) - \Delta_a^b n(\beta)\, \Delta_c^d p(\gamma) \\ - \Delta_a^b n(\beta)\, \Delta_c^d p(\gamma) + \Delta_a^b n(\beta)\, \Delta_c^d n(\gamma).\end{aligned}$$

It follows that the positive and negative variation functions $p(\alpha; x, y)$ and $n(\alpha; x, y)$ associated with $\alpha(x, y)$ can be written

$$p(\alpha; x, y) = p(\beta, x)p(\gamma; y) + n(\beta, x)n(\gamma; y)$$

and

$$n(\alpha; x, y) = p(\beta; x)n(\gamma; y) + n(\beta; x)p(\gamma; y).$$

If now $\int_{X\times Y} fd\alpha$ exists, then $\int_{X\times Y} fdp(\alpha)$ and $\int_{X\times Y} fdn(\alpha)$ both exist and $\int_{X\times Y} fd\alpha = \int_{X\times Y} fdp(\alpha) - \int_{X\times Y} fdn(\alpha)$. Since

$$\int_{X\times Y} fdp(\alpha) = \int_{X\times Y} f(x, y)d[p(\beta; x)p(\gamma, y) + n(\beta; x)n(\gamma, y)]$$

and for any rectangle R

$$\begin{aligned}\Delta_{xy}[p(\beta; x)p(\gamma; y) + n(\beta; x)n(\gamma; y);\ R] &\geqq \Delta_{xy}[p(\beta; x)p(\gamma; y); R] \\ \text{and} \qquad &\geqq \Delta_{xy}\, [n(\beta; x)n(\gamma; y); R]\end{aligned}$$

it follows from VII.10.4 that the existence of the integral $\int_{X\times Y} f(x, y)\, dp(\alpha; x, y)$ carries with it the existence of the integrals $\int_{X\times Y} f(x, y)$

$d(p(\beta;\ x)p(\gamma;\ y)$ and $\int_{X\times Y} f(x,\ y)d(n(\beta;\ x)n(\gamma;\ y)$. Similarly from the existence of $\int_{X\times Y} f(x, y)\ dn(\alpha;\ x, y)$ we derive the existence of $\int_{X\times Y} f(x, y)d(p(\beta; x)n(\gamma; y))$ and $\int_{X\times Y} f(x, y)d(n(\beta; x)p(\gamma; y))$. To each of these integrals we can apply the Fubini theorem for monotone functions. As a consequence, we have that $\int_Y f(x, y)dp(\gamma;\ y)$ and $\int_Y f(x,\ y)dn(\gamma;\ y)$ each exists except for a $p(\beta)$-null set. Then $\int_Y f(x,\ y)d(p(\gamma;\ y) - n(\gamma;\ y)) = \int_Y f(x,\ y)d\gamma(y)$ will exist except for a $p(\beta)$-null set and

$$\int_{X\times Y} f(x, y)d(p(\beta; x)p(\gamma; y)) - \int_{X\times Y} f(x, y)d(p(\beta; x)n(\gamma; y)$$
$$= \int_X dp(\beta;\ x) \int_Y f(x,\ y)d\gamma(y).$$

Similarly,

$$\int_{X\times Y} f(x,\ y)d(n(\beta;x)p(\gamma;\ y)) - \int_{X\times Y} f(x,\ y)d(n(\beta;\ x)n(\gamma;\ y)$$
$$= \int_X dn(\beta;\ x) \int_Y f(x,\ y)d\gamma(y)$$

and the integral $\int_Y f(x, y)d\gamma(y)$ will exist except for a $n(\beta)$-null set. Consequently, $\int_Y f(x, y)d\gamma(y)$ will exist excepting for a $v(\beta)$ null set and

$$\int_{X\times Y} f(x, y)d\alpha(x,\ \ y) - \int_X d\beta(x) \int_Y f(x, y)d\gamma(y).$$

Obviously the roles of X and Y can be interchanged. We have then shown:

3.3. THEOREM. If $X = -\infty < x < +\infty$, $Y = -\infty < x < +\infty$; $\beta(x)$ and $\gamma(y)$ are of bounded variation on every finite subinterval of X and Y, respectively; $\alpha(x,\ y) = \beta(x)\gamma(y)$; $f(x,\ y)$ on $X \times Y$ is such that $\int_{X\times Y} f(x,\ y)d\alpha(x,\ y)$ exists; then $\int_Y f(x,\ y)d\gamma(y)$ exists except possibly for a $v(\beta)$-null set and $\int_X f(x,\ y)d\beta(x)$ exists except possibly for a $v(\gamma)$-null set, and

$$\int_{X\times Y} f(x, y)d\alpha(x, y) = \int_X d\beta(x) \int_Y f(x, y)d\gamma(y)$$
$$= \int_Y d\gamma(y) \int_X f(x, y)d\beta(x)$$

in which the inner integrals may fail to exist on $v(\beta)$-null and $v(\gamma)$-null sets, respectively.

EXERCISE

The integration by parts formula for Riemann-Stieltjes integrals can be written:

$$\int_a^b df(x) \int_a^x dg(y) = \int_a^b dg(y) \int_y^b df(x) = \int_a^b \int_a^b \chi(E; x, y) df(x) dg(y),$$

where E is the triangle $a \leqq x \leqq y \leqq b$. Suppose that $\beta(x)$ and $\gamma(y)$ are of bounded variation on $a \leqq x \leqq b$ and $a \leqq y \leqq b$, respectively. What does the Fubini theorem yield concerning the relation between the Lebesgue-Stieltjes integrals $\int_a^b \beta(y) d\gamma(y)$ and $\int_a^b \gamma(x) d\beta(x)$?

CHAPTER XI

DERIVATIVES AND INTEGRALS

1. Riemann Integrals and Derivatives

In elementary calculus, we find a close relationship between integrals and derivatives for functions $f(x)$ on a finite interval: $a \leqq x \leqq b$. This relationship is embodied in the two fundamental theorems of the integral calculus:

1.1. THEOREM A. If $f(x)$ is Riemann integrable on $[a, b]$ and $g(x) = \int_a^x f(x)dx$, then the derivative $g'(x)$ exists for all points x for which $f(x)$ is continuous and $g'(x) = f(x)$ at these points.

1.2. THEOREM B. If $f(x)$ on $[a, b]$ is such that $f'(x)$ exists for all x of $[a, b]$ and is Riemann integrable, then $\int_a^b f'(x)dx = f(b) - f(a)$, or $\int_a^x f'(x)dx = f(x) - f(a)$ for $a \leqq x \leqq b$.

The proof of Theorem A is well known and quite simple. For

$$g(x_0 + \Delta x) - g(x_0) = \int_a^{x_0+\Delta x} f(x)dx - \int_a^{x_0} f(x)dx = \int_{x_0}^{x_0+\Delta x} f(x)dx.$$

Then since $f(x_0)\Delta x = \int_{x_0}^{x_0+\Delta x} f(x_0)\Delta x$:

$$\begin{aligned} &| (g(x_0 + \Delta x) - g(x_0))/\Delta x - f(x_0) | \\ &= | (\int_{x_0}^{x_0+\Delta x} (f(x) - f(x_0))dx)/\Delta x | \\ &\leqq \int_{x_0}^{x_0+\Delta x} |f(x) - f(x_0)| dx/| \Delta x |. \end{aligned}$$

If $f(x)$ is continuous at x_0, then $e > 0$, d_{ex_0}, $| x - x_0 | < d_{ex_0}$: $| f(x) - f(x_0) | < e$. If $| \Delta x | < d_{ex_0}$, then

$$\int_{x_0}^{x_0+\Delta x} |f(x) - f(x_0)| dx / | \Delta x | < e,$$

or

$$|(g(x_0 + \Delta x) - g(x_0))/\Delta x - f(x_0)| < e.$$

This means that $g'(x_0) = f(x_0)$.

An immediate consequence of Theorem A is:

1.2.1. Corollary. If $f(x)$ is continuous on $[a, b]$, then $g'(x) = f(x)$ for all x of $[a, b]$. That is for every function $f(x)$ continuous on $[a, b]$, there exists a function $g(x) = \int_a^x f(x)dx$ such that $g'(x) = f(x)$ for all x of $[a, b]$, or every continuous function is the inverse derivative of a (continuous) function.

We note further that since any Riemann integrable function is continuous except for a set of Lebesgue measure zero, Theorem A asserts that $d/dx \int_a^x f(x)dx$ exists and is equal to $f(x)$ except for a set of x of Lebesgue measure zero.

Theorem B tells us that the indefinite Riemann integral recovers the function $f(x)$ from its derivative if this latter is R-integrable. The usual proof is as follows: Let σ be any subdivision of $[a, b]$. Then by the mean value theorem of the differential calculus there exists points x_i' on $[x_{i-1}, x_i]$ such that

$$f(b) - f(a) = \sum_\sigma (f(x_i) - f(x_{i-1})) = \sum_\sigma f'(x_i')\,(x_i - x_{i-1}).$$

But the last expression is one of the approximating sums for $\int_a^b f'(x)dx$. Consequently, $f(b) - f(a) = \int_a^b f'(x)dx$, and this holds also if b is replaced by any point x in $[a, b]$.

This proof uses the mean value theorem of the differential calculus. It is natural to ask whether it is possible to prove this theorem using only the existence of the derivative $f'(x)$ for each x of $[a, b]$ and the R-integrability of this function. This has been done for the Riemann-Stieltjes integral relative to a strictly monotone function $g(x)$ in II. 16.3, so that the proof is also valid for the special case $g(x) = x$.

The main object of this chapter is to obtain the extension of these two fundamental theorems to the case when Lebesgue integration is involved. Since the proofs above depend on the properties of Riemann integration, different procedures will be necessary for Lebesgue integrable functions. Instead of taking up the L-S integral with respect to a function of bounded variation, we shall limit ourselves to Lebesgue integrals with $\alpha(x) = x$ on a finite interval $[a, b]$. Measurable sets are then Lebesgue measurable or simply measurable, and derivatives are with respect to x. We shall denote by $\mu(E)$ the Lebesgue measure of a measurable set E, and by $\mu^*(E)$ the Lebesgue upper measure of any set E.

We note in passing that the two fundamental theorems of the integral calculus give a partial solution of what might be called the inverse derivative problem: Given a finite valued function $f(x)$ on $[a, b]$; under what conditions does there exist a (continuous) function $g(x)$ such that $g'(x) = f(x)$ for all x of $[a, b]$ and how can one construct such a function $g(x)$ when it exists.

EXERCISES

1. Show that if $f(x)$ is Riemann integrable, then $g(x) = \int_a^x f(x)dx$ has a right-hand derivative at all points where $f(x)$ is continuous on the right.

2. Prove the following interval lemma: If to every point x of $a \leq x < b$, there corresponds one subinterval to the right: $[x, x + r_x]$, and to every x of $a < x \leq b$, there exists a d_x such that all subintervals to the left of x: $[x - l_x, x]$ with $l_x < d_x$ correspond to x, then there exists a finite number of these intervals which laid end to end reach from a to b. Is this lemma equivalent to the Borel theorem on $[a, b]$?

3. Is the following theorem true: If $\alpha(x)$ is of bounded variation on $[a, b]$, if $f(x)$ is continous at x_0 and such that $\int_a^b f(x)d\alpha(x)$ exists in either norm or σ-sense, and if $g(x) = \int_a^x f(x)d\alpha(x)$, then

$$\lim_{\Delta x \to 0} \frac{g(x_0 + \Delta x) - g(x_0)}{\alpha(x_0 + \Delta x) - \alpha(x_0)} = f(x_0),$$

where Δx is limited to values for which $\alpha(x_0 + \Delta x) \neq \alpha(x_0)$.

2. On Derivatives

Before attacking the problem of derivatives as related to Lebesgue integration, it seems desirable to review briefly some of the properties of derivatives of finite valued functions $f(x)$ on a finite interval $[a, b]$.

If, as usual, we say that $f(x)$ on $[a, b]$ has a derivative at x_0 if $\lim_{\Delta x \to 0} (f(x_0 + \Delta x) - f(x_0))/\Delta x$ exists finite or $+\infty$ or $-\infty$, then we have:

2.1. THEOREM. If $f(x)$ on $[a, b]$ has a derivative $f'(x_0)$ at x_0 with $a < x_0 < b$, then if $h > 0$, $k > 0$, we have

$$\lim_{(h,k)\to(0,0)} \frac{f(x_0 + h) - f(x_0 - k)}{h + k} = f'(x_0).$$

If $f'(x_0)$ is finite, then $e > 0$, d_{ex_0}, $0 < h < d_{ex_0}$, $0 < k < d_{ex_0}$:

$$-he < f(x_0 + h) - f(x_0) - hf'(x_0) < he$$

and

$$-ke < f(x_0) - f(x_0 - k) - kf'(x_0) < ke.$$

Consequently:

$$-(h + k)e < f(x_0 + h) - f(x_0 - k) - (h + k)f'(x_0) < (h + k)e.$$

This leads at once to the conclusion of the theorem when $f'(x_0)$ is finite. If $f'(x_0) = +\infty$, then $M > 0$, d_{Mx_0}, $0 < h < d_{Mx_0}$, $0 < k < d_{Mx_0}$:

$$f(x_0 + h) - f(x_0) > hM, \quad \text{and} \quad f(x_0) - f(x_0 - k) > kM$$

so that $f(x_0 + h) - f(x_0 - k) > M(h + k)$. Similarly for $f'(x_0) = -\infty$.

We note that since $f'(x_0)$ exists, we could assume $h \geqq 0$, $k \geqq 0$, $(h, k) \neq (0, 0)$ in the double limit.

Conversely we have:

2.2. THEOREM. If $f(x)$ on $[a, b]$ is such that

$$\lim_{(h,k)\to(0,0)} \frac{f(x_0 + h) - f(x_0 - k)}{h + k} = A$$

with either $h \geqq 0$, $k \geqq 0$, $(h, k) \neq (0, 0)$, or $h > 0$, $k > 0$ with $f(x)$ continuous at x_0, then $f'(x_0)$ exists with $f'(x_0) = A$.

We prove this theorem only for the case when A is finite, the case where $A = +\infty$ or $-\infty$ follows similarly. The first of the two alternatives in the hypothesis leads to the existence of the derivative by assuming $h = 0$, $k > 0$ and $h > 0$, $k = 0$. In the case of the second alternative, we note first:

$$e > 0, d_{ex_0}, 0 < h < d_{ex_0}; 0 < k < d_{ex_0}: \left| \frac{f(x_0 + h) - f(x_0 - k)}{h + k} - A \right| < e.$$

If in the final inequality we allow $k \to 0$, or $h \to 0$, then because of the continuity of $f(x)$ at x_0, we have

$$e > 0, \ d_{ex_0}, \ 0 < h < d_{ex_0}: \ |(f(x_0 + h) - f(x_0))/h - A| < e$$

$$e > 0, \ d_{ex_0}, \ 0 < k < d_{ex_0}: \ |(f(x_0) - f(x_0 - k))/k - A| < e.$$

These two statements together yield $f'(x_0) = A$.

These theorems are useful in connection with the study of non-differentiable continuous functions, since it is sometimes easier to deal with secants straddling a point than with those going through a given point.

We note in passing that if we define relative to the function $f(x)$ the interval function $F(I) = f(d) - f(c)$, where $I = [c, d]$, then $(f(x + \Delta x) - f(x))/\Delta x = F(I)/l(I)$, where $I = [x + \Delta x; \ x]$ for $\Delta x < 0$ and $I = [x, x + \Delta x]$ for $\Delta x > 0$ and $l(I) = |\Delta x|$ is the length of I. $f(x)$ then possesses a derivative at x if $\lim_{l(I) \to 0} F(I)/l(I)$ exists, I being limited to the intervals which have x as an end point. Theorem 2.2 points up the fact that a continuous function $f(x)$ possess a derivative at x when the class of intervals allowed for $F(I)/l(I)$ is extended to those containing x either as an end point or an interior point. There is here the germ of a derivative notion of one function of intervals with respect to another such function, leading possibly to a derivative in higher dimensional space.

If $f(x)$ does not have a derivative at x_0, that is,

$$\lim_{\Delta x \to 0} (f(x_0 + \Delta x) - f(x_0))/\Delta x$$

may fail to exist, then we have values approached by this ratio, which are called *derivates*. The greatest of such values or greatest of the limits is the upper derivate at x_0: $\overline{D}f(x_0)$ and the least, the lower derivate at x_0: $\underline{D}f(x_0)$. On a linear interval we can also distinguish between the left $(\Delta x < 0)$ and the right $(\Delta x > 0)$ approaches giving unilateral derivatives: $f'(x_0 - 0)$, $f'(x_0 - 0)$, as well as unilateral extreme derivates: $D^+f(x_0)$, $D_+f(x_0)$, $D^-f(x_0)$, $D_-f(x_0)$. Obviously $\overline{D}f(x_0)$ is the larger of $D^+f(x_0)$ and $D^-f(x_0)$ and $\underline{D}f(x_0)$ is the smaller of $D_+f(x_0)$ and $D_-f(x_0)$. Note that at a given point the "tangent" line representing $D^-f(x_0)$ is below that representing $D_-f(x_0)$.

2.3. If $\overline{D}$ is any fixed upper derivate and $\underline{D}$ the corresponding lower derivate, then for two functions f and g we have by I.4.6,

$$\underline{D}f + \underline{D}g \leq \underline{D}(f + h) \leqq \underline{D}f + \overline{D}g \leq \overline{D}(f + g) \leqq \overline{D}f + \overline{D}g,$$

provided no expressions of the form $+\infty - \infty$ occur. In particular, if f has a finite unilateral or bilateral derivative $(\overline{D}f = \underline{D}f$ and finite$)$, then

$$\overline{D}(f + g) = f' + \overline{D}g \quad \text{and} \quad \underline{D}(f + g) = f' + \underline{D}g$$

and $\overline{D}$ and $\underline{D}$ are distributive in this case.

The following theorems are easily proved:

2.4. If all the extreme derivates of $f(x)$ at a point are finite then $f(x)$ is continuous at this point.

2.5. If $f(x)$ is continuous on $[a, b]$ then at any point x_0 of $[a, b]$ the values approached by $(f(x_0 + \Delta x) - f(x_0))/\Delta x$ as $\Delta x \to 0$, that is the values of the derivates fill up the closed interval $[\overline{D}f(x_0), \underline{D}(f(x_0)]$.

2.6. Necessary condition that x_0 be a relative maximum of $f(x)$ [that is, $f(x) \leqq f(x_0)$ for some vicinity of x_0] is that $D^+f(x_0) \leqq 0$ and $D\_f(x_0) \geqq 0$.

We state without proving the:

2.7. Mean Value Theorem of the Differential Calculus. If $f(x)$ is continuous on $a \leqq x \leqq b$ and $f'(x)$ exists for $a < x < b$, then there exists an x_1 with $a < x_1 < b$ such that $(f(b) - f(a))/(b - a) = f'(x_1)$.

Following are consequences of the mean value theorem:

2.8. If $f(x)$ on $[a, b]$ is such that $f'(x) = 0$ for all x, then $f(x)$ is constant on $[a, b]$. The conclusion also holds if $f'(x) = 0$ except for a finite number of points, provided $f(x)$ is continuous.

2.9. If $f(x)$ is continuous on $[a, b]$, $f'(x)$ exists for $0 < |x - x_0| < d$ with $a < x_0 < b$, and $\lim_{x\to x_0} f'(x)$ exists, then $f'(x_0)$ exists and $\lim_{x\to x_0} f'(x) = f'(x_0)$. Changes in the statement of the theorem when $x_0 = a$, or $x_0 = b$ are obvious.

The mean value theorem applies to $f(x)$ on the intervals $[x_0; x_0 + d]$ and $[x_0 - d, x_0]$, so that if $0 < |x - x_0| < d$, then $(f(x) - f(x_0))/(x - x_0) = f'(x')$, where x' is between x and x_0. Under the hypotheses of the theorem we then find $\lim_{x\to x_0}(f(x) - f(x_0))/(x - x_0) = \lim_{x\to x_0} f'(x)$.

2.10. If $f(x)$ is continuous on $[a, b]$ and $f'(x)$ exists as a finite value for all x of $[a, b]$, then $f'(x)$ takes on all values between any two of its values.

Let $a \leqq c < d \leqq b$. On $[c, d]$ consider the functions

$$g_1(x) = (f(d) - f(x))/(d - x) \text{ for } x \neq d; \; = f'(d) \text{ for } x = d;$$
$$g_2(x) = (f(x) - f(c))/(x - c) \text{ for } x \neq c; \; = f'(c) \text{ for } x = c.$$

Then $g_1(x)$ and $g_2(x)$ are continuous on $[c, d]$, and so $g_1(x)$ takes on all values between $(f(d) - f(c))/(d - c)$ and $f'(d)$, and $g_2(x)$

takes on all values between $f'(c)$ and $(f(d) - f(c))/(d - c)$. If y_0 lies between $f'(c)$ and $f'(d)$, then either $g_1(x)$ or $g_2(x)$ takes on the value y_0 in $[c, d]$. Suppose it is $g_1(x)$. Then there exists x_1 with $c < x_1 < d$, such that $y_0 = g_1(x_1) = (f(d) - f(x_1))/(d - x_1)$. The mean value theorem applied to $f(x)$ now gives a point x_2 between x_1 and d such that

$$f'(x_2) = (f(d) - f(x_1))/(d - x_1) = g_1(x_1) = y_0.$$

The same method of proof can be applied even if $f'(c)$ and $f'(d)$ are not finite, so that the theorem holds provided $f(x)$ is continuous and $f'(x)$ exists for all x of $[a, b]$.

The theorem is of importance in connection with the inverse derivative problem, in that it says that a function $g(x)$ can be the derivative of a continuous function $f(x)$ for all x of $[a, b]$ only if for all $a \leqq c < d \leqq b$, $g(x)$ takes on all values between $g(c)$ and $g(d)$ on $[c, d]$. For instance, the function $g(x) = 0$ for $0 \leqq x < 1$; $= 1$ for $x = 1$, is not the derivative of any continuous function on $[0, 1]$.

A function $f(x)$ on $[a, b]$ having the property that for every $a \leqq c < d \leqq b$, $f(x)$ assumes all of the values between $f(c)$ and $f(d)$ on $[c, d]$ is sometimes called *Darboux continuous*. Continuous functions and derivative functions of continuous functions then have this property. H. Lebesgue ("Leçons sur l'Integration," Gauthier-Villars, Paris, 1928, p. 97) has given an example of a Darboux continuous function on $[0, 1]$ which is not continuous at any point.

2.11. THEOREM. If $f_n(x)$ are defined on $[a, b]$ such that the derivatives $f_n'(x)$ exist as finite numbers for all n and x, and if $f_n'(x)$ converge uniformly on $[a, b]$, then $f_n(x) - f_n(a)$ converges uniformly to a continuous function $f(x)$ such that $f'(x) = \lim_n f_n'(x)$.

This theorem is usually proved by using the fundamental theorems A and B of the integral calculus, but this requires in addition that the derivative functions be Riemann integrable. The following proof uses mainly the mean value theorem of the differential calculus.

Since the $f_n'(x)$ are finite, $f_n(x)$ are continuous on $[a, b]$. We then apply the mean value theorem to the functions $g_{mn}(x) = f_m(x) - f_n(x)$ to give

$$\begin{aligned}&(f_m(x) - f_m(a)) - (f_n(x) - f_n(a))\\ &= (f_m(x) - f_n(x)) - (f_m(a) - f_n(a))\\ &= (f_m'(x_{mn}) - f_n'(x_{mn}))\,(x - a),\end{aligned}$$

where $a < x_{mn} < x$. Since $\lim_{mn} (f_m'(x) - f_n'(x)) = 0$ uniformly on $[a, b]$, we have

$$e>0, n_e, m, n>n_e : |(f_m(x)-f_m(a))-f_n(x)-f_n(a))| < e(x-a) < e(b-a).$$

Then the sequence $f_n(x) - f_n(a)$ converges uniformly to a necessarily continuous function $f(x)$. If we replace x by $x_0 + \Delta x$, and a by x_0, then

$$e > 0,\ n_e,\ n,\ m > n_e,\ |\Delta x| > 0 : \left| \frac{f_n(x_0 + \Delta x) - f_n(x_0)}{\Delta x} - \frac{f_m(x_0 + \Delta x) - f_m(x_0)}{\Delta x} \right| < e.$$

Taking limits as to m gives:

$$e > 0,\ n_e,\ n > n_e,\ |\Delta x| > 0 : \left| \frac{f_n(x_0 + \Delta x) - f_n(x_0)}{\Delta x} - \frac{f(x_0 + \Delta x) - f(x_0)}{\Delta x} \right| < e.$$

On the other hand, if we set $\lim_n f_n'(x) = g(x)$, then for any x_0 of $[a, b]$

$$e > 0,\ n_e',\ n > n_e' : |f_n'(x_0) - g(x_0)| < e.$$

Further, since $f_n'(x_0)$ exists:

$$e > 0,\ n,\ d_{en},\ 0 < |\Delta x| < d_{en} : \left| \frac{f_n(x_0 + \Delta x) - f_n(x_0)}{\Delta x} - f_n'(x_0) \right| < e$$

If now we select an $n_0 > n_e$ and n_e' and take $d_e = d_{en_0}$, then

$$e > 0,\ d_e,\ 0 < |\Delta x| < d_e : |(f(x_0 + \Delta x) - f(x_0))/\Delta x - g(x_0)| < 3e.$$

This means that $f'(x_0) = g(x_0) = \lim_n f_n'(x_0)$ for all x_0 of $[a, b]$.

With the aid of this theorem it is possible to show that for any continous function $f(x)$ on $[a, b]$ there exists a continuous function $g(x)$ so that $g'(x) = f(x)$ on $[a, b]$. For by the Weierstrass polynomial approximation theorem there exists a sequence of polynomials $P_n(x)$ converging uniformly to $f(x)$ on $[a, b]$. For polynomials $P_n(x)$ we have formulas giving us polynomials $Q_n(x)$ such that $Q_n'(x) = P_n(x)$. Then $Q_n'(x)$ converge uniformly to $f(x)$ and so

$Q_n(x) - Q_n(a)$ converges uniformly to a function $g(x)$ such that $g'(x) = f(x)$. The proof of the Weierstrass approximation theorem in II.18.3. was made by the use of Bernstein polynomials and does not involve integration. It could then be used to give us a formula for the inverse derivative of a given continuous function $f(x)$ on $[a, b]$ without integration. Note that whether we use indefinite integrals or the Weierstrass approximation theorem, the desired inverse derivative depends on the convergence of some sequence of functions (see H. Lebesgue: "Leçons sur l'Integration," Gauthier-Villars, Paris, 1928, p. 95).

For the case when $f(x)$ is continuous but the derivative does not exist at all points of $[a, b]$, we have:

2.12. THEOREM. If $f(x)$ is continuous on $[a, b]$; if $Df(x)$ is one of the four extreme unilateral derivate functions of $f(x)$: $D^+f(x)$, $D_+f(x)$, $D^-f(x)$ or $D_-f(x)$; and if $Df(x) \geqq A$ for all x of $[a, b]$, then $(f(d) - f(c))/(d - c) \geqq A$ for all $[c, d]$ such that $a \leqq c < d \leqq b$.

It is sufficient to prove this theorem for $c = a$ and $d = b$.

We take $Df = D^+f$. Then for $e > 0$ and $x = a$, we can find a point x_1 to the right of a such that $f(x_1) - f(a) \geqq (A - e)(x_1 - a)$. Then there exists a point x_2 to the right of x_1 such that $f(x_2) - f(x_1) \geqq (A - e)(x_2 - x_1)$ and consequently

$$f(x_2) - f(a) \geqq (A - e)(x_2 - a).$$

And so on. Let x' be the least upper bound of points such that if $x < x'$ there exists an x_0 with $x < x_0 < x'$ and such that $f(x_0) - f(a) \geqq (A - e)(x_0 - a)$. Then because of the continuity of $f(x)$ we also have $f(x') - f(a) \geqq (A - e)(x' - a)$. Either $x' = b$ or $x' < b$. But in the latter case there exist points $x'' > x'$ such that $f(x'') - f(x') \geqq (A - e)(x'' - x')$ and so $f(x'') - f(a) \geqq (A - e)(x'' - a)$. Consequently, $x'' = b$ and for all $e > 0: f(b) - f(a) \geqq (A - e)(b - a)$. Then $f(b) - f(a) \geqq A(b - a)$.

The same procedure works for the other derivates excepting that for D^-f and D_-f we start from b and go to the left. If the condition $Df(x) \geqq A$ for all x of $[a, b]$ is replaced by $Df(x) \leqq A$, then the conclusion becomes $(f(d) - f(c))/(d - c) \leqq A(d - c)$ for all $a \leqq c < d \leqq b$. Note that the proof depends on the unilateral character of the derivates involved.

This theorem leads at once to the following:

2.13. THEOREM. A necessary and sufficient condition that the continuous function $f(x)$ be monotonic nondecreasing on $[a, b]$ is that one of the four extreme unilateral derivatives satisfies the condition $Df(x) \geqq 0$ for all x of $[a, b]$.

2.14. THEOREM. If $f(x)$ is continuous on $[a, b]$ and has a zero right (left) derivate at each point of $a \leqq x < b$ $(a < x \leqq b)$, then $f(x)$ is constant on $[a, b]$.

For then $D^+f(x) \geqq 0$ for all x so that $f(x) - f(a) \geqq 0$ for $a \leqq x \leqq b$. Similarly $D_+ f(x) \leqq 0$ for all x so that $f(x) - f(a) \leqq 0$ for all $a \leqq x \leqq b$. Then $f(x) = f(a)$ for x on $[a, b]$. The proof for the "left" case is the same.

2.15. THEOREM. If $f(x)$ is continuous on $[a, b]$ and M and m are the least upper bound and greatest lower bound, respectively, of a fixed extreme unilateral derivate $Df(x)$ on $[a, b]$ then $m(d - c) \leqq f(d) - f(c) \leqq M(d - c)$ for all $[c, d]$ with $a \leqq c < d \leqq b$.

This theorem is a sort of generalisation of the mean value theorem of the differential calculus. It has a number of interesting consequences.

2.16. THEOREM. If $f(x)$ is continuous on $[a, b]$, then all the extreme unilateral derivates have the same least upper and greatest lower bounds on all subintervals of $[a, b]$.

For suppose $D_1 f(x)$ has M_1 and $D_2 f(x)$ has M_2 as least upper bound on $[c, d]$ and suppose $M_1 > M_2$. Then there exists an x_1 of $[c, d]$ such that $M_1 \geqq D_1 f(x_1) > N > M_2$, and consequently a point x_2 in $[c, d]$ in a vicinity of x_1 such that $(f(x_2) - f(x_1))/(x_2 - x_1) \geqq N$. But since $D_2 f(x) \leqq M_2$ for all x on $[a, b]$ it would follow that

$$(f(x_2) - f(x_1))/(x_2 - x_1) \leqq M_2 < N.$$

For the bilateral upper derivate $\overline{D}f(x)$ and lower derivate $\underline{D}f(x)$ we can assert only that the l.u.b. of $\overline{D}f(x)$ is the same as that for $D^+ f(x)$ and $D^- f(x)$, while the g.l.b. of $\underline{D}f(x)$ is the same as that for $D_+ f(x)$ and $D_- f(x)$.

2.17. THEOREM. If $f(x)$ is continuous on $[a, b]$ and one of the extreme unilateral derivates is Riemann integrable, then all of these derivates are, and the integrals on $[a, b]$ have $f(b) - f(a)$ as value.

Moreover, the bilateral upper and lower derivates are also integrable to the same value. All of the extreme derivates are equal except for a set of measure zero and $f(x)$ has a derivative except for a set of measure zero on $[a, b]$.

For if for any subdivision σ of $[a, b]$ into intervals we set up the upper and lower sums $\Sigma_\sigma M_i(x_i - x_{i-1})$ and $\Sigma_\sigma m_i(x_i - x_{i-1})$, then these sums will be the same for all extreme unilateral derivates since all have the same l.u.b. and g.l.b. on each of the intervals $[x_{i-1}, x_i]$. This means that if one of the unilateral extreme derivates is integrable, then all are and have the same value for their integrals. Since on $[x_{i-1}, x_i]$:

$$m_i(x_i - x_{i-1}) \leqq f(x_i) - f(x_{i-1}) \leqq M_i(x_i - x_{i-1}),$$

it follows that when $\int_a^b Df(x)dx$ exists, then its value is $f(b) - f(a)$.

Since the l.u.b. of $\overline{D}f(x)$ on any interval agrees with that of $D^+f(x)$ and $D^-f(x)$, it follows that

$$\overline{\int_a^b} \overline{D}f(x)dx = \int_a^b D^+f(x)dx = f(b) - f(a).$$

Similarly since the g.l.b. of $\underline{D}f(x)$ on any interval agrees with that of D_+f and D_-f, we have

$$\underline{\int_a^b} \underline{D}f(x)dx = \int_a^b D_+f(x)dx = f(b) - f(a).$$

Then since

$$\underline{\int_a^b} \underline{D}f(x)dx \leqq \overline{\int_a^b} \underline{D}f(x)dx \leqq \overline{\int_a^b} \overline{D}f(x)dx$$

and

$$\underline{\int_a^b} \underline{D}f(x)dx \leqq \underline{\int_a^b} \overline{D}f(x)dx \leqq \overline{\int_a^b} \overline{D}f(x)dx,$$

we conclude that $\underline{D}f(x)$ and $\overline{D}f(x)$ are both integrable with $\int_a^b \underline{D}f(x)dx = \int_a^b \overline{D}f(x)dx$. Then $\int_a^b (\overline{D}f(x) - \underline{D}f(x))dx = 0$, which since $\overline{D}f(x) - \underline{D}f(x) \geqq 0$ for all x, implies that $\overline{D}f(x) = \underline{D}f(x)$ except at most at their points of discontinuity, a set of measure zero, where we use II.15, Ex. 6. This means also that $f(x)$ has a derivative except for a set of measure zero. (For these results compare H. Lebesgue: "Leçons sur l'Integration," Gauthier-Villars, Paris, 1928, Chapter V.)

EXERCISES

1. Show that if $f(x)$ is continuous on $[a, b]$ and if $\overline{D}f(x) \leqq A$ for all x of $[a, b]$, then for all $a \leqq c < d \leqq b$, we have $f(d) - f(c) \leqq A(d - c)$; and if $\underline{D}f(x) \geqq A$, then $f(d) - f(c) \geqq A(d - c)$. Will these statements still be valid if in the first $\overline{D}f(x) \leqq A$ is replaced by $\underline{D}f(x) \leqq A$, and in the second $\underline{D}f(x) \geqq A$ by $\overline{D}f(x) \geqq A$?

2. Is the following theorem true: If $f(x)$ is continuous on $[a, b]$ and has a zero derivate for all x of $[a, b]$ then $f(x) = f(a)$ for all x?

3. In the proof of theorem XI.2.17. deduce the existence of a derivative for $f(x)$ except for a set of measure zero from the fact that $f(x) - f(a) = \int_a^x Df(x)dx$, where $Df(x)$ is any of the four extremal unilateral derivates.

3. The Vitali Theorem

The Vitali theorem is of the nature of a covering theorem in that it gives a means of reducing a system of intervals to a finite or denumerable number of intervals. It is particularly concerned with the class of intervals arising in connection with derivatives and proves to be a powerful tool in the extension of the fundamental theorems of the integral calculus to Lebesgue integrals, that is, in determining the relation between indefinite integrals and their derivatives.

3.1. Definitions. A *point* x of the finite interval $[a, b]$ is said to be *Vitali covered* by a system of intervals $\mathfrak{J} = [I]$, if there exists a sequence of intervals I_{nx} in $\mathfrak{J}$, each containing x either as an interior or end point, and such that $\lim_n l(I_{nx}) = 0$.

3.1.1. A *set* E of $[a, b]$ is *Vitali covered* by a set of intervals $\mathfrak{J}$, if every point x of E is Vitali covered by $\mathfrak{J}$.

For instance, if $f(x)$ is a function on $[a, b]$ and E consists of the set of points x of $[a, b]$ for which $f(x)$ has A as a derivate at x, and if $\mathfrak{J}$ consists of the intervals $[x, x + \Delta_n x]$ such that

$$\lim_n (f(x + \Delta_n x) - f(x))/\Delta_n x) = A,$$

then E is Vitali covered by $\mathfrak{J}$.

The basic theorem is:

3.2. Vitali Theorem. If E is any subset of the finite closed interval $[a, b]$ and $\mathfrak{I}$ is a Vitali covering for E, then for $e > 0$, there exists a sequence of disjoint intervals I_n from $\mathfrak{I}$, such that

$$\sum_n l(I_n) < \mu^*(E) + e, \quad \text{and} \quad \mu^*(E - E\sum_n I_n) = 0.$$

Consequently, for $e > 0$, there exists a finite set $I_1 \ldots I_n$ of disjoint intervals in $\mathfrak{I}$, such that

$$\sum_1^n l(I_k) < \mu^*(E) + e, \quad \text{and} \quad \mu^*(E - E\sum_1^n I_k) < e.$$

For any $e > 0$, there exists an open set $G \geqq E$ such that $\mu(G) < \mu^*(E) + e$. If we delete from the set $\mathfrak{I}$ all intervals which are not contained in G, we will still have a Vitali covering $\mathfrak{I}'$ for E, and also for any sequence $\{I_n\}$ of disjoint intervals chosen from $\mathfrak{I}'$, we shall have $\Sigma_n l(I_n) < \mu^* E + e$. We can then assume that our original set of intervals $\mathfrak{I}$ lies entirely in G. Let $c_1 =$ l.u.b. $[l(I)$ for I in $\mathfrak{I}]$. Select as I_1 any I of $\mathfrak{I}$ such that $l(I_1) > c_1/2$. Delete from $\mathfrak{I}$ any interval which intersects I_1 and call $\mathfrak{I}_1$ the remaining set. $\mathfrak{I}_1$ will be a Vitali covering for $E - I_1E$. Let $c_2 =$ l.u.b. $[l(I)$ for I in $\mathfrak{I}_1]$, and take I_2 in $\mathfrak{I}_1$ so that $l(I_2) > c_2/2$. Delete from $\mathfrak{I}_1$ all intervals intersecting I_2 and call $\mathfrak{I}_2$ the remaining intervals which will be a Vitali covering for $E - (I_1 + I_2)E$. Continuing in this way, at the nth stage we get a set of intervals $\mathfrak{I}_n$, no one of which intersects $I_1 \ldots I_n$, we let $c_{n+1} =$ l.u.b. $[l(I)$ for I in $\mathfrak{I}_n]$, and I_{n+1} an interval of $\mathfrak{I}_n$ such that $l(I_{n+1}) > c_{n+1}/2$; and $\mathfrak{I}_{n+1}$ the intervals of $\mathfrak{I}_n$ not intersecting I_{n+1}. Since the intervals I_n are disjoint and subintervals of $[a, b]$ it follows that $\Sigma_n l(I_n) < \infty$, so that $\lim_n c_n = 0$, with $c_{n+1} \leqq c_n$.

Let I_n^* be the interval of length $5l(I_n)$, obtained by extending I_n on each side by double its length. Then we show that for every n, every point of E belongs to one of the sequence of intervals $I_1, \ldots, I_n, I_{n+1}^*, I_{n+2}^*, \ldots$. The only points which cause trouble are those which do not belong to any I_n. Since x is Vitali covered by the interval set $\mathfrak{I}_n$, there exists an interval I_x in $\mathfrak{I}_n$ with length $l(I_x) \leqq c_{n+1}$ containing x. Now I_x is eventually deleted. Suppose that $c_{m+1} < l(I_x) \leqq c_m$. Then I_x has been deleted by the time the mth stage has been reached, that is, I_x intersects one of the intervals $I_{n+1} \ldots I_m$, say I_k, with $n + 1 \leqq k \leqq m$. Now $l(I_k) > c_k/2$. Then I_x lies entirely in the extended interval I_k^*, since $l(I_x) \leqq c_k$, as a simple diagram will show. Then I_k^* contains x. Since $l(I_n^*) = 5l(I_n)$, and $\Sigma_n l(I_n) < \infty$, it follows that $\lim_k \Sigma_k^\infty l(I_n^*)$

$= 0$. For $d > 0$, take k so that $\Sigma_{k+1}^{\infty} l(I_n^*) < d$. Then since $E - E\,\Sigma_1^k I_n$ is contained in $\Sigma_{k+1}^{\infty} I_n^*$, it follows that

$$\mu^*(E - E \sum_1^k I_n) \leqq \sum_{k+1}^{\infty} l(I_n^*) < d, \quad \text{and} \quad \mu(E - E \sum_1^{\infty} I_n) = 0.$$

A useful form of this Vitali theorem is:

3.3. If E is any bounded set of the real line, and $\mathfrak{I}$ is any Vitali covering for E, then for every $e > 0$, there exists a finite set of disjoint intervals: $I_1 \ldots I_n$ of $\mathfrak{I}$, such that

$$\mu^*(E) - e < \mu^*(E \sum_1^n I_k) = \sum_1^n \mu^*(E \cdot I_k) \leqq \sum_1^n l(I_k) < \mu^*(E) + e.$$

For:

$$\mu^*(E) \leqq \mu^*(E \sum_1^n I_k) + \mu^*(E - E \sum_1^n I_k) < \mu^*(E \sum_1^n I_k) + e$$

if the $I_1 \ldots I_n$ have been chosen in such a way that $\mu^*(E - E\,\Sigma_1^n I_k) < e$. Further, since the intervals I_k are disjoint and measurable, μ^* is by V.10.5 additive on the sets $E \cdot I_k$, $k = 1 \ldots n$, so that

$$\mu^*(E \sum_1^n I_k) = \sum_1^n \mu^*(E \cdot I_k).$$

The remaining inequalities are obvious.

The Vitali theorem gives us a generalization of Theorems XI.2.8 and XI.2.14 under which the vanishing of derivates of a function guarantee that the function is a constant on an interval:

3.4. THEOREM. If $f(x)$ is absolutely continuous on $[a, b]$ and $f'(x) = 0$ except for a set of zero measure, then $f(x)$ is constant on $[a, b]$.

Absolute continuity can be taken in the interval sense that for an interval function $F(I)$, the expression $\Sigma_1^n F(I_m)$ for I_m disjoint converges to zero as $\Sigma_1^n l(I_m)$ approaches zero. A point function $f(x)$ is then absolutely continuous if the corresponding interval function $f(I) = f(d) - f(c)$ for $I = [c, d]$ is absolutely continuous. An absolutely continuous point function is continuous and also of bounded variation.

Suppose $e > 0$, d_e, $\Sigma_1^n l(I_m) < d_e$: $|\Sigma_1^n f(I_m)| < e$. If E is the set for which $f'(x) = 0$, then for $e > 0$, there exist for every x of E, intervals $I_{nx} = [x, x + d_n]$, or $I_{nx} = [x + d_n, x]$ with $\lim_n d_n = 0$ such that

$$|f(x + d_n) - f(x)| / |d_n| = |f(I_{nx})| / l(I_{nx}) < e.$$

The set of intervals I_{nx} for all n and x of E, form a Vitali covering for E. By the Vitali theorem we then obtain a finite number of these intervals $I_1 \ldots I_m$ such that $\mu(E) - \Sigma_1^m l(I_k) < d_e$. If I_j' denote intervals complementary to $\Sigma_1^m I_k$, then $\Sigma_j l(I_j') < d_e$. Then

$$\sum_1^n |f(I_k)| < e \sum_1^n l(I_k) \leqq e(b - a) \quad \text{and} \quad |\sum_j f(I_j')| < e.$$

Consequently,

$$|f(b) - f(a)| \leqq \sum_1^n |f(I_k)| + |\sum_j f(I_j')| \leqq (b - a + 1)\, e.$$

Since this is true for all e, it follows that $f(b) = f(a)$. Also, since the the hypothesis of the theorem is valid for all intervals $[a, c]$ with $a \leqq c \leqq b$, we have $f(x) = f(a)$ for all c, that is $f(x)$ is constant on $[a, b]$.

3.5. Corollary. If $f(x)$ and $g(x)$ have the same finite derivative on a set E of $[a, b]$ whose complement CE is of zero measure, and if $f(x) - g(x)$ is absolutely continuous on $[a, b]$, then $f(x)$ differs from $g(x)$ by a constant.

It is to be noted that the condition that $f(x)$ be absolutely continuous in the hypothesis of the theorem is ncccssary. For example the Cantor function [defined as follows: if $x = \Sigma_n a_n/3^n$ and all a_n are 0 or 2, then $f(x) = \frac{1}{2}(\Sigma_n a_n/2^n)$: if $x = a_1/3 + \ldots + a_k/3^k + \ldots$ and $a_i = 0$ or 2 for $i < k$ with $a_k = 1$, then $f(x) = \frac{1}{2}(a_1/2 + \ldots + (a_k + 1)/2^k)$] is continuous and constant on the intervals complementary to the Cantor nondense perfect set. Consequently, $f'(x) = 0$ except on the Cantor set which is of content and so measure zero. Obviously the Cantor function is not absolutely continuous since it maps the Cantor set on the unit interval.

4. Derivatives of Monotonic Functions and of Functions of Bounded Variation

If $f(x)$ is finite valued and monotonic nondecreasing on $[a, b]$ then all of its derivates are positive or zero and may be $+\infty$.

4.1. THEOREM. If $f(x)$ is finite valued and monotonic nondecreasing on $[a, b]$ and E is the set of values for which $\overline{D}f(x) = +\infty$, then $\mu(E) = 0$.

If M is any fixed large positive number, then for any x of E, there exist intervals I_{nx} of the form $(x, x + d_n)$ or $(x + d_n, x)$ with $\lim_n d_n = 0$ such that

$$|f(x + d_n) - f(x)| / |d_n| = f(I_{nx}) / l(I_{nx}) > M$$

or

$$f(I_{nx}) > M\, l(I_{nx}) .$$

Then the set of intervals I_{nx} form a Vitali covering for the set E. Consequently, by the Vitali theorem XI.3.2 for $e > 0$, there exists a finite number of these intervals $I_1 \dots I_m$ such that $\mu^*(E) - e < \Sigma_1^m l(I_k)$. Since for all intervals I, we have $f(I) \geqq 0$, it follows that

$$f(b) - f(a) \geqq \sum_1^m f(I_k) > M \sum_1^m l(I_k) > M(\mu^*(E) - e).$$

Then for all $e > 0$,

$$\mu^*(E) < e + (f(b) - f(a))/M.$$

Since e and M are arbitrary, it follows that $\mu^*(E) = 0$.

The derivates of a monotonic nondecreasing functions are then finite excepting possibly at a set of x of zero measure. It is possible to say more.

4.2. THEOREM. If $f(x)$ is finite valued and monotonic nondecreasing on $[a, b]$, then with the exception of a set of points of zero measure, the derivative $f'(x)$ exists as a finite number.

If x is any point for which $\overline{D}f(x) > \underline{D}f(x) \geqq 0$, then there exist rational numbers r_1 and r_2 such that $\overline{D}f(x) > r_1 > r_2 > \underline{D}f(x)$. So that

$$E[\overline{D}f(x) > \underline{D}f(x)] = \sum_{r_1 r_2} E[\overline{D}f(x) > r_1 > r_2 > \underline{D}f(x)] = \sum_{r_1 r_2} E_{r_1 r_2}.$$

Now the sets $E_{r_1 r_2}$ as r_1 and r_2 range over the rationals is a denumerable collection of sets. If then we prove that for any two rationals $r_1 > r_2$ we have $\mu(E_{r_1 r_2}) = 0$, then $\mu(E[\overline{D}f(x) > \underline{D}f(x)]) = 0$ also. Let then $E = E_{r_1 r_2} = E[\overline{D}f(x) > r_1 > r_2 > \underline{D}f(x)]$. If $\underline{D}f(x) < r_2$, then there exists a sequence of intervals I_{nx} with x as one end point such that $f(I_{nx}) < r_2 l(I_{nx})$ with $\lim_n l(I_{nx}) = 0$. Such intervals form a Vitali covering for E. Then by the Vitali theorem XI.3.2 for $e > 0$, there exists a finite number of disjoint intervals $I_1 \ldots I_m$ such that

$$\mu^*(E) - e < \sum_1^m \mu^*(I_k \cdot E) \leqq \sum_1^m l(I_k) < \mu^*(E) + e$$

and for which

$$\sum_1^m f(I_k) < r_2 \sum_1^m l(I_k) < r_2(\mu^*(E) + e).$$

If we assume that the intervals I_k are open, which we can do without changing the right-hand side of these inequalities, then for every point x of $I_k \cdot E$, we have $\overline{D}f(x) > r_1$ so that there exists a sequence of intervals I_{knx} interior to I_k having x as one end point and such that

$$f(I_{knx}) > r_1 l(I_{knx}).$$

These in turn yield a finite set for each k: I_{kn}, $n = 1 \ldots n_k$, such that

$$\mu^*(I_k \cdot E) - e/m < \sum_{n=1}^{n=n_k} l(I_{kn}) < \mu^*(I_k \cdot E) + e/m.$$

Then since $f(x)$ is monotone nondecreasing:

$$f(I_k) \geqq \sum_{n=1}^{n=n_k} f(I_{kn}) > r_1 \sum_{n=1}^{n=n_k} l(I_{kn}) > r_1(\mu^*(I_k \cdot E) - e/m),$$

and so

$$\sum_{k=1}^{k=m} f(I_k) > r_1 (\sum_{k=1}^{k=m} \mu^*(I_k \cdot E) - e).$$

But

$$\sum_1^m \mu^*(I_k \cdot E) > \mu^*E - e \quad \text{and} \quad \sum_1^m f(I_k) < r_2(\mu^*E + e).$$

Then

$$r_1(\mu^*E - 2e) < \sum_1^m f(I_k) < r_2(\mu^*E + e)$$

and

$$\mu^*E < e(2r_1 + r_2)/(r_1 - r_2).$$

This is true for every $e > 0$, and so $\mu^*(E) = \mu^*(E_{r_1 r_2}) = 0$.

Since any function of bounded variation on $[a, b]$ is the difference of two monotonic nondecreasing functions, it follows at once:

4.3. THEOREM. If $f(x)$ is of bounded variation on $[a, b]$ then $f(x)$ has a finite derivative $f'(x)$ except at most for a set of a zero measure.

We apply this theorem to the function $f(x) = \mu^*(E[a, x])$, where E is any subset of $[a, b]$. This function is monotonic nondecreasing in x and consequently has a finite derivative except for a set of zero measure. Now since intervals are measurable sets by V.10.5 the interval function $\mu^*(E \cdot I)$ is additive relative to I, so that for any interval $[c, d]$ we have:

$$f(I) = f(d) - f(c) = \mu^*(E[a, d]) - \mu^*(E[a, c)]$$
$$= \mu^*(E[c, d]) \leqq d - c = l(I).$$

Consequently, if I_x is any interval with x as end point, we have $f(I_x)/l(I_x) \leqq 1$, so that any derivates or derivatives of $\mu^*(E[a, x])$ have values between 0 and 1, inclusive. We can say more:

4.4. THEOREM. The derivative of $f(x) = \mu^*(E[a, x])$ is unity at all points of E excepting at most a set of zero measure on E.

For $0 < c < 1$, denote by E_c the set x of E such that $\underline{D}\mu^*(E[a, x]) < c$. Then we determine a Vitali covering for E_c by taking for all x of E_c, the intervals I_x having x as one end point such that $\mu^*(E \cdot I_x) < c\, l(I_x)$. Let $e > 0$ and $I_1 \ldots I_m$ be those intervals determined by the Vitali theorem for which

$$\mu^*(E_c) - e < \sum_1^m \mu^*(E_c \cdot I_k) \leqq \sum_1^m l(I_k) < \mu^*(E_c) + e.$$

Then since E_c is contained in E:

$$\mu^*(E_c) - e < \sum_1^m \mu^*(E_c \cdot I_k) \leqq \sum_1^m \mu^*(E \cdot I_k) < c \sum_1^m l(I_k)$$
$$< c(\mu^*(E_c) + e).$$

It follows that

$$(1 - c)\mu^*(E_c) < e(1 + c) \quad \text{or} \quad \mu^*(E_c) < e(1 + c)/(1 - c).$$

Since this holds for all $e > 0$, it follows that $\mu^*(E_c) = 0$ for all $0 <$

$c < 1$. If $\{c_n\}$ is a monotone sequence such that $\lim_n c_n = 1$, for instance $c_n = 1 - 1/n$ and E_0 is the subset of E for which

$$\underline{D}\mu^*(E[a, x]) < 1,$$

then $E_0 = \Sigma_n E_{c_n}$, and consequently $\mu^*(E_0) = 0$.

The derivative of $\mu^*E[a, x])$ at any point x is called the *metric density* of E at x, so that the theorem says that the metric density of a set E is 1 at points of E except at most for a subset of E of zero measure.

If E is measurable then

$$\mu(E[a, x]) + \mu(CE[a, x]) = x - a.$$

Then at any point of E where $(d/dx)\mu E[a, x]) = 1$, we also have $(d/dx)\mu(CE[a, x]) = 0$. Similarly if $(d/dx)\mu(CE[a, x]) = 1$, then $(d/dx)\mu(E[a, x]) = 0$. Consequently:

4.5. THEOREM. If E any measurable subset of $[a, b]$, then except for a set of zero measure on $[a, b]$, the derivative of $\mu(E[a, x])$ is 1 for x on E and 0 for x on CE.

5. Derivatives of Indefinite Lebesgue Integrals

If E is measurable, then $\mu(E[a, x]) = \int_a^x \chi(E; x)dx$. The last theorem (XI.4.5) can then be restated:

5.1. For the characteristic function $\chi(E; x)$ of a measurable set E of $[a, b]$, the derivative of the indefinite integral $\int_a^x \chi(E; x)dx$ exists and is $\chi(E; x)$ except at most for a set of zero measure on $[a, b]$.

This extends at once to:

5.2. THEOREM. If $f(x)$ is a measurable step function assuming at most a finite number of values, that is, $f(x) = \Sigma_1^n c_m \chi(E_m; x)$, where the measurable sets E_m are disjoint and $\Sigma_1^n E_m = [a, b]$, then $(d/dx) \int_a^x f(x)dx$ exists and is equal to $f(x)$ except for a set of zero measure.

This follows at once from the linearity of the integration and the derivative processes.

In order to extend this theorem to the case when $f(x)$ is any integrable function, we need additional information on the interchange of derivatives and limits. The following theorem due to G. Fubini [*Atti Accad. Naz. Lincei Rend. Classe sci. fis. mat. e nat.* (5) 24 (1915) 204-206] serves this purpose:

5.3. THEOREM. If $f_n(x)$ are monotonic nondecreasing in x on $[a, b]$ and monotone in n in a strong sense that for every interval $[c, d]$ of $[a, b]$ we have $f_n(d) - f_n(c) \leqq f_{n+1}(d) - f_{n+1}(c)$, and if $\lim_n f_n(x) = f(x)$, a finite valued function on $[a, b]$, then $\lim_n f_n'(x) = f'(x)$ except for a set of zero measure.

The monotoneity conditions of the theorem are fulfilled in case $h_n(x)$ is a sequence of monotonic nondecreasing functions and $f_n(x) = \Sigma_1^n h_m(x)$. Also if $k_n(x)$ are integrable and satisfy the conditions: $k_n(x) \geqq 0$ and $k_{n-1}(x) \leqq k_n(x)$ in n and x on $[a, b]$, then the indefinite integrals $f_n(x) = \int_a^x k_n(x)\, dx$ satisfy the monotoneity conditions.

Since a monotonic function has a finite derivative except at most for a set of zero measure, let E_1 be the set of x such that if $E_0 = CE_1$ then $\mu(E_0) = 0$ and $f_n'(x)$ and $f'(x)$ exist as finite values for all x of E_1. If we set $g_n(x) = f(x) - f_n(x)$, then the sequence of functions $g_n(x)$ has the following properties: (1) $g_n(x) \geqq 0$ for all n and x; (2) $\lim_n g_n(x) = 0$ for all x; (3) $g_n(x)$ are monotone nondecreasing in x for each n; (4) for every $[c, d]$ of $[a, b]$ and every n:

$$g_n(d) - g_n(c) \geqq g_{n+1}(d) - g_{n+1}(c);$$

and (5) $g_n'(x) \geqq g_{n+1}'(x) \geqq 0$, for all n and x in E_1.

The first two of these properties are obvious. As for (3) let us denote by Δg the expression $g(d) - g(c)$ for $c < d$ in $[a, b]$. Then

$$\Delta g_n = \Delta(f - f_n) = \Delta(\lim_m f_m - f_n) = \lim_m \Delta(f_m - f_n) \geqq 0.$$

For (4) we have:

$$\Delta g_n - \Delta g_{n+1} = \Delta(f_{n+1} - f_n) = \Delta f_{n+1} - \Delta f_n \geqq 0.$$

(5) is an immediate consequence of (3) and (4).

We show that $\lim_n g_n'(x) = 0$ except for a set of zero measure on E_1 and so on $[a, b]$, from which the conclusion of the theorem is immediate. For $e > 0$, and fixed n, let E_{ne} be the set of x on E_1 for which $g_n'(x) > e$. Then in the usual way, we can use the Vitali theorem to produce for a given $d > 0$, a finite number of disjoint intervals $I_1 \ldots I_m$ such that

$$\mu^*(E_{ne}) - d < \sum_1^m l(I_k) < \mu^*(E_{ne}) + d$$

and

$$g_n(I_k) > e\, l(I_k) \quad \text{for} \quad k = 1 \dots m.$$

Then

$$g_n(b) - g_n(a) \geqq \sum_1^m g_n(I_k) > e \sum_1^m l(I_k) > e(\mu^*(E_{ne}) - d).$$

This holds for any $d > 0$ so that for fixed $e > 0$

$$\mu^*(E_{ne}) < (g_n(b)) - g_n(a))/e.$$

Since $\lim_n(g_n(b) - g_n(a)) = 0$, it follows that $\lim_n \mu^*(E_{ne}) = 0$. This means that the sequence $g_n'(x)$ converges to zero relative to the measure function $\mu^*(E)$ and therefore by VI.5.5 there exists a subsequence $g'_{n_m}(x)$ such that $\lim_m g'_{n_m} x) = 0$, except for a set of measure zero. Since the $g_n'(x)$ are monotone nonincreasing in n on E_1, we conclude that $\lim_n g_n'(x) = 0$, except for a set of measure zero on E_1 and so on $[a, b]$.

In the statement of the theorem, the increasing monotoneity condition in n of the functions $f_n(x)$ can be replaced by a corresponding decreasing condition, that is, $f_{n+1}(d) - f_{n+1}(c) \leq f_n(d) - f_n(c)$ for all $[c, d]$ of $[a, b]$ and n. We now prove:

5.4. THEOREM. If $f(x)$ is any measurable step function which is integrable on $[a, b]$, then $(d/dx) \int_a^x f(x)dx$ exists and has $f(x)$ as value except for a set of measure zero.

The measurability condition is redundant, for if $f(x)$ is an integrable step function, then there exists a sequence of disjoint measurable sets E_n such that $\Sigma_n E_n = [a, b]$ and

$$f(x) = \textstyle\sum_1^\infty c_n\, \chi(E_n; x) \qquad \text{with} \qquad \sum_1^\infty |c_n|\, \mu(E_n) < \infty.$$

If c_n^+ are the positive c_n and c_n^- the negative ones and if the theorem holds for $\Sigma_n c_n^+\, \chi(E_n; x)$ and $- \Sigma_n c_n^-\, \chi(E_n; x)$, that is, for positive valued step functions, then it holds for any step function.

Suppose then $c_n \geq 0$ for all n. Then the sequence of functions $f_m(x) = \int_a^x \Sigma_1^m c_n\, \chi(E_n; x)dx$ satisfies the conditions of the Fubini convergence theorem (XI.5.3) and we can conclude that if $f(x) = \lim_m f_m(x)$, then except for a set of measure zero,

$$d/dx \int_a^x f(x)dx = d/dx \int_a^x \sum_1^\infty c_n\, \chi(E_n; x)dx$$

$$= \lim_m\, d/dx \int_a^x \sum_1^m c_n\, \chi(E_n; x)dx = \sum_1^\infty c_n\, \chi(E; x) = f(x).$$

A second application of the Fubini convergence theorem gives us the result we seek relative to the derivative of the indefinite integral:

5.5. THEOREM. If $f(x)$ is integrable on $[a, b]$ then $(d/dx) \int_a^x f(x)dx$ exists and is equal to $f(x)$ except at most for a set of zero measure.

It is sufficient to prove this for the case when $f(x) \geqq 0$ on $[a, b]$ since any integrable function is expressible as the difference of two positive integrable functions, the positive and the negative part of $f(x)$.

By the definition of integral: $\int_a^b f(x)dx = \lim_\sigma \Sigma_\sigma m(f, E_n)\mu(E_n)$ where $\sigma \equiv \{E_n\}$ is a subdivision of $[a, b]$ into measurable sets, and $m(f, E_n) =$ g.l.b. of $f(x)$ on E_n. Let σ_k be a sequence of subdivisions of $[a, b]$ such that $\sigma_k \geqq \sigma_{k+1}$ and $\lim_k \Sigma_{\sigma_k} m(f, E_{nk})\mu(E_{nk}) = \int_a^b f(x)dx$. If we set $g_k(x) = \Sigma_n m(f, E_{nk})\ \chi(E_{nk}; x)$, then $f(x) \geqq g_{k+1}(x) \geqq g_k(x)$ for all k and x, and

$$\int_a^b f(x)dx = \lim_k \sum_{\sigma_k} m(f, E_{nk})\mu(E_{nk}) = \lim_k \int_a^b g_k(x)dx.$$

In the proof of Theorem VII.8.11 we showed that we also have $\lim_k g_k(x) = f(x)$ except for a set of zero measure. Consequently, since for all k and x: $g_k(x) \leqq f(x)$, and $f(x)$ is integrable it follows that

$$\lim_k \int_a^x g_k(x)dx = \int_a^x \lim_k g_k(x)dx = \int_a^x f(x)dx$$

for all x. The sequence of functions $h_k(x) = \int_a^x g_k(x)dx$ satisfy the hypotheses of the Fubini convergence theorem. Moreover, $g_k(x)$ are step functions so that $h_k'(x) = g_k(x)$ except for a set of zero measure. Then except for a set of zero measure:

$$f(x) = \lim_k g_k(x) = \lim_k d/dx \int_a^x g_k(x)dx = d/dx \lim_k \int_a^x g_k(x)dx$$
$$= d/dx \int_a^x f(x)dx.$$

This theorem is the generalization of the fundamental theorem A of the integral calculus to Lebesgue integrable functions. In one way it tells us more than Theorem A in that it applies to a larger group of integrable functions. In another way it tells less since in the case of Riemann integrable functions, the set of points at which the derivative of the indefinite integral exists and is equal to the function integrated includes the points of continuity of this function.

We note that in the proof of the theorem we could also have used the functions $h_\sigma(x) = \Sigma_\sigma M(f, E_n)\ \chi(E_n; x)$, where σ is a subdivision of $[a, b]$ into measurable sets on each of which $f(x)$ is bounded and $M(f, E) =$ l.u.b. of f on E. We observe further that if we define $\varphi_\sigma(x) = \int_a^x h_\sigma(x)dx$ and $\psi_\sigma(x) = \int_a^x g_\sigma(x)dx$, where

$$g_\sigma(x) = \sum_\sigma m(f, E_n)\chi(E_n; x),$$

then the functions $\varphi_\sigma(x)$ and $\psi_\sigma(x)$ are absolutely continuous and such that $\varphi_\sigma'(x) \geqq f(x) \geqq \psi_\sigma'(x)$ except for a set of zero measure. Moreover, $\lim_\sigma \varphi_\sigma(x) = \lim_\sigma \psi_\sigma(x) = \int_a^x f(x)dx$ for every x. Then g.l.b.$_\sigma \varphi_\sigma(b) = \lim_\sigma \varphi(b) = \lim_\sigma \psi_\sigma(b) =$ l.u.b. $\psi_\sigma(b) = \int_a^b f(x)dx$.

6. Lebesgue Integrals of Derivatives

In considering an extension of fundamental Theorem B of the integral calculus (XI.1.2) which recovers a continuous function from its derivative function, we note the following:

6.1. THEOREM. If $f(x)$ is continuous on $[a, b]$ and has a finite derivative $f'(x)$ at all points x of $[a, b]$, then $f'(x)$ is a measurable function.

We extend $f(x)$ to the left of a and the right of b by the conditions: $f(x) = f(a) + f_+'(x)\ (x - a)$ for $x < a$, and $f(x) = f(b) + f_-'(b)$ $(x - b)$ for $x > b$. Then for any x of $[a, b]$ and any sequence $h_n \to 0$, we have $f'(x) = \lim_n (f(x + h_n) - f(x))/h_n$. Since the function $(f(x + h) - f(x))/h$ for fixed $h \neq 0$ is continuous on $[a, b]$ and consequently measurable, it follows that $f'(x)$ as the limit of a sequence of measurable functions is also measurable.

In the same way we prove:

6.2. THEOREM. If $f(x)$ is measurable on $[a, b]$ and such that $f'(x)$ exists and is finite except for a set E_0 of zero measure on $[a, b]$, then the function $g(x) = f'(x)$ on CE_0 and arbitrary on E_0 is measurable. Consequently if $f(x)$ is of bounded variation on $[a, b]$, the function $g(x) = f'(x)$ where $f'(x)$ is exists and is finite, and arbitrary elsewhere is measurable.

We can extend the first theorem to extreme derivates.

6.3. THEOREM. If $f(x)$ is continuous on $[a, b]$, then the six extreme derivates: $\bar{D}f(x)$, $\underline{D}f(x)$, $D^+f(x)$, $D_+f(x)$, $D^-f(x)$, $D_-f(x)$ are all measurable.

The difficulty in the proof of this theorem is that the sequence h_{nx} involved in the intervals $(x, x + h_{nx})$ leading to a particular derivate at a given point varies with x. We proceed to show that because of the fact that $f(x)$ is continuous, it is possible to determine a sequence $h_n \to 0$ independent of x such that for all x of $[a, b]$ the class of values approached by $(f(x + h_n) - f(x))/h_n$ is the same as that of $(f(x + h) - f(x))/h$ as $h \to 0$. It then follows that the extreme derivates are greatest and least limits of a sequence of continuous functions: $(f(x + h_n) - f(x))/h_n$ and consequently measurable.

We assume that $f(x)$ is extended beyond a and b by the conditions $f(x) = f(a)$ for $x < a$, and $f(x) = f(b)$ for $x > b$. Then on the closed rectangles: $[a \leqq x \leqq b, 1/(n + 1) \leqq |h| \leqq 1/n)$, the function $(f(x + h) - f(x))/h$ is continuous in x and h, and so uniformly continuous. Then for each n, there exists d_{en} such that for any rectangle of side at most d_{en} of $[a \leqq x \leqq b, 1/(n + 1) \leqq h \leqq 1/n]$, the oscillation of $(f(x + h) - f(x))/h$ is less than $1/n$. Subject the intervals $[1/(n + 1), 1/n]$ and $[- 1/n, - 1/(n + 1)]$ to a subdivision σ by the points h_{ni}, $i = 1 \ldots m_n$, so that $|\sigma| < d_{en}$. Then if $1/(n + 1) \leqq |h| \leqq 1/n$, there will exist an h_{ni} such that

$$|(f(x + h) - f(x))/h - (f(x + h_{ni}) - f(x))/h_{ni}| \leq 1/n$$

for all x of $[a, b]$. Consequently if the h_{ni} are arranged as a single sequence k_m, then the values approached by $(f(x + h) - f(x))/h$ will be the same as those of $(f(x + k_m) - f(x))/k_m$ as $m \to \infty$.

Following is a simple but limited extension of fundamental theorem B:

6.4. THEOREM. If the function $f(x)$ on $[a, b]$ is such that it has a bounded derivative on all of $[a, b]$, then $f(x) - f(a) = \int_a^x f'(x)dx$ for all x of $[a, b]$.

It is sufficient to prove this theorem for the case $x = b$.

Since $f(x)$ has a finite derivative at each point of $[a, b]$ it is continuous on $[a, b]$. Consequently, $f'(x)$ is measurable. Since $f'(x)$ is also bounded, the integral $\int_a^b f'(x)dx$ exists. Extend $f(x)$ beyond a and b by the conditions $f(x) = f(a) + f'(a)(x - a)$ for $x < a$ and $f(x) = f(b) + f'(b)(x - b)$ for $x > b$. Then $(f(x + h_n) - f(x))/h_n$ with $h_n \neq 0$ is a sequence of continuous functions, which converges to $f'(x)$ for every x as $h_n \to 0$. This sequence is uniformly bounded in x for every such sequence h_n, since by the mean value theorem of the differential calculus:

$$(f(x+h_n)-f(x))/h_n = f'(x+\theta_{xn}h_n), \qquad 0<\theta_{xn}<1.$$

Consequently, by the Lebesgue convergence theorem VII.8.8.3,

$$\lim_n \int_a^b [(f(x+h_n)-f(x))/h_n]dx$$
$$= \int_a^b [\lim_n (f(x+h_n)-f(x))/h_n]dx = \int_a^b f'(x)dx.$$

Now

$$\int_a^b f(x+h_n)dx = \int_{a-h_n}^{b-h_n} f(y)dy$$
$$= \int_a^b f(y)dy + \int_{a-h_n}^a f(y)dy - \int_{b-h_n}^b f(y)dy.$$

Then

$$\lim_n \int_a^b [(f(x+h_n)-f(x))/h_n]dx$$
$$= \lim_n [(1/h_n)\int_{a-h_n}^a f(y)dy - (1/h_n)\int_{b-h_n}^b f(y)dy] = f(b)-f(a),$$

since $f(x)$ is continuous at $x=a$, and $x=b$. This completes the proof of the theorem.

Since the boundedness of $f'(x)$ plays a decisive role in the proof of this theorem, it is not obvious how to extend it to the case when we know only that $f'(x)$ is finite for all x of $[a, b]$ and $\int_a^b f'(x)dx$ exists.

Since for any Lebesgue integrable function $f(x)$ the indefinite integral $\int_a^x f(x)dx$ is of bounded variation, we consider the integrability of the derivatives of functions of bounded variation and show:

6.5. THEOREM. If $f(x)$ is of bounded variation on $[a, b]$, and $f'(x)$ denotes its derivative where it exists as a finite number, and is arbitrary on the set of zero measure where this derivative does not exist or is infinite, then $\int_a^b f'(x)dx$ exists.

Since by XI.6.2 $f'(x)$ is measurable, it is only necessary to show that there exists a subdivision σ_y of $0 \leq y < \infty$, with $|\sigma_y| < \infty$, such that $\Sigma_i y_i \mu(E[y_{i-1} < |f'(x)| \leqq y_i]) < \infty$. Since $f(x)$ is of bounded variation the total variation function $v(f; x)$ defines an upper measure $v^*(f; E)$ and a class of sets measurable relative to $v(f)$, which includes the Borel measurable sets. We have:

6.6. Lemma. If E is any set such that $|f'(x)| > A$ for all x of E, then

$$A\mu^*(E) \leqq v^*(f; E).$$

Let $e > 0$. Then there exists an open set $G \geqq E$ such that

$$v(f; G) \leqq v^*(f; E) + e.$$

For any x in E, we can find a sequence of intervals I_{nx} interior to G with x as an end point and $\lim_n l(I_{nx}) = 0$, such that $|f(I_{nx})| / l(I_{nx}) > A$. These I_{nx} form a Vitali covering for E and, consequently, for $d > 0$, we can select a finite number of disjoint intervals $I_1 \dots I_m$ from this set such that $\mu^*(E) - d < \Sigma_1^m l(I_k)$. Then:

$$A\mu^*(E) < \sum_1^m Al(I_k) + Ad \leqq \sum_1^m |f(I_k)| + Ad \leqq v(f; G) + Ad$$
$$\leqq v^*(f; E) + e + Ad.$$

Since d and e are arbitrary, we conclude that $A\mu^*(E) \leqq v^*(f; E)$.

As a special case of this lemma we have:

6.6.1. If $f(x)$ is of bounded variation on $[a, b]$, and if E is any Lebesgue measurable set which is also measurable relative to the total variation function $v(f; x)$, and if $|f'(x)| > A$ on E, then for x on E $A\mu(E) \leqq v(f; E)$.

Let now $\sigma_y = \{y_i\}$ be any subdivision of $0 \leqq y < +\infty$ of finite norm and let $E_i = E[y_i < |f'(x)| \leqq y_{i+1}]$, $i = 0, 1, \dots$. Then the sets E_i are Lebesgue measurable, and there exists a Borel measurable set B_i contained in E_i such that $\mu(B_i) = \mu(E_i)$. Then by our lemma we have on B_i:

$$y_i\mu(B_i) \leqq v(f; B_i).$$

Consequently,

$$\sum_i y_i\mu(E_i) = \sum_i y_i\mu(B_i) \leqq \sum_i v(f; B_i) \leqq v(f; [a, b]).$$

It follows then that $|f'(x)|$ is Lebesgue integrable, and this is also true of $f'(x)$. Moreover,

$$\int_a^b |f'(x)| \, dx \leqq v(f; [a, b]).$$

We can now complete the extension of fundamental theorem B in:

6.7. THEOREM. If $f(x)$ is any function of bounded variation, on $[a, b]$ then a necessary and sufficient condition that $f(x) - f(a) = \int_a^x f'(x)dx$ for all x of $[a, b]$ is that $f(x)$ be absolutely continuous.

The absolute continuity is obviously necessary. For the sufficiency we note that if $f(x)$ is absolutely continuous on $[a, b]$ it is also of bounded variation. Then the indefinite integral function $g(x) = \int_a^x f'(x)dx$ exists and is absolutely continuous. But by XI.5.4, $g'(x) = f'(x)$ except for a set of zero measure. Consequently, by XI.3.5, $g(x) = f(x) + c$, or $g(x) = f(x) - f(a)$, so that

$$f(x) - f(a) = \int_a^x f'(x)dx.$$

7. Lebesgue Decomposition of Functions of Bounded Variation

The above generalizations of the fundamental theorems of the integral calculus to Lebesgue integration throw additional light on the structure of functions of bounded variation. For if $f(x)$ is of bounded variation on $[a, b]$, then $f'(x)$ exists as a finite value except for a set of zero measure, and is Lebesgue integrable on $[a, b]$. If we set $g(x) = \int_a^x f'(x)dx$, then $g'(x) = f'(x)$ except for a set of zero measure. If we denote $g(x) = \int_a^x f'(x)dx$, the absolutely continuous part of $f(x)$, by $f_{ac}(x)$, then the difference $f(x) - f_{ac}(x)$ will be a function which will have a derivative zero except for a set of zero measure, which latter may include the points where $f'(x)$ is not finite or does not exist. If

$$f_b(x) = \sum_{a \leqq y < x} (f(y+0) - f(y-0)) + f(x) - f(x-0),$$

the function of the breaks of $f(x)$, then $f_{zc}(x) = f(x) - f_b(x) - f_{ac}(x)$ will be a continuous function, which has derivative zero except at most a set of zero measure [since $f_b(x)$ has zero derivative except at a set of zero measure]. Consequently, we have:

7.1. THEOREM. Every function of bounded variation is expressible as the sum of three functions of different types:

$$f(x) = f_{ac}(x) + f_b(x) + f_{zc}(x),$$

where $f_{ac}(x)$ is absolutely continuous, $f_b(x)$ is a pure break function, and $f_{zc}(x)$ is continuous but has derivative zero except for a set of zero measure. This decomposition is unique if $f_{zc}(a) = f(a)$.

For the uniqueness, we have already shown that $f_b(x)$ is unique, and that $f(x) - f_b(x)$ is continuous. Suppose then $f(x)$ is continuous and assume, if possible that $f(x) = f_1(x) + f_2(x) = g_1(x) + g_2(x)$, where $f_1(x)$ and $g_1(x)$ are absolutely continuous with $f_1(a) = g_1(a) = 0$ and $f_2(x)$ and $g_2(x)$ have zero derivative except for a set of zero measure. Then $f_1(x) - g_1(x) = f_2(x) - g_2(x)$ has zero derivative except for a set of zero measure, and is absolutely continuous, consequently by XI.3.5, a constant, which is zero. This decomposition of a function of bounded variation is called a *Lebesgue decomposition*. The function $f_{ac}(x)$ is determined by the function $f'(x)$ where it exists finitely, $f_b(x)$ depends only on the points of discontinuity of $f(x)$, $f_{zc}(x)$ would seem to depend on the values of $f(x)$ at a set of zero measure. If we think of $f(x)$ as a weight distribution, then $f_b(x)$ depends on weights concentrated at individual points, $f_{zc}(x)$ depends on weights distributed over a set of zero measure, and $f_{ac}(x)$ is the continuous (derivable) distribution.

A simple example of a function of the type $f_{zc}(x)$, which has derivative zero, except at a set of zero measure, is the Cantor function, the continuous monotonic function, constant on the intervals complementary to the Cantor set, which maps the Cantor set of [0, 1] on the unit interval [0, 1]. There are however, monotonic continuous functions of this type, where the set of zero measure on which the derivative of $f(x)$ is nonexistent or not zero, is everywhere dense on $[a, b]$. As an illustration, suppose $g(x)$ is the Cantor function on [0, 1]. Extend $g(x)$ to the interval $0 \leq x < \infty$ by the condition that $g(x) = n + g(x - n)$ for $n \leq x \leq n + 1$. Then $g(x)$ is continuous and monotonic nondecreasing for $x > 0$, and has zero derivative on the translations of the Cantor set to $[n, n + 1]$. Let $h(x) = \Sigma_{n=0}^{\infty} g(2^n x)/2^{2n}$ for $0 \leq x \leq 1$. Then $h(x)$ being the sum of a uniformly convergent sequence of positive monotone functions is a monotone nondecreasing continuous function on [0, 1]. If E_n is the set of points of [0, 1] belonging to the Cantor sets on $m/2^n \leq x \leq (m + 1)/2^n$, $m = 0, 1, \ldots, 2^n - 1$, reduced in the ratio $1 : 2^n$, then $g(2^n x)$ has zero derivative on the complement of E_n, so that $\Sigma_0^m g(2^n x)/2^{2n}$ has zero derivative except on $\Sigma_0^m E_n$, which is of zero measure. Consequently, by the Fubini convergence theorem XI.5.3, $h(x)$ has zero derivative except at most for a set of zero measure E_z which may include the points of $\Sigma_0^{\infty} E_n$, a set of zero measure.

Each of the functions $f(x)$, $f_{ac}(x)$, $f_b(x)$, and $f_{zc}(x)$ gives rise to an s-additive class of measurable sets, which includes the Borel measurable sets, and an s-additive set function. The measurable sets for $f_{ac}(x)$ include the Lebesgue measurable sets. Any subset of $[a, b]$ is measurable relative to $f_b(x)$. If E_b is the set of all discontinuities of $f(x)$, then for any set E:

$$f_b(E) = \sum_{x \text{ in } E} (f(x+0) - f(x-0)) = f_b(E \cdot E_b),$$

since $f(x+0) - f(x-0) \neq 0$ only if x is in E_b. In the same way one might perhaps guess that for $f_{zc}(x)$ or the corresponding set function $f_{zc}(E)$, there exists a set E_z of zero measure such that for certain sets measurable relative to $f_{zc}(x)$, we have $f_{zc}(E \cdot E_z) = f_{zc}(E)$. In order to show that this is the case, we make a study of the set function $f(E)$ defined by $f(x)$ of bounded variation from another angle.

For a given function $f(x)$ of bounded variation let $\mathfrak{E}$ be the class of subsets of $[a, b]$ which are both Lebesgue measurable and measurable relative to $f(x)$ or rather relative to the variation function $v(f; x)$. Then $\mathfrak{E}$ is an s-algebra on which both Lebesgue measure and $v(f; E)$ are s-additive and which includes the Borel measurable sets. Then we have:

7.2. THEOREM. If $f(x)$ is any regular function of bounded variation [with $(f(x+0) - f(x))\,(f(x) - f(x-0)) \geq 0$ for all x], and $f(E)$ is the corresponding set function, which will be defined on $\mathfrak{E}$, then there exists a Borel measurable set E_z of Lebesgue measure zero, such that if $f_1(E) = f(E \cdot E_z)$, then $f_1(E) = f_1(E \cdot E_z)$ for all E of $\mathfrak{E}$. Further, if $f_2(E) = f(E) - f_1(E)$ on $\mathfrak{E}$, then $f_2(E)$ is absolutely continuous on $\mathfrak{E}$.

We prove this theorem first for the case when $f(x)$ is monotonic nondecreasing in x, so that $f(E) \geq 0$ for all E of $\mathfrak{E}$. Since $f(E)$ is bounded on $\mathfrak{E}$, we let c = l.u.b. $[f(E)$ for all Borel measurable subsets E of $[a, b]$ with $\mu(E) = 0]$. If E_n is a set with $\mu(E_n) = 0$, such that $f(E_n) \geq c - 1/n$, then for $E_z = \Pi_n E_n$, we have $c \geq f(E_z) \geq c - 1/n$ for all n, so that $f(E_z) = c$ with $\mu(E_z) = 0$. If E is any subset of $\mathfrak{E}$, then a similar procedure yields a function $f_1(E)$ = l.u.b. $[f(E')$ for all E', Borel measurable with $\mu(E') = 0$ and $E' \leq E]$, as well as a Borel measurable set E_B contained in E such that $\mu(E_B) = 0$, and $f_1(E) = f(E_B)$.

We note that the function $f_1(E)$ is s-additive on $\mathfrak{E}$. For if we order sets of $\mathfrak{E}$ for which $\mu(E) = 0$ by inclusion, then for any set E of $\mathfrak{E}$, $f_1(E) = \lim_{E_0} f(E_0)$, where the limit is taken relative to the directed set of E_0 satisfying the conditions $\mu(E_0) = 0$, and $E_0 \leq E$. Because of the additivity of $f(E)$ on $\mathfrak{E}$ and linearity of limit, we obtain the finite additivity of $f_1(E)$. The s-additivity follows from the inequality $f_1(E) \leq f(E)$ for all E of $\mathfrak{E}$, and the s-additivity of $f(E)$.

We can now show that the set E_B, with $\mu(E_B) = 0$ such that $f_1(E) = f(E_B)$ can be taken to be the set $E \cdot E_z$, where E_z is the set E_B for the interval $[a, b]$. For since there exists a Borel measurable set $B \leq E \cdot E_z$ such that $f(B) = f(E \cdot E_z)$, with $\mu(B) = \mu(E \cdot E_z) = 0$, it follows that $f_1(E) \geq f(B) = f(E \cdot E_z)$. Then

$$f(E_z) = f_1([a, b]) = f_1(E) + f_1(CE) \geq f(E \cdot E_z) + f(CE \cdot E_z) = f(E_z).$$

Hence equality holds throughout and $f_1(E) = f(E \cdot E_z)$ for all E of $\mathfrak{E}$. Then $f_1(E) = f(E \cdot E_z) = f(E \cdot E_z \cdot E_z) = f_1(E \cdot E_z)$ for all E of $\mathfrak{E}$. This completes the demonstration of the first part of the theorem, when $f(x)$ is monotone.

To prove that $f_2(E) = f(E) - f_1(E)$ is absolutely continuous on $\mathfrak{E}$ it is sufficient to show that for any E_0 of $\mathfrak{E}$ with $\mu(E_0) = 0$, we have $f_2(E_0) = 0$, since for an s-algebra of sets this condition implies absolute continuity (see VII.7.3). For given E_0, there exists a Borel measurable set B_0 contained in E_0 such that $f(E_0) = f(B_0)$ and obviously $\mu(B_0) = 0$. Then

$$f_2(E_0) = f(E_0) - f_1(E_0) = f(B_0) - f_1(E_0) \leqq 0.$$

Consequently, $f_2(E_0) = 0$.

In case $f(x)$ is of bounded variation on $[a, b]$, we make use of the Jordan decomposition of $f(x)$ into the difference of two monotonic nondecreasing functions $p(x)$ and $n(x)$. This leads to two positive valued set functions $p(f; E)$ and $n(f; E)$ defined on the sets measurable relative to $v(f; E)$. Also by VII.11.6 there exist two disjoint sets E^+ and E^-, which can be assumed to be Borel measurable, such that $p(f; E) = f(E \cdot E^+)$ and $n(f; E) = -f(E \cdot E^-)$ for all E measurable relative to $v(f; E)$. We can then determine Borel measurable sets E_z^+, a subset of E^+, and E_z^-, a subset of E^-, such that $\mu(E_z^+) = 0$ and $\mu(E_z^-) = 0$, and decompositions of $p(f; E) = p_1(f; E) + p_2(f; E)$ and $n(f; E) = n_1(f; E) + n_2(f; E)$, with $p(f; E \cdot E_z^+) = p_1(f; E) = p_1(f; E \cdot E_z^+)$ and $n(f; E \cdot E_z^-) = n_1(f; E) = n_1(f; E \cdot E_z^-)$ for all E of $\mathfrak{E}$, while $p_2(f; E)$ and $n_2(f; E)$ are absolutely continuous on $\mathfrak{E}$. This leads to functions:

$$f_1(E) = p_1(f; E) - n_1(f; E) \quad \text{and} \quad f_2(E) = p_2(f; E) - n_2(f; E)$$

and a Borel measurable set $E_z = E_z^+ + E_z^-$, such that $f(E) = f_1(E) + f_2(E), f_1(E) = f_1(E \cdot E_z)$ for all E of $\mathfrak{E}$, and $f_2(E)$ absolutely continuous on $\mathfrak{E}$. This completes the proof of the theorem.

An s-additive set function $f(E)$ on an s-algebra for which there exists a set E_z of a subclass $\mathfrak{E}_0$ of $\mathfrak{E}$, such that $f(E \cdot E_z) = f(E)$ for all E of $\mathfrak{E}$ is said to be *singular* relative to $\mathfrak{E}_0$. Then the break function $f_b(E)$ of a function of bounded variation $f(x)$ is singular relative to the sets consisting of a denumerable number of points, the function $f_1(E)$ above is singular relative to the sets of zero measure of $\mathfrak{E}$.

Our theorem could then be stated:

7.3. The s-additive set function $f(E)$ relative to a regular function of bounded variation on a finite interval $[a, b]$ admits of a decomposition into the sum of two functions $f_1(E)$ and $f_2(E)$ on the class $\mathfrak{E}$ of sets which are Lebesgue measurable and measurable relative to $f(E)$, such that $f_1(E)$ is singular relative to sets of Lebesgue zero measure and $f_2(E)$ is absolutely continuous on $\mathfrak{E}$. This decomposition is unique.

The uniqueness of the decomposition is obvious. This decomposition is called the *Lebesgue decomposition* of the set function $f(E)$. We might note that for a function of bounded variation the set E_z^+ is a Borel measurable set such that $f(E_z^+) = \text{l.u.b.} f(E)$ for E ranging over the Borel measurable subsets of $[a, b]$ for which $\mu(E) = 0$, while $f(E_z^-) = \text{g.l.b.}\ f(E)$ for the same class of sets.

To complete the identification of this second decomposition with the one previously obtained, viz., $f(x) = f_b(x) + f_{ac}(x) + f_{zc}(x)$, we show:

7.4. THEOREM. If the continuous function of bounded variation $f(x)$ is such that the corresponding s-additive set function is singular with respects to sets of Lebesgue zero measure, then $f(x) - f(a) = f([a, x])$ has derivative zero except for a set of zero measure.

We limit ourselves to the case when $f(x)$ is monotonic nondecreasing so that $f(E) \geq 0$ for all E measurable relative to f. The extension to the case when $f(x)$ is of bounded variation can be made without difficulty by using the Jordan decomposition. Suppose if possible that $f'(x) \neq 0$ on a set of positive measure. Then $\int_a^b f'(x)dx > 0$. Set $f(x) = g(x) + \int_a^x f'(x)dx$. Then for any Borel measurable set B: $f(B) = g(B) + \int_B f'(x)dx$. In particular, $f([a, b]) = g([a, b]) + \int_a^b f'(x)dx$ with $g([a, b]) < f([a, b])$. Since f is singular, there exists a set E_z with $\mu(E_z) = 0$, such that $f([a, b] \cdot E_z = f([a, b])$.

But

$$f([a, b] \cdot E_z) = g([a, b] \cdot E_z) \leq g([a, b]) < f([a, b]),$$

which involves a contradiction.

In the Lebesgue decomposition by sets, we have $f(E) = f_1(E) + f_2(E)$ where $f_1(E)$ is singular relative to sets of measure zero, and $f_2(E)$ is absolutely continuous, we can decompose $f_1(E) = f_b(E) + f_{1c}(E)$, where $f_b(E)$ is a break function and $f_{1c}(E)$ is continuous. It follows that

$$f_{1c}([a, x]) = f_{zc}(x) - f(a), \quad f_2([a, x]) = f_{ac}(x) = \int_a^x f'(x)dx$$

where we use the uniqueness of the two types of decomposition. Summarizing, we have that for any function $f(x)$ of bounded variation, there are two types of decomposition:

(A) $$f(x) = f_b(x) + f_{ac}(x) + f_{zc}(x)$$

where $f_b(x)$ is a pure break function, $f_{ac}(x)$ is absolutely continuous and has value $\int_a^x f'(x)dx$, and $f_{zc}(x)$ is continuous and has zero derivative except for a set of zero measure; and

(B) $$f(E) = f_b(\mathrm{E}) + f_{ac}(E) + f_{zc}(E)$$

where $f_b(E)$ is a pure break function, that is there exists a set E_b consisting of a denumerable set of points such that for any subset E of $[a, b]$: $f_b(E) = f(E \cdot E_b) = \Sigma_P f(P)$, where P ranges over the points of $E \cdot E_b$; $f_{ac}(E)$ is absolutely continuous and has as value $\int_E f'(x)dx$ for every Lebesgue measurable set; and $f_{zc}(E)$ is singular relative to sets of Lebesgue measure zero, that is there exists a Borel measurable set E_z with $\mu(E_z) = 0$, such that for all sets E Lebesgue measurable and measurable relative to f, we have $f_{zc}(E \cdot E_z) = f_{zc}(E)$; moreover, $f_{zc}(E)$ is continuous in the sense that if a set consists of a single point P then $f_{zc}(E) = f_{zc}(P) = 0$.

EXERCISES

1. Show that if $f(x)$ is absolutely continuous on $[a, b]$ and $f'(x) \geq 0$ except for a set of zero measure, then $f(x)$ is monotonic nondecreasing on $[a, b]$.

2. Show that if $f_n(x)$ is a sequence of functions of bounded variation on $[a, b]$ such that for all $[c, d]$ of $[a, b]$ and all n: $f_n(d) - f_n(c) \geq f_{n-1}(d) -$

$f_{n-1}(c)$, and $\lim_n f_n(x) = f(x)$ as a finite valued function, then $\lim_n f_n'(x) = f'(x)$ except at most at a set of zero measure.

3. Is it possible to show that if $f(x)$ is Lebesgue integrable on $[a, b]$, then $(d/dx) \int_a^x f(x)dx = f(x)$ except for a set of zero measure, without decomposing $f(x)$ into the difference of two positive integrable functions?

4. Suppose that $f(x)$ is such that its upper and lower integrals on $[a, b]$ exist as finite numbers. What can be said of the derivatives of the corresponding indefinite integrals $\overline{\int_a^x} f(x)dx$ and $\underline{\int_a^x} f(x)dx$?

5. Suppose that Df stands for a fixed extremal derivate of $f(x)$ on $[a, b]$, and suppose that Df is bounded on $[a, b]$. Is $\int_a^x Df(x)dx = f(x) - f(a)$?

6. If $f(x)$ is absolutely continuous on $[a, b]$, and has a zero derivate (zero as a value approached by $\Delta f/\Delta x$) at all points of a set E whose complement is of zero measure , then $f(x)$ is a constant on $[a, b]$.

7. Is it possible to have a continuous function $f(x)$ on $[a, b]$ such that $f'(x)$ exists as a finite number at each point and is Lebesgue integrable, and still not have $\int_a^x f'(x)dx = f(x) - f(a)$?

8. To what extent are the theorems relating integrals and derivatives valid for a function Lebesgue (and so absolutely) integrable on $(-\infty, +\infty)$?

9. Suppose that $g(x)$ is the Cantor function on $[0, 1]$. Define $g(x)$ on $[1, 2]$ by the condition $g(x) = g(2 - x)$, and then extend $g(x)$ to the interval $-\infty < x < \infty$ to have period 2, i.e., $g(x) = g(x + 2)$ for all x. Let $h(x) = \Sigma_{n=0}^{\infty} g(2^n x)/2^n$. Show that $h(x)$ has zero derivative except for a set of zero measure.

10. Show that a pure break function has derivative zero except for a set of zero measure. Is this set of zero measure necessarily the set of points of discontinuity of the function?

11. What information does the Lebesgue decomposition of a regular function of bounded variation $\alpha(x)$ give relative to the value of an R-S integral $\int_a^b f(x)d\alpha(x)$, or an L-S integral $\int_E f(x)d\alpha(x)$?

8. The Radon-Nikodym Theorem

The developments of the preceding section have an equivalent in an abstract setting. The basic result is embodied in the:

8.1. Radon-Nikodym Theorem. If X is an abstract space, $\mathfrak{E}$ an s-algebra of subsets of X, α a finite valued s-additive function on $\mathfrak{E}$ with

$\alpha(E) \geq 0$ for all E of $\mathfrak{E}$, and β a finite valued s-additive function on $\mathfrak{E}$, then there exists a set E_0 of $\mathfrak{E}$ such that $\alpha(E_0) = 0$, and a point function f on X, Lebesgue integrable with respect to α, such that for any set E of $\mathfrak{E}$, we have

$$\beta(E) = \beta(EE_0) + \int_E f d\alpha \quad \text{with} \quad \beta(E - EE_0) = \int_E f d\alpha.$$

If we set $\beta_s(E) = \beta(EE_0)$ and $\beta_{ac}(E) = \beta(E - EE_0)$, then β_{ac} is absolutely continuous relative to α, and β_s is singular relative to α, that is, we have a Lebesgue decomposition of $\beta(E)$.

Since $\beta(E)$ is s-additive and finite valued on the s-algebra $\mathfrak{E}$, it is bounded and expressible as the difference of two positive valued functions: $\beta(E) = p(\beta; E) - n(\beta; E)$. Under the circumstances, it will be sufficient to prove the theorem for the case when $\beta(E) \geq 0$ for all E of $\mathfrak{E}$.

Let $\{r\}$ be a denumerable set of real numbers with $r \geq 0$, and dense on the positive real axis. Consider the functions: $\gamma_r(E) = \beta(E) - r\alpha(E)$ on $\mathfrak{E}$. These will be bounded and s-additive. Then as indicated in IX.4.3, for each r there exist disjoint sets E_r^+ and E_r^- such that $X = E_r^+ + E_r^-$ and $\gamma_r(E) = \beta(E) - r\alpha(E) \geq 0$ for all E contained in E_r^+ and $\gamma_r(E) = \beta(E) - r\alpha(E) \leq 0$ for all E contained in E_r^-. For any $y > 0$, let $E_y = \Pi_{r<y} E_r^+$. Since $\mathfrak{E}$ is s-additive, E_y will be in $\mathfrak{E}$ for each y. Then the sets E_y have the following properties:

(1) If $y_1 \geq y_2$ then $E_{y_1} \leq E_{y_2}$.

This is obvious.

(2) $\Pi_{y<y_1} E_y = E_{y_1}$.

For if an element x of X is in E_{y_1}, then for $r < y_1$, x is in E_r^+ and consequently in all E_y with $y < y_1$. On the other hand, if x is in all E_y with $y < y_1$, then it is in all E_r^+ with $r < y$.

(3) If E is any subset of E_y in $\mathfrak{E}$, then $\beta(E) - y\alpha(E) \geq 0$. For if E is any subset of E_y, it is a subset of all E_r^+ for $r < y$, so that

$$\beta(E) - r\alpha(E) \geq 0 \qquad \text{for all } r < y.$$

(4) If E is any subset of the complement CE_y of E_y, then $\beta(E) - y\alpha(E) \leq 0$. Obviously $CE_y = \Sigma_{r<y} CE_r = \Sigma_{r<y} E_r^-$. Now the set of numbers r was assumed to be denumerable, and so $\Sigma_{r<y} E_r^-$ can be

expressed as the sum of a sequence of disjoint sets of the form $E^-_{r'} - E^-_{r''}$. Since $E^-_{r'} - E^-_{r''}$ is a subset of $E^-_{r'}$, we will have

$$\beta(E^-_{r'} - E^-_{r''}) \leq r'\alpha(E^-_{r'} - E^-_{r''}) < y\alpha(E^-_{r'} - E^-_{r''}).$$

By summing these inequalities and using the s-additivity of α and β, we obtain $\beta(CE_y) \leq y\alpha(CE_y)$. In the same way we show that if E is any subset of CE_y in E, then $\beta(E) \leq y\alpha(E)$.

Since $\beta(E) \geq 0 = 0 \cdot \alpha(E)$ for all E of $\mathfrak{E}$ we can set $E_{y=0} = X$. Then:

(5) $\sum_{y \geq 0} E_y = X.$

On the other hand, suppose $E_\infty = \Pi_r E^+_r = \Pi_y E_y$. Then if E is any subset in $\mathfrak{E}$ of E_∞, we have $\beta(E) \geq n\alpha(E)$ for all n. It follows that $\alpha(E) = \alpha(E_\infty) = 0$.

Relative to the set $X - E_\infty$, the class of sets $E_y(X - E_\infty)$ satisfies the conditions of VI.2.5 for a point function determined by the condition $f(x) = y$ if x belongs to $(E_y - \Sigma_{y' > y} E_{y'})$ $(X - E_\infty)$, with $E[f \geq y] = E_y CE_\infty$. We can extend $f(x)$ to all X by the condition that $f(x) = 0$ on E_∞, that is a set of α-measure zero. Then since E_y and E_∞ are in $\mathfrak{E}$, f satisfies the measurability conditions on $\mathfrak{E}$. We show that f is Lebesgue integrable with respect to α and that

$$\beta(X - E_\infty) = \int_X f d\alpha.$$

Let y_k be any subdivision of the positive Y-axis of finite norm. Let $E_k = E[y_k \leq f(x) < y_{k+1}]$. Then E_k is contained in $E_{y_k} - E_{y_{k+1}}$. As a consquence,

$$y_k\alpha(E_k) \leq \beta(E_k) \leq y_{k+1}\alpha(E_k).$$

Then

$$\sum_k y_k\alpha(E_k) \leq \sum_k \beta(E_k) \leqq \beta(X).$$

Then $\Sigma_k y_k \alpha(E_k)$ is convergent and $f(x)$ is Lebesgue integrable. On the other hand, since the subdivision $\{y_k\}$ is of finite norm, and $\alpha(X)$ is finite, it follows that $\Sigma_k y_{k+1}\alpha(E_k)$ is convergent also, and

$$\sum_k y_k\alpha(E_k) \leq \sum_k \beta(E_k) \leq \sum_k y_{k+1}\alpha(E_k).$$

It follows that $\int_X f d\alpha$ which is the limit of $\Sigma_k y_k \alpha(E_k)$ as $|\sigma_y| \to 0$ is equal to $\Sigma_k \beta(E_k)$ or $\beta(X - E_\infty)$.

It is obvious that the same procedure could be applied to the case when X is replaced by any set E of $\mathfrak{E}$, and the function $f(x)$ is $f(x)\chi(E; x)$, so that we have

$$\beta(E - E_\infty) = \int_E f d\alpha$$

for all E of $\mathfrak{E}$. Since $\int_E f d\alpha$ is absolutely continuous relative to α, it follows that $\beta_{ac}(E) = \beta(E - E_\infty)$ is absolutely continuous. In particular:

8.2. If $\beta(E)$ is absolutely continuous relative to α, then $\beta(E_\infty) = 0$, so that for any set E of $\mathfrak{E}$, we have

$$\beta(E) = \int_E f d\alpha\,.$$

The Radon-Nikodym theorem for the case when X is an n-dimensional Euclidean space was derived by J. Radon in "Absolute additive Mengenfunktionen": *Sitzber. Akad. Wiss. Wien* 122, Abt. 2a (1913) 1295-1438. The abstract setting setting is due to O. Nikodym: Sur une generalisation des integrales de Radon, *Fundamenta Math.* 15 (1930) 131-179, particularly pp. 169-179. The proof given above is a slight modification of Nikodym's proof. See also J. M. H. Olmsted: Lebesgue theory on a Boolean algebra, *Trans. Am. Math. Soc.* 51 (1942) 185-191; and C. Caratheodory, "Mass und Integral und ihre Algebraisierung," Birkhäuser, Basel, 1956, p. 190.

Some Reference Books on Integration

Bourbaki, N. " Integration" (" Eléments de Mathématiques," XIII and XXI, Livre VI). Hermann, Paris, 1952 and 1956.

Caratheodory C. " Vorlesungen über reelle Funktionen," 2nd Ed. Teubner, Leipzig, 1927.

Caratheodory, C. " Mass und Integral und ihre Algebraisierung." Birkhäuser, Basel, 1956.

Graves, L. M. " Theory of Functions of Real Variables," 2nd Ed. McGraw-Hill, New York, 1956.

Hahn, H., and Rosenthal, A. " Set Functions." Univ. of New Mexico Press, Albuquerque, 1944.

Halmos, P. R. " Measure Theory." Van Nostrand, New York, 1947.

Kestelman, H. " Modern Theories of Integration," 2nd Ed. Dover, New York, 1960.

Lebesgue, H. " Leçons sur l'Intégration," 2nd Ed. Gauthier-Villars, Paris, 1928.

McShane, E. J. " Integration." Princeton Univ. Press, Princeton, New Jersey, 1944.

Munroe, M. E. " Measure and Integration." Addison-Wesley, Cambridge, Massachusetts, 1953.

Picone, M., and Viole, T. " Lezioni sulla Teoria Moderna dell'Integrazione." Einaudi, Turin, Italy, 1952.

Saks, S. "Theory of the Integral" (L. C. Young, trans.). Warsaw, Poland, 1937.

Zaanen, A. C. " An Introduction to the Theory of Integration." North-Holland, Amsterdam, 1958.

INDEX

I

J

L

M

N

V

W

Y

Z

Pure and Applied Mathematics

A Series of Monographs and Textbooks

1: Arnold Sommerfeld. Partial Differential Equations in Physics. 1949 (Lectures on Theoretical Physics, Volume VI)
2: Reinhold Baer. Linear Algebra and Projective Geometry. 1952
3: Herbert Busemann and Paul Kelly. Projective Geometry and Projective Metrics. 1953
4: Stefan Bergman and M. Schiffer. Kernel Functions and Elliptic Differential Equations in Mathematical Physics. 1953
5: Ralph Philip Boas, Jr. Entire Functions. 1954
6: Herbert Busemann. The Geometry of Geodesics. 1955
7: Claude Chevalley. Fundamental Concepts of Algebra. 1956
8: Sze-Tsen Hu. Homotopy Theory. 1959
9: A. M. Ostrowski. Solution of Equations and Systems of Equations. Second Edition. 1966
10: J. Dieudonné. Treatise on Analysis. Volume I, Foundations of Modern Analysis, enlarged and corrected printing, 1969. Volume II, 1970.
11: S. I. Goldberg. Curvature and Homology. 1962.
12: Sigurdur Helgason. Differential Geometry and Symmetric Spaces. 1962
13: T. H. Hildebrandt. Introduction to the Theory of Integration. 1963.
14: Shreeram Abhyankar. Local Analytic Geometry. 1964
15: Richard L. Bishop and Richard J. Crittenden. Geometry of Manifolds. 1964
16: Steven A. Gaal. Point Set Topology. 1964
17: Barry Mitchell. Theory of Categories. 1965
18: Anthony P. Morse. A Theory of Sets. 1965

Pure and Applied Mathematics

A Series of Monographs and Textbooks

19: GUSTAVE CHOQUET. Topology. 1966
20: Z. I. BOREVICH AND I. R. SHAFAREVICH. Number Theory. 1966
21: JOSÉ LUIS MASSERA AND JUAN JORGE SCHAFFER. Linear Differential Equations and Function Spaces. 1966
22: RICHARD D. SCHAFER. An Introduction to Nonassociative Algebras. 1966
23: MARTIN EICHLER. Introduction to the Theory of Algebraic Numbers and Functions. 1966
24: SHREERAM ABHYANKAR. Resolution of Singularities of Embedded Algebraic Surfaces. 1966
25: FRANÇOIS TREVES. Topological Vector Spaces, Distributions, and Kernels. 1967
26: PETER D. LAX and RALPH S. PHILLIPS. Scattering Theory. 1967
27: OYSTEIN ORE. The Four Color Problem. 1967
28: MAURICE HEINS. Complex Function Theory. 1968
29: R. M. BLUMENTHAL AND R. K. GETOOR. Markov Processes and Potential Theory. 1968
30: L. J. MORDELL. Diophantine Equations. 1969
31: J. BARKLEY ROSSER. Simplified Independence Proofs: Boolean Valued Models of Set Theory. 1969
32: WILLIAM F. DONOGHUE, JR. Distributions and Fourier Transforms. 1969
33: MARSTON MORSE AND STEWART S. CAIRNS. Critical Point Theory in Global Analysis and Differential Topology. 1969
34: EDWIN WEISS. Cohomology of Groups. 1969
35: HANS FREUDENTHAL AND H. DE VRIES. Linear Lie Groups. 1969
36: LASZLO FUCHS. Infinite Abelian Groups: Volume I. 1970
37: KEIO NAGAMI. Dimension Theory. 1970
38: PETER L. DUREN. Theory of H^p Spaces. 1970
39: BODO PAREIGIS. Categories and Functors. 1970
40: PAUL L. BUTZER AND ROLF J. NESSEL. Fourier Analysis and Approximation: Volume 1, One-Dimensional Theory, 1971
41: EDUARD PRUGOVEČKI. Quantum Mechanics in Hilbert Space. 1971
42: D. V. WIDDER: An Introduction to Transform Theory. 1971

In preparation

MAX LARSEN and PAUL J. MCCARTHY. Multiplicative Theory of Ideals.

ERNST-AUGUST BEHRENS. Ring Theory.